Fundamentals of
Geometry
and Algebra

Book Staff and Contributors

Paul Thomas   *Senior Content Specialist*
Kay McCarthy   *Senior Text Editor*
Wendi Russell   *Text Editor*
Suzanne Montazer   *Creative Director, Print and ePublishing*
Vicki Croghan, Betsy Simpson   *Print Visual Designer*
Carol Leigh   *Print Visual Designer, Cover Designer*
Steve Mawyer   *Illustrations Editor*
Jean Stringer   *Rights Manager*
Amy Eward   *Senior Manager, Writers*
Susan Raley   *Manager, Editors*
Trish Heiman   *Senior Project Manager*

Maria Szalay   *Senior Vice President for Product Development*
John Holdren   *Senior Vice President for Content and Curriculum*
David Pelizzari   *Vice President, Content and Curriculum*
Kim Barcas   *Vice President, Creative*
Laura Seuschek   *Instructional Design and Evaluation & Research*
Aaron Hall   *Vice President, Program Management*

Lisa Dimaio Iekel   *Production Manager*
John Agnone   *Director of Publications*

About K12 Inc.

K12 Inc., a technology-based education company, is the nation's leading provider of proprietary curriculum and online education programs to students in grades K–12. K12 provides its curriculum and academic services to online schools, traditional classrooms, blended school programs, and directly to families. K12 Inc. also operates the K12 International Academy, an accredited, diploma-granting online private school serving students worldwide. K12's mission is to provide any child the curriculum and tools to maximize success in life, regardless of geographic, financial, or demographic circumstances. K12 Inc. is accredited by CITA. More information can be found at www.K12.com.

ISBN 978-1-60153-124-7

Printed by RR Donnelley & Sons, Roanoke, VA, USA, April 2013, Lot 040513

Fundamentals of
Geometry
and Algebra

Contents

Chapter 6 Comparisons: Ratios

Chapter 7 Angles and Circles

Chapter 8   Probability

Chapter 9   Statistics

Chapter 10 The Second Dimension

Chapter 11 Rates

Chapter 12 Working with Positives and Negatives

Chapter 13 Making and Moving Figures

Chapter 14 Patterns, Primes, and Puzzles

Appendices

How to Use This Book

This book contains 14 chapters. Each chapter begins with a chapter opener and a Foundations topic. Each chapter then presents the core math topics, ending with a Chapter Review.

The chapter opener introduces the content of the chapter.

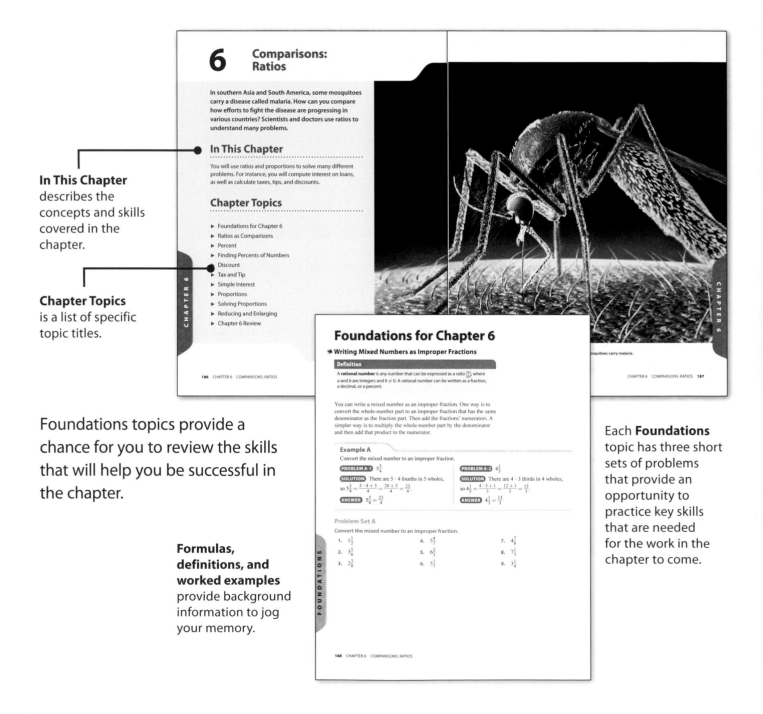

In This Chapter describes the concepts and skills covered in the chapter.

Chapter Topics is a list of specific topic titles.

Foundations topics provide a chance for you to review the skills that will help you be successful in the chapter.

Formulas, definitions, and worked examples provide background information to jog your memory.

Each **Foundations** topic has three short sets of problems that provide an opportunity to practice key skills that are needed for the work in the chapter to come.

Each core math topic has two reference pages that include definitions, examples, and other helpful information.

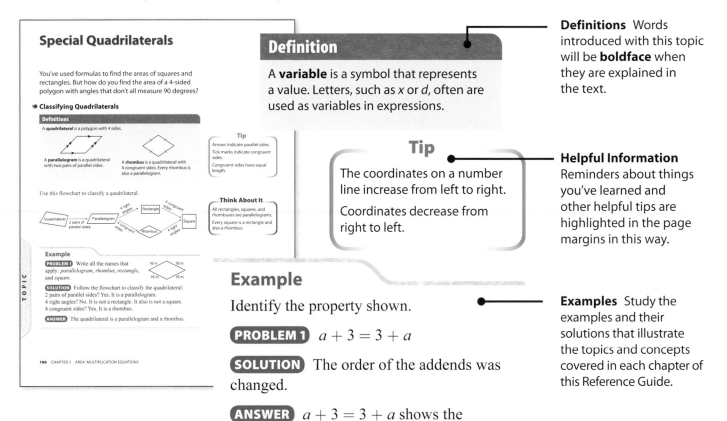

Definitions Words introduced with this topic will be **boldface** when they are explained in the text.

Helpful Information Reminders about things you've learned and other helpful tips are highlighted in the page margins in this way.

Examples Study the examples and their solutions that illustrate the topics and concepts covered in each chapter of this Reference Guide.

A pair of Problem Set pages follows each pair of reference pages.

Problem Set The end of each topic is where you will do the math so you can learn the math.

Stepping Stones are partially worked examples that can help you see how to approach problems.

Each Chapter Review is a set of problems that will help you make sure you have mastered the content of the chapter.

The first part of the **Chapter Review** Problem Set is made up of multiple choice problems. The problems in the second part are free response.

The **Topic Lookup** shows you which topics in the chapter you should look to for help with specific problems from the Chapter Review Problem Set.

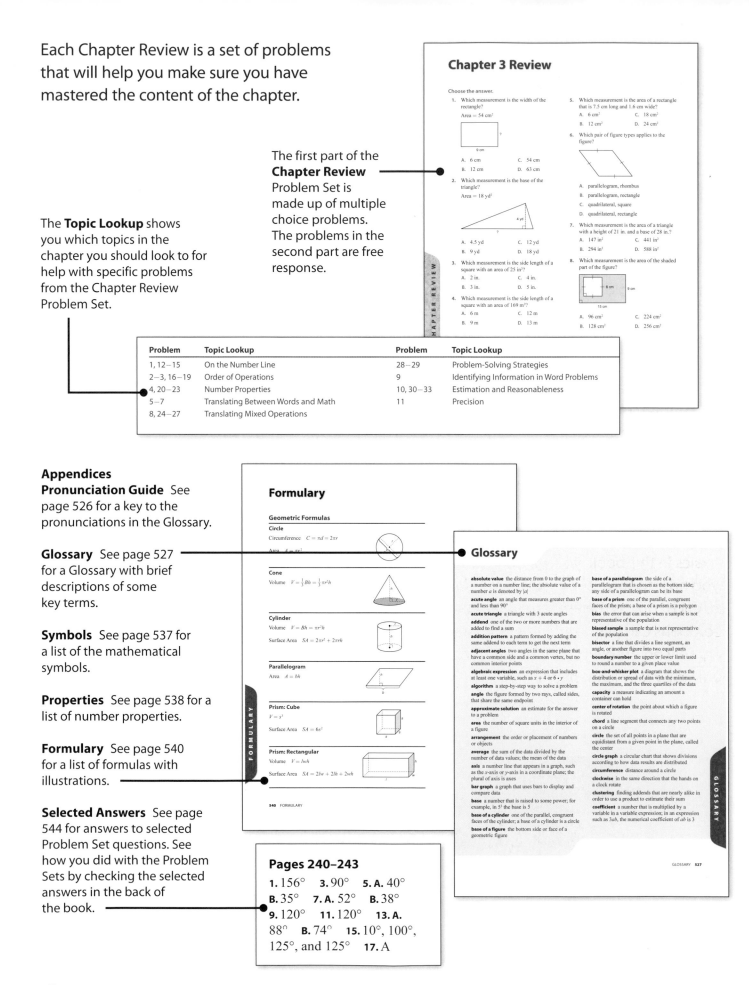

Chapter 3 Review

Choose the answer.

1. Which measurement is the width of the rectangle?

Area = 54 cm²

A. 6 cm   C. 54 cm
B. 12 cm   D. 63 cm

2. Which measurement is the base of the triangle?

Area = 18 yd²

A. 4.5 yd   C. 12 yd
B. 9 yd   D. 18 yd

3. Which measurement is the side length of a square with an area of 25 in²?
A. 2 in.   C. 4 in.
B. 3 in.   D. 5 in.

4. Which measurement is the side length of a square with an area of 169 m²?
A. 6 m   C. 12 m
B. 9 m   D. 13 m

5. Which measurement is the area of a rectangle that is 7.5 cm long and 1.6 cm wide?
A. 6 cm²   C. 18 cm²
B. 12 cm²   D. 24 cm²

6. Which pair of figure types applies to the figure?

A. parallelogram, rhombus
B. parallelogram, rectangle
C. quadrilateral, square
D. quadrilateral, rectangle

7. Which measurement is the area of a triangle with a height of 21 in. and a base of 28 in.?
A. 147 in²   C. 441 in²
B. 294 in²   D. 588 in²

8. Which measurement is the area of the shaded part of the figure?

A. 96 cm²   C. 224 cm²
B. 128 cm²   D. 256 cm²

Problem	Topic Lookup	Problem	Topic Lookup
1, 12–15	On the Number Line	28–29	Problem-Solving Strategies
2–3, 16–19	Order of Operations	9	Identifying Information in Word Problems
4, 20–23	Number Properties	10, 30–33	Estimation and Reasonableness
5–7	Translating Between Words and Math	11	Precision
8, 24–27	Translating Mixed Operations		

Appendices
Pronunciation Guide See page 526 for a key to the pronunciations in the Glossary.

Glossary See page 527 for a Glossary with brief descriptions of some key terms.

Symbols See page 537 for a list of the mathematical symbols.

Properties See page 538 for a list of number properties.

Formulary See page 540 for a list of formulas with illustrations.

Selected Answers See page 544 for answers to selected Problem Set questions. See how you did with the Problem Sets by checking the selected answers in the back of the book.

Formulary

Geometric Formulas
Circle

Circumference $C = \pi d = 2\pi r$

Area $A = \pi r^2$

Cone

Volume $V = \frac{1}{3}Bh = \frac{1}{3}\pi r^2 h$

Cylinder

Volume $V = Bh = \pi r^2 h$

Surface Area $SA = 2\pi r^2 + 2\pi rh$

Parallelogram

Area $A = bh$

Prism: Cube

$V = s^3$

Surface Area $SA = 6s^2$

Prism: Rectangular

Volume $V = lwh$

Surface Area $SA = 2lw + 2lh + 2wh$

540   FORMULARY

Glossary

absolute value the distance from 0 to the graph of a number on a number line; the absolute value of a number a is denoted by $|a|$

acute angle an angle that measures greater than 0° and less than 90°

acute triangle a triangle with 3 acute angles

addend one of the two or more numbers that are added to find a sum

addition pattern a pattern formed by adding the same addend to each term to get the next term

adjacent angles two angles in the same plane that have a common side and a common vertex, but no common interior points

algebraic expression an expression that includes at least one variable, such as $x + 4$ or $6 \cdot y$

algorithm a step-by-step way to solve a problem

angle the figure formed by two rays, called sides, that share the same endpoint

approximate solution an estimate for the answer to a problem

area the number of square units in the interior of a figure

arrangement the order or placement of numbers or objects

average the sum of the data divided by the number of data values; the mean of the data

axis a number line that appears in a graph, such as the x-axis or y-axis in a coordinate plane; the plural of axis is axes

bar graph a graph that uses bars to display and compare data

base a number that is raised to some power; for example, in 5^3 the base is 5

base of a cylinder one of the parallel, congruent faces of the cylinder; a base of a cylinder is a circle

base of a figure the bottom side or face of a geometric figure

base of a parallelogram the side of a parallelogram that is chosen as the bottom side; any side of a parallelogram can be its base

base of a prism one of the parallel, congruent faces of the prism; a base of a prism is a polygon

bias the error that can arise when a sample is not representative of the population

biased sample a sample that is not representative of the population

bisector a line that divides a line segment, an angle, or another figure into two equal parts

boundary number the upper or lower limit used to round a number to a given place value

box-and-whisker plot a diagram that shows the distribution or spread of data with the minimum, the maximum, and the three quartiles of the data

capacity a measure indicating an amount a container can hold

center of rotation the point about which a figure is rotated

chord a line segment that connects any two points on a circle

circle the set of all points in a plane that are equidistant from a given point in the plane, called the center

circle graph a circular chart that shows divisions according to how data results are distributed

circumference distance around a circle

clockwise in the same direction that the hands of a clock rotate

clustering finding addends that are nearly alike in order to use a product to estimate their sum

coefficient a number that is multiplied by a variable in a variable expression; in an expression such as $3ab$, the numerical coefficient of ab is 3

GLOSSARY   527

Pages 240–243

1. 156°   3. 90°   5. A. 40°
B. 35°   7. A. 52°   B. 38°
9. 120°   11. 120°   13. A. 88°   B. 74°   15. 10°, 100°, 125°, and 125°   17. A

Introduction

Welcome to *Fundamentals of Geometry and Algebra*

This Reference Guide was developed to accompany the online portion of K12's Fundamentals of Geometry and Algebra program. The topics and Problem Sets in this book make sense on their own, but they are not the entire story. The online component of the course is critical. Online, you will find audio-visual explanations, interactive problems, and dynamic explorations. The online component and this Reference Guide work together to tell the entire story.

Don't just read it—do the math!

Math is learned at the tip of a pencil. As you work through the topics in this book, you will see worked examples that show you how to solve some problems, but the most important part of each topic is the Problem Set at the end. Reading problem solutions can help you find good strategies and best practices for solving problems, but only when you solve problems yourself will you really learn math.

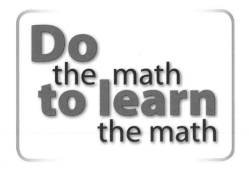

1 Problem Solving

When you are solving a tough problem, it can seem as daunting as climbing a mountain. Climbers know that to scale a mountain, you need to have a solid strategy and the correct tools, but you also need to do the little things right. Every climb starts with a single, solid handhold.

In This Chapter

You will learn about number lines and the order of operations. The big point of the unit is problem solving. To solve problems, you will learn how to translate between words and math symbols, and you will use strategies such as drawing figures, estimating, and breaking a problem down into smaller parts. You'll also learn how to tend to precision and reasonableness.

Chapter Topics

- ► Foundations for Chapter 1
- ► On the Number Line
- ► Order of Operations
- ► Number Properties
- ► Translating Between Words and Math
- ► Translating Mixed Operations
- ► Problem-Solving Strategies
- ► Identifying Information in Word Problems
- ► Estimation and Reasonableness
- ► Precision
- ► Chapter 1 Review

A climber scales a mountain.

Foundations for Chapter 1

➜ **Expressions**

Definitions

An **expression** is a group of mathematical symbols that represents a certain value. An expression can be as simple as one number, such as 8, or can contain several numbers and symbols, such as $2 + 3$, $12 \cdot 12$, or $2.4 \cdot (6 + 1.8)$.

You **simplify** an expression by finding its value.

You can simplify an expression that contains a $+$, $-$, $\cdot$, or $\div$ symbol by performing the operation with the given numbers. Use mental math and your recall of basic facts.

Example A

Simplify the expression.

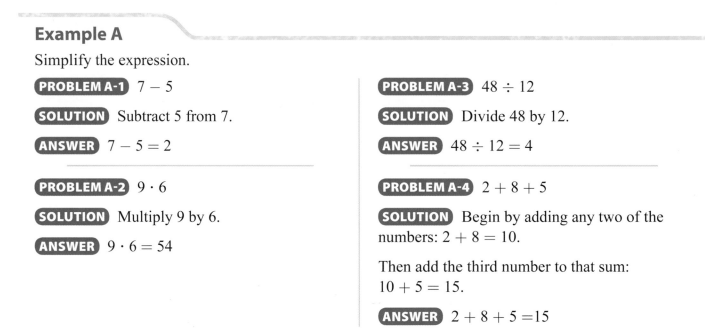

PROBLEM A-1 $7 - 5$

SOLUTION Subtract 5 from 7.

ANSWER $7 - 5 = 2$

PROBLEM A-2 $9 \cdot 6$

SOLUTION Multiply 9 by 6.

ANSWER $9 \cdot 6 = 54$

PROBLEM A-3 $48 \div 12$

SOLUTION Divide 48 by 12.

ANSWER $48 \div 12 = 4$

PROBLEM A-4 $2 + 8 + 5$

SOLUTION Begin by adding any two of the numbers: $2 + 8 = 10$.

Then add the third number to that sum: $10 + 5 = 15$.

ANSWER $2 + 8 + 5 = 15$

Problem Set A

Simplify the expression.

1. $7 + 0$
2. $15 - 8$
3. $4 \cdot 3$
4. $14 \div 2$
5. $12 + 7$

6. $19 - 9$
7. $7 \cdot 8$ 56
8. $4 \cdot 9$
9. $24 \div 6$ 4
10. $36 \div 4$

11. $72 - 52$
12. $6 + 1 + 1$
13. $8 + 0 + 4$
14. $2 \cdot 3 \cdot 8$
15. $4 \cdot 1 \cdot 9$ 36

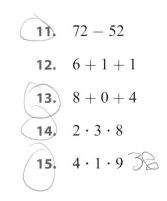

➔ Equations

To determine whether an equation is true, you can find the values of the expressions on each side of the equals sign. If the values are the same, the equation is true.

Example B

State whether the equation is true.

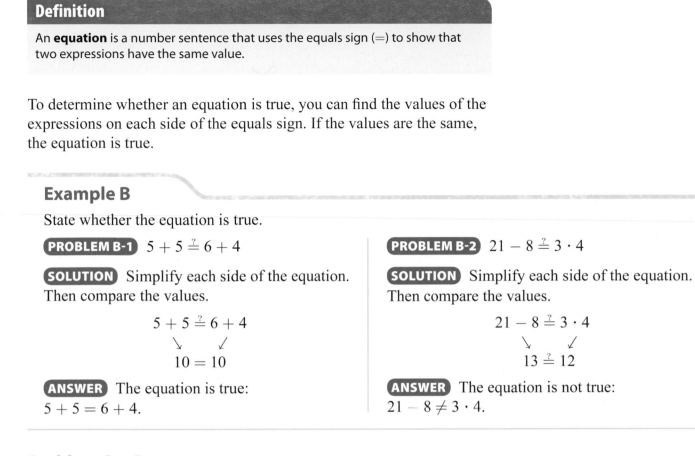

PROBLEM B-1 $5 + 5 \overset{?}{=} 6 + 4$

SOLUTION Simplify each side of the equation. Then compare the values.

$$5 + 5 \overset{?}{=} 6 + 4$$
$$10 = 10$$

ANSWER The equation is true:
$5 + 5 = 6 + 4$.

PROBLEM B-2 $21 - 8 \overset{?}{=} 3 \cdot 4$

SOLUTION Simplify each side of the equation. Then compare the values.

$$21 - 8 \overset{?}{=} 3 \cdot 4$$
$$13 \overset{?}{=} 12$$

ANSWER The equation is not true:
$21 - 8 \neq 3 \cdot 4$.

Problem Set B

State whether the equation is true.

1. $7 + 4 \overset{?}{=} 10 + 1$

2. $14 - 4 \overset{?}{=} 13 - 5$

3. $2 \cdot 3 \overset{?}{=} 5 \cdot 1$

4. $4 \div 4 \overset{?}{=} 7 \div 7$

5. $6 + 5 \overset{?}{=} 18 - 9$

6. $17 - 11 \overset{?}{=} 2 \cdot 3$

7. $6 \cdot 1 \overset{?}{=} 12 \div 3$

8. $21 \div 3 \overset{?}{=} 3 + 3$

9. $10 + 18 \overset{?}{=} 4 \cdot 7$

10. $1 + 1 \overset{?}{=} 24 \div 12$

11. $17 + 18 \overset{?}{=} 19 + 16$

12. $44 - 24 \overset{?}{=} 36 - 26$

13. $8 \cdot 11 \overset{?}{=} 22 \cdot 5$

14. $100 \div 4 \overset{?}{=} 50 \div 3$

15. $14 + 16 \overset{?}{=} 90 \div 3$

➜ Evaluating Expressions with Variables

Definitions

A **variable** is a symbol that represents a value. Letters, such as *x* or *d*, often are used as variables in expressions.

You **evaluate** an expression by substituting a value for a variable and then simplifying the expression.

To evaluate an expression with one or more variables, replace each variable with the given value. Then simplify the expression.

Example C

PROBLEM C-1 Evaluate the expression $n + 3$ when $n = 8$.

SOLUTION Replace *n* with 8. Then simplify.

$$n + 3$$
$$8 + 3$$
$$11$$

ANSWER When $n = 8$, $n + 3 = 11$.

PROBLEM C-2 Evaluate the expression $x \cdot y$ when $x = 4$ and $y = 11$.

SOLUTION Replace *x* with 4 and *y* with 11. Then simplify.

$$x \cdot y$$
$$4 \cdot 11$$
$$44$$

ANSWER When $x = 4$ and $y = 11$, $x \cdot y = 44$.

Problem Set C

Evaluate the expression for the given value or values.

1. $4 + y$ when $y = 9$

2. $f - 3$ when $f = 12$

3. $5 \cdot j$ when $j = 5$

4. $18 \div r$ when $r = 6$

5. $c + 18$ when $c = 12$

6. $24 - n$ when $n = 24$

7. $a \cdot 12$ when $a = 8$

8. $g \div 7$ when $g = 56$

9. $x \cdot 30$ when $x = 20$

10. $v + g$ when $v = 17$ and $g = 14$

11. $s - y$ when $s = 23$ and $y = 8$

12. $e \cdot r$ when $e = 9$ and $r = 11$

13. $m \div k$ when $m = 169$ and $k = 13$

14. $d + y$ when $d = 75$ and $y = 25$

15. $z \cdot h$ when $z = 20$ and $h = 40$

A climber scales a mountain.

Planting a Seed

The language of math can help you describe and solve many types of problems. Math provides the tools, but you still need to develop solid strategies that help you become a great problem solver.

On the Number Line

A number line is one of the tools that you can use to solve math problems.

➡ Finding Coordinates on a Number Line

Definition

A **coordinate** is a number that gives the location of a point on a number line. The coordinates 1 through 8 are labeled on the scale of this number line.

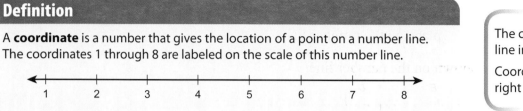

> ### Tip
>
> The coordinates on a number line increase from left to right.
>
> Coordinates decrease from right to left.

You can find the coordinate for a point shown on a number line by looking at the scale.

Example

Identify the coordinate of the point shown on the number line.

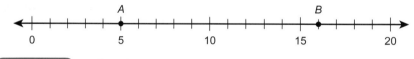

PROBLEM 1 point *A*

SOLUTION The number shown underneath point *A* is 5.

ANSWER The coordinate of point *A* is 5.

PROBLEM 2 point *B*

SOLUTION The point lies on the first tick mark between the tick marks for 15 and 20. The first whole number after 15 is 16.

ANSWER The coordinate of point *B* is 16.

PROBLEM 3 point *C*

SOLUTION The minor tick marks show tenths and the point is 8 minor tick marks to the right of 15.

ANSWER The coordinate of point *C* is 15.8.

➔ Graphing Points on a Number Line

Example

Draw a number line from 0 through 20 and graph a point with the given coordinate.

PROBLEM 4 point *D* with a coordinate of 15

SOLUTION Find the tick mark labeled 15. Graph point *D* at that place on the number line.

PROBLEM 5 point *E* with a coordinate of 11

SOLUTION Find the tick mark labeled 10. Move 1 unit to the right. Graph point *E* at that place on the number line.

ANSWER Points *D* and *E* are shown on the number line.

➔ Comparing and Ordering Numbers

Numbers increase in value as you move farther right on the number line.

Example

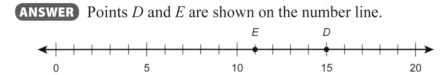

PROBLEM 6 Order 23, 26, and 19 from least to greatest.

SOLUTION The coordinate 26 is farthest to the right on the number line, and the coordinate 19 is farthest to the left. The coordinate 23 falls between 19 and 26 on the number line, so its value is between 19 and 26.

ANSWER $19 < 23 < 26$

TOPIC

Problem Set

Identify the coordinate of the point shown on the number line.

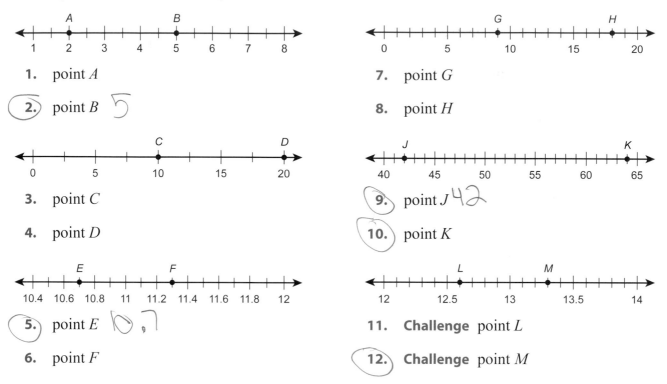

1. point A

2. point B 5

3. point C

4. point D

5. point E 0.7

6. point F

7. point G

8. point H

9. point J 42

10. point K

11. **Challenge** point L

12. **Challenge** point M

Draw a number line from 15 to 30, and then graph the point with the given coordinate.

13. point T with coordinate 18

14. point Y with coordinate 22

15. point M with coordinate 25

16. point W with coordinate 19

Draw a number line from 35 to 37, and then graph the point with the given coordinate.

17. point A with a coordinate of 35.9

18. point L with a coordinate of 36.7

19. point N with a coordinate of 36.2

20. **Challenge** point R with a coordinate of 36.45

Use the number line to compare or order the numbers.

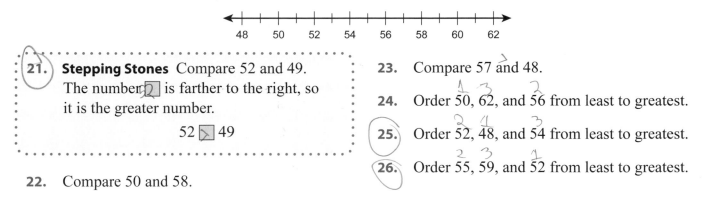

21. **Stepping Stones** Compare 52 and 49. The number ⬜ is farther to the right, so it is the greater number.

52 ⬞ 49

22. Compare 50 and 58.

23. Compare 57 and 48.

24. Order 50, 62, and 56 from least to greatest.

25. Order 52, 48, and 54 from least to greatest.

26. Order 55, 59, and 52 from least to greatest.

Use the number line to compare or order the numbers.

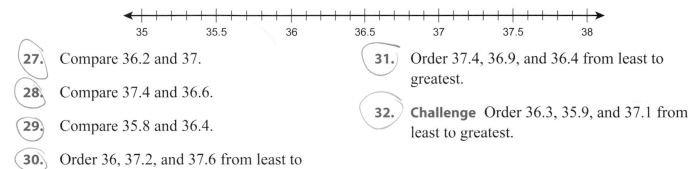

27. Compare 36.2 and 37.

28. Compare 37.4 and 36.6.

29. Compare 35.8 and 36.4.

30. Order 36, 37.2, and 37.6 from least to greatest.

31. Order 37.4, 36.9, and 36.4 from least to greatest.

32. **Challenge** Order 36.3, 35.9, and 37.1 from least to greatest.

Choose the answer.

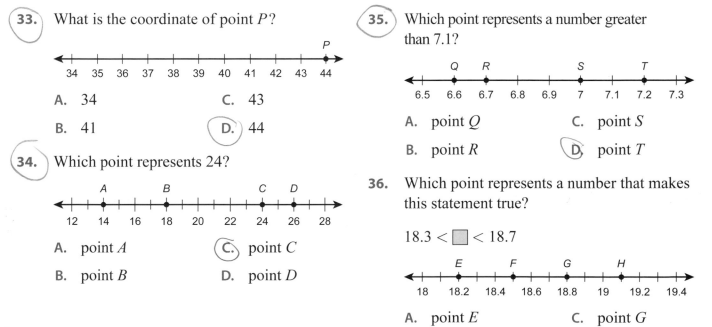

33. What is the coordinate of point P?

A. 34   C. 43

B. 41   D. 44

34. Which point represents 24?

A. point A C. point C

B. point B D. point D

35. Which point represents a number greater than 7.1?

A. point Q C. point S

B. point R D. point T

36. Which point represents a number that makes this statement true?

$18.3 < \square < 18.7$

A. point E C. point G

B. point F D. point H

Order of Operations

If an expression has more than one operation, then you need to perform the operations in the proper order.

➜ Identifying Addends and Factors in Expressions

Definitions

An **algebraic expression** is an expression that includes at least one variable, such as $x + 4$ or $6 \cdot y$.

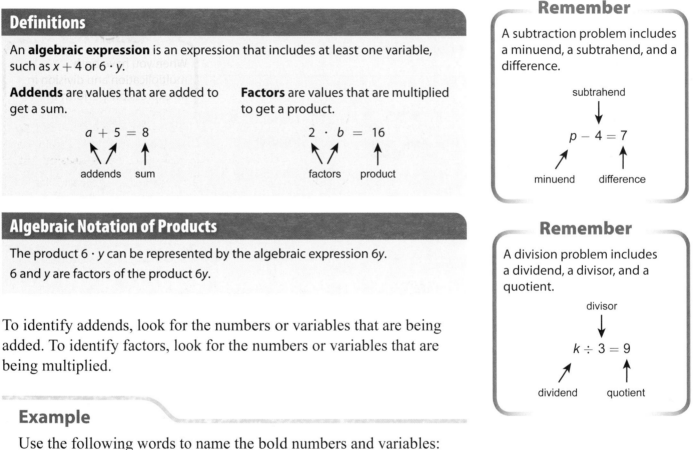

Addends are values that are added to get a sum.

$$a + 5 = 8$$

addends   sum

Factors are values that are multiplied to get a product.

$$2 \cdot b = 16$$

factors   product

Algebraic Notation of Products

The product $6 \cdot y$ can be represented by the algebraic expression $6y$.
6 and y are factors of the product $6y$.

To identify addends, look for the numbers or variables that are being added. To identify factors, look for the numbers or variables that are being multiplied.

Example

Use the following words to name the bold numbers and variables: *addend*, *sum*, *factor*, *product*, *minuend*, *subtrahend*, *difference*, *dividend*, *divisor*, or *quotient*.

PROBLEM 1 $\mathbf{m + 2} = 7$

SOLUTION m and 2 are being added to give the sum 7.

ANSWER 2 and m are addends.

PROBLEM 2 $\mathbf{3x + 2} = 11$

SOLUTION $3x$ and 2 are being added.
3 and x are being multiplied.

ANSWER $3x$ and 2 are addends. 3 and x are factors.

Using the Order of Operations

Simplify an expression with two or more operations by performing the operations in the proper order.

Example

Simplify the expression.

PROBLEM 3 $3 + 36 \div 4$

SOLUTION

$3 + 36 \div 4$ Divide 36 by 4.

$\downarrow$

$3 + \quad 9$ Add 3 and 9.

$\downarrow$

12

ANSWER $3 + 36 \div 4 = 12$

PROBLEM 4 $5 \cdot (12 - 4)$

SOLUTION

$5 \cdot (12 - 4)$ Subtract 4 from 12.

$\downarrow$

$5 \cdot \quad 8$ Multiply 5 by 8.

$\downarrow$

40

ANSWER $5 \cdot (12 - 4) = 40$

Tip

Remember *PMDAS* to help you keep the order straight.

Parentheses

Multiply

Divide

Add

Subtract

Remember

When you have both multiplication and division in an expression, perform the operations as they come in the expression from left to right. So, if the division comes first in the expression, do the division first.

The same is true for addition and subtraction. Perform the operations from left to right as they appear in the expression.

Finding an Error

Example

PROBLEM 5 Find the error and correct the mistake.

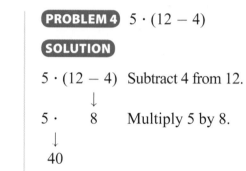

$5 + 7 \cdot 2$

$12 \cdot 2$

24

SOLUTION You should multiply before adding. The numbers 5 and 7 were added to get 12. Then 12 was multiplied by 2 to get 24. Instead, multiply 7 and 2 to get 14. Then add 5 to get a result of 19.

ANSWER The correct result is 19.

TOPIC

Problem Set

Use the following words to name the bold numbers and variables: *addend, sum, factor, product, minuend, subtrahend, difference, dividend, divisor,* or *quotient.*

1. **Stepping Stones** $8 + x = 17$

   The values being added are ▢ and ▢.
   8 and x are ▢.

2. $7c = 42$ *factor*

3. $9n = \mathbf{27}$

4. $\mathbf{9} + \mathbf{x} = 14$

5. $x - \mathbf{2} = 8$

6. $y - \mathbf{3} = 24$ *sub*

7. $18 - z = \mathbf{10}$

8. $\mathbf{2x} + \mathbf{5} = 17$ *factor addend*

9. $7 + \mathbf{4z} = 43$

10. $12 + \mathbf{6n} = 84$ *addend factor*

11. $56 - \mathbf{5h} = 34$

12. $9 + 3j = \mathbf{22}$

13. $\mathbf{81} \div 3d = \mathbf{2}$

14. **Challenge** $\mathbf{5a} + \mathbf{6b} = 140$

15. **Challenge** $\mathbf{5c} - \mathbf{6d} = 3$

Simplify the expression.

16. **Stepping Stones**

    $\mathbf{12} \div \mathbf{2} \cdot 3$

    ▢ $\cdot 3$

    ▢

17. $14 - 7 + 20$

18. $12 \cdot 4 \div 4$

19. $5 + 10 - 15$

20. $28 \div 4 \cdot 3$ 21

21. $40 - 16 \div 8$

22. $4 \cdot (6 + 3)$ 36

23. $46 - 18 \div 9$

24. $7 \cdot 3 + 7$

25. $36 \div (5 + 4)$

26. $(12 - 5)(11 + 3)$

27. $(5 + 2)[6 - (3 + 2)]$

28. $(4 \div 1)[(1 + 6) + 2]$ 27

29. **Challenge** $2 \cdot (5 + 9) \div 7 - 3$

30. **Challenge** $100 \div (14 - 4) \cdot 2 + 8$

Find the error and correct the mistake.

31. Stepping Stones $20 - 14 \div 2$

$20 - 14 \div 2$

$6 \div 2$

3

The first step should have been to [____] the numbers 14 and [ ].

Then the second step should have been to [____] the numbers [ ] and [ ].

The correct result is [ ].

32.

$18 + 6 \cdot 2$

$24 \cdot 2$

48

33.

$3 \cdot 2 + 4$

$3 \cdot 6$

18

34.

$48 \div 6 + 2$

$48 \div 8$

6

35.

$(18 - 6) \div 3$

$18 - 2$

16

36.

$(3 + 4) \cdot 2$

$3 + 8$

11

37.

Challenge

$4 \cdot (6 - 5)$

$24 - 5$

19

Choose the answer.

38. Which number is the sum in $5 + 8 + 2$?

   A. 2   C. 8

   B. 5   D. 15

39. What is the value of $90 \div (10 + 5)$?

   A. 6   C. 14

   B. 10   D. 15

40. What is the value of $6 + 3 \cdot 2$?

   A. 0   C. 12

   B. 18   D. 15

41. Which expression has the greatest value?

   A. $10 - (3 - 2)$ C. $(10 - 2) - 3$

   B. $10 - 3 - 2$ D. $10 - 2 - 3$

Number Properties

Properties can make simplifying expressions . . . simpler!

➔ Identifying Number Properties

Number Properties	
Properties	**Examples**
Associative Properties The grouping of addends or factors doesn't change the sum or the product.	
$a + (b + c) = (a + b) + c$	$2 + (3 + 4) = (2 + 3) + 4$
$a \cdot (b \cdot c) = (a \cdot b) \cdot c$	$5 \cdot (7 \cdot 9) = (5 \cdot 7) \cdot 9$
Commutative Properties The order of addends or factors doesn't change the sum or the product.	
$a + b = b + a$	$4 + 6 = 6 + 4$
$a \cdot b = b \cdot a$	$8 \cdot 9 = 9 \cdot 8$
Distributive Properties For all numbers a, b, and c,	
$a(b + c) = ab + ac$	$3 \cdot (6 + 4) = 3 \cdot 6 + 3 \cdot 4$
$a(b - c) = ab - ac$	$8 \cdot (5 - 2) = 8 \cdot 5 - 8 \cdot 2$
Symmetric Property If $a = b$, then $b = a$.	If $2 + 3 = 5$, then $5 = 2 + 3$.
Transitive Property If $a = b$ and $b = c$, then $a = c$.	If $a = b$ and $b = 5$, then $a = 5$.

Think About It

The commutative properties apply only to addition and multiplication.

There are no commutative properties for subtraction or division.

$6 - 4 \neq 4 - 6$

$12 \div 3 \neq 3 \div 12$

Example

Identify the property shown.

PROBLEM 1 $a + 3 = 3 + a$

SOLUTION The order of the addends was changed.

ANSWER $a + 3 = 3 + a$ shows the commutative property of addition.

PROBLEM 2 $2 \cdot (b + 7) = 2b + (2 \cdot 7)$

SOLUTION The factor 2 is being distributed through the two addends in the parentheses.

ANSWER $2 \cdot (b + 7) = 2b + (2 \cdot 7)$ shows the distributive property.

TOPIC C

→ Justifying Steps in Simplifying Expressions

If you can identify the properties being used to simplify an expression, you will be able to use them yourself to make simplifying expressions easier.

Example

Justify each step in the solution.

PROBLEM 3

ANSWER

Operation or Property

$$5 \cdot (75 \cdot 2) = 5 \cdot (2 \cdot 75)$$ commutative property of multiplication
$$= (5 \cdot 2) \cdot 75$$ associative property of multiplication
$$= 10 \cdot 75$$ multiplication
$$= 750$$ multiplication

→ Using Properties to Simplify Expressions

You can use the properties to rewrite expressions so that you can simplify them using mental math.

Example

Use properties to simplify the expression.

PROBLEM 4 $6 \cdot 28$

SOLUTION
$6 \cdot (20 + 8)$ Break 28 into the sum $20 + 8$.
$6 \cdot 20 + 6 \cdot 8$ distributive property
$120 + 48$ Multiply.
168 Add.

ANSWER $6 \cdot 28 = 168$

PROBLEM 5 $8 + (19 + 12)$

SOLUTION
$8 + (12 + 19)$ commutative property of addition
$(8 + 12) + 19$ associative property of addition
$20 + 19$ Add.
39 Add.

ANSWER $8 + (19 + 12) = 39$

Think About It

There are many different ways to use properties to simplify expressions. The ways shown in these problems are just examples.

Problem Set

Identify the property shown.

1. **Stepping Stones** $2 + x = x + 2$

   The addends are the same, but their [____] has changed.

   This equation shows the [____] property of addition.

2. $3 \cdot (2 \cdot v) = (3 \cdot 2) \cdot v$

3. $5 \cdot (p + 7) = 5p + (5 \cdot 7)$

4. If $x = y$ and $y = 7$, then $x = 7$.

5. If $k = 8$, then $8 = k$.

6. $(2 + a) + 7 = 2 + (a + 7)$

7. $7 \cdot p = p \cdot 7$

8. If $p = 12$ and $12 = q$, then $p = q$.

9. If $4 = n$, then $n = 4$.

10. $9 + x = x + 9$

11. $(14 \cdot p) \cdot 12 = 14 \cdot (p \cdot 12)$

12. $f + (1 + 4) = (f + 1) + 4$

13. $5 \cdot 6p = 6p \cdot 5$

14. If $6a = 12$ and $12 = 3b$, then $6a = 3b$.

15. $6j + (2k + 3) = (6j + 2k) + 3$

16. $3p \cdot 2k = 2k \cdot 3p$

17. $3p \cdot (2 + k) = 6p + 3pk$

18. If $8k = 56$, then $56 = 8k$.

19. $3x + 7y = 7y + 3x$

20. $(7 \cdot p) \cdot 2k = 7 \cdot (p \cdot 2k)$

21. $6p \cdot 125 = 125 \cdot 6p$

22. **Challenge** $(5p \cdot 2k) \cdot 9g = 5p \cdot (2k \cdot 9g)$

23. **Challenge** $4 \cdot 3p + (4 \cdot 6) = 4 \cdot (3p + 6)$

Justify each step in the solution.

24. **Stepping Stones**

Step		Justification
$5 + (15 + 23) = (5 + 15) + 23$	A.	[____] property of addition
$= 20 + 23$	B.	Add within the parentheses.
$= 43$	C.	Add.

25. $2 \cdot 7 \cdot 5$
    $2 \cdot 5 \cdot 7$ A. [____]
    $10 \cdot 7$ B. [____]
    70 C. [____]

26. $21 + 17 + 9$
    $21 + 9 + 17$ A. [____]
    $30 + 17$ B. [____]
    47 C. [____]

27. $5 \cdot 34$
    $(5 \cdot 30) + (5 \cdot 4)$ A. [____]
    $150 + 20$ B. [____]
    170 C. [____]

28. $(17 \cdot 4) \cdot 25$
    $17 \cdot (4 \cdot 25)$ A. [____]
    $17 \cdot 100$ B. [____]
    1700 C. [____]

29. $(32 \cdot 13) - (32 \cdot 3)$
$32 \cdot (13 - 3)$ **A.** �
$32 \cdot 10$ **B.** ▢
320 **C.** ▢

30. $8 \cdot 47$
$(8 \cdot 40) + (8 \cdot 7)$ **A.** ▢
$320 + 56$ **B.** ▢
376 **C.** ▢

31. $67 + (45 + 33)$
$67 + (33 + 45)$ **A.** comm
$(67 + 33) + 45$ **B.** assoc
$100 + 45$ **C.** add
145 **D.** add

32. Challenge $68 + 8 \cdot 44$
$68 + (8 \cdot 40) + (8 \cdot 4)$ **A.** ▢
$68 + 320 + 32$ **B.** ▢
$68 + 32 + 320$ **C.** ▢
$100 + 320$ **D.** ▢
420 **E.** ▢

Use properties to evaluate the expression.

33. Stepping Stones $18 + 9 + 12$

$$18 + (9 + 12) = 18 + (12 + 9)$$
$$= (\square + \square) + 9$$
$$= \square + 9$$
$$= \square$$

34. $5 \cdot 7 \cdot 8$

35. $14 + (16 + 28)$

36. $(2 \cdot 9) \cdot 4$ 72

37. $(13 + 6) + 4$

38. $5 \cdot 14 \cdot 2$

39. $36 + 17 + 24$

40. $46 + (14 + 39)$

41. $4 \cdot 9 \cdot 5$

42. $19 + (28 + 21)$

43. $7 \cdot 23$

44. $(13 + 2) + 7$ 22

45. $9 \cdot 47$

46. $4 \cdot (8 \cdot 2)$ 64

47. $5 \cdot 84$

48. $(36 + 42) + 24$

49. $6 \cdot 64$

50. $57 + (19 + 43)$

51. Challenge $37 + 7 \cdot 49$

Choose the answer.

52. Which statement shows the associative property of multiplication?
   A. If $7m = 28$, then $28 = 7m$.
   B. $(5 + a) + 6 = 5 + (a + 6)$
   C. $(6 \cdot y) \cdot 4 = 6 \cdot (y \cdot 4)$
   D. $3 \cdot s = s \cdot 3$

53. What is the value of $25 \cdot (7 \cdot 4)$?
   A. 36
   B. 100
   C. 175
   D. 700

54. If $p = c$ and $c = g$, which statement is true?
   A. $p = g$ C. $p < g$
   B. $p > g$ D. $p > c > g$

55. Which expression is equivalent to $84 \cdot 6$?
   A. $(80 \cdot 4) + (4 \cdot 6)$
   B. $(40 \cdot 6) + (8 \cdot 6)$
   C. $(60 \cdot 4) + (80 \cdot 4)$
   D. $(80 \cdot 6) + (4 \cdot 6)$

Translating Between Words and Math

To solve a word problem, translate the words of the problem into a math expression that you can simplify.

➡ Translating Word Phrases into Expressions

Look for clues in the problem that can tell you what operation to use. Then choose a variable for any unknown.

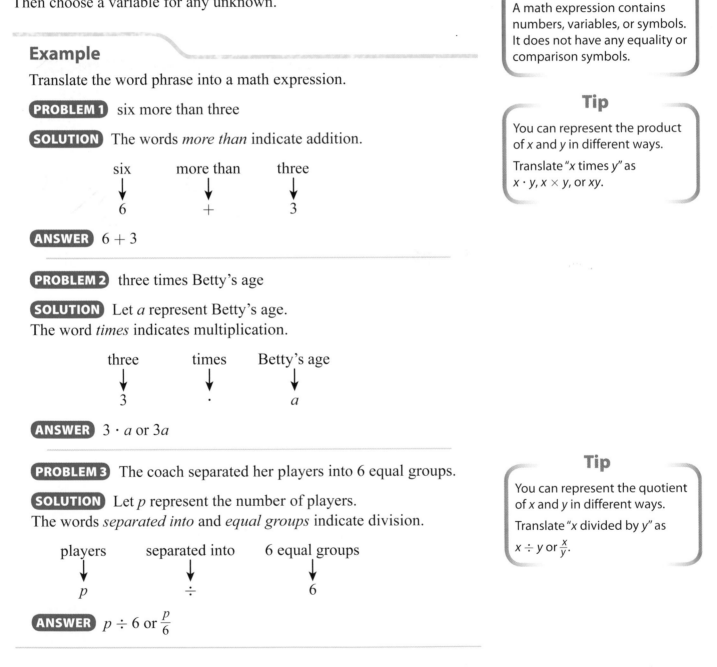

Example

Translate the word phrase into a math expression.

PROBLEM 1 six more than three

SOLUTION The words *more than* indicate addition.

six	more than	three
↓	↓	↓
6	+	3

ANSWER $6 + 3$

PROBLEM 2 three times Betty's age

SOLUTION Let *a* represent Betty's age.
The word *times* indicates multiplication.

three	times	Betty's age
↓	↓	↓
3	·	a

ANSWER $3 \cdot a$ or $3a$

PROBLEM 3 The coach separated her players into 6 equal groups.

SOLUTION Let *p* represent the number of players.
The words *separated into* and *equal groups* indicate division.

players	separated into	6 equal groups
↓	↓	↓
p	÷	6

ANSWER $p \div 6$ or $\frac{p}{6}$

Remember

A math expression contains numbers, variables, or symbols. It does not have any equality or comparison symbols.

Tip

You can represent the product of *x* and *y* in different ways.

Translate "*x* times *y*" as $x \cdot y$, $x \times y$, or xy.

Tip

You can represent the quotient of *x* and *y* in different ways.

Translate "*x* divided by *y*" as $x \div y$ or $\frac{x}{y}$.

TOPIC

⇥ Writing Word Phrases for Expressions

A math expression, such as $n - 10$, can represent many different situations. The expression could mean you spend $10 from your savings. Or it could be the height difference between a 10 ft tree and another tree with an unknown height. To write a word phrase for an expression, choose words to represent the operations in the expression.

Example

PROBLEM 4 Write two different word phrases for the math expression $12x$.

SOLUTION Use the words *times* and *product* to represent multiplication.

ANSWER 12 times a number or the product of a number and 12

PROBLEM 5 Write an everyday situation for the math expression $\frac{d}{3}$. Use the idea of going to a restaurant with two of your friends.

SOLUTION The expression $\frac{d}{3}$ shows a number divided by 3. You could divide the total cost of a meal into 3 equal parts.

ANSWER Three friends went to a restaurant. The total bill was d dollars. They shared the bill equally. The expression $\frac{d}{3}$ represents each person's share.

Problem Set

Translate the word phrase into a math expression.

1. **Stepping Stones** five more than seven

   five   more than   seven
   ↓   ↓   ↓
   ▢   ▢   ▢

   Expression: ▭

2. fourteen increased by two

3. the product of six and eight 6×8

4. fifty-four divided by nine

5. seventeen less than thirty

6. the quotient of twenty-one and three

7. eight groups of ten $8 \cdot 10$

8. four more than eleven

9. 11 times a number

10. 12 more than a number

11. 1 fewer than a number

12. 20 cards in some equal piles

13. 12 meters longer than his throw

14. total miles walked at a constant rate per day for 6 days

15. an amount spent taken from $40 $40 - a$

16. the profit divided into 3 equal shares

17. Antwan pays $12 per hour to rent a canoe for the afternoon.

18. Josie reads the same number of pages each day in her 200-page book.

19. Hank can swim twice as far now as when he started taking lessons 3 months ago.

20. The temperature drops 5°C overnight.

21. Last month, the puppy weighed 14 pounds. It gains more weight this month.

22. Sheila buys some boxes of pens, with 20 pens in each box.

23. He and his brother each paint the same number of sections of fence.

24. Kim gets 4 more answers correct on this math test than on her last test.

25. **Challenge** The number of visitors to a new website triples in just one month.

Write two different word phrases for the math expression.

26. **Stepping Stones** $g - 2$

    ▢ less than the number g
    the difference between ▢ and ▢

27. $3n$

28. $b + 6$

29. $18 \div h$

30. $14 - f$

31. $25 + m$

32. $\dfrac{b}{5}$

33. $5 \cdot d$

34. $q - 6$

35. $11 - w$

36. $w \cdot 3$

37. $17 + p$

38. $\frac{6}{x}$

Write an everyday situation for the math expression with the context provided.

39. $m - 20$; giving your friend a gift certificate

40. $\frac{75}{n}$; sharing something equally

75 cookies to share

41. $45d$; doing something for the same number of minutes each day

42. $18 - c$; comparing people's ages

Choose the answer.

43. Which expression shows the sum of five and forty?

    A. $40 - 5$

    B. $5 + 40$

    C. $40 \div 5$

    D. $5 \cdot 40$

44. Which expression describes the total growth of a plant that grew 2 cm each week for w weeks?

    A. $2w$

    B. $w + 2$

    C. $w - 2$

    D. $2 - w$

45. Which word phrase describes the expression $30 - n$?

    A. n less than 30

    B. 30 increased by n

    C. 30 less than n

    D. the product of 30 and n

46. Which situation can be described by the expression $\frac{z}{4}$?

    A. Four less than the number of apples.

    B. Four apples each weigh the same amount.

    C. There are 4 more apples in the bag.

    D. She cut up 4 of the apples into equal pieces.

Translating Mixed Operations

When translating an everyday situation into a math expression, you might need two or more operations.

Remember

Order of operations:

1. Operate inside parentheses.

2. Multiply and divide from left to right.

3. Add and subtract from left to right.

➜ **Translating Word Phrases into Expressions**

Look for clues to help you decide which operations to use. Then identify variables for unknown quantities. Put the operations in the correct order in the expression. Use parentheses to show operations to be performed first.

Example

Translate the phrase into a math expression.

PROBLEM 1 five less than the quotient of eight and four

SOLUTION The words *less than* indicate subtraction and the word *quotient* indicates division.

quotient of eight and four	less	five
↓	↓	↓
$8 \div 4$	$-$	5

The wording of the problem indicates that $8 \div 4$ should be calculated first. In the order of operations, division is performed before subtraction, so the expression doesn't need parentheses.

ANSWER $8 \div 4 - 5$

PROBLEM 2 six times the sum of seven and a number

SOLUTION The word *times* indicates multiplication and the word *sum* indicates addition.
Let n represent the number.

six	times	sum of seven and a number
↓	↓	↓
6	$\cdot$	$7 + n$

Use parentheses so that the sum is calculated before the product.

ANSWER $6 \cdot (7 + n)$

Example

PROBLEM 3 Valerie has one climbing rope that is 150 ft long. She has some other ropes that are each 300 ft long. Write an expression that shows the total length of Valerie's climbing ropes.

SOLUTION The word *each* indicates multiplication and the word *total* indicates addition.

Let r represent the number of ropes that are 300 ft long.

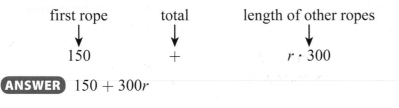

first rope	total	length of other ropes
↓	↓	↓
150	+	$r \cdot 300$

ANSWER $150 + 300r$

➤ Writing Word Phrases for Expressions

When writing a word phrase to represent a math expression with more than one operation, keep the order of operations in mind. Look for parentheses to tell you what operation to perform first. Choose words to represent the operations in the order that they should be performed.

Example

Write a situation for the math expression.

PROBLEM 4 $6n - 4$

SOLUTION The situation should represent subtracting 4 from the product of 6 and n.

ANSWER Michael buys some 6-packs of bottled water and gives away 4 bottles.

PROBLEM 5 $(18 + 32) \div p$

SOLUTION The parentheses indicate that the sum $18 + 32$ is divided by p.

ANSWER Carlos has 18 pennies and 32 nickels. He divides the coins into equal piles.

Problem Set

Translate the phrase into a math expression.

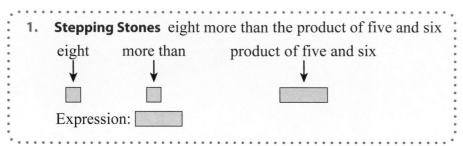

1. **Stepping Stones** eight more than the product of five and six

    eight   more than   product of five and six

    Expression:

2. twelve more than the quotient of six divided by three

3. the quotient of twenty divided by four more than one

4. six times the product of eleven and two

5. twice a number decreased by 12

6. 15 divided by a number, then decreased by 2

7. 30 added to a number that is decreased by 5

8. 6 times the sum of a number and 5

9. one-third of the difference between 10 and a number

10. 5 plus 8 times the number of hours

11. the sum of 6 and a number divided by 5

12. twenty less a quantity divided into 16 equal parts

13. the quotient of 75 and the difference of a number and 10

Write a math expression for the situation.

14. Dinner cost $72, plus a tip of $13. Six people split the total bill evenly. Write an expression to show how much each person paid.

15. A carpenter charges $50, plus $65 per hour. Write an expression to show the total charge for 3 hours of work.

16. Julia ships some books that weigh 18 oz each in a box that weighs 4 oz. Write an expression to show the total weight of the shipped box.

17. Barb wants to save $350 for a trip. She has been saving $85 each week. Write an expression to show how much more she needs to save.

18. **Challenge** Cherries cost $2.79 per lb. Raspberries cost $3.99 per lb. Write an expression to show the total cost of c pounds of cherries and a bag of raspberries that weighs twice as much.

Write a situation for the math expression.

19. $3 \cdot (k + 7)$

20. $(4 + a) \div 2$

21. $6p - 2$

22. $45 + (q + 9)$

23. $5 \cdot p + 11$

24. $20 - m \div 3$

25. $36 - 2w$

26. $4 \cdot \frac{n}{8}$

27. $\frac{3}{r} \cdot 7$

28. $15 + \frac{g}{3}$

29. $x + 3y$

30. Challenge $\frac{5a + b}{2}$

Choose the answer.

31. Which expression shows the sum of 18 and y, divided into 2 equal parts?

   A. $18 \div 2 + y$

   B. $18 \div y + 2$

   C. $(18 + y) \div 2$

   D. $18 + y \div 2$

32. The basketball league orders 50 new basketballs. Each coach receives 4 new balls. Which expression shows the number of basketballs that are left after some are given to coaches?

   A. $4 \cdot c - 50$

   B. $50 - 4 \div c$

   C. $(50 - 4) \cdot c$

   D. $50 - 4c$

33. Which expression describes a $5 discount on the purchase of some tickets that cost $15 each?

   A. $15t - 5$

   B. $5t - 15$

   C. $15t + 5$

   D. $5t + 15$

34. Which situation can be described by the expression $3x + 9$?

   A. 9 shirts in each of 3 stacks

   B. 9 shirts more than 3 shirts

   C. 9 equal stacks of shirts on 3 tables

   D. 3 equal stacks of shirts plus 9 more shirts

Problem-Solving Strategies

When you solve problems, it helps to have a plan and a set of sound strategies.

Pólya's 4-Step Problem-Solving Plan

Hungarian mathematician George Pólya developed this general approach to solving problems:

1. Understand the problem.
2. Devise a plan.
3. Carry out the plan.
4. Look back.

➤ Guess-and-Test Strategy

When you need to find different quantities that are related to each other, you can try guessing an answer and then testing it to see if it is correct. If the guess is not correct, refine your guess and try again.

Example

PROBLEM 1 Kim has 7 coins in her pocket that have a total value of 50¢. Each coin is either a nickel or a dime. How many nickels does Kim have?

SOLUTION Guess that Kim has 3 nickels and 4 dimes. Find the value of the coins.

$$(3 \cdot 5) + (4 \cdot 10) = 55$$
$$55 > 50$$

The value is too high, so adjust the guess to 4 nickels and 3 dimes.

$$(4 \cdot 5) + (3 \cdot 10) = 50$$

ANSWER Kim has 4 nickels and 3 dimes.

➤ Draw-a-Figure Strategy

Sometimes, drawing a figure can help you visualize a problem situation. This strategy works well with problems involving distances or areas.

Example

PROBLEM 2 Andre leaves his campsite and hikes west 450 m. Then he turns south and hikes 300 m. Finally, he turns east and hikes another 450 m. How far is Andre from his campsite?

SOLUTION Andre has hiked three sides of a rectangle. His distance from the campsite is the length of the opposite side of the rectangle.

ANSWER Andre is 300 m from his campsite.

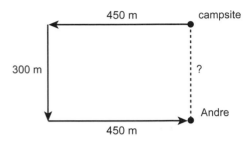

→ Relate-to-a-Simpler-Problem Strategy

Sometimes you can solve a simpler problem, and then extend the solution to the original problem.

Example

PROBLEM 3 A farmer sets posts 12 ft apart to build a new fence. How many posts will he need to set to build a fence 180 ft long?

SOLUTION Start by thinking about the number of posts it takes to build a smaller fence. The farmer needs 2 posts for one 12 ft section of fence. He needs 3 posts for two 12 ft sections, and 4 posts for three 12 ft sections.
So for *n* sections, the farmer needs $n + 1$ posts.

There are $180 \div 12 = 15$ sections of fence. $15 + 1 = 16$

ANSWER The farmer needs 16 posts.

→ Break-into-Parts Strategy

You can break some problems into smaller parts.

Example

PROBLEM 4 A factory ships 280 boxes to Maryland, 155 boxes to Delaware, and 165 boxes to Virginia. Each box weighs 40 lb. What is the total weight of the boxes shipped?

SOLUTION First find the total number of boxes.
$280 + 155 + 165 = 600$

Then find the total weight of the boxes. $600 \cdot 40 = 24,000$

ANSWER The total weight of the boxes shipped is 24,000 lb.

Problem Set

Solve using the guess-and-test strategy.

1. **Stepping Stones** Michael and Susan have a combined age of 17 years. Michael is 5 years older than Susan. How old is Michael?

$$m + s = 17 \text{ and } m - s = 5$$

Try $m = 10$.

$10 + s = 17; s = \square$

$10 - s = 5; s = \square$

Try $m = \square$.

$\square + s = 17; s = \square$

$\square - s = 5; s = \square$

Michael is $\square$ years old.

2. Ella's two puppies weigh a total of 37 oz. One puppy weighs 3 oz more than the other. How much does the lighter puppy weigh?

3. The math club has 57 members who are in sixth or seventh grades. There are twice as many sixth graders as seventh graders. How many sixth graders are in the club?

4. Ira has 28¢ in his pocket. He has 20 coins that are either pennies or nickels. How many nickels does Ira have?

Solve using the draw-a-figure strategy.

5. Four friends are standing in line to buy tickets. Carlos is not first in line. Paige is ahead of Kate. Lisa is last in line. Who is first in line?

6. A snail is at the bottom of a 10 ft wall. Each day it climbs up 3 ft. Each night it slides back down 1 ft. On which day will it reach the top of the wall? *5th*

7. **Challenge** There are 30 players at lacrosse camp. Twelve of the players are girls. Eight players have played lacrosse before. Three players are girls who have played lacrosse before. How many players are boys who have not played lacrosse before?

8. **Challenge** There are juice boxes in the refrigerator. One-sixth of them are apple juice. One-fourth of them are grape juice. The other 14 boxes are cranberry juice. How many boxes of apple juice are there?

Solve using the relate-to-a-simpler-problem strategy.

9. **Stepping Stones** Three people can sit at each long side of a rectangular table, and 1 person can sit at each end. How many people can sit at 13 tables that are all placed end-to-end?

8 people can sit at 1 table.

$\square$ people can sit at 2 tables.

$\square$ people can sit at 3 tables.

So $\square$ people can sit at n tables.

$\square$ people can sit at 13 tables.

10. The population of Medfield is 7000. Capital City's population is $\frac{8}{25}$ of Medfield's. What is Capital City's population? *2240*

11. **Challenge** Rosita is building models of prisms using foam balls and straws. How many of each will she need to make a prism with 16-sided bases?

Solve using the break-into-parts strategy.

12. Stepping Stones What is the area of this figure? Use the formula $A = lw$ to find the area of a rectangle with length l and width w.

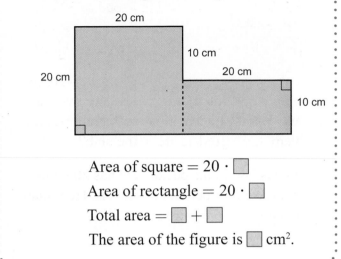

Area of square = $20 \cdot \square$

Area of rectangle = $20 \cdot \square$

Total area = $\square + \square$

The area of the figure is $\square$ cm².

13. The month of January is 744 hours long. How many minutes are there in January? (Hint: 1 hour = 60 minutes)

14. Challenge What is the area of this figure?

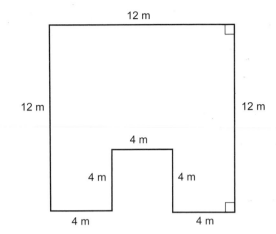

Solve.

15. A farmer keeps a total of 17 cows and chickens on his farm. His animals have a total of 40 legs. How many cows does the farmer have? 3

16. A rectangular tent is 16 ft long and 5 ft wide. Each 4 ft section of tent has a post on each end, except for the 5 ft sides. How many posts are there in the tent?

17. There are labels on the front and top of each box of auto parts. How many labels are showing if there are boxes stacked in 4 equal rows of 8?

18. Martin starts at one corner of a square field and walks 40 steps along one side to another corner of the field. He turns and walks 30 steps, and then walks straight back to where he started. What is the area of the part of the field he walked around?

19. Max spends a total of 150 minutes studying math, science, and social studies. He spends twice as much time on his math as on either his science or social studies. How much time does Max spend studying science?

Choose the answer.

20. A carpenter makes legs for 3-legged stools and 4-legged tables. He makes a total of 68 legs. For how many stools did he make legs?

   A.   8   C.   24

   B.   11   D.   36

21. One-third of the balls in the gym closet are basketballs. One-fourth of the balls are footballs. The other 10 are soccer balls. How many balls are in the closet?

   A.   16   C.   24

   B.   18   D.   34

Identifying Information in Word Problems

Before solving any problem, decide which facts you need and which you don't.

➤ Identifying Needed Information

You can identify what information in a word problem is needed by first looking at what the problem asks you to find. Think about the information you will use to solve the problem. The remaining facts aren't needed.

Example

Solve. Identify the information that is needed to solve the problem.

PROBLEM 1 Games, toys, and books are all on sale at the toy store. Mark buys 4 games. How much does he save by buying the games on sale?

	Game	Toy	Book
Regular Price	$6.50	$8.00	$3.00
Sale Price	$5.00	$6.50	$2.75

SOLUTION The problem asks for the amount saved, which is the regular price minus the sale price for the 4 games.

Needed information: regular price of games: $6.50
     sale price of games: $5.00
     number of games Mark buys: 4

Information not needed: prices of toys and books

Write an expression to represent the amount saved.

$4 \cdot 6.5 - 4 \cdot 5$
$26 - 20$ Simplify.
6

ANSWER Mark saves $6.00.

Think About It

You also could write and simplify the expression $4 \cdot (6.5 - 5)$ to solve Problem 1.

The distributive property shows that the expression is equivalent to $(4 \cdot 6.5) - (4 \cdot 5)$.

Example

PROBLEM 2 Gerri has 40 math practice problems to solve. It takes her 2 minutes to solve each problem. It takes her 4 minutes to read each page in her literature book. How long will it take Gerri to read 27 pages in her literature book?

SOLUTION The problem asks for the amount of time Gerri will spend reading 27 pages in her literature book.

Needed information: number of pages: 27
time it takes to read each page: 4 minutes

Information not needed: number of math practice problems: 40
time it takes to solve each math problem: 2 minutes

Write an expression to represent the amount of time Gerri will spend reading the pages.

$4 \cdot 27$
108   Simplify.

ANSWER It will take Gerri 108 minutes to read the pages in her literature book.

➡ Identifying Missing Information

You might be asked to solve a problem, but not be given all the information you need to solve it. Look first at what the problem asks you to find. Then search through the problem for the information you need to solve it. Identify any information that is missing.

Example

State what information is needed to solve the problem.

PROBLEM 3 Jason's family got a 2-month-old puppy. The puppy gained 7 oz in one week and 11 oz the next week. How much does the puppy weigh now?

SOLUTION The problem asks for the puppy's weight now.

Needed information: puppy's original weight: ?
amount of weight gained the first week: 7 oz
amount of weight gained the next week: 11 oz

ANSWER The missing information is the puppy's original weight.

TOPIC

Problem Set

Solve. Identify the information that is needed to solve the problem.

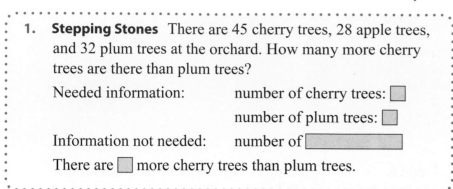

1. **Stepping Stones** There are 45 cherry trees, 28 apple trees, and 32 plum trees at the orchard. How many more cherry trees are there than plum trees?

   Needed information: number of cherry trees: ☐

   number of plum trees: ☐

   Information not needed: number of ▭

   There are ☐ more cherry trees than plum trees.

2. Gary buys some $3 raffle tickets. He gives 5 tickets to his sister and keeps 8 tickets for himself. How many raffle tickets did Gary buy?

3. Linda walks 3 miles in 40 minutes on Friday. She walks twice that far on Saturday. How far did she walk on both days?

4. A store has a special offer on a pack of 12 pencils, 4 pens, and 8 colored markers. The special price is $12.50 for the pack. What fraction of the tools are pencils?

5. Trudy is making punch for a party. She plans to use 4 cans of frozen lemonade, 2 baskets of strawberries, and 1 can of frozen orange juice. What is the ratio of lemonade to orange juice?

6. The length and width of a rectangular garden are 40 m and 20 m. The area is 800 m². How many meters of fence are needed to go around this garden?

7. Last month the pet store sold 48 birds, 58 fish, and 17 hamsters. The average cost of each pet was $9.25. How many more fish than birds did the store sell?

8. Ralph pays $15 plus $3 per hour to rent a bicycle. He has the bike for 3.5 hours and travels 8.2 miles. How much did it cost Ralph to rent the bike? 53

9. Lionel is saving money to buy a new music player. So far he has saved $35 and the player costs $129. He can save $16 per week from his allowance. How much more does Lionel have to save?

10. **Challenge** Carla buys a notebook, 2 pens, and a box of markers. She spends $12. The pens are $1.50 each, pencils are $3 per box, and a box of markers is $4. How much does the notebook cost?

State what information is missing but is needed to solve the problem.

11. **Stepping Stones** Todd pays $8 for lunch, which includes a salad, a sandwich, and a drink. The salad costs $3, and the sandwich costs more than the salad. How much does the drink cost?

    Needed information: total cost of lunch: 2

    cost of salad: 3

    cost of sandwich: 4

    The cost of the ⎡Soda⎤ is missing from the problem.

12. Students are enrolled in grades 6, 7, and 8. There are 358 students in the sixth grade and 278 students in the eighth grade. How many students are in the seventh grade?

13. At the first bus stop, 5 passengers get on the bus. Then 12 people get off at the next stop. How many people are on the bus now?

14. Mr. Randall uses 86 square tiles for the kitchen floor. The floor has the shape of a rectangle. Find the width of the floor.

15. **Challenge** In Patrick's neighborhood, 28% of the students have mobile phones. How does the percent change if 5 more students get mobile phones?

Choose the answer.

16. Benji needs 120 in. of wire for a school project. What information is needed to find out if 3 spools of wire will be enough?

    A. cost of one spool of wire

    B. number of inches in each spool

    C. the time it will take to complete the project

    D. length and width of poster board for the project

17. There are 168 students signed up for a field trip. A special exhibit has 285 examples of butterflies from all over the world. Each student pays $3 for the bus, plus the cost of the admission ticket. What is the cost per student for this trip?

    A. $56

    B. $504

    C. cannot solve; there is extra information

    D. cannot solve; there is not enough information

Estimation and Reasonableness

Estimation can help you solve problems and check for reasonable answers.

➠ Estimating by Rounding

Definitions

An **estimate** is a good guess or a rough calculation of an answer. It is a number close to the exact answer.

One way to estimate is by rounding. You **round** a number by changing it to the nearest given place value.

How to Round Numbers

Rounding using a number line:
To round 43 to the nearest ten, locate the number on a number line. The number 43 is closer to 40 than to 50, so it rounds to 40.

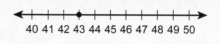
40 41 42 43 44 45 46 47 48 49 50

Rounding rules for a number:
1. In the number, look at the digit one place to the right of the place value you will round to.
2. If that digit is greater than 5, round the number up by adding 1 to the digit in the rounding place.
3. If that digit is less than 5, round the number down by keeping the digit in the rounding place the same.
4. If that digit is 5 *and* the digits to its right are all zeros, round to the nearest even number. If the digits to the right are nonzero, then round up.
5. Change all the digits to the right of the rounding place to zeros.

Tip

Underlining the digit in the place you are rounding to can help you keep that place in mind. Then circle the digit to its right.

For example, mark if you want to round 4539 to the nearest hundred: 45③9.

Tip

2581 rounded to the nearest thousand is 3000.

2500 rounded to the nearest even thousand is 2000.

3500 rounded to the nearest even thousand is 4000.

Example

PROBLEM 1 Estimate $37 + 22$ by rounding to the nearest ten.

SOLUTION 37 rounds up to 40. 22 rounds down to 20.
$40 + 20 = 60$

ANSWER The sum $37 + 22$ is about 60.

➥ Estimating with Friendly Numbers

Friendly numbers are numbers that are easy to work with for a given operation.

Example

Use friendly numbers to estimate the value of the expression.

PROBLEM 2 $35 \div 3$

SOLUTION The number 36 is close to 35, and you can use mental math to divide 36 by 3. The quotient of $35 \div 3$ is close to the quotient of $36 \div 3$.
$36 \div 3 = 12$

ANSWER $35 \div 3 \approx 12$

PROBLEM 3 $27 \cdot 4$

SOLUTION The number 25 is close to 27, and you can use mental math to multiply $25 \cdot 4$. The product of $27 \cdot 4$ is close to the product of $25 \cdot 4$.
$25 \cdot 4 = 100$

ANSWER $27 \cdot 4 \approx 100$

➥ Finding Upper and Lower Bound Estimates

Definitions

An **upper bound estimate** is an estimate to a problem that is greater than the actual solution could be.

A **lower bound estimate** is an estimate that is less than the actual solution could be.

Think about how rounding each number up or down will affect the estimate. Then round the numbers in the problem so that the estimate is either higher or lower than the exact answer.

Tip

Look at the context of the problem to help you decide whether you need to find an upper bound estimate or a lower bound estimate. Look for key words like *at most* or *at least*.

Think About It

When rounding numbers to find a lower bound or an upper bound estimate, you won't always be finding the nearest place value.

Example

PROBLEM 4 Find lower bound and upper bound estimates for $27 + 64$.

SOLUTION

$20 + 60 = 80$ To find a lower bound estimate, round both addends down.

$30 + 70 = 100$ To find an upper bound estimate, round both addends up.

ANSWER A lower bound estimate of $27 + 64$ is 80, and an upper bound estimate is 100.

TOPIC

Problem Set

Round the number to the given place value.

1. **Stepping Stones** 86; tens

   The digit in the tens place is ☐.

   The digit in the ones place is ☐.

   6 ☐ 5, so round ▭.

   The number 86 rounded to the nearest ten is ☐.

2. 43; tens

3. 661; hundreds

4. 4889; thousands

5. 7.2; ones

6. 3.8; ones

7. 8.14; tenths

8. 6.02; tenths

9. 24.617; hundredths

10. 1.044; hundredths   10.40

11. 561; tens

12. 9211; hundreds

13. 54,839; thousands

14. 287.5; ones

15. 500.24; tenths

Estimate the value of the expression by rounding each number to the given place value.

16. $14 + 43$; tens

17. $35 + 62$; tens

18. $665 + 234$; hundreds

19. $6092 + 3614$; thousands

20. $2968 + 9912$; thousands

21. $68 - 29$; tens

22. $425 - 137$; hundreds

23. $3447 - 1922$; thousands

24. $56 \cdot 9$; round 56 to the nearest ten

25. $249 \cdot 8$; round 249 to the nearest hundred

26. $46 \div 5$; round 46 to the nearest ten

Solve.

27. Marcus has 78 baseball cards and 45 basketball cards. Estimate the total number of cards Marcus has.

28. Shelley's family is traveling 430 miles to visit her grandparents. So far they have driven 274 miles. Estimate how much farther they have to drive.

29. Penn earns $6.57 per hour at his job. Estimate how much Penn earns for working 40 hours.

30. **Challenge** Explain which is greater: the number 3895 rounded to the nearest ten or to the nearest hundred.

Use friendly numbers to estimate the value of the expression.

31. **Stepping Stones** $47 \div 6$

The number ☐ is close to 47 and is easily divisible by 6.

The quotient ☐ $\div 6$ is close to $47 \div 6$.

☐ $\div 6 =$ ☐

The quotient $47 \div 6$ is about ☐.

32. $48 + 49$

33. $197 - 120$

34. $47 \cdot 5$

35. $25 \div 6$

36. $243 \cdot 4$

37. $268 \div 9$

38. $488 \cdot 2$

39. $487 + 611$

40. $897 \div 3$

41. $19 \cdot 43$

42. $467 \div 70$

43. $748 \div 23$

44. $329 \cdot 30$

45. **Challenge** $3549 \div 58$

Find the lower bound estimate and upper bound estimate by rounding to the greatest place.

46. **Stepping Stones** $45 + 38$

Lower bound: round down

45 rounds down to ☐.

38 rounds down to ☐.

☐ $+$ ☐ $=$ ☐

Upper bound: round up

45 rounds up to ☐.

38 rounds up to ☐.

☐ $+$ ☐ $=$ ☐

47. $92 \cdot 30$

48. $47 - 29$

49. $259 - 118$

50. $875 - 493$

51. $377 \div 18$

52. **Challenge** $7634 \div 31$

Choose the answer.

53. What is 348 rounded to the nearest hundred?

A. 300

B. 340

C. 350

D. 400

54. Which number rounds up when rounded to the nearest tenth?

A. 55.24

B. 170.93

C. 0.12

D. 8.15

55. Which is the estimated sum when the addends in $439 + 528$ are rounded to the nearest hundred?

A. 800

B. 700

C. 1000

D. 900

56. What are the lower bound estimate and upper bound estimate of $976 - 205$?

A. 600; 800

B. 500; 800

C. 600; 700

D. 500; 700

Precision

You measure with different tools and units depending on how exact you need to be.

➤ Calculating with a Given Precision

Definitions

Precision is an indication of how finely a measurement was made. Precision depends on the unit of measure you use. The smaller the unit of measure used, the more precise the measurement is.

When you calculate with measurements, your answer shouldn't be any more precise than the least-precise measurement. First perform the calculation. Then round your answer to the same place to which the least-precise measurement is given.

> **Remember**
>
> To round, look at the digit one place to the right of the place you are rounding to. If that digit is greater than 5, round up. If the digit is less than 5, round down. Then change all the digits to the right to zeros.

Example

Solve. Give your answer with the appropriate precision.

PROBLEM 1 Three rock samples have masses of 2.97 kg, 3.8 kg, and 8.946 kg. What is the total mass of the rocks?

SOLUTION

$2.97 + 3.8 + 8.946$ Write an expression to show the total mass.
15.716   Add.

ANSWER The total mass of the rocks is 15.7 kg.

PROBLEM 2 A runner completes a 26.2-mile marathon in 4.1 hours. What is her average speed?

SOLUTION

$\text{rate} = \frac{\text{distance}}{\text{time}}$ Use the rate formula.

$= \frac{26.2}{4.1}$ Substitute distance and time.

$= 6.3902439$ Use a calculator to divide.

The distance and time are given to the tenths place, so round the answer to the tenths place: 6.3902439 rounds to 6.4.

ANSWER The runner's average speed is 6.4 miles per hour.

TOPIC

➜ Estimating or Finding an Exact Answer

Some problems require you to find an exact answer. But sometimes an estimate is all that's required. When deciding whether to estimate or find the exact answer, carefully consider the situation.

Example

State whether you should estimate or find the exact answer. Then solve.

PROBLEM 3 Riley wants to fill a sandbox with 500 lb of sand. He can move sand from a pile by using a bucket that will carry $22\frac{3}{8}$ lb of sand. About how many buckets full of sand will he need to carry?

SOLUTION The word *about* in the problem tells you that you can estimate.

Replace $22\frac{3}{8}$ with friendly numbers and divide to find upper and lower bound estimates.

Find a lower bound estimate.   Find an upper bound estimate.
Replace $22\frac{3}{8}$ with 25.   Replace $22\frac{3}{8}$ with 20.
$500 \div 25 = 20$ $500 \div 20 = 25$

ANSWER An estimate can be used. Riley will need to carry between 20 and 25 buckets of sand.

> **Tip**
> Look for words such as *about*, *around*, *at least*, or *at most* that will tell you the answer should be an estimate.

PROBLEM 4 Carol is making fruit punch to sell at the farmers' market. She will mix 300 mL of orange juice, 175 mL of apple juice, and 250 mL of ginger ale in each 1 L bottle. Then she will fill the bottle with pineapple juice. How much pineapple juice will she need to add to each bottle?

SOLUTION It is important that Carol use the exact amount of pineapple juice so the containers don't have too much punch or not enough punch. Find an exact answer.

$300 + 175 + 250$	Write an expression to show the volume of the first three ingredients.
725	Simplify.
$1000 - 725$	Write an expression to show how much pineapple juice to add.
275	Simplify.

ANSWER An exact answer is needed. Carol needs to add 275 mL of pineapple juice to each container.

Problem Set

Solve. Give your answer with the appropriate precision.

1. **Stepping Stones** Three wires are 6.5 m, 8.19 m, and 4.457 m long. What is the total length of the wires?

   $6.5 + 8.19 + 4.457 = \boxed{}$

   The least-precise measure is $\boxed{}$.
   Round the sum to the nearest $\boxed{}$.
   $\boxed{}$ rounds to $\boxed{}$.
   The total length of the wires is $\boxed{}$.

2. Sheila lives 4.75 km from the park. The library is 3.8 km farther away. How far does Sheila live from the library?

3. The ocean club collects 24.93 kg of trash on the first weekend of the summer. The club collects 18.3 kg the next weekend. How much more trash is collected the first weekend?

4. A scientist records a temperature of 234.566°C in an experiment. The temperature then falls 48.01°C. What was the temperature after it fell?

5. What is the average price per pound of 2 steaks that weigh 0.7 lb and 0.75 lb and cost a total of $8.68?

6. Ricardo's dog weighs 78 lb. A weight of 2.2 lb is equivalent to about 1 kg in mass. What is Ricardo's dog's mass?

7. Patrice buys 15.70 gallons of gas for $2.799 per gallon. How much does Patrice pay for gas?

8. Michael bikes 36 mi last week and 38.4 mi this week. What is the average distance he bikes?

9. **Challenge** Maggie spent 3.5 hours working on her science project, 126 minutes doing her math assignment, and 2 hours working on an English assignment. How long did she spend in all on the schoolwork?

State whether you should estimate or find the exact answer. Then solve.

10. **Stepping Stones** Kelly is filling a 1 qt container with colored sand for an art project. She has used $\frac{1}{2}$ c of red sand, $1\frac{3}{4}$ c of blue sand, and $1\frac{1}{3}$ c of yellow sand. How much green sand does she need to add to fill the container? (Hint: 1 qt = 4 c)

    Kelly can't use too much sand and she can't leave any empty space in the container, so find an $\boxed{}$.

    $\frac{1}{2} + 1\frac{3}{4} + 1\frac{1}{3} = \boxed{}$

    $4 - \boxed{} = \boxed{}$

    Kelly needs to add $\boxed{}$ of green sand.

11. Jeremy is having a party. He plans for each of his 12 guests to have a $\frac{1}{3}$ lb burger. He buys three packages of ground beef weighing $\frac{9}{10}$ lb, $1\frac{1}{8}$ lb, and 2 lb. Does Jeremy need to buy more ground beef?

12. The record rainfall in Centerville for the first six months of a year is 304.8 cm. This year, the first six monthly rain totals were 49.7 cm, 18.2 cm, 61.7 cm, 74.4 cm, 25.7 cm, and 12.6 cm. How many centimeters below the record is the first six months total from this year?

13. Renaldo wants to make 3 cushions that take 89.8 cm of trim each. He has 300 cm of trim. Does he have enough trim to make the cushions?

14. Anisa is going to make 6 same-size banners to hang around the school for spirit week. She wants to use the entire $37\frac{1}{2}$ ft of banner paper she has. How many feet long will each of the banners be?

15. In order to make the cross-country team, Leslie must have run at least 25 mi over the past three days. Her running distances for the last three days were $9\frac{4}{10}$ mi, $8\frac{9}{10}$ mi, and $6\frac{6}{10}$ mi. Did Leslie run at least 25 mi over the last three days?

16. Martin's youth group held an aluminum-can drive over the last six weeks. The group has a goal of collecting 400 lb of aluminum cans. On the first two weeks of the drive, the group collected $70\frac{1}{4}$ lb each week. For the next four weeks of the drive, the youth group collected $85\frac{7}{8}$ lb each week. Did the group meet its goal?

17. Tamika wants to make 3 picture frames that will take 42.8 cm of trim each and 2 picture frames that take 74.5 cm of trim each. She has 280 cm of picture frame trim. Does she have enough trim to make the picture frames?

18. Jorge bought a phone card that has 120 minutes of phone use on it. The first week he used 37.7 minutes, the second week he used 12.7 minutes, and the third and fourth weeks he used 31.9 minutes each week. How many minutes of phone use does he have left on the card?

19. John is going to paint some rooms in his house. He will be painting a total of 2300 square feet. He buys 7 gallons of paint that will cover 306 square feet per gallon. Does John need to buy more paint?

20. **Challenge** Reggie is putting a fence around the perimeter of three sides of his front yard and four sides of his backyard. Two sides of his front yard are each 15.75 m long and the third side is 28.2 m long. Three sides of his backyard are each 18.25 m long and the other side is 15.6 m long. Reggie bought enough supplies to fence in a total of 130 m. Does Reggie need to buy more materials to be able to complete the job?

Choose the answer.

21. There are 0.459 L of blue liquid and 0.77 L of red liquid. What is the total volume of liquid to the appropriate degree of precision?

   A. 1 L   C. 1.23 L

   B. 1.3 L   D. 1.259 L

22. Wes has 150 m of tape to mark the boundaries of a piece of land with side lengths of 36.2 m, 41.6 m, 39.4 m, and 31.2 m. How much tape will he have left over?

   A. 1.2 m   C. 2 m

   B. 1.6 m   D. 3 m

Chapter 1 Review

Choose the answer.

1. Which point represents 36?

E	F		G				H			

   34 35 36 37 38 39 40 41 42 43 44

   A. point E C. point G

   B. point F D. point H

2. What value is equivalent to the expression $3 \cdot (4 - 2)$?

   A. 6   C. 10

   B. 8   D. 12

3. What value is equivalent to the expression $6 + 6 \div 2$?

   A. 6   C. 24

   B. 9   D. 48

4. Which equation demonstrates the commutative property of addition?

   A. $p + (9 + g) = (p + 9) + g$

   B. $6r \cdot 125 = 125 \cdot 6r$

   C. If $4m = 28$, then $28 = 4m$.

   D. $p + 3 = 3 + p$

5. Which expression represents the word phrase "an amount less than 41"?

   A. $41 - x$ C. $41 + x$

   B. $x - 41$ D. $x \cdot 41$

6. David is 3 years older than his brother. They have a combined age of 23. How old is David?

   A. 7   C. 13

   B. 10   D. 16

7. Which situation can be described by the expression $8 \cdot c$?

   A. He worked 8 more hours than another day.

   B. He worked 8 hours each day for some days.

   C. He earned an $8 bonus in addition to his pay.

   D. He spent $8 from his pay.

8. Which expression describes a single $7 shipping fee for any number of items costing $29 each?

   A. $29 \cdot (k + 7)$ C. $7 \cdot 29 + k$

   B. $7 \cdot k + 29$ D. $29 \cdot k + 7$

9. Paulina ran 3.1 mi on Monday and 3.8 mi on Wednesday. She cycled 13.2 mi on Tuesday and 6.8 mi on Thursday. How much farther did Paulina cycle on Tuesday than on Thursday?

   A. 0.7 mi   C. 10.1 mi

   B. 6.4 mi   D. 3 mi

10. What is 6347 rounded to the nearest ten?

    A. 6350   C. 6300

    B. 6340   D. 6000

11. The masses of two soil samples are 45.6 g and 43.77 g. What is the total mass of the samples to the appropriate degree of precision?

    A. 89 g   C. 89.37 g

    B. 89.4 g   D. 90 g

Draw a number line, and then plot and label each point.

12. point A with a coordinate of 12.6

13. point B with a coordinate of 12.9

14. point C with a coordinate of 13.4

15. point D with a coordinate of 13.2

Simplify the expression.

16. $25 + 10 \div 5$

17. $12 \cdot 6 + 6$

18. $7 \cdot (8 - 2)$

19. $80 \div (8 + 12)$

Use properties to evaluate the expression.

20. $2 \cdot 7 \cdot 5$

21. $39 + (78 + 41)$

22. $9 \cdot 36$

23. $(23 + 8) + 17$

Translate into a math expression.

24. the sum of 8 and a number multiplied by 4

25. the quotient of 24 and the difference between a number and 6

26. A scooter costs $36 per day to rent, plus $0.25 per mile.

27. Shari saved $13 per week for some weeks, and then spent $25.

Solve.

28. Maria has a total of 36 white and blue socks in her drawer. She has 16 more white socks than she has blue socks. How many blue socks does Maria have?

29. Mr. Barrows averaged 60 mi/h while driving his car 693 mi. For how long did Mr. Barrows drive?

Estimate the value of the expression by rounding each number to the given place value.

30. $45 + 67$; tens

31. $618 - 472$; hundreds

32. $42 \cdot 68$; tens

33. $5690 + 3412$; hundreds

2 Distance: Addition Equations

If a farmer has painted part of a fence, how much more does she need to paint? Addition equations can help the farmer solve a problem like that one.

In This Chapter

You will learn how to use units to measure distance and perimeter. You'll also solve addition and subtraction equations and discover how those equations can give rise to the idea of negative numbers. Finally, you will use absolute value and operations with positive and negative numbers to solve problems.

Chapter Topics

- ▶ Foundations for Chapter 2
- ▶ Units of Distance
- ▶ Polygons and Perimeter
- ▶ Addition and Subtraction Equations
- ▶ Applications of Addition and Subtraction Equations
- ▶ Negative Numbers
- ▶ Absolute Value and Distance
- ▶ Addition and Subtraction with Negative Numberss
- ▶ Solving Addition Equations with Negative Numbers
- ▶ Chapter 2 Review

Many units can be used to measure the length of a fence.

CHAPTER 2   DISTANCE: ADDITION EQUATIONS   **47**

Foundations for Chapter 2

➡ **Adding Whole Numbers and Decimals**

How to Add Numbers

Vertical Addition
1. Align the addends by place value.
2. Add the digits in each place, beginning with the farthest place on the right and working to the left.
3. If the sum of the digits in any place is greater than 9, regroup 10 units from that place as 1 unit in the next-greater place.

Tip
When adding decimals, align the addends at the decimal point. Sometimes addends show different numbers of places to the right of the decimal point. When the numbers of places aren't the same, you can write zeros to the right of the last place in the addend(s) with fewer places.

Example A

Add. Use estimation to check that your answer is reasonable.

PROBLEM A-1 $824 + 469$

SOLUTION
$$\begin{array}{r} \overset{1}{8}24 \\ +469 \\ \hline 1293 \end{array}$$

ANSWER $824 + 469 = 1293$

CHECK Use estimation to check.
$800 + 500 = 1300$ ✓
The answer is close to the estimate, so the answer is reasonable.

PROBLEM A-2 $4.638 + 7.7$

SOLUTION Use the equivalent decimal 7.700 so that the addends have the same number of digits to the right of the decimal point.
$$\begin{array}{r} \overset{1}{4}.638 \\ +7.700 \\ \hline 12.338 \end{array}$$

ANSWER $4.638 + 7.7 = 12.338$

CHECK Use estimation to check.
$5 + 8 = 13$ ✓
The answer is close to the estimate, so the answer is reasonable.

Problem Set A

Add. Use estimation to check that your answer is reasonable.

1. $34 + 26$
2. $5.1 + 4.4$
3. $67 + 19$ 86
4. $3.8 + 2.7$
5. $482 + 466$

6. $671 + 358$
7. $4.53 + 6.8$ 11.33
8. $9.37 + 8.04$
9. $550 + 679$
10. $1383 + 4296$

11. $1.037 + 2.493$
12. $3.82 + 5.819$
13. $2.094 + 9.926$
14. $8712 + 8493$
15. $23.47 + 10.89$

➥ Subtracting Whole Numbers and Decimals

How to Subtract Numbers

Vertical Subtraction

1. Align the numbers by place value, with the greater number above the other.
2. Subtract the digits in each place, beginning with the farthest place on the right and working to the left.
3. If the greater digit is in the second number for any place value you are subtracting, then you must regroup.

Tip

Record any regrouping carefully. You might need to regroup in the same place twice.

Example B

Subtract. Use estimation to check your answer.

PROBLEM B-1 $467 - 283$

SOLUTION

$$\begin{array}{r} {\scriptstyle 3\ 16} \\ \cancel{46}7 \\ -283 \\ \hline 184 \end{array}$$

There are not enough tens to subtract, so regroup 1 of the 4 hundreds as 10 tens. Then there are 3 hundreds and 16 tens.

ANSWER $467 - 283 = 184$

CHECK Use estimation to check.
$500 - 300 = 200$ ✓

PROBLEM B-2 $8.23 - 4.77$

SOLUTION

$$\begin{array}{r} {\scriptstyle 11} \\ {\scriptstyle 7\ \cancel{8}\ 13} \\ 8.23 \\ -4.77 \\ \hline 3.46 \end{array}$$

There are not enough hundredths to subtract, so regroup 1 tenth as 10 hundredths. Then regroup 1 one as 10 tenths.

ANSWER $8.23 - 4.77 = 3.46$

CHECK Use estimation to check.
$8 - 5 = 3$ ✓

Problem Set B

Subtract. Use estimation to check your answer.

1. $87 - 42$
2. $93 - 51$
3. $8.7 - 4.5$
4. $7.694 - 3.987$
5. $4.3 - 2.8$

6. $549 - 86$
7. $344 - 52$
8. $6.72 - 5.8$
9. $8.2 - 4.603$
10. $4.02 - 0.55$ 3.47

11. $783 - 485$
12. $6.72 - 5.81$
13. $920 - 876$
14. $70.3 - 64.9$
15. $400 - 192$ 208

➔ Working with Units

Adding or Subtracting Measures

Numbers that represent measures with units can be added or subtracted only if the units are the same.

Look at the values' units. If the values have the same unit, you can add or subtract directly. If not, you will have to convert one of the values so both are written with the same units. If they can't be converted to the same units, they cannot be added or subtracted.

Example C

State whether the values can be added or subtracted. If one value needs to be converted to another, describe the conversion.

PROBLEM C-1 13 yd + 27 ft

SOLUTION The units are different: yards and feet. Either convert the yards to feet or convert the feet to yards. Once one value is converted, the measures can be added.

ANSWER The values can be added once one is converted to the other's measure.

PROBLEM C-2 45 kg − 4.6 kg

SOLUTION The units are the same: kilograms.

ANSWER The numbers can be subtracted.

PROBLEM C-3 3 people + 4 stereos

SOLUTION The units are different: people and stereos. Neither unit can be converted to the other.

ANSWER The numbers cannot be added.

Problem Set C

State whether the values can be added or subtracted. If one value needs to be converted to another, describe the conversion.

1. 3 m + 14 km

2. 6.7 g − 3.3 ft

3. 12 in. + 11 in.

4. 6 shovels + 8 snowballs

5. 4.55 L − 300 mL

6. 26.2 mi + 4224 yd

7. 14 dogs + 1 dog

8. 5 pt − 3.5 c

9. 1600 mm − 23 mg

10. 3.7 mg + 8.944 kg

FOUNDATIONS

Many units can be used to measure the length of a fence.

Planting the Seed

A number line can help you see whole numbers, decimals, and even negative numbers that are to the left of zero.

Units of Distance

How do you know which unit to use when measuring a distance? It depends on what you're measuring!

➡ Choosing the Best Unit

Common Units of Distance	
English Units	**Metric Units**
1 ft = 12 in.	1 cm = 10 mm
1 yd = 36 in.	1 m = 100 cm
1 yd = 3 ft	1 km = 1000 m
1 mi = 5280 ft	

When measuring a distance, such as the length, height, or width of an object, you need to choose a unit for the most useful measure.

Example

State the most appropriate English and metric units, if any, to use to measure.

PROBLEM 1 length of a grasshopper

SOLUTION A grasshopper is small and its length is much less than 1 ft and 1 m. Its length is much greater than 1 mm.

ANSWER Use inches or centimeters to measure the length of a grasshopper.

PROBLEM 2 height of a 4-story office building

SOLUTION A 4-story office building is hundreds of inches and thousands of centimeters high. Its height is also much less than 1 mi or 1 km.

ANSWER Use feet, yards, or meters to measure the height of a 4-story office building.

Example

PROBLEM 3 thickness of a human hair

SOLUTION A human hair is very small. Its thickness is much less than 1 in. or 1 cm.

ANSWER Use millimeters to measure the thickness of a human hair. There is no appropriate English unit to measure a distance this small.

➔ Converting Measurements

To convert from a larger unit to a smaller unit, you can multiply by the conversion factor. When converting from a smaller unit to a larger unit, you can divide by the conversion factor.

Example

Convert to the given unit.

PROBLEM 4 6 yd = ? ft

SOLUTION $6 \cdot 3 = 18$ Since a yard is a larger unit than a foot, multiply by 3.

ANSWER 6 yd = 18 ft

PROBLEM 5 8000 m = ? km

SOLUTION $8000 \div 1000 = 8$ Since a meter is a smaller unit than a kilometer, divide by 1000.

ANSWER 8000 m = 8 km

Problem Set

State the most appropriate English and metric units, if any, to use to measure.

....
1. **Stepping Stones** width of a book

   The width of a book could be less than or just greater than 1 ft.

   So it would be best to use [____] to measure its width.

   Its width would be much greater than 1 mm and much less than 1 m. It would be best to use [____] to measure the width of a book.
....

2. distance between Los Angeles and New York

3. length of a pencil

4. length of a paper clip

5. distance from the top of a table to the floor

6. length of a small greeting card

7. length of the front of a house

8. length of a brick

9. width of a human hand

10. length of an adult alligator

11. height of a mountain

12. length of a very small ant

13. height of a 12 oz can of juice

14. width of an eyelash

15. length of a marathon

16. length of a calculator

17. distance between Seattle and San Francisco

18. **Challenge** length of 40 pencils set in a line end to end

Convert to the given unit.

....
19. **Stepping Stones** 21,120 ft = [ ] mi

    Use the conversion factor, 1 mi = 5280 ft. A foot is a smaller unit than a mile, so [____] by the conversion factor.

    21,120 [ ] 5280 = [ ]
....

20. 600 cm = [ ] m

21. 12 ft = [ ] yd

22. 17 cm = [ ] mm

23. 8 ft = [ ] in.

24. 4 km = [ ] m

25. 15 m = [ ] cm

26. 400 mm = [ ] cm

27. 12 yd = [ ] ft

28. 17 km = [ ] m

29. 350 cm = [ ] m

30. 1759 m = [ ] km

31. 592 cm = [ ] m

32. 6.8 yd = [ ] in.

33. **Challenge** 7 km = [ ] cm

34. **Challenge** 3 mi = [ ] in.

Measure the length of the object. Give your answer in inches and feet.

35.

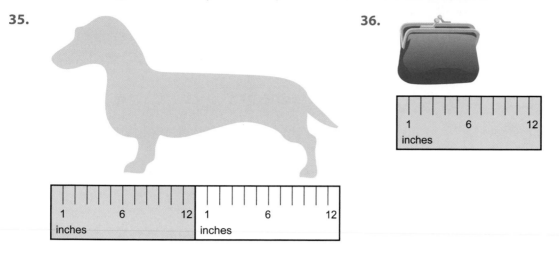

36.

Find the object and measure its length. Give your answer in inches, feet, centimeters, and meters.

37. bed

38. door

39. computer keyboard

40. chair

41. refrigerator

42. pencil

43. table

44. key

Choose the answer.

45. Which unit is the most appropriate choice to measure the height of a tree?

   A. millimeters

   B. centimeters

   C. feet

   D. miles

46. Which measure is equivalent to 24 ft?

   A. 2 in.

   B. 8 in.

   C. 220 in.

   D. 288 in.

Polygons and Perimeter

If you know the length of each side of a figure, you can find its perimeter.

➔ Finding the Perimeter of a Square or a Rectangle

Definition

The **perimeter** of a plane figure is the distance around it. The perimeter equals the sum of the lengths of the sides.

Formulas

The perimeter of a square with side length s is
$$P = 4s.$$
The perimeter of a rectangle with length l and width w is
$$P = 2l + 2w \text{ or } P = 2(l + w).$$

Remember

The opposite sides of any rectangle are the same length.

All 4 sides of a square are the same length.

Think About It

You know that $2l + 2w$ and $2(l + w)$ are equivalent because of the distributive property.

When finding the perimeter of a figure, remember to label your answer with the units for the side lengths.

Example

PROBLEM 1 Write two equations you could use to find the perimeter of the rectangle. Then find the perimeter.

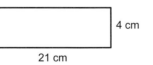

4 cm

21 cm

SOLUTION Substitute 21 for l and 4 for w into each formula.

$P = 2l + 2w = 2 \cdot 21 + 2 \cdot 4 = 42 + 8 = 50$

$P = 2(l + w) = 2(21 + 4) = 2 \cdot 25 = 50$

ANSWER The perimeter of the rectangle is 50 cm.

Example

Find the perimeter.

PROBLEM 2 square with $s = 8$ in.

SOLUTION Use the formula for the perimeter of a square. Substitute 8 for the side length s.

$$P = 4s$$
$$= 4 \cdot 8$$
$$= 32$$

ANSWER The perimeter is 32 in.

PROBLEM 3 rectangle with $l = 10$ cm and $w = 3.5$ cm

SOLUTION Use either formula. Substitute the given dimensions.

$$P = 2l + 2w$$
$$= 2 \cdot 10 + 2 \cdot 3.5$$
$$= 20 + 7$$
$$= 27$$

ANSWER The perimeter is 27 cm.

Tip

The numbers given in the problem can help you decide which formula to use.

In Problem 3, $P = 2l + 2w$ might be easier to use than $P = 2(l + w)$.

➔ Finding the Perimeter of Any Polygon

You can find the perimeter of any polygon by adding the lengths of its sides. Use what you know about polygons to find any missing side length.

Example

PROBLEM 4 Find the perimeter.

SOLUTION Add the lengths of the sides.

$$5.7 + 6.3 + 2 + 6.3 + 4.5 = 24.8$$

ANSWER The perimeter is 24.8 cm.

6.3 cm
5.7 cm
2 cm
4.5 cm
6.3 cm

PROBLEM 5 A farmer uses a long rectangular area to grow corn and a smaller square area for tomatoes. Find the amount of fence needed to go around both the rectangle and the square.

8 m
a
8 m
c
b
10 m
34 m

SOLUTION Side a is the side length for the square, so its measure is 8 m. In the rectangle, side b is opposite the side with length 10 m, so side b's measure is also 10 m. The length of side c is $34 \text{ m} - 8 \text{ m} = 26 \text{ m}$.

Add: $8 + 8 + 10 + 34 + 10 + 26 + 8 = 104$

ANSWER The farmer needs 104 m of fence.

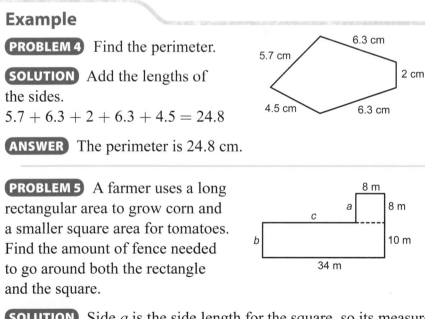

TOPIC

Problem Set

Write two equations you could use to find the perimeter of the rectangle.
Then find the perimeter.

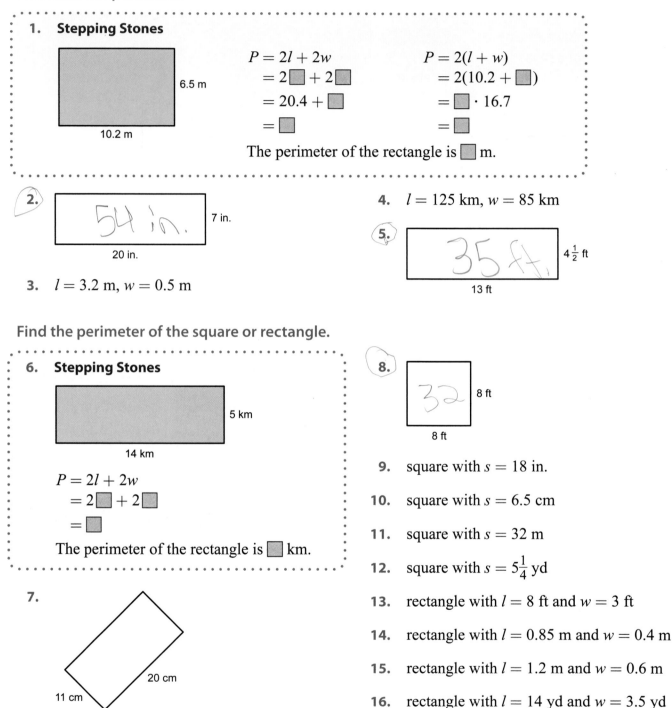

1. **Stepping Stones**

   6.5 m

   10.2 m

   $P = 2l + 2w$
   $= 2\square + 2\square$
   $= 20.4 + \square$
   $= \square$

   $P = 2(l + w)$
   $= 2(10.2 + \square)$
   $= \square \cdot 16.7$
   $= \square$

   The perimeter of the rectangle is $\square$ m.

2. 54 in.

   7 in.

   20 in.

3. $l = 3.2$ m, $w = 0.5$ m

4. $l = 125$ km, $w = 85$ km

5. 35 ft.

   $4\frac{1}{2}$ ft

   13 ft

Find the perimeter of the square or rectangle.

6. **Stepping Stones**

   5 km

   14 km

   $P = 2l + 2w$
   $= 2\square + 2\square$
   $= \square$

   The perimeter of the rectangle is $\square$ km.

7.

   20 cm

   11 cm

8. 32

   8 ft

   8 ft

9. square with $s = 18$ in.

10. square with $s = 6.5$ cm

11. square with $s = 32$ m

12. square with $s = 5\frac{1}{4}$ yd

13. rectangle with $l = 8$ ft and $w = 3$ ft

14. rectangle with $l = 0.85$ m and $w = 0.4$ m

15. rectangle with $l = 1.2$ m and $w = 0.6$ m

16. rectangle with $l = 14$ yd and $w = 3.5$ yd

17. **Challenge** square with $s = 0.004$ m

18. **Challenge** rectangle with $l = 2\frac{1}{8}$ in. and $w = 1\frac{1}{2}$ in.

Find the perimeter of the polygon.

19. Stepping Stones

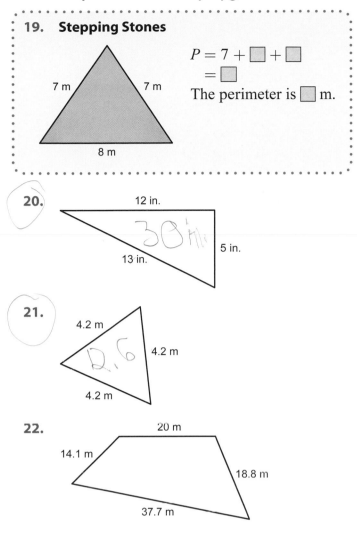

$P = 7 + \square + \square$

$= \square$

The perimeter is $\square$ m.

20.

12 in.

13 in.

5 in.

30 in.

21.

4.2 m

4.2 m

4.2 m

12.6

22.

20 m

14.1 m

18.8 m

37.7 m

23.

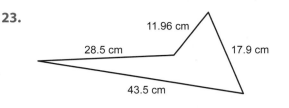

11.96 cm

28.5 cm

17.9 cm

43.5 cm

24. Challenge This figure has a vertical line of symmetry.

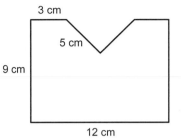

3 cm

5 cm

9 cm

12 cm

25. Challenge This design for a garden is made from two rectangles with a square in the middle. How far would you walk if you went all the way around the garden?

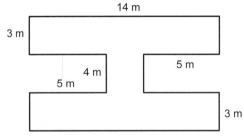

14 m

3 m

4 m

5 m

5 m

3 m

Choose the answer.

26. Which equation could be used to find the perimeter of a rectangle that has width 10 inches and length 20 inches?

A. $P = 2 \cdot 10 + 2 \cdot 10$

B. $P = 20 \cdot 10$

C. $P = 10 + 20$

D. $P = 2 \cdot 20 + 2 \cdot 10$

27. Which rectangle has the greatest perimeter?

A. 4 cm by 8 cm 24

B. 5 cm by 6 cm 22

C. 6 cm by 7 cm 26

D. 9 cm by 1 cm 20

Addition and Subtraction Equations

An addition equation can represent many problem situations.

➥ Solving Equations

Definitions
A **solution** of an equation with one variable is a value of the variable that makes the equation a true statement.
Equivalent equations are equations with the exact same solutions.

➥ Strategy: Guess-and-Test

One strategy you can use to solve addition equations is guess-and-test. With this method, guess a value for the variable that you think will make the equation true, and then test your guess. If your guess is wrong, make another guess using what you learned from your previous guesses.

Example

PROBLEM 1 The perimeter of this figure is 14 m. What is the length of the side labeled x?

SOLUTION The sum of the lengths of the sides is 14 m. Write an equation. Simplify.

$$x + 2 + 5 + 4 = 14$$
$$x + 11 = 14$$

Use guess-and-test.
Test $x = 2$: $2 + 11 \stackrel{?}{=} 14$
$$13 \neq 14$$

The equation is not true. Try a greater value.
Test $x = 3$: $3 + 11 \stackrel{?}{=} 14$
$$14 = 14$$

ANSWER Side x is 3 m long.

➥ Strategy: Using Properties

You'll find it easier to solve an equation if you can get the variable alone on one side of the equation. Properties can help you do that.

Addition and Subtraction Properties of Equality

The **addition and subtraction properties of equality** state that if you add or subtract the same number from both sides of an equation, the sides remain equal.

$$\text{If } a = b, \text{ then } a + c = b + c$$
$$\text{and } a - c = b - c.$$

Identity Property of Addition

The **identity property of addition** states that adding zero to a number gives a sum identical to that number.

$$a + 0 = a$$

Think About It

An equation is like a set of scales. To keep scales in balance, you must add equal weights to each side. Whatever you do to one side of the equation, you also must do to the other side to keep the sides equal.

Example

PROBLEM 2 Solve for y: $y - 7 = 19$

SOLUTION

$$y - 7 = 19$$
$$y - 7 + 7 = 19 + 7 \qquad \text{Add 7 to both sides.}$$
$$y + 0 = 26 \qquad \text{Simplify.}$$
$$y = 26 \qquad \text{Apply the identity property of addition.}$$

ANSWER $y = 26$

CHECK Replace y with 26 in the original equation. Then simplify and see if you have a true equation.

$$y - 7 = 19$$
$$26 - 7 \overset{?}{=} 19$$
$$19 = 19 \checkmark$$

Remember

Addition and subtraction are inverse operations. They undo each other.

So to "undo" the subtraction of 7, you can add 7.

PROBLEM 3 Jaime's car can travel 500 km on a tank of gas. If she began with a full tank of gas and traveled 350 km, how much farther can she travel on that tank?

SOLUTION Write an equation to represent the situation. Let d represent how much farther Jaime can travel.

$$d + 350 = 500 \qquad \text{Write an equation.}$$
$$d + 350 - 350 = 500 - 350 \qquad \text{Subtract 350 from both sides.}$$
$$d + 0 = 150 \qquad \text{Simplify.}$$
$$d = 150$$

ANSWER Jaime can travel 150 km farther.

TOPIC

Problem Set

Find the value of the unknown side length for the given perimeter *P*.

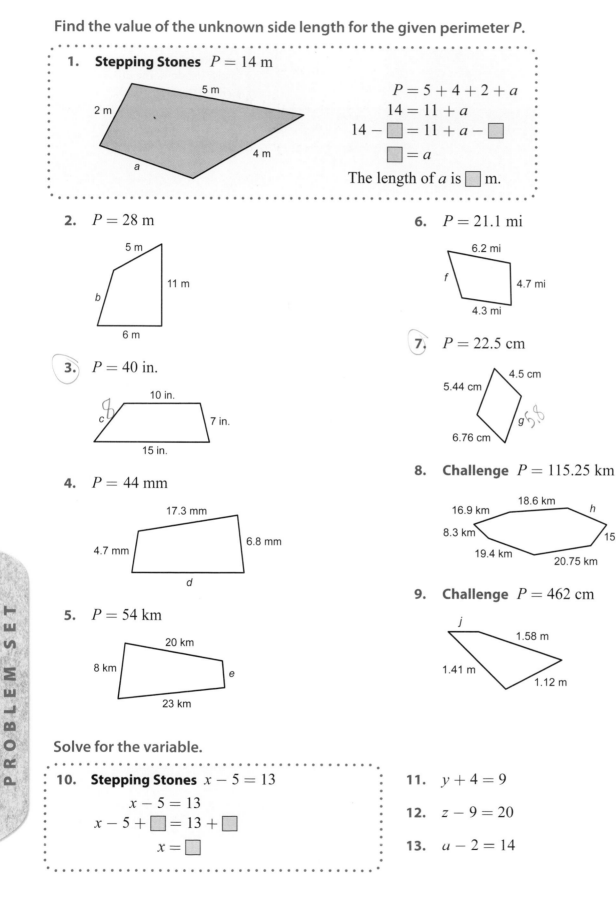

1. **Stepping Stones** $P = 14$ m

   5 m
   2 m
   4 m
   a

   $$P = 5 + 4 + 2 + a$$
   $$14 = 11 + a$$
   $$14 - \square = 11 + a - \square$$
   $$\square = a$$

   The length of *a* is $\square$ m.

2. $P = 28$ m

   5 m
   11 m
   b
   6 m

3. $P = 40$ in.

   10 in.
   c   7 in.
   15 in.

4. $P = 44$ mm

   17.3 mm
   4.7 mm   6.8 mm
   d

5. $P = 54$ km

   20 km
   8 km   *e*
   23 km

6. $P = 21.1$ mi

   6.2 mi
   f   4.7 mi
   4.3 mi

7. $P = 22.5$ cm

   4.5 cm
   5.44 cm
   g 5.8
   6.76 cm

8. **Challenge** $P = 115.25$ km

   18.6 km
   16.9 km   *h*
   8.3 km   15.1 km
   19.4 km
   20.75 km

9. **Challenge** $P = 462$ cm

   j
   1.58 m
   1.41 m
   1.12 m

Solve for the variable.

10. **Stepping Stones** $x - 5 = 13$

    $$x - 5 = 13$$
    $$x - 5 + \square = 13 + \square$$
    $$x = \square$$

11. $y + 4 = 9$

12. $z - 9 = 20$

13. $a - 2 = 14$

14. $16 = b + 7$

15. $22 = c - 4$ $c = 26$

16. $p + 12 = 17$

17. $q + 8 = 36$

18. $r - 5 = 14$

19. $n + 3.9 = 5.4$

20. $15 = k + 7.3$

21. $8.8 = m - 6.5$ $m = 2.3$

22. $x - 23.9 = 5.47$

23. $y + 16.46 = 42.7$

24. $z - 28.64 = 19.99$

25. Challenge $x + 5\frac{2}{3} = 7\frac{6}{7}$

26. Challenge $y - 8\frac{9}{11} = 13\frac{4}{5}$

Write and solve an equation to find the answer.

27. **Stepping Stones** Conner has a baseball card collection. He gives 17 cards to his friend and now has 49 baseball cards left. How many baseball cards did Conner originally have in his collection?

Let n represent the number of baseball cards Conner originally had.

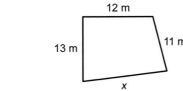

$$n - 17 = 49$$
$$n - 17 + \blacksquare = 49 + 17$$
$$n = \blacksquare$$

28. The drama teacher chose 19 students to be in the play and had to turn away 23 students. How many students wanted to be in the play?

29. In the championship football game, the Knights won with a score of 72 points, which was 66 points more than their opponent, the Gators, scored. How many points did the Gators score?

30. A fence with four sections has a perimeter of 43 ft. Three of the sections have lengths of 8 ft, 12 ft, and 11 ft. What is the length of the fourth section?

31. The amount of time James spends exercising each day, plus 45 minutes, is equal to 2.5 hours, which is the amount of time he spends reading and watching TV each day. How many hours does James spend exercising each day?

Choose the answer.

32. The perimeter of the polygon is 50 m. What is the value of x in meters?

A. $x = 11$

B. $x = 14$

C. $x = 66$

D. $x = 86$

12 m
13 m
11 m
x

33. What is the value of y in the equation $y - 8 = 12$?

A. $y = 4$

B. $y = 12$

C. $y = 20$

D. $y = 96$

Applications of Addition and Subtraction Equations

Writing and solving addition and subtraction equations can help you solve many practical problems.

➔ Using Addition and Subtraction Equations to Solve Problems

When writing an equation to solve a problem, you can first write a short sentence or set of phrases about the situation. Then you can change the words to numbers, symbols, and variables. Solve the equation by isolating the variable.

You can use the subtraction property of equality to isolate the variable when solving addition equations. When you're solving subtraction equations, you can use the addition property of equality to isolate the variable.

Remember

The addition and subtraction properties of equality allow you to add or subtract the same number from both sides of an equation, since the sides will remain equal.

➔ Application: Temperature

Example

Write and solve an equation to find the answer. Check your answer for reasonableness.

PROBLEM 1 At noon, the temperature was 17.3°C. That temperature is 2.4°C warmer than the temperature was at 8:00 a.m. What was the temperature at 8:00 a.m.?

SOLUTION Write an equation to represent the situation.

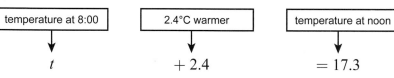

temperature at 8:00	2.4°C warmer	temperature at noon
t	$+\ 2.4$	$=\ 17.3$

Think About It

If it got warmer, then the temperature is increasing. So use an addition equation.

Solve the equation for t.

$$t + 2.4 = 17.3$$
$$t + 2.4 - 2.4 = 17.3 - 2.4 \quad \text{Subtract 2.4 from each side.}$$
$$t + 0 = 14.9 \quad \text{Simplify.}$$
$$t = 14.9 \quad \text{Apply the identity property of addition.}$$

ANSWER The temperature at 8:00 a.m. was 14.9°C.

CHECK Check the answer with the original problem. The answer 14.9 is about 2.5 less than the temperature was at noon. It warmed up by about that much, so the answer is reasonable. ✓

➔ Applications: Population and Money

Example

Write and solve an equation to find the answer. Check your answer for reasonableness.

PROBLEM 2 From 2000 to 2030, Florida's population is expected to grow by 12.7 million. In 2030, Florida's population is expected to be 28.7 million. What was Florida's population in 2000?

SOLUTION Write an equation to represent the situation.

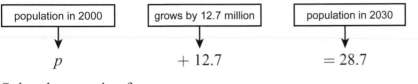

population in 2000	grows by 12.7 million	population in 2030
p	$+\ 12.7$	$=28.7$

Solve the equation for p.
$$p + 12.7 = 28.7$$
$$p + 12.7 - 12.7 = 28.7 - 12.7$$
$$p + 0 = 16$$
$$p = 16$$

ANSWER The population of Florida in 2000 was 16 million.

CHECK Check the answer with the original problem. The answer 16 million is about 13 million less than the population is expected to be in 2030. This difference is close to the expected growth of 12.7 million, so the answer is reasonable. ✓

PROBLEM 3 Hania put $225 from her paycheck into her savings account. She had $879.43 left. What was the total of Hania's paycheck?

SOLUTION Write an equation to represent the situation.

amount of paycheck	$225 into savings	amount left
t	$-\ \$225$	$=\ \$879.43$

Solve the equation for t.
$$t - 225 = 879.43$$
$$t - 225 + 225 = 879.43 + 225$$
$$t + 0 = 1104.43$$
$$t = 1104.43$$

ANSWER Hania's paycheck totaled $1104.43.

CHECK Check the answer with the original problem. The answer is about $1100, which is about $200 more than the amount left (about $900). The answer is reasonable. ✓

Think About It

If Florida's population is growing, then people are being *added* to the population total. So use an addition equation.

Think About It

If Hania is putting money from her paycheck into her savings account, she is *subtracting* money from her paycheck. So use a subtraction equation.

T O P I C

Problem Set

Write and solve an equation to find the answer. Check your answer
for reasonableness.

1. **Stepping Stones** On the second day of a two-day trip, Raul drove 142.7 mi.
He drove a total of 436.2 mi on the trip. How many miles did Raul drive on
the first day?

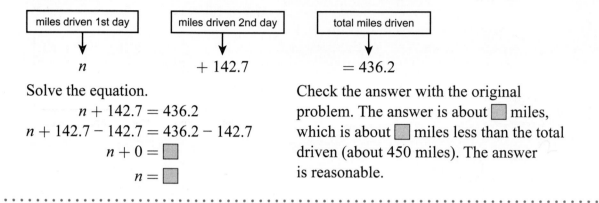

miles driven 1st day	miles driven 2nd day	total miles driven
n	$+ 142.7$	$= 436.2$

Solve the equation.

$$n + 142.7 = 436.2$$
$$n + 142.7 - 142.7 = 436.2 - 142.7$$
$$n + 0 = \boxed{}$$
$$n = \boxed{}$$

Check the answer with the original
problem. The answer is about $\boxed{}$ miles,
which is about $\boxed{}$ miles less than the total
driven (about 450 miles). The answer
is reasonable.

2. Palmer pours 17 cL of milk from a container
into a glass. He leaves 87 cL of milk in the
container. How many centiliters of milk are
in the container right before Palmer pours his
glass of milk?

3. Usman paints the entire length of a fence in a
day. He paints the last 12 m of the 38 m fence
in the afternoon. How many meters of the
fence does he paint in the morning? 26m

4. After two months, Rachel has saved enough
money to buy an MP3 player. During the
second month, she saves $87 and she pays
$199 for the MP3 player. How much does
Rachel save during the first month?

5. Sharifa spends $51 on the first day of her
vacation. This leaves her with $127 to spend
during the rest of her vacation. How much
money did Sharifa bring to spend during
her vacation?

6. Scott works a total of 14.5 hours after school
from Monday to Friday. After the weekend,
he has worked a total of 27.75 hours for the
entire week. How many hours does Scott
work on the weekend?

7. Christina climbs to the top of Mount Graham
in Arizona. On the first day, she climbs to an
elevation of 1029 ft. The elevation of Mount
Graham is 10,724 ft. How many total feet of
Mount Graham's elevation does Christina
climb on the other days? 9695

8. While stacking dominoes in a pattern on
her table, Katie accidentally knocks over 94
of them. There are still 279 dominoes left
standing on the table. How many dominoes
were standing on the table before Katie
knocked some of them over?

9. Dania marks off 18.7 m of a playing field for
a sports festival. She needs to mark off a total
of 29 m to finish the field. How many more
meters does Dania have left to mark off?

10. Ramon is painting the outside of his house. He needs a total of 42 gallons of paint and he already has 16 gallons of paint in his garage. How many more gallons of paint does Ramon need to buy?

11. Alex spends 96 minutes exercising. How many minutes does Alex jog?

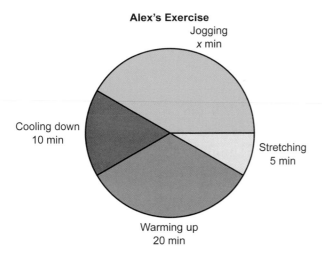

Alex's Exercise

Jogging
x min

Cooling down
10 min

Stretching
5 min

Warming up
20 min

12. Bianca sells 49 spoons that were in her spoon collection. She now has 156 spoons left in her collection. How many spoons were originally in Bianca's collection?

13. Brad is saving money to buy a new video game. The game costs $34.95. So far he has saved $26. How much more does Brad have to save?

Choose the answer.

16. Colin put 42 new pictures in his picture album, which now has a total of 501 pictures in it. How many pictures were in Colin's picture album before he added the 42 new pictures?

   A. 42

   B. 459

   C. 501

   D. 543

14. The amount of money in Courtney's savings account from January to May is shown below.

Money in Savings Account

Balance in dollars

Jan. Feb. Mar. Apr. May

Month

Sumaya has $51.33 more in her savings account than Courtney had in her savings account in April. How much does Sumaya have in her savings account?

15. **Challenge** Ian collected the following amounts of newspaper for the first six months of a newspaper drive: 5.7 lb, 6.4 lb, 8.9 lb, 11.1 lb, 13.5 lb, 16 lb. After another year, he'd collected 9.4 lb less than the 152.3 lb Justin has collected. How many pounds of newspaper did Ian collect during the one year after his first six months of collecting?

17. Sally takes a test and gets 17 answers wrong. She gets 59 questions right. How many questions are on the test?

   A. 76

   B. 59

   C. 42

   D. 17

Negative Numbers

If the temperature starts at 7°C and then drops by 12°C, the result is a negative temperature.

➔ Locating Integers on a Number Line

You have seen number lines used to show counting numbers like 1, 2, 20, and maybe even 13,597. You can extend the number line in the direction that is on the opposite side of zero as well. When you do, call the counting numbers *positive* and the numbers on the opposite side of zero *negative*.

Definition

An **integer** is any whole number or its opposite.

The integers: $\ldots -3, -2, -1, 0, 1, 2, 3, \ldots$

Example

PROBLEM 1 Identify the coordinate of point A.

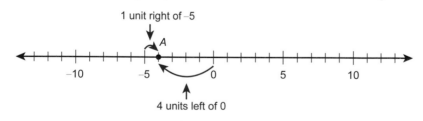

SOLUTION Look at the relationship between 0 and point A. Also look at the relationship of point A to the closest labeled integer.

Point A is 4 units to the left of 0 and 1 unit to the right of -5. Both of these facts indicate that point A is located at -4.

ANSWER The coordinate of point A is -4.

➔ Comparing and Ordering Integers

You can use a number line to compare and order integers. The farther to the left a number is on a number line, the lesser its value. The farther to the right a number is on a number line, the greater its value.

Example

Use < or > to compare or order the integers.

PROBLEM 2 Compare −7 and −12.

SOLUTION Draw a number line. Locate −7 and −12.

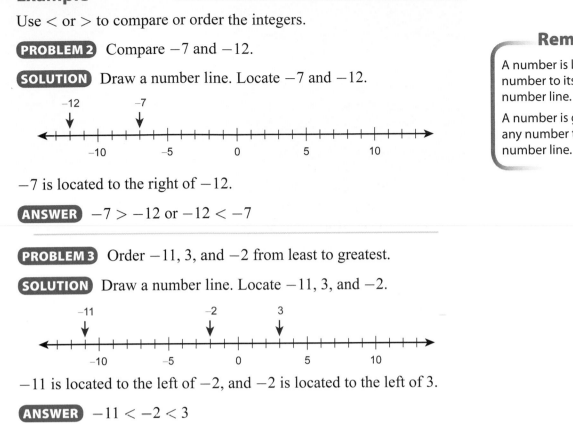

−7 is located to the right of −12.

ANSWER −7 > −12 or −12 < −7

PROBLEM 3 Order −11, 3, and −2 from least to greatest.

SOLUTION Draw a number line. Locate −11, 3, and −2.

−11 is located to the left of −2, and −2 is located to the left of 3.

ANSWER −11 < −2 < 3

➔ Representing Situations Using Integers

The table shows some words representing positive and negative situations.

Positive		Negative	
up	gain	down	loss
increase	filling	decrease	emptying
above	rise	below	drop

Example

Use an integer to represent the situation.

PROBLEM 4 The temperature rises 12°C.

SOLUTION *Rises* indicates a positive integer.

ANSWER +12 represents a rise of 12°C.

PROBLEM 5 A diver dives 43 ft below sea level.

SOLUTION *Below* indicates a negative integer.

ANSWER −43 represents a position of 43 ft below sea level.

TOPIC

Problem Set

Identify the coordinate of the point shown on the number line.

1. Stepping Stones point A

2 units right of −10

A

8 units left of 0

Point A is ☐ units to the left of 0 and ☐ units to the right of −10.
The coordinate of point A is ☐.

2. point D **3.** point E **4.** point F 3

5. point G **6.** point H −15   **7.** point J

8. point K −116   **9.** point L **10.** point M −99

11. point N **12.** point P **13.** point Q −3

14. Challenge point R **15. Challenge** point S **16. Challenge** point T

Use $<$ or $>$ to compare or order the integers.

17. Stepping Stones −8 and −3

−8 is to the left of −3, so −8 $<$ −3.

18. Compare −5 and −9.   −5 > −9

19. Compare −2 and −3.

20. Compare −12 and −9.

21. Compare 2 and −2.

22. Compare −13 and −5.   −13 < −5

23. Compare −15 and 4.   −15 ⬚ 4

24. Compare −19 and −21.

25. Compare −31 and −26.

26. Compare 474 and −2678.

27. Compare −12 and 3290.   −12 ⬚ 3290

28. Order 0, −2, and −3 from least to greatest.

29. Order −5, −4, and −13 from least to greatest.

30. Order −21, 10, and 4 from greatest to least.

31. Order −7, −5, and −9 from least to greatest.

32. Order 22, −6, and −7 from greatest to least.

33. Order −17, −18, and −2 from greatest to least.   −2, −17, −18

34. Order 0, −11, and −4 from least to greatest.

35. Order −65, −47, and −96 from greatest to least.

36. Order −1047, 256, and 1 from greatest to least.

37. Order −4, 367, and −6444 from least to greatest.

38. **Challenge** Order −24, −31, 27, −33, and −29 from greatest to least.

Use an integer to represent the situation.

39. **Stepping Stones** The price of gasoline decreases by 11 cents per gallon.

Decreases indicates a negative integer.

⬚ represents the decrease in the price per gallon of gasoline.

40. Jim gains 5 yd on a football play.

41. The rent for an apartment goes down by $35 per month.

42. The elevation of Mount Elbert in Colorado is 14,433 ft above sea level.

43. The water level in the river drops by 16 cm.

44. The elevation of Death Valley, California, is 232 ft below sea level.

45. The amount of money in Joanne's checking account increases $727.

46. Ryan fills the gas tank with 19 gal of gasoline.

47. The deepest part of the Mariana Trench is at least 11,000 m below sea level.

48. **Challenge** Use an integer to represent the end position of Jerry if he starts hiking 7 m below sea level, hikes up 10 m, and then down 8 m.

Choose the answer.

49. What is the location of point X on the number line?

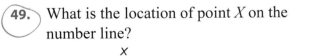

A. 8

B. 6

C. −6

D. −8

50. Which statement shows the integers ordered from greatest to least?
$$-6, 2, -11$$

A. $-11 > -6 > 2$

B. $-11 < -6 < 2$

C. $2 < -6 < -11$

D. $2 > -6 > -11$

Absolute Value and Distance

You can use a simple formula to find the distance between any two points on a line.

➡ Finding the Absolute Value and the Opposite of an Integer

Definitions

The **absolute value** of an integer is its distance from the origin, or 0, on the number line. The absolute value of *a* is written $|a|$.

Opposites are pairs of numbers whose distance from 0 is the same.

Tip

You can easily find a number's opposite by changing its sign.

To find the opposite and the absolute value of an integer, use the distance the integer is from 0 on the number line.

Example

Find the absolute value and the opposite of the integer.

PROBLEM 1 7

SOLUTION Draw a number line and locate 7. To find the absolute value of 7, find the distance from 7 to 0. To find the opposite of 7, find the other number that is the same distance from 0.

Think About It

A number without any sign is assumed to be positive. So 7 is the same as +7.

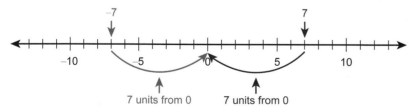

7 is 7 units from 0. The other number that is 7 units from 0 is −7.

ANSWER $|7| = 7$ and the opposite of 7 is −7.

PROBLEM 2 −9

SOLUTION −9 is 9 units from 0. The other number that is 9 units from 0 is 9.

ANSWER $|-9| = 9$ and the opposite of −9 is 9.

TOPIC

➡ Finding Distance

You can use the formula below to find the distance between two points on the number line.

Distance Between Two Points

The distance d between two points with coordinates a and b on a number line can be found using

$$d = |b - a|.$$

Example

PROBLEM 3 Find the distance between the two points on the number line.

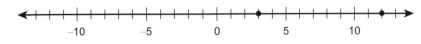

SOLUTION Use the formula.

$d = |b - a|$
$\quad = |12 - 3|$ Replace b with 12 and a with 3.
$\quad = |9|$ Simplify.
$\quad = 9$

ANSWER The distance between the two points is 9 units.

Think About It

It doesn't matter which point you select for a and which you select for b. The answer is the same:

$|3 - 12| = |-9| = 9.$

➡ Application: Finding Locations

Example

PROBLEM 5 Ken hooked his dog's 7 ft leash on a fence. The number line represents the fence with 1 unit = 1 ft. The point is where Ken hooked the leash. Where are the farthest locations that Ken's dog can go along the fence?

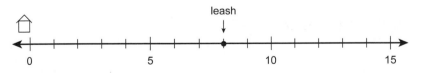

SOLUTION The leash is 7 ft long. Since Ken hooked the leash at the 8 ft location, subtract 7 from 8 and add 7 to 8.

$$8 - 7 = 1 \qquad \text{and} \qquad 8 + 7 = 15$$

ANSWER The farthest locations along the fence that Ken's dog can go are at 1 ft and 15 ft.

T O P I C

Problem Set

Find the absolute value and the opposite of the integer.

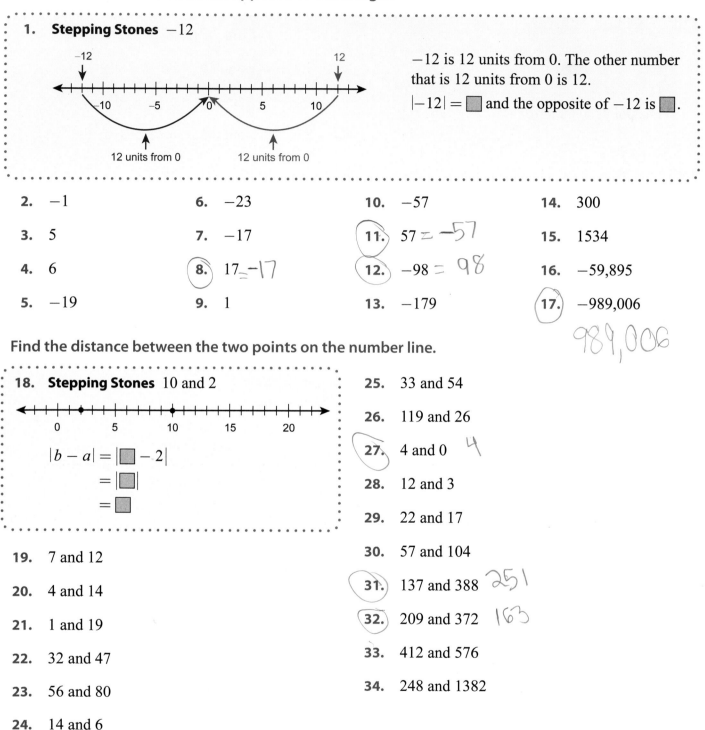

1. **Stepping Stones** -12

−12 is 12 units from 0. The other number that is 12 units from 0 is 12.

$|-12| = $ ⬛ and the opposite of -12 is ⬛.

12 units from 0   12 units from 0

2. -1

3. 5

4. 6

5. -19

6. -23

7. -17

8. $17 = -17$

9. 1

10. -57

11. $57 = -57$

12. $-98 = 98$

13. -179

14. 300

15. 1534

16. $-59,895$

17. $-989,006$

989,006

Find the distance between the two points on the number line.

18. **Stepping Stones** 10 and 2

$$|b - a| = |\;⬛\; - 2|$$
$$= |\;⬛\;|$$
$$= ⬛$$

19. 7 and 12

20. 4 and 14

21. 1 and 19

22. 32 and 47

23. 56 and 80

24. 14 and 6

25. 33 and 54

26. 119 and 26

27. 4 and 0   4

28. 12 and 3

29. 22 and 17

30. 57 and 104

31. 137 and 388   251

32. 209 and 372   163

33. 412 and 576

34. 248 and 1382

Find all points that are the given distance from the given point.

35. **Stepping Stones** 6 units from the point located at 15

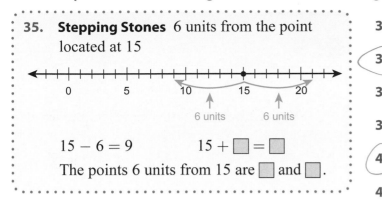

$15 - 6 = 9$ $15 + \square = \square$

The points 6 units from 15 are $\square$ and $\square$.

36. 4 units from the point located at 9

37. 12 units from the point located at 21   33, 9

38. 24 units from the point located at 31

39. 12 units from the point located at 5

40. 19 units from the point located at 53   72, 34

41. 37 units from the point located at 28

Solve.

42. Is -7 or 5 closer to 0 on the number line?

43. Is 24 or -23 closer to 0 on the number line? -23

44. Is -17 or -18 closer to 0 on the number line?

45. What two numbers are a distance of 43 units from 0 on the number line? 43, -43

46. **Challenge** Lisa drove along the highway between the mile-markers shown on number line A. Rodney drove along another highway between the mile-markers shown on number line B. How many more miles did Rodney drive than Lisa?

Number Line A

110   115   120   125   130

Number Line B

495   500   505   510   515

47. **Challenge** A sprinkler head is located at point *S*. The water stream from the sprinkler will spray a distance of 55 ft. Will the water reach the rose bush located at *R* and the palm tree located at *P*?

P   *S*   *R*

10   20   30   40   50   60   70   80   90   100   110   120

Choose the answer.

48. Evaluate: $|-13|$

A. -13 C. 3

B. 0   D. 13

49. What is the distance between the two points?

0   5   10   15   20

A. 2 units   C. 17 units

B. 15 units   D. 19 units

Addition and Subtraction with Negative Numbers

How do you add and subtract positive and negative numbers?

➡ Adding Integers

Example

PROBLEM 1 Add: $3 + (-7)$

SOLUTION Use a number line. Start at 0. Move 3 units to the right. Then move 7 units to the left.

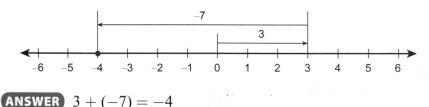

ANSWER $3 + (-7) = -4$

Rules for Adding Integers

Addends with same signs:
Add the absolute values. The sum has the same sign as the addends.
$3 + 2 = 5 \qquad -4 + (-7) = -11$

Addends with different signs:
Subtract the absolute values. The sum has the same sign as the addend with the greater absolute value.
$8 + (-7) = 1 \qquad 3 + (-5) = -2$

Example

PROBLEM 2 Add: $-8 + 5$

SOLUTION The signs of the addends are different, so subtract the absolute values.

$|-8| - |5| = 8 - 5 = 3$

$|-8| > |5|$, so the sum is negative.

ANSWER $-8 + 5 = -3$

PROBLEM 3 Add: $-6 + (-9)$

SOLUTION The signs of the addends are the same, so add the absolute values.

$|-6| + |-9| = 6 + 9 = 15$

The addends are negative, so the sum is, too.

ANSWER $-6 + (-9) = -15$

➤ Subtracting Integers

Subtracting a Number

To subtract a number, add its opposite.

$$a - b = a + (-b)$$

Remember

The graph of a number's opposite is the same distance on the other side of the 0 from the number.

You can find a number's opposite by changing its sign.

Example

PROBLEM 4 Subtract: $-2 - (-8)$

SOLUTION The opposite of -8 is 8.
$-2 - (-8) = -2 + 8 = |8| - |-2| = 8 - 2 = 6$

ANSWER $-2 - (-8) = 6$

PROBLEM 5 Subtract: $-5 - 12$

SOLUTION The opposite of -12 is 12.
$-5 - 12 = -5 + (-12)$

The signs of the addends are the same.
$|-12| + |-5| = 12 + 5$ Add the absolute values.
$\qquad\qquad = 17$ Simplify.

ANSWER $-5 - 12 = -17$

➤ Application: Dartboard Game

Example

PROBLEM 6 Greg and his friends are playing a game using the dartboard. Greg throws 3 darts and gets -9, 7, and -2. What is Greg's score for this round?

SOLUTION Add the three integers.

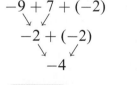

$-2 + (-2)$ Add -9 and 7.
$\qquad -4$ Add -2 and -2.

ANSWER Greg's score for this round is -4.

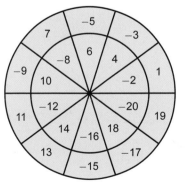

T O P I C

Problem Set

Add.

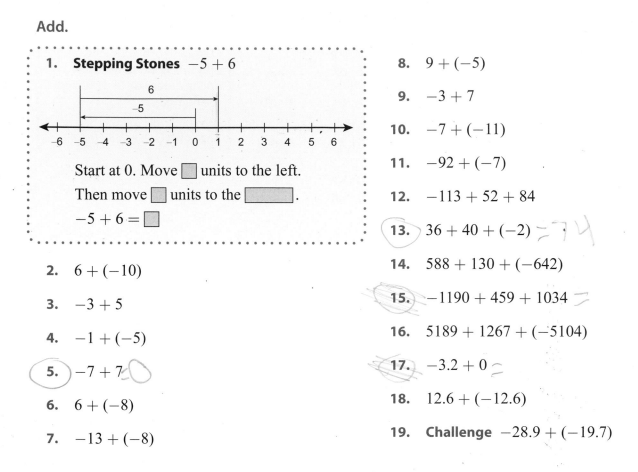

1. Stepping Stones $-5 + 6$

Start at 0. Move ☐ units to the left.

Then move ☐ units to the ▭.

$-5 + 6 =$ ☐

2. $6 + (-10)$

3. $-3 + 5$

4. $-1 + (-5)$

5. $-7 + 7$ 0

6. $6 + (-8)$

7. $-13 + (-8)$

8. $9 + (-5)$

9. $-3 + 7$

10. $-7 + (-11)$

11. $-92 + (-7)$

12. $-113 + 52 + 84$

13. $36 + 40 + (-2) = 74$

14. $588 + 130 + (-642)$

15. $-1190 + 459 + 1034 =$

16. $5189 + 1267 + (-5104)$

17. $-3.2 + 0 =$

18. $12.6 + (-12.6)$

19. **Challenge** $-28.9 + (-19.7)$

Subtract.

20. Stepping Stones $9 - (-14)$

$9 - (-14) = 9 +$ ☐ $=$ ☐

21. $7 - (-3)$

22. $8 - (-9)$

23. $-5 - 9$ -14

24. $3 - 5$

25. $5 - 8$

26. $-46 - 74$

27. $-1066 - 464 = 1530$

28. $-2842 - (-5427)$

29. $-19.4 - 5.6$

30. **Challenge** $417.2 - 334.9$

31. **Challenge** $-418.01 - 11.24$

Solve.

32. Yesterday morning at dawn the temperature was −2°C. By noon it had dropped to −12°C. What was the change in temperature?

33. One winter day it was 3°C at noon. The temperature dropped 11 degrees by sunset. What was the temperature at sunset? −9

34. The average daily low temperature in Fairbanks, Alaska, in April is −3°C. The average daily high temperature is 10°C warmer. What is the average daily high temperature in Fairbanks, Alaska, in April?

35. The bottom of a valley is 10 m below sea level. A nearby city is 120 m above sea level. What is the difference in elevations between the valley floor and the city?

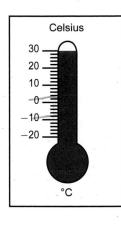

Use the formula and table to write the profit or loss for the month.

profit/loss = revenue − expenses

Revenue and Expenses (thousands of dollars)						
	Jan.	Feb.	Mar.	Apr.	May	June
Revenue	3.2	3.3	4.1	6.8	2.8	2.7
Expenses	2.7	3.4	3.3	4.9	4.1	3.6

36. January

37. February

38. March

39. April 1.9

40. May −1.3

41. June

42. **Challenge** Find the total profit or loss for these six months.

Choose the answer.

43. What is the value of −23 + (−10)?
    A. −33
    B. −13
    C. 13
    D. 33

44. What is the value of 14 − (−3)?
    A. −17
    B. −11
    C. 11
    D. 17

45. A submarine travels at a depth of 156 m below the ocean surface. It rises 27 m and then dives 44 m. Which integer represents the new depth, in meters, of the submarine relative to the ocean surface?
    A. −139
    B. −173
    C. 139
    D. 173

P R O B L E M   S E T

Solving Addition Equations with Negative Numbers

What does the solution to an equation like $t + 32 = 20$ look like? Solutions can be positive or negative.

➡ Solving Equations with Negative Solutions

One way to see how equations work is to model them with algebra tiles.

Using Algebra Tiles

Use these algebra tiles to model equations.

A rectangle represents a variable.

A white square represents one positive unit.

A gray square represents one negative unit.

Example

PROBLEM 1 $x + (-3) = -5$

SOLUTION Model the equation using algebra tiles.

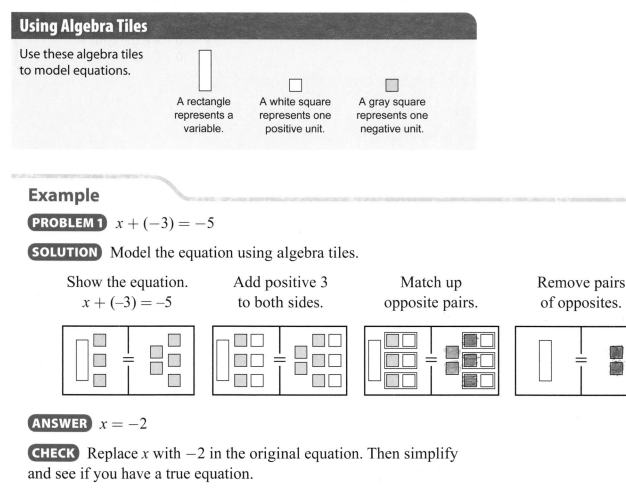

Show the equation.
$x + (-3) = -5$

Add positive 3 to both sides.

Match up opposite pairs.

Remove pairs of opposites.

ANSWER $x = -2$

CHECK Replace x with -2 in the original equation. Then simplify and see if you have a true equation.

$$x + (-3) = -5$$
$$-2 + (-3) \stackrel{?}{=} -5$$
$$-5 = -5 \checkmark$$

Solving Equations That Include Negative Numbers

Solve equations that include negative numbers in the same way as you solve equations with only positive numbers.

Think About It

The properties of equality apply to negative numbers as well as positive numbers.

Example

PROBLEM 2 Solve: $h + 4 = -10$

SOLUTION

$$h + 4 = -10$$
$$h + 4 - 4 = -10 - 4 \qquad \text{Subtract 4 from both sides.}$$
$$h + 0 = -14 \qquad \text{Simplify.}$$
$$h = -14$$

ANSWER $h = -14$

Tip

Subtracting a number is the same as adding its opposite.

$-10 - 4$ is the same as $-10 + (-4)$.

CHECK Replace h with -14 in the original equation. Then simplify and see if you have a true equation.

$$h + 4 = -10$$
$$-14 + 4 \stackrel{?}{=} -10$$
$$-10 = -10 \checkmark$$

Application: Savings Account

Example

PROBLEM 3 Lori withdrew $40 from her savings account, deposited $150 the next day, and then made another withdrawal. The result was an increase of $50 in her account. Find the amount of the second withdrawal.

Think About It

Positive and negative numbers can be used to show gains and losses, the distance above or below sea level, and temperatures.

SOLUTION Let w represent the second withdrawal.

$$-40 + 150 + w = 50 \qquad \text{Write an equation.}$$
$$110 + w = 50 \qquad \text{Simplify.}$$
$$110 - 110 + w = 50 - 110 \qquad \text{Subtract 110 from both sides.}$$
$$0 + w = -60 \qquad \text{Simplify.}$$
$$w = -60$$

ANSWER The second withdrawal was $60.

CHECK Read the original problem again. Check that your answer is reasonable. There are two withdrawals of $40 and $60. So Lori took out $100 and deposited $150. The result is an increase of $50. The answer makes sense. $\checkmark$

Problem Set

Solve. Model the equation using algebra tiles.

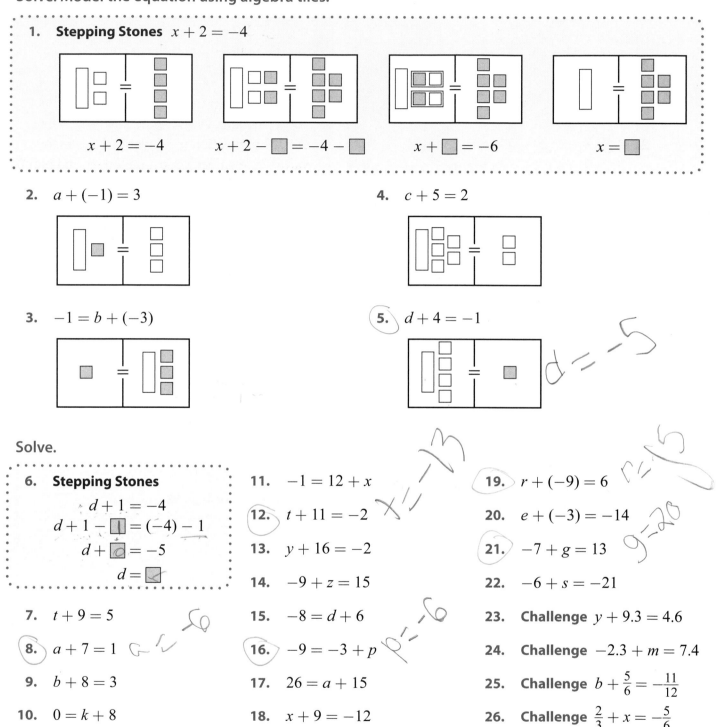

1. **Stepping Stones** $x + 2 = -4$

   $x + 2 = -4$ $x + 2 - \blacksquare = -4 - \blacksquare$ $x + \blacksquare = -6$ $x = \blacksquare$

2. $a + (-1) = 3$

4. $c + 5 = 2$

3. $-1 = b + (-3)$

5. $d + 4 = -1$ $d = -5$

Solve.

6. **Stepping Stones**

   $d + 1 = -4$
   $d + 1 - \boxed{1} = (-4) - 1$
   $d + \boxed{0} = -5$
   $d = \boxed{}$

7. $t + 9 = 5$

8. $a + 7 = 1$

9. $b + 8 = 3$

10. $0 = k + 8$

11. $-1 = 12 + x$

12. $t + 11 = -2$ $x = -13$

13. $y + 16 = -2$

14. $-9 + z = 15$

15. $-8 = d + 6$

16. $-9 = -3 + p$ $p = -6$

17. $26 = a + 15$

18. $x + 9 = -12$

19. $r + (-9) = 6$ $r = 15$

20. $e + (-3) = -14$

21. $-7 + g = 13$ $g = 20$

22. $-6 + s = -21$

23. **Challenge** $y + 9.3 = 4.6$

24. **Challenge** $-2.3 + m = 7.4$

25. **Challenge** $b + \frac{5}{6} = -\frac{11}{12}$

26. **Challenge** $\frac{2}{3} + x = -\frac{5}{6}$

Write and solve an equation to find the answer.

27. **Stepping Stones** Fred withdrew $22 more than the amount he had in his checking account. Then he transferred money from his savings account into his checking account. His checking balance was then $85. How much money did Fred transfer?

Let t represent the amount transferred.

$$-22 + t = \boxed{85}$$
$$-22 + \boxed{22} + t = \boxed{85} + 22$$
$$0 + t = \boxed{107}$$
$$t = \boxed{}$$

He transferred $\boxed{}$.

107

28. The temperature starts at 13°F and changes quickly, ending at −6°F. What is the change in temperature?

29. In Jackie's town, the average daily low temperature in January is −2°C. That temperature is 14 degrees less than the average daily low temperature in her uncle's town. What is the average daily low temperature in January in her uncle's town?

30. A football team loses 12 yards on one play, and then gains yards on the next play. The change in position is −2 yards. How many yards were gained or lost on the second play? Write the solution as an integer.

31. The bottom of a valley is 50 m below sea level. A helicopter takes off from the valley floor and rises 400 m above the valley floor. What is the final elevation of the helicopter?

Choose the answer.

32. Solve: $x + 18 = -13$

   A. $x = -31$ C. $x = 5$

   B. $x = -5$ D. $x = 13$

33. A scuba diver is 80 ft below sea level. How far must she ascend to reach a depth of 30 ft below sea level?

   A. 110 ft   C. −50 ft

   B. 50 ft   D. −110 ft

34. Solve: $15 = x + (-6)$

   A. $x = -21$ C. $x = 9$

   B. $x = -9$ D. $x = 21$

35. The temperature yesterday was 10°C. That was 15°C less than it is today. Which equation can be used to find today's temperature?

   A. $x + 10 = -15$

   B. $15 + x = -10$

   C. $x + (-10) = -15$

   D. $x + (-15) = 10$

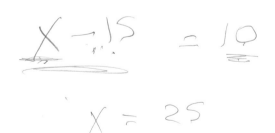

$$x - 15 = 10$$
$$x = 25$$

Chapter 2 Review

Choose the answer.

1. Which unit is the best choice to measure the distance from New York City to Washington, D.C.?

   A. millimeter   C. meter

   B. centimeter   D. kilometer

2. Which measure is equivalent to 3.4 m?

   A. 0.034 mm   C. 3400 cm

   B. 340 mm   D. 340 cm

3. What is the perimeter of this triangle with all three sides the same length?

   33 cm

   A. 11 cm   C. 66 cm

   B. 99 cm   D. 198 cm

4. What is the side length of a square that has the same perimeter as a rectangle with a length of 13 m and a width of 11 m?

   A. 48 m   C. 36 m

   B. 24 m   D. 12 m

5. What is the value of p in the equation $p + 18 = 42$?

   A. 24   C. 34

   B. 60   D. 26

6. The bakery sells 156 walnut muffins. It sells 27 more blueberry muffins than walnut muffins. How many blueberry muffins does the bakery sell?

   A. 128   C. 183

   B. 173   D. 138

7. Which list of integers is in order from greatest to least?

   A. 2, 4, −5   C. 4, 2, −5

   B. −5, 2, −4   D. −5, 2, 4

8. What is the distance between the points −6 and 12 on the number line?

   A. 22 units   C. 28 units

   B. 18 units   D. 62 units

9. What is the sum $-4 + (-23)$?

   A. −19   C. 19

   B. −27   D. 27

10. Yesterday's low temperature was −5°C. Today's low temperature was 11°C warmer. What was today's low temperature?

    A. 6°C   C. −6°C

    B. −16°C   D. 16°C

Name the English and metric units you would use to measure each length. Explain your choice.

11. length of a bicycle

12. height of a telephone pole

13. thickness of a dime

14. length of a swimming pool

CHAPTER REVIEW

Find the perimeter.

15. square with side = 8 in.

16. rectangle with length 4.5 m and width 37 m

17. rectangle with length 1.9 m and width 0.7 m

18. square with side = 6.8 cm

Solve.

19. $y + 7 = 12$

20. $20 = 16 + z$

21. $a + 44 = 63$

22. $105 = 7 + b$

Write and solve an equation to find the answer. Check your answer for reasonableness.

23. Carlos walks 245 m to his friend's house. Then he and his friend walk 317 m together to the park. How far does Carlos walk in all?

24. Kate has 240 pages to read in her book. She reads 34 pages on Monday and 40 pages on Tuesday. How many more pages does Kate have to read?

Use the number line to compare or order the integers.

25. Compare -6 and -5.

26. Compare 3 and 2.

27. Order $7, -7,$ and -2 from least to greatest.

28. Order $8, 4,$ and 0 from greatest to least.

Find the distance between the two points on the number line.

29.

30.

Add or subtract.

31. $4 + (-12)$

32. $-7 + 9$

33. $-54 + (-56)$

34. $-183 + 206$

35. $5 - 17$

36. $-3 - 4$

37. $-1 - (-5)$

38. $9 - (-1)$

Solve.

39. $k + 8 = 2$

40. $141 + a = 12$

41. $t + 387 = -569$

42. $85 + e = 0$

CHAPTER REVIEW

3

Area: Multiplication Equations

A general contractor needs to calculate area to determine the amount of carpet, tile, or wood for a floor.

In This Chapter

You will learn how to compute the areas of squares, triangles, rectangles, and other polygons. You'll also learn how to divide to find an unknown side length and how a square root relates a side length to the area of a square.

Chapter Topics

▶ Foundations for Chapter 3

▶ Units of Area

▶ Areas of Rectangles

▶ Special Quadrilaterals

▶ Areas of Triangles

▶ Figures Made Up of Triangles and Parallelograms

▶ Unknown Side Lengths: Division

▶ Unknown Side Lengths: Square Roots

▶ Chapter 3 Review

Flooring is measured in square units.

CHAPTER 3

Foundations for Chapter 3

➔ **Finding the Area of a Square**

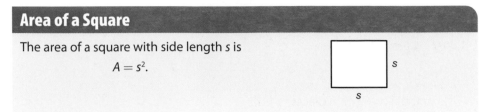

Area of a Square

The area of a square with side length *s* is

$$A = s^2.$$

Area is expressed in square units such as square feet or square centimeters. When the problem doesn't give units, express your answer as a measurement of "square units."

Example A

PROBLEM A-1 Find the area of the square.

3 m
3 m

SOLUTION $A = s^2$
$= 3^2$
$= 3 \cdot 3 = 9$

ANSWER The area of the square is 9 square meters.

PROBLEM A-2 Find the area of the infield of a square-shaped baseball diamond that measures 90 feet on each side.

SOLUTION $A = s^2$
$= 90^2$
$= 90 \cdot 90 = 8100$

ANSWER The area of the infield is 8100 square feet.

Problem Set A

Find the area of the square. Include appropriate units in your answer.

1.

8 cm
2 cm

2.

16 m
4 m

3.

7

4.

6 mm
1.2 mm

5. a tile that is 3 feet long on each side 12 ft.

6. a cornfield that is 2 km long on each side

7. a square chessboard that measures 15 inches on each side 60 in.

8. a computer's central processing unit that measures 2.2 cm on each side

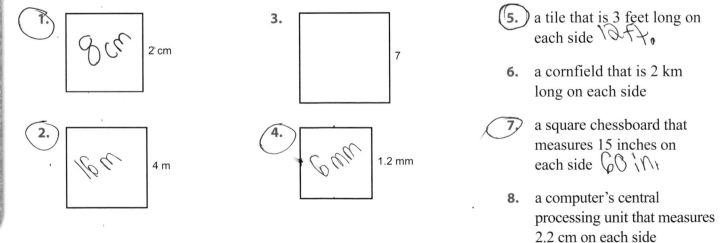
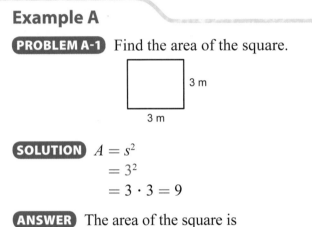

➔ Multiplying Whole Numbers and Decimals

Definitions

A **product** is the result of multiplying two or more factors.

How to Multiply Numbers

Vertical Multiplication
1. Multiply the value of each digit in the second factor by each digit in the first factor.
2. Place zeros to the right of each partial product to reflect the place value.
3. Add all the partial products.
4. Use estimation to check your answer.

Tip
When multiplying decimals, count the number of places to the right of the decimal point in each factor. The total tells you how many places are to the right of the decimal point in the product.

Example B

PROBLEM B-1 Multiply: $83 \cdot 36$

SOLUTION

$$
\begin{array}{r}
\overset{1}{8}3 \\
\times 36 \\
\hline
498 \\
+2490 \\
\hline
2988
\end{array}
$$

ANSWER $83 \cdot 36 = 2988$

CHECK Use estimation to check.
$80 \cdot 40 = 3200$
The estimate and the answer are close, so the answer seems reasonable. ✓

PROBLEM B-2 Multiply: $4.7 \cdot 2.9$

SOLUTION Count decimal places in the factors to know where to place the decimal point in the product.

$$
\begin{array}{r}
\overset{1}{\underset{6}{}}\,4.7 \\
\times 2.9 \\
\hline
423 \\
+940 \\
\hline
13.63
\end{array}
$$

ANSWER $4.7 \cdot 2.9 = 13.63$

CHECK Use estimation to check.
$5 \cdot 3 = 15$
The estimate and the answer are close, so the answer seems reasonable. ✓

Problem Set B

Multiply.

1. $45 \cdot 20$
2. $28 \cdot 1.6$
3. $37 \cdot 37$
4. $312 \cdot 18$

5. $71 \cdot 6.2$
6. $8.12 \cdot 33$
7. $7610 \cdot 84$
8. $560.9 \cdot 2.8$

9. $38,026 \cdot 49$
10. $608,391 \cdot 37$
11. $40.631 \cdot 0.17$
12. $1.00793 \cdot 9.8$

➔ Dividing Whole Numbers and Decimals

Definitions

The result of dividing a dividend by a divisor is the **quotient**.

$$\begin{array}{r} 14 \\ 7\overline{)98} \end{array}$$ ← quotient
divisor → $7\overline{)98}$ ← dividend

How to Divide Numbers

Long Division
1. Divide the divisor into the first digits of the dividend.
2. Multiply.
3. Subtract the partial product.
4. Divide the divisor into the difference.
5. Repeat.

Tips
When dividing, place digits exactly where they should be in the quotient. Be careful when you place the decimal point.

Always rewrite a decimal division problem as an equivalent problem with a whole-number divisor.

Example C

PROBLEM C-1 Divide: $859 \div 3$

SOLUTION

$$\begin{array}{r} 286 \text{ r } 1 \\ 3\overline{)859} \\ -6 \\ \hline 25 \\ -24 \\ \hline 19 \\ -18 \\ \hline 1 \end{array}$$

ANSWER $859 \div 3 = 286 \text{ r } 1$

CHECK Multiply to check.
$(286 \cdot 3) + 1 = 859 \checkmark$

PROBLEM C-2 Divide: $67.2 \div 3.2$

SOLUTION First, write the problem as an equivalent problem with a whole-number divisor. $67.2 \div 3.2 = 672 \div 32$

$$\begin{array}{r} 21 \\ 32\overline{)672} \\ -64 \\ \hline 32 \\ -32 \\ \hline 0 \end{array}$$

ANSWER $67.2 \div 3.2 = 21$

CHECK Multiply to check.
$21 \cdot 3.2 = 67.2 \checkmark$

Problem Set C

Divide.

1. $81 \div 3$

2. $92 \div 4$

3. $2.1 \div 3$

4. $4.2 \div 7$

5. $573 \div 9$

6. $79.2 \div 9$

7. $409 \div 22$

8. $1728 \div 36$

9. $3985 \div 51$

10. $278.8 \div 0.4$

11. $391.6 \div 2.2$

12. $67{,}427 \div 39$

Flooring is measured in square units.

Planting the Seed

You can multiply to find the area of a figure. To find a missing length when you know the area of a figure, you can solve a multiplication equation. Multiplication and division are inverse operations, so you can use division to solve multiplication equations.

Units of Area

If you say a square has an area of 8, what do you mean? Is the area 8 square inches or 8 square miles? You need to think about units when describing area.

➔ Counting Square Units to Find Area

Definitions

The **area** of a figure is the number of square units inside the figure.

A **square unit** is a square with sides 1 unit long.

You can use the superscript 2 after a unit name to record square units. For example, use m^2 for square meters and cm^2 for square centimeters.

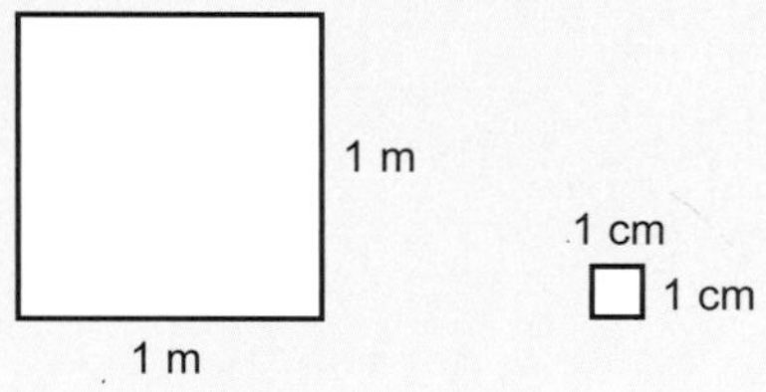

1 m

1 m

1 cm

1 cm

You can count the square units inside a figure drawn on a grid to find its area. If a figure isn't on a grid, you can divide the figure into square units.

Example

PROBLEM 1 Find the area of the shaded figure.

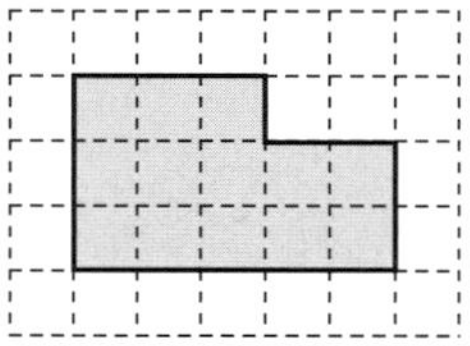

SOLUTION Count the squares.

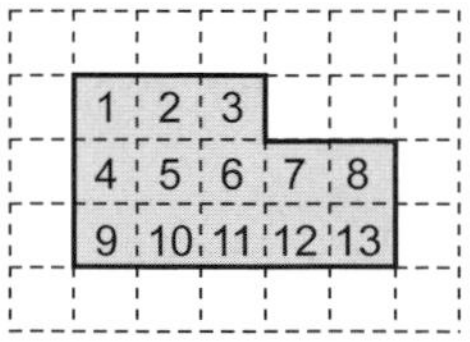

1	2	3		
4	5	6	7	8
9	10	11	12	13

There are 13 squares. Each square is 1 square unit.

ANSWER The area of the figure is 13 square units.

Example

PROBLEM 2 Find the area.

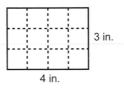

SOLUTION Divide the rectangle's length into 4 equal parts, and its width into 3 equal parts. Each square will be 1 square inch.

Count the squares. There are 12 squares.

ANSWER The area of the figure is 12 in².

➔ Converting Square Units

To use a different unit when you find the area of a square, you can first convert the side length to the new unit and then use the area formula. Look at the squares to the right. The smaller the unit, the more square units there will be.

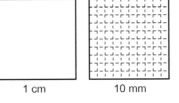

1 cm   10 mm

Example

PROBLEM 3 Find the area of the square in square feet and in square inches.

3 ft

Remember

The area of a square with side length s is
$$A = s^2.$$

SOLUTION Convert feet to inches. Then find the area in feet and in inches.

1 ft = 12 in.	Write the conversion factor for feet and inches.
3 ft = 3 · (12 in.)	Multiply to find the number of inches.
3 ft = 36 in.	Multiply.

Area in square feet:

$A = s^2$
$\quad = (3 \text{ ft})^2$ Substitute for s.
$\quad = 9 \text{ ft}^2$

Area in square inches:

$A = s^2$
$\quad = (36 \text{ in.})^2$
$\quad = 1296 \text{ in}^2$

ANSWER The area of the square is 9 ft², or 1296 in².

Problem Set

Find the area.

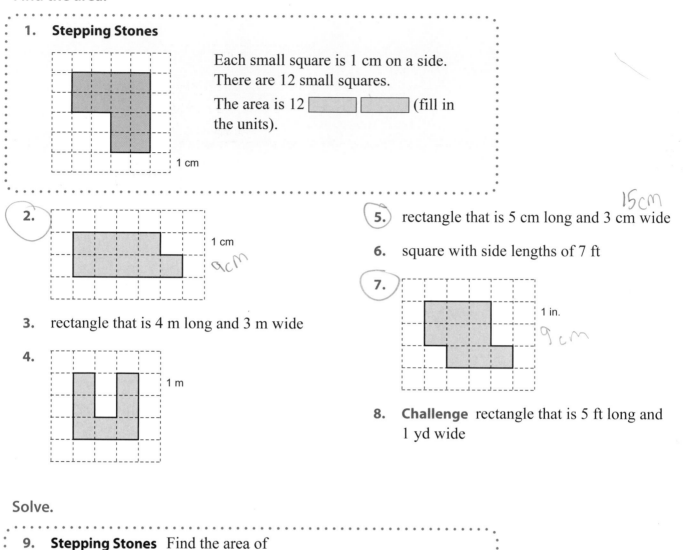

1. Stepping Stones

Each small square is 1 cm on a side. There are 12 small squares.

The area is 12 ▭ ▭ (fill in the units).

2. *1 cm* — 9cm

3. rectangle that is 4 m long and 3 m wide

4. *1 m*

15cm

5. rectangle that is 5 cm long and 3 cm wide

6. square with side lengths of 7 ft

7. *1 in.* — 9cm

8. Challenge rectangle that is 5 ft long and 1 yd wide

Solve.

9. Stepping Stones Find the area of the square in square feet and in square yards.

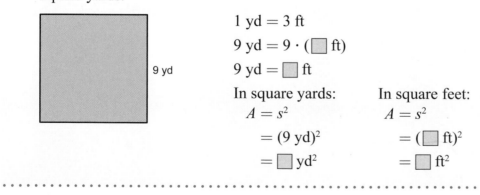

9 yd

$1 \text{ yd} = 3 \text{ ft}$

$9 \text{ yd} = 9 \cdot (\square \text{ ft})$

$9 \text{ yd} = \square \text{ ft}$

In square yards:

$A = s^2$

$= (9 \text{ yd})^2$

$= \square \text{ yd}^2$

In square feet:

$A = s^2$

$= (\square \text{ ft})^2$

$= \square \text{ ft}^2$

PROBLEM SET

10. Find the area of the square in square meters and in square centimeters.

5 m

11. Find the area of the square in square inches and in square feet.

24 in.

12. Find the area of the rectangle in square centimeters and in square millimeters.

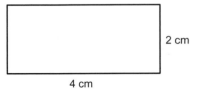

2 cm

4 cm

13. Find the area of the rectangle in square yards and in square feet.

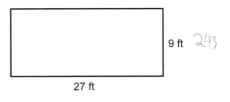

9 ft   243

27 ft

14. Find the area of the figure in square millimeters and in square centimeters.

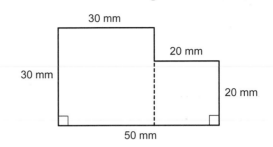

30 mm

20 mm

30 mm

20 mm

50 mm

15. **Challenge** Find the area of the figure in square meters and in square millimeters.

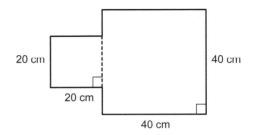

20 cm

40 cm

20 cm

40 cm

Choose the answer.

16. Which measurement is the area of this rectangle?

A. 9 units

B. 9 square units

C. 18 units

D. 18 square units

17. Which measurement is the area of a rectangle that is 12 in. long and 6 in. wide?

A. 36 in.

B. 36 in^2

C. 72 in.

D. 72 in^2

Areas of Rectangles

You've used the formula $A = s^2$ to find the area of a square with side length s. You can use a similar formula to find the area of any rectangle.

➔ Finding the Area of a Rectangle

Definition

A **rectangle** is a plane figure with 4 sides and 4 square corners.

Area of a Rectangle

The area of a rectangle with length l and width w is

$$A = lw.$$

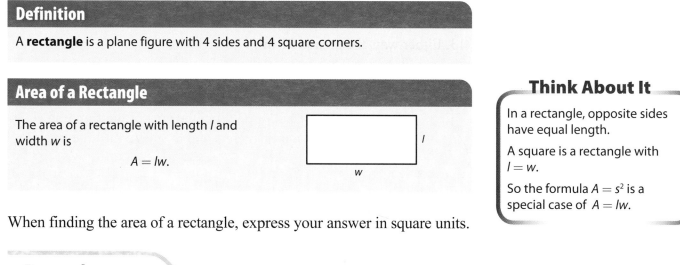

When finding the area of a rectangle, express your answer in square units.

Think About It

In a rectangle, opposite sides have equal length.

A square is a rectangle with $l = w$.

So the formula $A = s^2$ is a special case of $A = lw$.

Example

PROBLEM 1 Find the area of the rectangle.

SOLUTION

$A = lw$
$\quad = 24 \cdot 12$ Substitute 24 for l and 12 for w.
$\quad = 288$ Multiply.

ANSWER The area is 288 in².

Tip

The commutative property of multiplication states that the order of the factors does not affect the product.

➔ Choosing Length and Width

The area of a rectangle is the same whether you multiply $l \cdot w$ or $w \cdot l$. So you can use either dimension as the length.

    The way the rectangle is turned doesn't matter either. All three of the rectangles shown have the same area. You could use length 6 m and width 2 m or use length 2 m and width 6 m for any of the three.

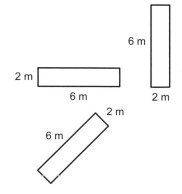

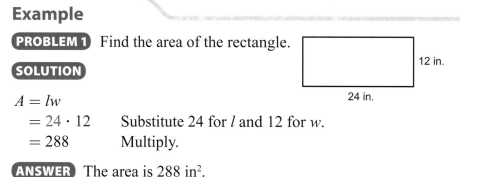

Example

PROBLEM 2 Write two equations that you could use to find the area of the rectangle. Then find the the area both ways.

SOLUTION Use the area formula, $A = lw$. Substitute values for l and w.

13 m

7 m

For $l = 13$ and $w = 7$:

$$A = lw$$
$$= 13 \cdot 7$$
$$= 91$$

For $l = 7$ and $w = 13$:

$$A = lw$$
$$= 7 \cdot 13$$
$$= 91$$

ANSWER The area of the rectangle can be found using the equation $A = 13 \cdot 7$ or $A = 7 \cdot 13$. Either way, the area is 91 m².

➔ Application: Painting Walls

Example

PROBLEM 3 A painter uses a table to record the dimensions of some walls he will paint. How many square feet of wall will he paint in all?

Wall Measurements			
Wall	Length	Height	Area
1	22 ft	8 ft	
2	14 ft	8 ft	
3	16 ft	10 ft	
4	9 ft	10 ft	

SOLUTION Find the area of each wall. Then add to find the total area.

$$A_1 = l_1 w_1$$
$$= 22 \cdot 8$$
$$= 176$$

$$A_2 = l_2 w_2$$
$$= 14 \cdot 8$$
$$= 112$$

$$A_3 = l_3 w_3$$
$$= 16 \cdot 10$$
$$= 160$$

$$A_4 = l_4 w_4$$
$$= 9 \cdot 10$$
$$= 90$$

$$A = A_1 + A_2 + A_3 + A_4$$
$$= 176 + 112 + 160 + 90$$
$$= 538$$

ANSWER The painter will paint 538 ft² of wall.

TOPIC

Problem Set

Find the area of the rectangle.

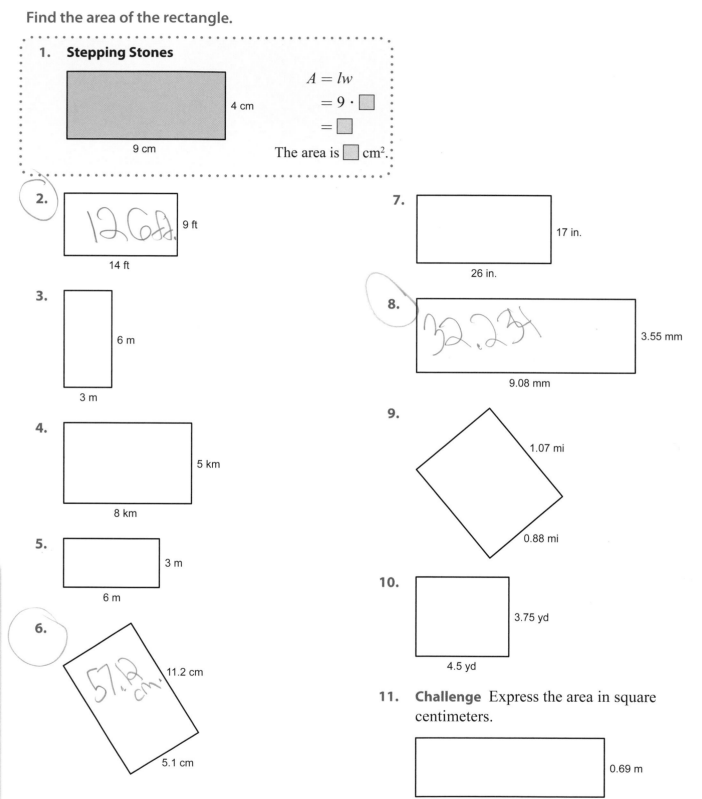

1. Stepping Stones

4 cm

9 cm

$A = lw$

$= 9 \cdot \square$

$= \square$

The area is $\square$ cm².

2. 12 ft.

9 ft

14 ft

3.

6 m

3 m

4.

5 km

8 km

5.

3 m

6 m

6. 57.12 cm.

11.2 cm

5.1 cm

7.

17 in.

26 in.

8. 32.234

3.55 mm

9.08 mm

9.

1.07 mi

0.88 mi

10.

3.75 yd

4.5 yd

11. Challenge Express the area in square centimeters.

0.69 m

4.2 m

Write two equations that you could use to find the area of the rectangle. Then find the area both ways.

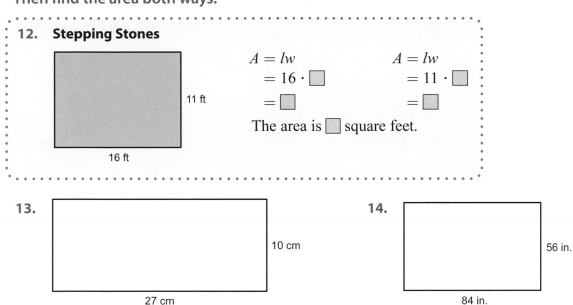

12. **Stepping Stones**

$A = lw$
$\quad = 16 \cdot \square$
$\quad = \square$

$A = lw$
$\quad = 11 \cdot \square$
$\quad = \square$

The area is $\square$ square feet.

11 ft
16 ft

13.

10 cm
27 cm

14.

56 in.
84 in.

Complete the table.

Rectangular Paddock Measurements			
Paddock	Base	Height	Area
1	14 yd	16 yd	224
2	30 yd	24 yd	
3	9 yd	33 yd	
4	22.5 yd	17 yd	
5	30.25 yd	31.75 yd	
6	17 yd	32 yd	544

15.
16.
17.
18.
19.
20.

21. **Challenge** Express the area of Paddock 2 in square feet.

22. **Challenge** Express the area of Paddock 4 in square feet.

23. **Challenge** Express the area of Paddock 6 in square feet.

Choose the answer.

24. Which measurement is the closest approximation of the rectangle's area?

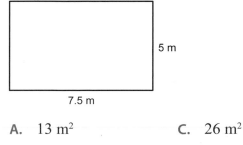

5 m
7.5 m

A. 13 m²
B. 20 m²
C. 26 m²
D. 40 m²

25. Which measurements are for a rectangle with an area of 15 square units?

A. 2 units wide, 13 units long
B. 3 units wide, 5 units long
C. 4 units wide, 4 units long
D. 5 units long, 2 units wide

Special Quadrilaterals

You've used formulas to find the areas of squares and rectangles. But how do you find the area of a 4-sided polygon with angles that don't all measure 90 degrees?

➔ Classifying Quadrilaterals

Definitions

A **quadrilateral** is a polygon with 4 sides.

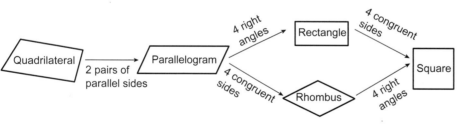

A **parallelogram** is a quadrilateral with two pairs of parallel sides.

A **rhombus** is a quadrilateral with 4 congruent sides. Every rhombus is also a parallelogram.

> **Tip**
>
> Arrows indicate parallel sides.
>
> Tick marks indicate congruent sides.
>
> Congruent sides have equal length.

Use this flowchart to classify a quadrilateral.

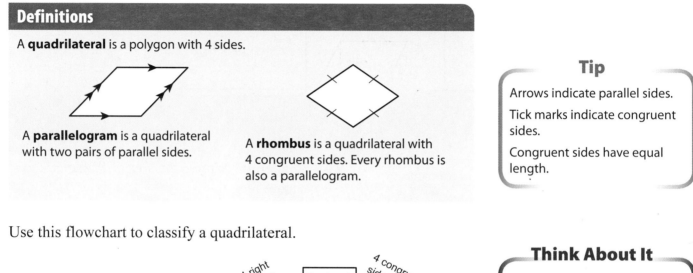

> **Think About It**
>
> All rectangles, squares, and rhombuses are parallelograms.
>
> Every square is a rectangle and also a rhombus.

Example

PROBLEM 1 Write all the names that apply: *parallelogram, rhombus, rectangle,* and *square*.

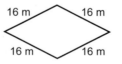

SOLUTION Follow the flowchart to classify the quadrilateral:
2 pairs of parallel sides? Yes. It is a parallelogram.
4 right angles? No. It is not a rectangle. It also is not a square.
4 congruent sides? Yes. It is a rhombus.

ANSWER The quadrilateral is a parallelogram and a rhombus.

➜ Finding the Area of a Parallelogram

Area of a Parallelogram

The area of a parallelogram with base b and height h is

$$A = bh.$$

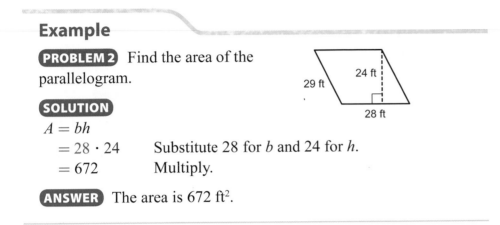

When finding the area of a parallelogram, express your answer in square units.

Example

PROBLEM 2 Find the area of the parallelogram.

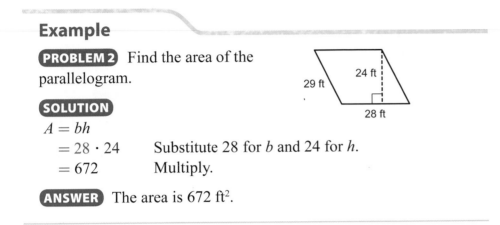

29 ft   24 ft   28 ft

SOLUTION

$A = bh$

$\quad = 28 \cdot 24 \qquad$ Substitute 28 for b and 24 for h.

$\quad = 672 \qquad\quad$ Multiply.

ANSWER The area is 672 ft².

➜ Application: Tessellations

To find the area of some figures, you can break them into parallelograms. First find the area of each parallelogram, and then add the areas to find the total area of the composite figure.

Remember

A tessellation is a pattern of congruent figures that covers a plane without overlaps or gaps.

Example

PROBLEM 3 This composite figure is made up of two parallelograms. Find the total area of a tessellation formed when this composite figure is repeated eight times.

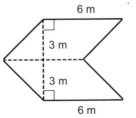

6 m   3 m   3 m   6 m

SOLUTION

Area of upper parallelogram: Area of lower parallelogram:

$\quad A = bh$ $\qquad\qquad\qquad\qquad\qquad A = bh$

$\quad\quad = 6 \cdot 3 \qquad$ Substitute for the variables. $\qquad = 6 \cdot 3$

$\quad\quad = 18 \qquad\qquad$ Multiply. $\qquad\qquad\qquad = 18$

Area of combined figure $= 18 + 18 = 36$

Area of tessellation $= 36 \cdot 8 = 288$

ANSWER The total area of the tessellation is 288 m².

Problem Set

Write all the names that apply: *parallelogram*, *rhombus*, *rectangle*, and *square*.

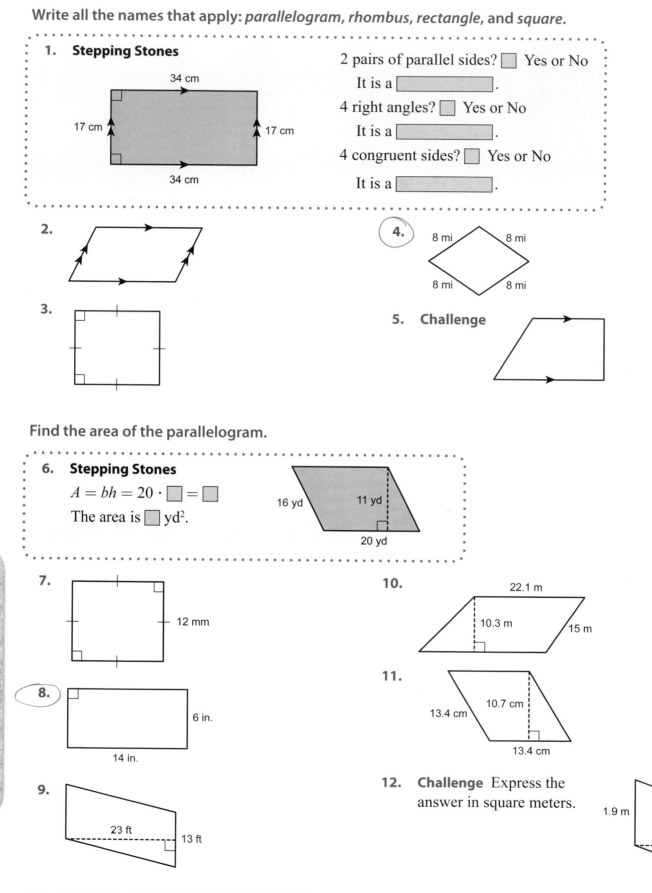

1. **Stepping Stones**

34 cm
17 cm   17 cm
34 cm

2 pairs of parallel sides? ☐ Yes or No

It is a ⬚⬚⬚⬚⬚⬚ .

4 right angles? ☐ Yes or No

It is a ⬚⬚⬚⬚⬚⬚ .

4 congruent sides? ☐ Yes or No

It is a ⬚⬚⬚⬚⬚⬚ .

2.

4.
8 mi   8 mi
8 mi   8 mi

3.

5. **Challenge**

Find the area of the parallelogram.

6. **Stepping Stones**

$A = bh = 20 \cdot \square = \square$

The area is ☐ yd².

16 yd   11 yd
20 yd

7.

12 mm

10.
22.1 m
10.3 m
15 m

11.
13.4 cm   10.7 cm
13.4 cm

8.

6 in.
14 in.

12. **Challenge** Express the answer in square meters.

295 cm
1.9 m
230 cm

9.

23 ft
13 ft

Find the area of the figure made up of parallelograms.

13. **Stepping Stones** Find the area of the figure that is made up of two rectangles.

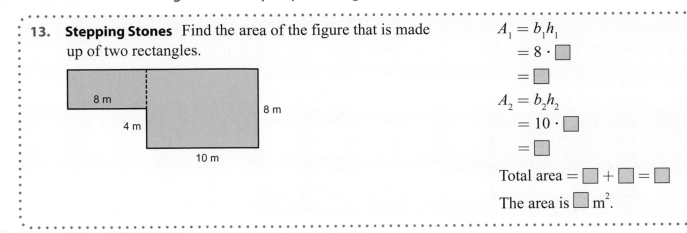

$A_1 = b_1 h_1$

$= 8 \cdot \square$

$= \square$

$A_2 = b_2 h_2$

$= 10 \cdot \square$

$= \square$

Total area $= \square + \square = \square$

The area is $\square$ m².

14. Find the area of the figure that is made up of a square and a parallelogram.

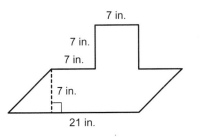

15. Find the area of the figure that is made up of two parallelograms.

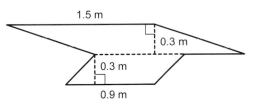

16. Find the total area of the figure that is made up of a square and a parallelogram.

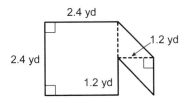

17. Find how much greater the area of the shaded section of this figure is than the unshaded section.

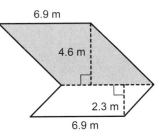

18. **Challenge** The figure in Problem 17 is repeated four times as a tessellation. Find the total area of the tessellation.

Choose the answer.

19. What is the area of the figure?

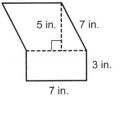

A. 70 in²

B. 56 in²

C. 70 in.

D. 56 in.

20. What is the area of the parallelogram?

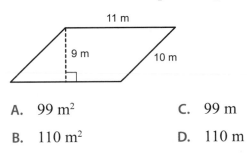

A. 99 m²

B. 110 m²

C. 99 m

D. 110 m

Areas of Triangles

If you divide any parallelogram in half, you create two triangles that have equal size.

➤ Bases and Heights of Triangles

Definitions

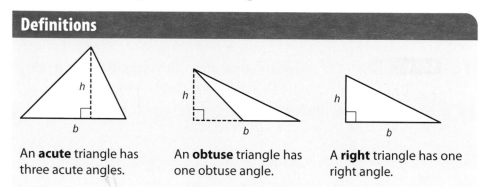

An **acute** triangle has three acute angles.

An **obtuse** triangle has one obtuse angle.

A **right** triangle has one right angle.

The base of a triangle always forms a right angle with the height.

Example

PROBLEM 1 Find the lengths of the three bases of the triangle and the corresponding height for each base.

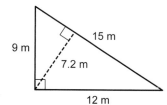

SOLUTION Find the height for each base.

For $b = 12$ m, $h = 9$ m.
For $b = 9$ m, $h = 12$ m.
For $b = 15$ m, $h = 7.2$ m.

ANSWER The three bases and corresponding heights for the triangle are 12 m, 9 m; 9 m, 12 m; and 15 m, 7.2 m.

Think About It

Any side of a triangle can be the base. The height will change accordingly.

For every acute triangle, all three heights are inside the triangle.

For every right triangle, two of the heights are sides of the triangle, while one height is inside the triangle.

For every obtuse triangle, two of the heights lie outside the triangle and one lies inside the triangle.

➤ Finding the Area of a Triangle

Area of a Triangle

The area of a triangle with base b and height h is

$$A = \tfrac{1}{2}bh$$

or $A = \dfrac{bh}{2}$.

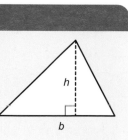

When finding the area of a triangle, express your answer in square units.

Example

Find the area of the triangle.

PROBLEM 2

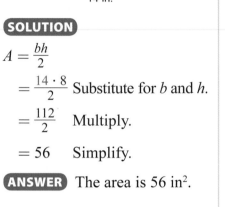

8 in.

14 in.

SOLUTION

$A = \dfrac{bh}{2}$

$= \dfrac{14 \cdot 8}{2}$ Substitute for b and h.

$= \dfrac{112}{2}$ Multiply.

$= 56$ Simplify.

ANSWER The area is 56 in².

PROBLEM 3

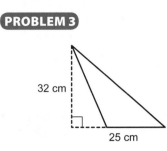

32 cm

25 cm

SOLUTION

$A = \dfrac{1}{2}bh$

$= \dfrac{1}{2}(25 \cdot 32)$ Substitute for b and h.

$= \dfrac{1}{2}(800)$ Multiply inside the parentheses.

$= 400$ Multiply.

ANSWER The area is 400 cm².

➔ Application: Sails

Example

PROBLEM 4 The table shows the dimensions of some triangular sails. Which sail has the greatest area?

SOLUTION Find the area of each sail. Then compare the areas.

$A_1 = \dfrac{1}{2}b_1h_1 = \dfrac{1}{2}(11 \cdot 32) = 176$

$A_2 = \dfrac{1}{2}b_2h_2 = \dfrac{1}{2}(9 \cdot 35) = 157.5$

$A_3 = \dfrac{1}{2}b_3h_3 = \dfrac{1}{2}(12 \cdot 30) = 180$

$A_4 = \dfrac{1}{2}b_4h_4 = \dfrac{1}{2}(10 \cdot 34) = 170$

$180 > 176 > 170 > 157.5$

ANSWER The greatest sail area is 180 ft². Sail 3 has the greatest area.

Sail Measurements			
Sail	Base	Height	Area
1	11 ft	32 ft	
2	9 ft	35 ft	
3	12 ft	30 ft	
4	10 ft	34 ft	

Problem Set

Find the lengths of the three bases of the triangle and the corresponding height for each base.

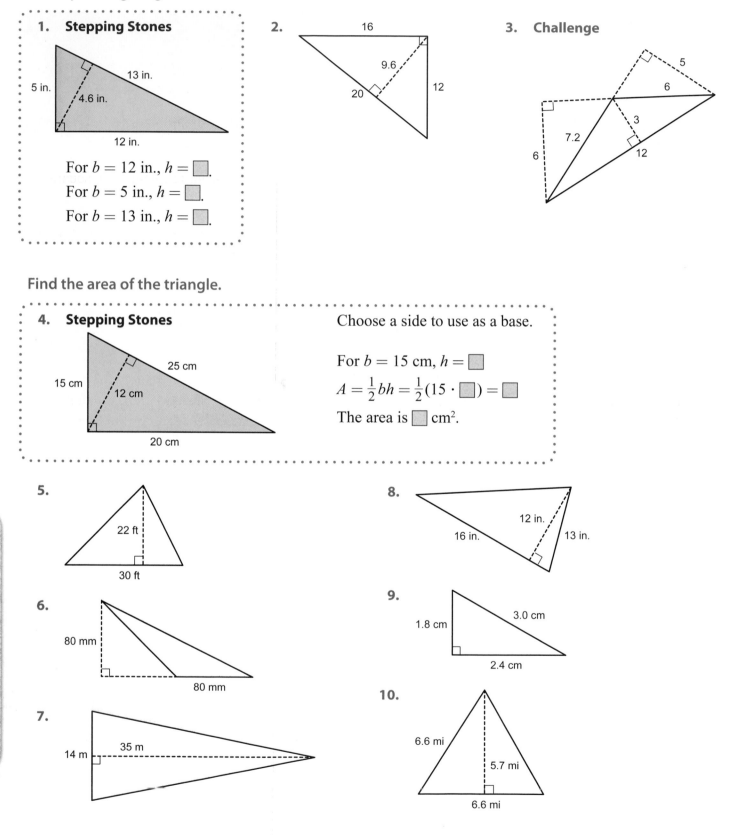

1. **Stepping Stones**

13 in.

5 in.

4.6 in.

12 in.

For $b = 12$ in., $h = \square$.
For $b = 5$ in., $h = \square$.
For $b = 13$ in., $h = \square$.

2.

16

9.6

20

12

3. **Challenge**

5

6

3

7.2

12

6

Find the area of the triangle.

4. **Stepping Stones**

25 cm

15 cm

12 cm

20 cm

Choose a side to use as a base.

For $b = 15$ cm, $h = \square$

$A = \frac{1}{2}bh = \frac{1}{2}(15 \cdot \square) = \square$

The area is $\square$ cm².

5.

22 ft

30 ft

6.

80 mm

80 mm

7.

35 m

14 m

8.

12 in.

16 in.

13 in.

9.

1.8 cm

3.0 cm

2.4 cm

10.

6.6 mi

5.7 mi

6.6 mi

11.

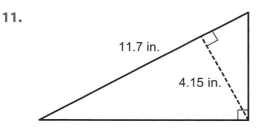

11.7 in.
4.15 in.

12. Challenge Express the area in square meters.

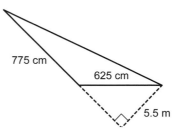

775 cm
625 cm
5.5 m

Complete the table.

Triangle Measurements		
Base	Height	Area
13. 6 cm	3 cm	
14. 8 ft	4 ft	
15. 7 km	7 km	
16. 6.5 m	8.25 m	
17. 5.75 mi	9.75 mi	
18. 7.25 mm	3.5 mm	

19. Express the area from Problem 16 in square centimeters.

20. Express the area from Problem 18 in square centimeters.

21. Challenge Express the area from Problem 15 in square centimeters.

Solve.

22. Sunset Park is shaped like a triangle. Two perpendicular sides of the park measure 1.4 miles and 2.3 miles. Find the park's area.

23. Does Triangle A or Triangle B have a greater area? Explain your answer.

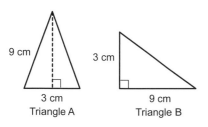

9 cm
3 cm
Triangle A

3 cm
9 cm
Triangle B

24. Challenge Find the least number of tiles shaped like this equilateral triangle that must be put together to cover an area of 70 m².

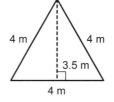

4 m   4 m
3.5 m
4 m

Choose the answer.

25. Which measurement is the area of the figure?

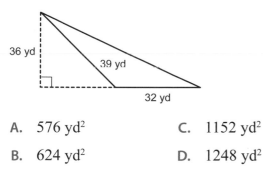

36 yd
39 yd
32 yd

A. 576 yd²   C. 1152 yd²

B. 624 yd²   D. 1248 yd²

26. Which measurement is the area of a triangle with a base of 5.5 cm and a height of 8.8 cm?

A. 12.1 cm²

B. 24.2 cm²

C. 36.3 cm²

D. 48.4 cm²

Figures Made Up of Triangles and Parallelograms

If you want to find the area of a complicated figure, you can get help by breaking it apart into simpler figures.

➔ Finding Areas by Breaking Up Figures

You can break apart, or decompose, a complex figure into smaller figures, such as triangles and parallelograms. Then use the formulas to find the areas of the triangles and parallelograms. Add their areas to find the total area of the complex figure.

> **Remember**
>
> Area of a rectangle:
> $$A = lw$$

Example

PROBLEM 1 Find the area of the figure.

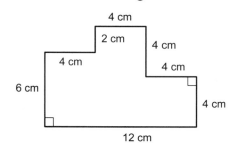

SOLUTION

Step 1 Break the figure into three rectangles.

Step 2 Find the area of each rectangle.
Substitute 4 for b_1 and 6 for h_1.
$A_1 = b_1 h_1 = 4 \cdot 6 = 24$

Substitute 4 for b_2 and 8 for h_2.
$A_2 = b_2 h_2 = 4 \cdot 8 = 32$

Substitute 4 for b_3 and 4 for h_3.
$A_3 = b_3 h_3 = 4 \cdot 4 = 16$

> **Think About It**
>
> A complex figure can be decomposed in many different ways.

Step 3 Add the areas of the rectangles.
$24 + 32 + 16 = 72$

ANSWER The area of the figure is 72 cm².

Example

PROBLEM 2 Find the area of the figure.

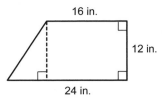

SOLUTION The figure is a right triangle and a rectangle.

Step 1 Find the area of the right triangle.
Subtract to find the length of the triangle's base.
$b = 24 - 16 = 8$

Substitute 8 for b and 12 for h. Then simplify.
$A = \frac{bh}{2} = \frac{8 \cdot 12}{2} = \frac{96}{2} = 48$

Step 2 Find the area of the rectangle.
Substitute 16 for b and 12 for h.
$A = bh = 16 \cdot 12 = 192$

Step 3 Add the areas of the triangle and rectangle.
$48 + 192 = 240$

ANSWER The area of the figure is 240 in².

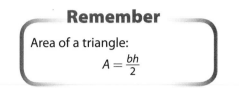

Remember

Area of a triangle:
$$A = \frac{bh}{2}$$

➤ Finding Areas of Figures with Missing Pieces

Sometimes a figure may have a piece missing from it. To find the area of the figure, first find the area of the larger figure. Then find the area of the missing piece, and subtract it from the total area to find the remaining area.

Example

PROBLEM 3 Find the area of the shaded part of the parallelogram.

SOLUTION Find the area of the parallelogram, and then subtract the area of the square.

Area of the parallelogram: $A = bh = 45 \cdot 30 = 1350$

Area of the square: $A = s^2 = 15^2 = 225$

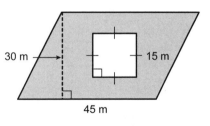

Subtract to find the area of the shaded part.
$1350 - 225 = 1125$

ANSWER The area of the shaded part of the figure is 1125 m².

TOPIC

Problem Set

Find the area of the figure. Assume all figures are made up of parallelograms and triangles.

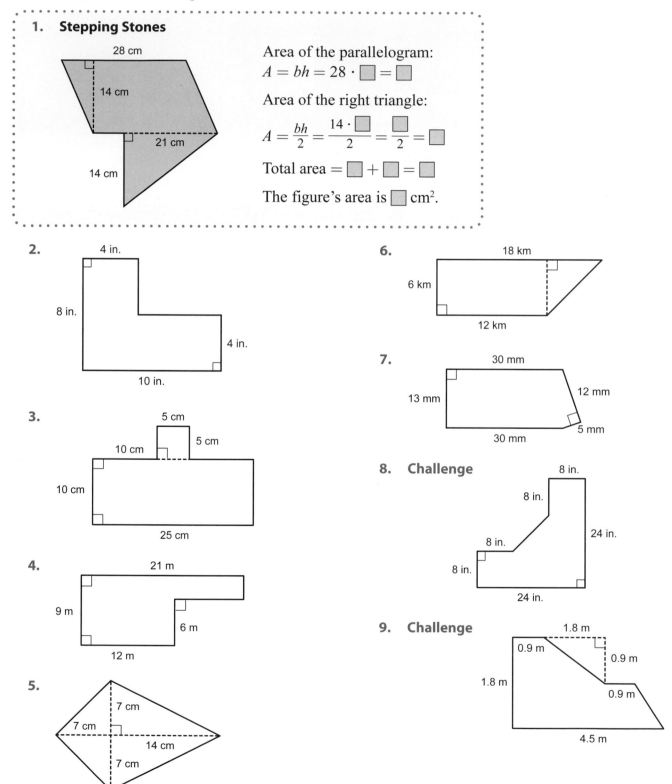

1. Stepping Stones

28 cm

14 cm

21 cm

14 cm

Area of the parallelogram:
$$A = bh = 28 \cdot \square = \square$$

Area of the right triangle:
$$A = \frac{bh}{2} = \frac{14 \cdot \square}{2} = \frac{\square}{2} = \square$$

Total area $= \square + \square = \square$

The figure's area is $\square$ cm^2.

2.

4 in.

8 in.

4 in.

10 in.

3.

5 cm

5 cm

10 cm

10 cm

25 cm

4.

21 m

9 m

6 m

12 m

5.

7 cm

7 cm

14 cm

7 cm

6.

18 km

6 km

12 km

7.

30 mm

13 mm

12 mm

30 mm

5 mm

8. Challenge

8 in.

8 in.

8 in.

24 in.

8 in.

24 in.

9. Challenge

1.8 m

0.9 m

0.9 m

1.8 m

0.9 m

4.5 m

Find the area of the shaded part of the figure.

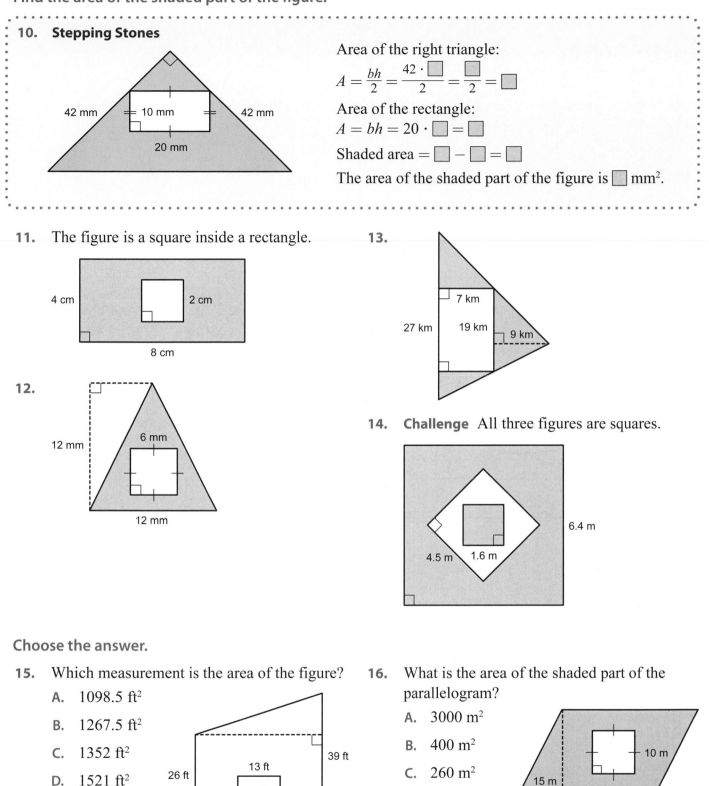

10. **Stepping Stones**

42 mm   = 10 mm =   42 mm

20 mm

Area of the right triangle:

$$A = \frac{bh}{2} = \frac{42 \cdot \boxed{}}{2} = \frac{\boxed{}}{2} = \boxed{}$$

Area of the rectangle:
$$A = bh = 20 \cdot \boxed{} = \boxed{}$$

Shaded area $= \boxed{} - \boxed{} = \boxed{}$

The area of the shaded part of the figure is $\boxed{}$ mm².

11. The figure is a square inside a rectangle.

4 cm   2 cm

8 cm

13.

7 km

27 km   19 km

9 km

12.

12 mm   6 mm

12 mm

14. **Challenge** All three figures are squares.

6.4 m

4.5 m   1.6 m

Choose the answer.

15. Which measurement is the area of the figure?

A. 1098.5 ft²

B. 1267.5 ft²

C. 1352 ft²

D. 1521 ft²

26 ft   39 ft

13 ft

13 ft

13 ft   13 ft

16. What is the area of the shaded part of the parallelogram?

A. 3000 m²

B. 400 m²

C. 260 m²

D. 200 m²

10 m

15 m

20 m

P R O B L E M   S E T

Unknown Side Lengths: Division

You can use area formulas to calculate unknown bases, heights, lengths, and widths.

➡ Finding an Unknown Side Length

When you're given a figure's area and asked to find an unknown side length, you can use the appropriate area formula to write an equation. Then you can find the unknown length.

Example

PROBLEM 1 The area of a rectangular room is 54 m². If the width of the room is 6 m, how long is the room?

6 m

SOLUTION First write an equation that relates length, width, and area for a rectangle.

$A = lw$
$54 = l \cdot 6$ Substitute 54 for A and 6 for w.

What value of l makes the equation true?
$l = 54 \div 6$ Write a related equation.
$l = 9$ Simplify.

ANSWER The length of the room is 9 m.

CHECK Substitute 9 for l in the original equation.
$54 = 9 \cdot 6 \checkmark$

➡ Using Division to Solve Multiplication Equations

You can use inverse operations like multiplication and division to solve equations.

Multiplication Property of Equality

If you multiply or divide both sides of an equation by the same number, you get an equation that is equivalent to the original equation.

If $x = a$ and b is not zero, then $x \cdot b = a \cdot b$,
and $x \div b = a \div b$.

Tip

When you want to find an unknown factor, you are looking for the answer to a division problem.

TOPIC

Writing simpler equations that are equivalent to the original is called *using transformations*.

Think About It

Solving an equation means finding all values of the variable that make the equation true. Any solution to an equation must make the original equation true.

Example

PROBLEM 2 Solve: $3p = 42$

SOLUTION The equation has multiplication, so divide to solve.

$$3p = 42$$
$$3p \div 3 = 42 \div 3 \qquad \text{Divide both sides by 3.}$$
$$p \cdot 3 \div 3 = 14 \qquad \text{commutative property}$$
$$p \cdot 1 = 14 \qquad \text{Divide 3 by 3 to get 1.}$$
$$p = 14 \qquad \text{Simplify.}$$

ANSWER $p = 14$

Remember

To keep an equation true, whatever you do to one side of the equation, you also need to do to the other side.

➔ Application: Counting Animals

Example

PROBLEM 3 How many wolves are in a pack that has 52 paws?

SOLUTION Choose variables and write an equation that models the situation.
Let w = the number of wolves and p = the number of paws.
$$4w = p$$

Solve the equation.

$$4w = 52 \qquad \text{Substitute 52 for } p.$$
$$4w \div 4 = 52 \div 4 \qquad \text{Divide each side by 4.}$$
$$w = 13 \qquad \text{Simplify.}$$

ANSWER If there are 52 paws, then there are 13 wolves.

CHECK Substitute 52 for p and 13 for w in the original equation.
$$4w = p$$
$$4 \cdot 13 = 52 \checkmark$$

Problem Set

Find the unknown side length for each figure that is a rectangle, parallelogram, or triangle.

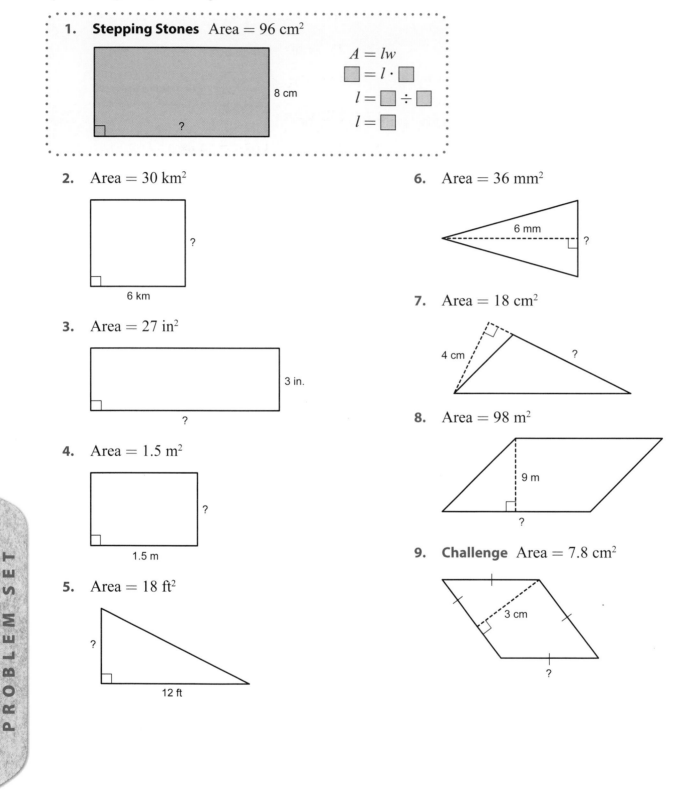

1. **Stepping Stones** Area = 96 cm²

8 cm

?

$$A = lw$$
$$\square = l \cdot \square$$
$$l = \square \div \square$$
$$l = \square$$

2. Area = 30 km²

?

6 km

3. Area = 27 in²

3 in.

?

4. Area = 1.5 m²

?

1.5 m

5. Area = 18 ft²

?

12 ft

6. Area = 36 mm²

6 mm

?

7. Area = 18 cm²

4 cm

?

8. Area = 98 m²

9 m

?

9. **Challenge** Area = 7.8 cm²

3 cm

?

Solve for the variable.

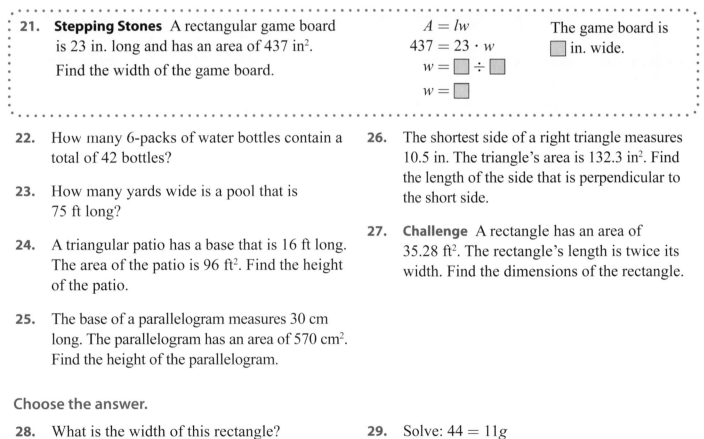

10. **Stepping Stones** $9g = 72$

$$9g = 72$$
$$9g \div 9 = 72 \div \square$$
$$g = \square$$

11. $6p = 24$

12. $8k = 64$

13. $63 = 9d$

14. $56 = 7m$

15. $11m = 187$

16. $169 = 13b$

17. $26r = 507$

18. $384 = 16w$

19. $132.8 = 8c$

20. **Challenge** $4.08p = 34.68$

Write an equation that models the situation and use it to solve the problem.

21. **Stepping Stones** A rectangular game board is 23 in. long and has an area of 437 in². Find the width of the game board.

$$A = lw$$
$$437 = 23 \cdot w$$
$$w = \square \div \square$$
$$w = \square$$

The game board is $\square$ in. wide.

22. How many 6-packs of water bottles contain a total of 42 bottles?

23. How many yards wide is a pool that is 75 ft long?

24. A triangular patio has a base that is 16 ft long. The area of the patio is 96 ft². Find the height of the patio.

25. The base of a parallelogram measures 30 cm long. The parallelogram has an area of 570 cm². Find the height of the parallelogram.

26. The shortest side of a right triangle measures 10.5 in. The triangle's area is 132.3 in². Find the length of the side that is perpendicular to the short side.

27. **Challenge** A rectangle has an area of 35.28 ft². The rectangle's length is twice its width. Find the dimensions of the rectangle.

Choose the answer.

28. What is the width of this rectangle?

Area = 108 cm²

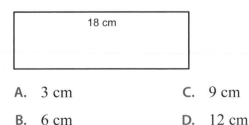

18 cm

A. 3 cm

B. 6 cm

C. 9 cm

D. 12 cm

29. Solve: $44 = 11g$

A. $g = 4$

B. $g = 15$

C. $g = 33$

D. $g = 55$

Unknown Side Lengths: Square Roots

If you're given the area of a square, you can use the formula $A = s^2$ to find the side lengths.

➔ Finding the Unknown Side Length of a Square

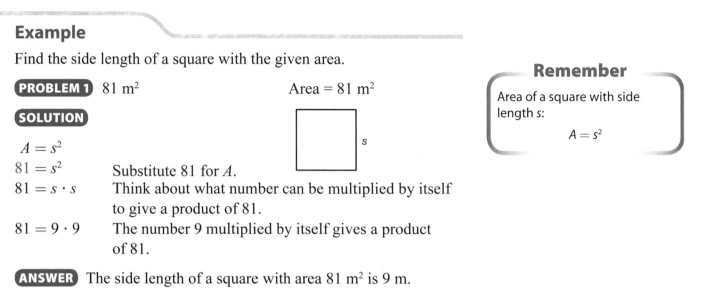

Example

Find the side length of a square with the given area.

PROBLEM 1 81 m²

Area = 81 m²

SOLUTION

$A = s^2$

$81 = s^2$ Substitute 81 for A.

$81 = s \cdot s$ Think about what number can be multiplied by itself to give a product of 81.

$81 = 9 \cdot 9$ The number 9 multiplied by itself gives a product of 81.

ANSWER The side length of a square with area 81 m² is 9 m.

Remember

Area of a square with side length s:

$$A = s^2$$

➔ Finding Square Roots

Definitions

A **square root** is a factor of a number that when multiplied by itself results in that number. For example, a square root of 9 is 3, because $3 \cdot 3 = 9$.

The square root is indicated by the $\sqrt{\ }$ symbol.

A whole number is a **perfect square** if its square root is also a whole number. Examples of perfect squares are 1, 4, 9, 16, 25, and 36.

If you don't recognize a number as a perfect square, you might be able to break it into the product of perfect squares. Then you can find the square root of each and multiply.

Tip

The square root of a product is the product of the square root of its factors:

$$\sqrt{a \cdot b} = \sqrt{a} \cdot \sqrt{b}.$$

The Square Root Property

For any positive numbers a and x:

$$\text{If } a = x^2, \text{ then } x = \sqrt{a}.$$

Example

Evaluate the square root.

PROBLEM 2 $\sqrt{64}$

SOLUTION

$64 = 8 \cdot 8$ The number 8 multiplied by itself gives a product of 64.

ANSWER $\sqrt{64} = 8$

PROBLEM 3 $\sqrt{1600}$

SOLUTION

$1600 = 16 \cdot 100$ Break 1600 into the product of perfect squares.

$1600 = 4 \cdot 4 \cdot 10 \cdot 10$ Factor the perfect squares.

$1600 = 40 \cdot 40$ commutative property

So $\sqrt{1600} = \sqrt{40 \cdot 40} = 40$.

ANSWER $\sqrt{1600} = 40$

➔ Application: Painting

Side Length of a Square

The side length of a square with area A is
$$s = \sqrt{A}.$$

Example

PROBLEM 4 A 2 L can of paint will cover about 25 m². What is the side length of the largest square that can be painted with 2 L of paint?

SOLUTION

$s = \sqrt{A}$ Use the formula for the side length of a square.

$s = \sqrt{25}$ Substitute 25 for A.

$= \sqrt{5 \cdot 5}$ The number 5 multiplied by itself gives a product of 25.

$= 5$

ANSWER The side length of the largest square that can be painted with 2 L of paint is 5 m.

Problem Set

Find the side length of a square with the given area.

1. **Stepping Stones** 121 in²

   $A = s^2$

   $\boxed{} = s^2$

   $= \boxed{} \cdot \boxed{}$

   So the side length is $\boxed{}$ in.

2. 49 ft²

3. 16 mi²

4. Area = 100 m²

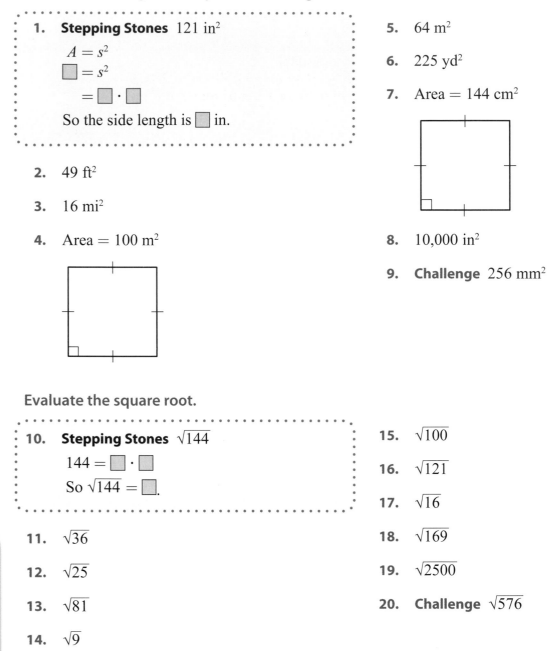

5. 64 m²

6. 225 yd²

7. Area = 144 cm²

8. 10,000 in²

9. **Challenge** 256 mm²

Evaluate the square root.

10. **Stepping Stones** $\sqrt{144}$

    $144 = \boxed{} \cdot \boxed{}$

    So $\sqrt{144} = \boxed{}$.

11. $\sqrt{36}$

12. $\sqrt{25}$

13. $\sqrt{81}$

14. $\sqrt{9}$

15. $\sqrt{100}$

16. $\sqrt{121}$

17. $\sqrt{16}$

18. $\sqrt{169}$

19. $\sqrt{2500}$

20. **Challenge** $\sqrt{576}$

Solve.

21. **Stepping Stones** A lawn mower can mow 1600 yd² of lawn on one tank of gas. What is the side length of the largest square that can be mown with one tank of gas?

$$s = \sqrt{A}$$
$$s = \sqrt{\boxed{}}$$
$$s = \sqrt{\boxed{} \cdot \boxed{}}$$
$$s = \boxed{}$$

The side length of the largest square of lawn that can be mown is $\boxed{}$ yd.

22. A batch of pizza dough can make a pizza with an area of 196 in². What is the side length of the largest square pizza that can be made with one batch of dough?

23. A 5-gallon drum of sealant can cover 6400 square yards of pavement. What is the side length of the largest square of pavement that can be covered with 5 gallons of sealant?

24. Two 2-liter cans of paint will cover about 49 m². How many cans of paint will it take to cover a square with a side length of 21 m?

25. **Challenge** A painter paints a wall that is 8 ft tall and 24 ft long. There are three equal-sized square windows in the wall that she does not paint. She paints a total of 165 ft². What is the width of each window?

Choose the answer.

26. Which square has an area of 121 cm²?

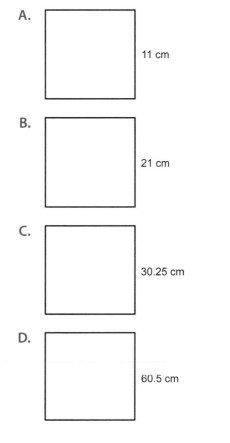

A. 11 cm

B. 21 cm

C. 30.25 cm

D. 60.5 cm

27. What is the square root of 900?

A. 30

B. 90

C. 300

D. 1800

28. A farmer has enough fertilizer to cover 500 ft² of field. Which square field is the largest that he could completely cover with fertilizer?

A. 18 ft by 18 ft

B. 20 ft by 20 ft

C. 22 ft by 22 ft

D. 25 ft by 25 ft

29. Which measurement is the side length of a square with an area of 36 ft²?

A. 4 ft

B. 6 ft

C. 9 ft

D. 18 ft

Chapter 3 Review

Choose the answer.

1. Which measurement is the width of the rectangle?

    Area = 54 cm^2

    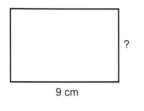

    9 cm

    A.   6 cm   C.   54 cm

    B.   12 cm   D.   63 cm

2. Which measurement is the base of the triangle?

    Area = 18 yd^2

    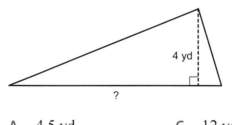

    4 yd

    ?

    A.   4.5 yd   C.   12 yd

    B.   9 yd   D.   18 yd

3. Which measurement is the side length of a square with an area of 25 in^2?

    A.   2 in.   C.   4 in.

    B.   3 in.   D.   5 in.

4. Which measurement is the side length of a square with an area of 169 m^2?

    A.   6 m   C.   12 m

    B.   9 m   D.   13 m

5. Which measurement is the area of a rectangle that is 7.5 cm long and 1.6 cm wide?

    A.   6 cm^2 C.   18 cm^2

    B.   12 cm^2 D.   24 cm^2

6. Which pair of figure types applies to the figure?

    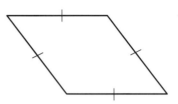

    A.   parallelogram, rhombus

    B.   parallelogram, rectangle

    C.   quadrilateral, square

    D.   quadrilateral, rectangle

7. Which measurement is the area of a triangle with a height of 21 in. and a base of 28 in.?

    A.   147 in^2 C.   441 in^2

    B.   294 in^2 D.   588 in^2

8. Which measurement is the area of the shaded part of the figure?

    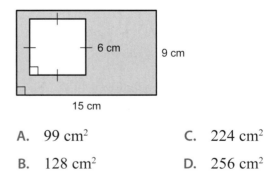

    6 cm

    9 cm

    15 cm

    A.   99 cm^2 C.   224 cm^2

    B.   128 cm^2 D.   256 cm^2

Solve.

9. Find the area of the square in square meters and square centimeters.

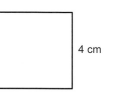

4 cm

10. Find the area of the square in square meters and square centimeters.

12 cm

Find the area of the rectangle or parallelogram.

11.

8 in.

23 in.

13.

2.5 m

4.7 m

12.

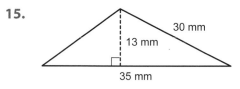

6 mm   7 mm

6 mm

14.

11.9 cm   14.2 cm

14.2 cm

Find the area of the figure.

15.

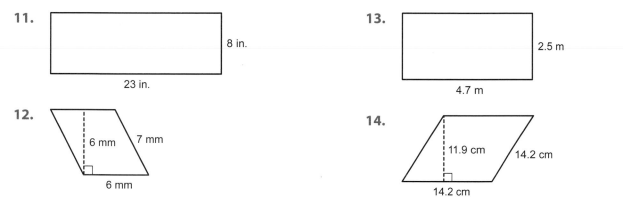

30 mm

13 mm

35 mm

16. The figure is made up of a square and a right triangle.

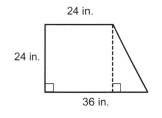

24 in.

24 in.

36 in.

Solve.

17. What is the area of a rectangular pool table that is 9 feet long and 4 feet wide?

18. What is the area of a triangular wall that has a base length of 2.4 m and a height of 6 m?

19. $9w = 81$

20. $39 = 13p$

21. What is the length of a rectangle with an area of 36 m² and a width of 3 m?

22. What is the side length of a square with an area of 16 cm²?

Problem	Topic Lookup
9, 10	Units of Area
5, 11, 13, 17	Areas of Rectangles
6, 12, 14	Special Quadrilaterals
7, 15, 18	Areas of Triangles

Problem	Topic Lookup
8, 16	Figures Made Up of Triangles and Parallelograms
1, 2, 19, 20, 21	Unknown Side Lengths: Division
3, 4, 22	Unknown Side Lengths: Square Roots

4 Working with Rational Numbers

Most two-by-fours are actually about $1\frac{1}{2}$ inches by $3\frac{1}{2}$ inches. Any carpenter working with lumber is also working with rational numbers.

In This Chapter

. . . .

You will learn how to change between various representations of rational numbers including equivalent fractions and decimals. You'll also add, subtract, multiply, and divide rational numbers and use these skills to solve practical problems.

Chapter Topics

. . . .

▶ Foundations for Chapter 4

▶ Equivalent Fractions

▶ Representing Rational Numbers

▶ Comparing Rational Numbers

▶ Perimeters with Fractions

▶ Areas with Fractions

▶ Dividing Fractions

▶ Solving Problems with Fraction Division

▶ Chapter 4 Review

A tape measure is a type of number line.

Foundations for Chapter 4

➔ **Expressing Fractions in Simplest Form**

Definitions

A **fraction** is a number in the form $\frac{a}{b}$, where a and b are integers and $b \neq 0$. Fractions can show part of a set, a point on a number line, a part of a whole, a quotient, or a ratio.

The **denominator** of a fraction is the number below the fraction bar. The denominator tells the number of equal parts.

The **numerator** of a fraction is the number above the fraction bar. The numerator tells the number of parts being described.

A fraction is in its **simplest form** or **lowest terms** when its numerator and denominator have no common factor other than 1.

To express a fraction in simplest form, find any common factors of the numerator and denominator. Then divide the numerator and denominator by the common factor. The value of the fraction does not change, because you are dividing both parts by the same number. Repeat until the only common factor is 1.

Example A
Express the fraction in simplest form.

PROBLEM A-1 $\frac{6}{8}$

SOLUTION Find common factors of 6 and 8.
Factors of 6: 1, 2, 3, 6
Factors of 8: 1, 2, 4, 8
Divide the numerator and the denominator by their greatest common factor, 2.

$$\frac{6}{8} = \frac{6 \div 2}{8 \div 2} = \frac{3}{4}$$

ANSWER $\frac{6}{8} = \frac{3}{4}$

PROBLEM A-2 $\frac{12}{36}$

SOLUTION Find common factors of 12 and 36. Divide the numerator and the denominator by their greatest common factor, 12.

$$\frac{12}{36} = \frac{12 \div 12}{36 \div 12} = \frac{1}{3}$$

ANSWER $\frac{12}{36} = \frac{1}{3}$

Problem Set A

Express the fraction in simplest form.

1. $\frac{3}{6}$

2. $\frac{4}{16}$

3. $\frac{3}{7}$

4. $\frac{2}{8}$

5. $\frac{9}{12}$

6. $\frac{14}{16}$

➔ Adding and Subtracting Fractions with Like Denominators

How to Add and Subtract Fractions with Like Denominators

To add or subtract fractions with like denominators, add or subtract the numerators and write the sum or difference over the common denominator.

$$\frac{1}{7} + \frac{5}{7} = \frac{1+5}{7} = \frac{6}{7} \qquad\qquad \frac{3}{5} - \frac{1}{5} = \frac{3-1}{5} = \frac{2}{5}$$

When adding or subtracting fractions, it's generally a good idea to express the answer in simplest form.

Example B
Add or subtract.

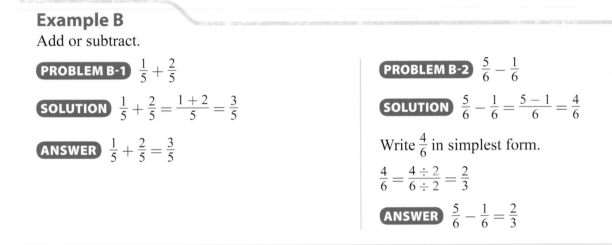

PROBLEM B-1 $\frac{1}{5} + \frac{2}{5}$

SOLUTION $\frac{1}{5} + \frac{2}{5} = \frac{1+2}{5} = \frac{3}{5}$

ANSWER $\frac{1}{5} + \frac{2}{5} = \frac{3}{5}$

PROBLEM B-2 $\frac{5}{6} - \frac{1}{6}$

SOLUTION $\frac{5}{6} - \frac{1}{6} = \frac{5-1}{6} = \frac{4}{6}$

Write $\frac{4}{6}$ in simplest form.

$$\frac{4}{6} = \frac{4 \div 2}{6 \div 2} = \frac{2}{3}$$

ANSWER $\frac{5}{6} - \frac{1}{6} = \frac{2}{3}$

Problem Set B

Add or subtract.

1. $\frac{1}{3} + \frac{1}{3}$

2. $\frac{3}{4} - \frac{2}{4}$

3. $\frac{2}{8} + \frac{5}{8}$

4. $\frac{11}{12} - \frac{6}{12}$

5. $\frac{2}{6} + \frac{1}{6}$

6. $\frac{1}{8} - \frac{1}{8}$

7. $\frac{3}{10} + \frac{5}{10}$

8. $\frac{6}{6} - \frac{4}{6}$

9. $\frac{3}{5} + \frac{4}{5}$

10. $\frac{6}{12} - \frac{4}{12}$

11. $\frac{1}{2} + \frac{1}{2}$

12. $\frac{7}{8} - \frac{3}{8}$

➡ Translating Among Different Forms of Decimals

Forms of Decimals

As with whole numbers, decimals can be written in different forms. The decimal model below represents 1 whole. The whole is divided into 100 equal parts, so each small square represents one hundredth, $\frac{1}{100}$, or 0.01. The number represented by the shaded part of the model can be written in the following forms:

Standard Form
0.45

Word Form
forty-five hundredths

Expanded Form
$0.4 + 0.05$

To convert among forms of decimals, consider the value of each digit in the number. The value of the digit is determined by its place.

Example C

PROBLEM C-1 Write 0.4 in word form.

SOLUTION The digit 4 is in the tenths place, so there are 4 tenths.

ANSWER 0.4 = four tenths

PROBLEM C-2 Write *thirty-seven thousandths* in standard form.

SOLUTION One thousandth is written as 0.001, so thirty-seven thousandths is $37 \cdot 0.001 = 0.037$.

ANSWER thirty-seven thousandths = 0.037

PROBLEM C-3 Write 12.75 in expanded form.

SOLUTION Write the number as the sum of the values of the digits.

The value of the tens digit, 1, is $1 \cdot 10 = 10$.

The value of the ones digit, 2, is $2 \cdot 1 = 2$.

The value of the tenths digit, 7, is $7 \cdot 0.1 = 0.7$.

The value of the hundredths digit is $5 \cdot 0.01 = 0.05$.

ANSWER $12.75 = 10 + 2 + 0.7 + 0.05$

Problem Set C

Write the decimal in word and expanded forms.

1. 0.3
2. 0.05
3. 2.16
4. 39.06

Write the decimal in standard and expanded forms.

5. fourteen hundredths

6. eighty-six hundredths

7. one and two tenths

8. sixty and five hundredths

Write the decimal in word and standard forms.

9. $40 + 7 + 0.3 + 0.09$
10. $80 + 4 + 0.2$
11. $100 + 3 + 0.08$

Planting the Seed

Every rational number can be written as a ratio of two integers, but a ratio can be written in many ways. For instance, you could write equivalent ratios such as $\frac{1}{2}$, $\frac{2}{4}$, and $\frac{4}{8}$. Changing the way rational numbers look can make it easier to add, subtract, multiply, or divide numbers.

FOUNDATIONS

Equivalent Fractions

You can use fractions that look very different to describe the same thing.

➡ Finding the Least Common Denominator

Definitions

A **multiple** of a number is the product of that number and a counting number.

The **least common multiple (LCM)** of two or more numbers is the least multiple that is common to all the numbers.

The **least common denominator (LCD)** of two or more fractions is the LCM of their denominators.

Tip

The counting numbers are 1, 2, 3, 4, 5, ….

To find the LCD of a set of fractions, find the LCM of their denominators. Find the LCM by listing the multiples of each denominator and then finding the least multiple that they share.

Example

Find the LCD for the fractions.

PROBLEM 1 $\frac{3}{8}$ and $\frac{1}{6}$

SOLUTION Multiples of 8: 8, 16, $\boxed{24}$, 32, 40, 48, …

Multiples of 6: 6, 12, 18, $\boxed{24}$, …

The LCM of 8 and 6 is 24.

ANSWER The LCD for $\frac{3}{8}$ and $\frac{1}{6}$ is 24.

PROBLEM 2 $\frac{1}{3}$ and $\frac{7}{12}$

SOLUTION Multiples of 3: 3, 6, 9, $\boxed{12}$, 15, 18, …

Multiples of 12: $\boxed{12}$, 24, 36, 48, …

The LCM of 3 and 12 is 12.

ANSWER The LCD for $\frac{1}{3}$ and $\frac{7}{12}$ is 12.

Tip

If one denominator is a factor of the other, then their LCM will be the greater denominator.

➽ Writing Equivalent Fractions

Definition

Equivalent fractions are fractions that name the same value.

One way to write an equivalent fraction for a given fraction is to multiply it by a form of 1. When you multiply by a fraction that looks like $\frac{a}{a}$, you are multiplying by a form of 1, so both fractions name the same value.

Example

PROBLEM 3 Write two fractions equivalent to $\frac{4}{9}$.

SOLUTION Multiply $\frac{4}{9}$ by two versions of $\frac{a}{a}$.

$$\frac{4}{9} = \frac{4}{9} \cdot \frac{2}{2} = \frac{4 \cdot 2}{9 \cdot 2} = \frac{8}{18}$$

$$\frac{4}{9} = \frac{4}{9} \cdot \frac{3}{3} = \frac{4 \cdot 3}{9 \cdot 3} = \frac{12}{27}$$

ANSWER $\frac{4}{9} = \frac{8}{18} = \frac{12}{27}$

PROBLEM 4 Complete to make equivalent fractions.

$$\frac{2}{3} = \frac{\square}{15}$$

SOLUTION Find the common factor. In the denominators, 3 is multiplied by 5 to get 15. The common factor is 5.

$$\frac{2}{3} \cdot \frac{5}{5} = \frac{10}{15}$$

ANSWER The missing number is 10.

> ### Think About It
>
> Remember that $\frac{2}{2} = 1$. So multiplying $\frac{4}{9}$ by $\frac{2}{2}$ is the same as multiplying by 1. The value of $\frac{4}{9}$ is unchanged, so you get equivalent fractions.

➽ Using the LCD to Compare Fractions

To compare fractions with different denominators, write equivalent fractions with a common denominator. Compare the numerators.

Example

Write $<$, $>$, or $=$ to compare.

PROBLEM 5 $\frac{7}{9} \;\square\; \frac{5}{6}$

SOLUTION The LCM of 9 and 6 is 18, so the LCD of the fractions is 18.

$$\frac{7}{9} = \frac{7}{9} \cdot \frac{2}{2} = \frac{7 \cdot 2}{9 \cdot 2} = \frac{14}{18} \qquad \frac{5}{6} = \frac{5}{6} \cdot \frac{3}{3} = \frac{5 \cdot 3}{6 \cdot 3} = \frac{15}{18}$$

Compare $\frac{14}{18}$ and $\frac{15}{18}$ by comparing the numerators: $14 < 15$.

ANSWER $\frac{7}{9} < \frac{5}{6}$

> ### Think About It
>
> This example shows comparing fractions using their LCD. But any common denominator will work for comparing fractions. It does not need to be the LCD.

Problem Set

Find the least LCD for the fractions.

1. **Stepping Stones** $\frac{2}{5}$ and $\frac{3}{4}$

   Multiples of 5: 5, 10, ☐, ☐, ☐, …

   Multiples of 4: 4, 8, ☐, ☐, ☐, …

   The LCD is ☐.

2. $\frac{1}{4}$ and $\frac{1}{8}$

3. $\frac{4}{9}$ and $\frac{2}{3}$

4. $\frac{1}{12}$ and $\frac{3}{4}$

5. $\frac{1}{3}$ and $\frac{5}{6}$

6. $\frac{1}{2}$ and $\frac{7}{16}$

7. $\frac{1}{6}$ and $\frac{3}{10}$

8. $\frac{5}{8}$ and $\frac{1}{9}$

9. $\frac{2}{7}$ and $\frac{9}{10}$

10. **Challenge** $\frac{11}{24}$ and $\frac{5}{16}$

Write two fractions equivalent to the fraction.

11. **Stepping Stones** $\frac{3}{4}$

    $$\frac{3}{4} \cdot \frac{☐}{2} = \frac{3 \cdot ☐}{4 \cdot 2} = \frac{☐}{8}$$

    $$\frac{3}{4} \cdot \frac{☐}{3} = \frac{3 \cdot ☐}{4 \cdot 3} = \frac{☐}{12}$$

12. $\frac{1}{2}$

13. $\frac{4}{5}$

14. $\frac{8}{10}$

15. $\frac{6}{5}$

16. $\frac{2}{3}$

17. $\frac{3}{7}$

18. $\frac{12}{2}$

19. $\frac{5}{1}$

20. **Challenge** $\frac{x}{y}$

Complete to make equivalent fractions.

21. **Stepping Stones** $\frac{5}{8} = \frac{☐}{24}$

    First, look at the denominators: $8 \cdot ☐ = 24$.

    Next, look at the numerators: $5 \cdot ☐ = ☐$.

    $$\frac{5}{8} = \frac{☐}{24}$$

22. $\frac{1}{4} = \frac{☐}{16}$

23. $\frac{3}{5} = \frac{☐}{30}$

24. $\frac{2}{3} = \frac{☐}{15}$

25. $\frac{5}{6} = \frac{20}{☐}$

26. $\frac{7}{3} = \frac{\square}{18}$

27. $\frac{12}{5} = \frac{60}{\square}$

28. $\frac{8}{\square} = \frac{16}{2}$

29. $\frac{7}{\square} = \frac{28}{40}$

30. **Challenge** $4 = \frac{\square}{16}$

Write $<$, $>$, or $=$ to compare.

31. **Stepping Stones** $\frac{4}{15} \square \frac{2}{6}$

The LCM is $\square$, so the LCD of the fractions is $\square$.

$\frac{4}{15} \cdot \frac{\square}{\square} = \frac{\square}{30}$ $\qquad$ $\frac{2}{6} \cdot \frac{\square}{\square} = \frac{\square}{30}$

Compare the numerators of the equivalent fractions:

$\square < \square$

So $\frac{4}{15} \square \frac{2}{6}$.

32. $\frac{3}{5} \square \frac{12}{20}$

33. $\frac{5}{7} \square \frac{11}{14}$

34. $\frac{15}{16} \square \frac{7}{8}$

35. $\frac{9}{24} \square \frac{3}{8}$

36. $\frac{3}{4} \square \frac{3}{5}$

37. $\frac{6}{8} \square \frac{7}{9}$

38. $\frac{5}{6} \square \frac{4}{5}$

39. $\frac{5}{8} \square \frac{12}{20}$

40. **Challenge** Order the fractions from least to greatest.

$\frac{5}{8}, \frac{3}{4}, \frac{1}{2}$

Choose the answer.

41. What is the LCM of 18 and 27?

   A. 90

   B. 108

   C. 54

   D. 270

42. Which one of these fractions is **not** equivalent to the others?

   A. $\frac{5}{20}$

   B. $\frac{8}{32}$

   C. $\frac{19}{76}$

   D. $\frac{14}{48}$

43. What is the LCD of $\frac{3}{8}$ and $\frac{19}{20}$?

   A. 16

   B. 40

   C. 60

   D. 160

44. Which pair of fractions shows $\frac{2}{3}$ and $\frac{5}{12}$ converted with their LCD?

   A. $\frac{8}{12}$ and $\frac{5}{12}$

   B. $\frac{24}{36}$ and $\frac{15}{36}$

   C. $\frac{11}{15}$ and $\frac{8}{15}$

   D. $\frac{8}{12}$ and $\frac{10}{24}$

Representing Rational Numbers

Improper fractions and mixed numbers are different ways to use fractions to name values greater than 1.

➤ Representing Mixed Numbers

Definitions

A **mixed number** is a number made up of a whole number and a proper fraction, or the opposite of such a number.

An **improper fraction** is a fraction greater than or equal to 1. The numerator of an improper fraction is greater than or equal to its denominator.

These models both show the mixed number $1\frac{3}{5}$ and the improper fraction $\frac{8}{5}$. The shaded parts of the rectangles show the number. The number line shows the number as the location of point P.

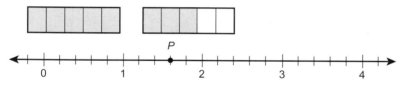

Example

PROBLEM 1 Write the mixed number and the improper fraction represented by the point on the number line.

SOLUTION Look at the marks between whole numbers to see what fractional parts are shown. Each whole unit is divided into 4 parts, so the number line shows fourths.

Find the mixed number. Point A is located at 2 whole units plus $\frac{1}{4}$ of a unit. That's $2\frac{1}{4}$.

Find the improper fraction. Start at 0 and count the fourths. There are 9 fourths. The improper fraction is $\frac{9}{4}$.

ANSWER Point A represents $2\frac{1}{4}$ and $\frac{9}{4}$.

➥ Converting Mixed Numbers to Improper Fractions

To write a mixed number as an improper fraction, convert the whole-number part to an improper fraction with the same denominator as the fraction part. Then add the numerators of the fractions. A short way to represent this method is to multiply the whole-number part by the denominator and then add that product to the numerator.

Example

Convert the mixed number to an improper fraction.

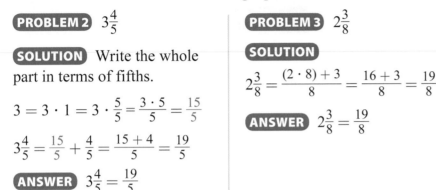

PROBLEM 2 $3\frac{4}{5}$

SOLUTION Write the whole part in terms of fifths.

$3 = 3 \cdot 1 = 3 \cdot \frac{5}{5} = \frac{3 \cdot 5}{5} = \frac{15}{5}$

$3\frac{4}{5} = \frac{15}{5} + \frac{4}{5} = \frac{15 + 4}{5} = \frac{19}{5}$

ANSWER $3\frac{4}{5} = \frac{19}{5}$

PROBLEM 3 $2\frac{3}{8}$

SOLUTION

$2\frac{3}{8} = \frac{(2 \cdot 8) + 3}{8} = \frac{16 + 3}{8} = \frac{19}{8}$

ANSWER $2\frac{3}{8} = \frac{19}{8}$

Remember

The number 1 can be written as any fraction with a numerator that is equal to its denominator.

➥ Converting Improper Fractions to Mixed Numbers

To convert an improper fraction to a mixed number, divide to find the quotient and remainder. Write the remainder over the divisor, and then express the fraction in simplest form.

Example

Convert the improper fraction to a mixed number.

PROBLEM 4 $\frac{9}{4}$

SOLUTION $9 \div 4 = 2 \text{ r } 1$

In the quotient, 2 represents the number of wholes and 1 is the number of fourths left over.

ANSWER $\frac{9}{4} = 2\frac{1}{4}$

CHECK Convert the answer back to an improper fraction.

$2\frac{1}{4} = \frac{(2 \cdot 4) + 1}{4}$

$= \frac{8 + 1}{4} = \frac{9}{4} \checkmark$

PROBLEM 5 $\frac{20}{6}$

SOLUTION $20 \div 6 = 3 \text{ r } 2$

There are 3 wholes, and 2 sixths are left over.

$3\frac{2}{6} = 3\frac{1}{3}$

ANSWER $\frac{20}{6} = 3\frac{1}{3}$

CHECK

$3\frac{1}{3} = \frac{(3 \cdot 3) + 1}{3}$

$= \frac{9 + 1}{3} = \frac{10}{3} = \frac{20}{6} \checkmark$

Think About It

In Problem 5, you also could have simplified the improper fraction $\frac{20}{6}$ to $\frac{10}{3}$ before converting.

TOPIC

Problem Set

Write the mixed number and the improper fraction represented by the point on the number line.

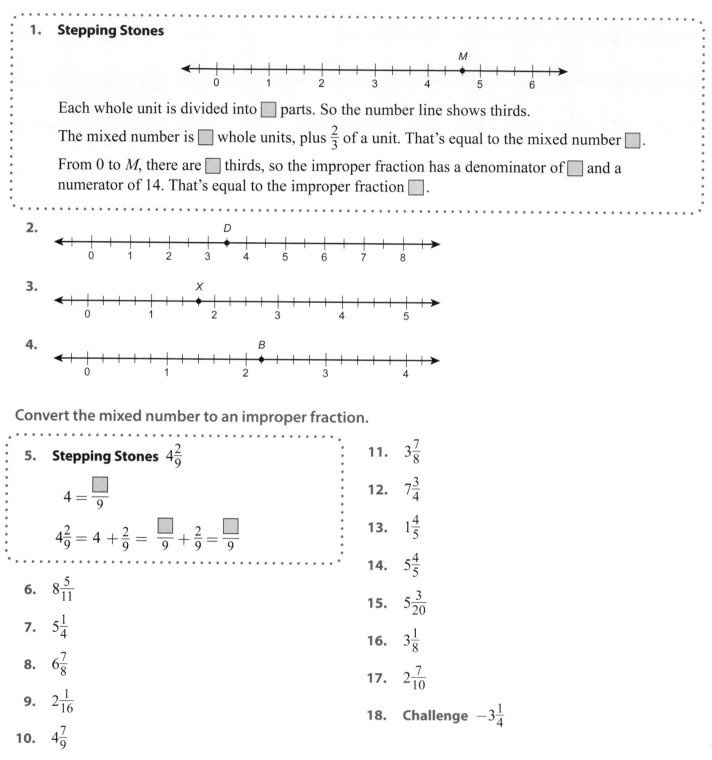

1. **Stepping Stones**

   Each whole unit is divided into ☐ parts. So the number line shows thirds.

   The mixed number is ☐ whole units, plus $\frac{2}{3}$ of a unit. That's equal to the mixed number ☐.

   From 0 to M, there are ☐ thirds, so the improper fraction has a denominator of ☐ and a numerator of 14. That's equal to the improper fraction ☐.

2.

3.

4.

Convert the mixed number to an improper fraction.

5. **Stepping Stones** $4\frac{2}{9}$

   $$4 = \frac{\square}{9}$$

   $$4\frac{2}{9} = 4 + \frac{2}{9} = \frac{\square}{9} + \frac{2}{9} = \frac{\square}{9}$$

6. $8\frac{5}{11}$

7. $5\frac{1}{4}$

8. $6\frac{7}{8}$

9. $2\frac{1}{16}$

10. $4\frac{7}{9}$

11. $3\frac{7}{8}$

12. $7\frac{3}{4}$

13. $1\frac{4}{5}$

14. $5\frac{4}{5}$

15. $5\frac{3}{20}$

16. $3\frac{1}{8}$

17. $2\frac{7}{10}$

18. **Challenge** $-3\frac{1}{4}$

Convert the improper fraction to a mixed number.

19. **Stepping Stones** $\frac{18}{5}$

$18 \div 5 = 3 \text{ r } \boxed{}$

There are 3 wholes and $\boxed{}$ is the number of fifths left over.

$$\frac{18}{5} = 3 + \frac{\boxed{}}{5}$$

$$= \boxed{}\frac{\boxed{}}{\boxed{}}$$

20. $\frac{49}{4}$

21. $\frac{32}{6}$

22. $\frac{39}{8}$

23. $\frac{21}{10}$

24. $\frac{61}{5}$

25. $\frac{13}{4}$

26. $\frac{34}{9}$

27. $\frac{17}{5}$

28. $\frac{16}{3}$

29. $\frac{9}{6}$

30. $\frac{24}{7}$

31. $\frac{23}{4}$

Choose the answer.

32. Which phrase best describes the location of $\frac{18}{5}$ on a number line?

A. at $1\frac{8}{5}$

B. at $3\frac{1}{2}$

C. closer to 3 than to 4

D. closer to 4 than to 3

33. The numerator of a fraction is twice the denominator. What is the value of this fraction?

A. $\frac{1}{2}$

B. $1\frac{1}{2}$

C. 2

D. $2\frac{1}{2}$

34. Which improper fraction is equal to the mixed number $6\frac{1}{3}$?

A. $\frac{7}{3}$

B. $\frac{19}{6}$

C. $\frac{19}{3}$

D. $\frac{61}{3}$

35. Which mixed number is equal to $\frac{34}{3}$?

A. $3\frac{4}{3}$

B. $11\frac{1}{3}$

C. $30\frac{4}{3}$

D. $33\frac{1}{3}$

Comparing Rational Numbers

When you convert a rational number from one form to another, the number keeps the same value.

➤ Converting Fractions to Decimals

A fraction is another way of writing a quotient. To convert a fraction to a decimal, divide the numerator by the denominator.

> **Remember**
>
> When you divide, you may get a decimal that repeats. You can show the repeating digit with three dots, such as 0.66 ...
>
> Or, you can put a bar over the digits that repeat, such as $0.\overline{6}$.

Example

Convert the fraction or mixed number to a decimal.

PROBLEM 1 $\frac{5}{16}$

SOLUTION

$\frac{5}{16} = 5 \div 16 = 0.3125$

ANSWER $\frac{5}{16} = 0.3125$

PROBLEM 2 $2\frac{3}{11}$

SOLUTION Divide to find the decimal part of the number. Then add the decimal part to the whole part.

$$2 + \frac{3}{11} = 2 + 3 \div 11$$
$$= 2 + 0.\overline{27} = 2.\overline{27}$$

ANSWER $2\frac{3}{11} = 2.\overline{27}$

➤ Converting Decimals to Fractions

Use place value to convert decimals to fractions. For instance, write the number of tenths or hundredths as the numerator over a denominator of 10 or 100. Then simplify the fraction if possible.

Example

Convert the decimal to a fraction or a mixed number.

PROBLEM 3 0.3

SOLUTION There are 3 tenths.

ANSWER $0.3 = \frac{3}{10}$

PROBLEM 4 0.67

SOLUTION There are 67 hundredths.

ANSWER $0.67 = \frac{67}{100}$

Example

Convert the decimal to a fraction or a mixed number.

PROBLEM 5 12.4

SOLUTION There are 12 wholes and 4 tenths.

$12.4 = 12\frac{4}{10}$ Write the fraction part as a fraction with a denominator of 10.

$ = 12\frac{2}{5}$ Simplify.

ANSWER $12.4 = 12\frac{2}{5}$

➜ Comparing and Ordering Rational Numbers

You can use a number line to compare rational numbers in different forms.

Example

PROBLEM 6 Write $<$, $>$, or $=$ to compare $\frac{3}{4}$ and 0.6.

SOLUTION Use a number line showing fractions and decimals.

The point for $\frac{3}{4}$ is to the right of the point for 0.6.

ANSWER $\frac{3}{4} > 0.6$

PROBLEM 7 Write the numbers in order from least to greatest.

$\frac{7}{2}$, 3.4, $3\frac{7}{20}$

SOLUTION Convert the fractions to decimals.

$\frac{7}{2} = 7 \div 2 = 3.5$ $3\frac{7}{20} = 3 + (7 \div 20) = 3.35$

Compare the decimals.

$3.35 < 3.4 < 3.5$

ANSWER $3\frac{7}{20} < 3.4 < \frac{7}{2}$

Problem Set

Convert the fraction or the mixed number to a decimal.

1. **Stepping Stones** $\frac{3}{8}$

   $\frac{3}{8} = 3 \div \boxed{} = \boxed{}$

2. $\frac{5}{10}$

3. $\frac{4}{25}$

4. $\frac{67}{100}$

5. $\frac{7}{20}$

6. $2\frac{5}{8}$

7. $1\frac{3}{50}$

8. $4\frac{6}{25}$

9. $\frac{5}{6}$

10. $2\frac{2}{3}$

11. $\frac{8}{9}$

12. $5\frac{11}{30}$

13. $\frac{8}{15}$

14. $1\frac{5}{24}$

15. $11\frac{3}{16}$

16. **Challenge** $\frac{36}{5}$

Convert the decimal to a fraction or a mixed number.

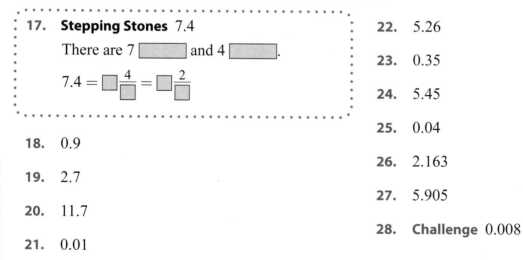

17. **Stepping Stones** 7.4

    There are 7 $\boxed{}$ and 4 $\boxed{}$.

    $7.4 = \boxed{}\frac{4}{\boxed{}} = \boxed{}\frac{2}{\boxed{}}$

18. 0.9

19. 2.7

20. 11.7

21. 0.01

22. 5.26

23. 0.35

24. 5.45

25. 0.04

26. 2.163

27. 5.905

28. **Challenge** 0.008

Write <, >, or = to compare the numbers.

29. **Stepping Stones** $\frac{3}{10}$ and 0.25

$\frac{3}{10}$ equals the decimal ☐.

$\frac{3}{10}$ ☐ 0.25

30. 0.75 and $\frac{3}{4}$

31. $\frac{4}{12}$ and 0.32

32. $1\frac{4}{13}$ and 1.27

33. $3\frac{3}{8}$ and 3.45

34. 0.625 and $\frac{5}{8}$

35. 0.36 and $\frac{3}{16}$

36. **Challenge** $1\frac{7}{16}$ and 1.45

Write the numbers in order from least to greatest.

37. 1.3, $1\frac{2}{5}$, $\frac{27}{24}$

38. $\frac{5}{10}$, 0.6, 0.4

39. 3.7, $2\frac{1}{2}$, 3.5

40. $5\frac{3}{5}$, 5.3, 5.43

Choose the answer.

41. Which decimal is equivalent to $\frac{8}{25}$?

   A. 0.28

   B. 0.32

   C. 0.34

   D. 0.825

42. Which decimal equals $\frac{19}{5}$?

   A. 1.95

   B. 3.4

   C. 3.8

   D. 19.5

43. Which list of numbers is in order from least to greatest?

   A. $1\frac{3}{15}$, $2\frac{2}{9}$, 1.6

   B. $1\frac{3}{15}$, 1.6, $2\frac{2}{9}$

   C. $2\frac{2}{9}$, $1\frac{3}{15}$, 1.6

   D. $2\frac{2}{9}$, 1.6, $1\frac{3}{15}$

44. Which mixed number is greater than 5.21?

   A. $5\frac{1}{5}$

   B. $5\frac{1}{4}$

   C. $4\frac{2}{5}$

   D. $5\frac{1}{6}$

Perimeters with Fractions

Surfaces in everyday life, such as tables and fields, rarely have all whole-number side lengths.

➔ Adding and Subtracting Fractions

How to Add and Subtract Fractions with Unlike Denominators

1. Find a common denominator.
2. Convert each fraction using the common denominator.
3. Add or subtract the numerators and write the sum or difference over the common denominator.

The commutative and associative properties of addition apply to addition with fractions and mixed numbers. Use these properties to reorder or regroup addends to make solving the problem easier.

Example
Add.

PROBLEM 1 $\frac{1}{8} + \frac{2}{3} + \frac{3}{8}$

SOLUTION

$$\frac{1}{8} + \frac{2}{3} + \frac{3}{8} = \frac{2}{3} + \frac{1}{8} + \frac{3}{8}$$ Reorder the addends.

$$= \frac{2}{3} + \left(\frac{1}{8} + \frac{3}{8}\right)$$ Associate the last two addends.

$$= \frac{2}{3} + \frac{1}{2}$$ Add inside the parentheses.

$$= \frac{2}{3} \cdot \frac{2}{2} + \frac{1}{2} \cdot \frac{3}{3}$$ Write each fraction with the LCD.

$$= \frac{4}{6} + \frac{3}{6}$$ Simplify.

$$= \frac{7}{6}$$ Add.

$$= 1\frac{1}{6}$$ Convert to a mixed number.

ANSWER $\frac{1}{8} + \frac{2}{3} + \frac{3}{8} = 1\frac{1}{6}$

> **Remember**
>
> The commutative property allows you to add numbers in any order.
>
> The associative property allows you to group the addends in any way.

TOPIC

Finding Perimeter with Fractions

You can use properties to help calculate perimeter involving fractions.

Example

PROBLEM 2 Find the perimeter.

SOLUTION $P =$ the sum of the side lengths

$P = 36\frac{2}{3} + 30\frac{5}{8} + 33\frac{1}{3} + 24\frac{1}{8}$ Write the sum of the lengths.

$= \left(36\frac{2}{3} + 33\frac{1}{3}\right) + \left(30\frac{5}{8} + 24\frac{1}{8}\right)$ Reorder and regroup the addends.

$= 70 + 54\frac{6}{8}$ Add inside the parentheses.

$= 124\frac{6}{8} = 124\frac{3}{4}$ Add and simplify.

ANSWER The perimeter is $124\frac{3}{4}$ ft.

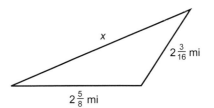

Solving Equations with Fractions

You can use the properties of equality to solve equations with fractions the same way you do with integers.

Example

PROBLEM 3 The perimeter of the triangle is 8 mi.
Find the unknown side length.

SOLUTION Write and solve an equation.

$P = x + 2\frac{3}{16} + 2\frac{5}{8}$ The perimeter equals the distance around the triangle.

$8 = x + 4\frac{13}{16}$ Replace P with 8. Add the mixed numbers.

$8 - 4\frac{13}{16} = x + 4\frac{13}{16} - 4\frac{13}{16}$ Subtract $4\frac{13}{16}$ from both sides.

$3\frac{3}{16} = x$ Simplify.

ANSWER The missing side length is $3\frac{3}{16}$ mi.

TOPIC

Problem Set

Add.

1. **Stepping Stones** $\frac{3}{5} + \frac{1}{8} + \frac{2}{5}$

$$\frac{3}{5} + \frac{1}{8} + \frac{2}{5} = \frac{1}{8} + \boxed{} + \frac{2}{5}$$

$$= \frac{1}{8} + \left(\boxed{} + \frac{2}{5}\right)$$

$$= \frac{1}{8} + \boxed{}$$

$$= \boxed{}$$

2. $\frac{1}{2} + \frac{3}{4} + \frac{1}{2}$

3. $\frac{5}{6} + \frac{7}{8} + 3\frac{1}{6}$

4. $3\frac{4}{9} + 1\frac{5}{12} + 4\frac{7}{12}$

5. $7\frac{3}{10} + 6\frac{1}{3} + 2\frac{7}{10}$

6. $5\frac{1}{8} + \frac{5}{6} + \frac{5}{12}$

7. $10\frac{5}{13} + 8\frac{7}{15} + 3\frac{8}{13}$

8. $7\frac{2}{7} + 20\frac{14}{19} + 5\frac{5}{19}$

9. $18\frac{5}{12} + 8\frac{10}{17} + 23\frac{7}{12} + 28\frac{7}{17}$

10. **Challenge** $1\frac{1}{3} + 8\frac{9}{10} + 4\frac{2}{3} + 51\frac{3}{22} + 48\frac{19}{22}$

Find the perimeter.

11. **Stepping Stones**

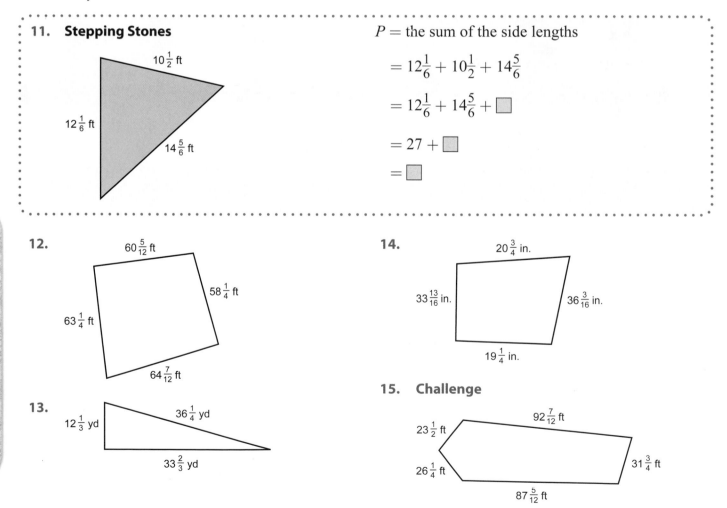

$10\frac{1}{2}$ ft

$12\frac{1}{6}$ ft

$14\frac{5}{6}$ ft

$P =$ the sum of the side lengths

$$= 12\frac{1}{6} + 10\frac{1}{2} + 14\frac{5}{6}$$

$$= 12\frac{1}{6} + 14\frac{5}{6} + \boxed{}$$

$$= 27 + \boxed{}$$

$$= \boxed{}$$

12.

$60\frac{5}{12}$ ft

$58\frac{1}{4}$ ft

$63\frac{1}{4}$ ft

$64\frac{7}{12}$ ft

13.

$12\frac{1}{3}$ yd

$36\frac{1}{4}$ yd

$33\frac{2}{3}$ yd

14.

$20\frac{3}{4}$ in.

$33\frac{13}{16}$ in.

$36\frac{3}{16}$ in.

$19\frac{1}{4}$ in.

15. **Challenge**

$92\frac{7}{12}$ ft

$23\frac{1}{2}$ ft

$26\frac{1}{4}$ ft

$31\frac{3}{4}$ ft

$87\frac{5}{12}$ ft

Find the unknown side length.

16. Stepping Stones $P = 19$ in.

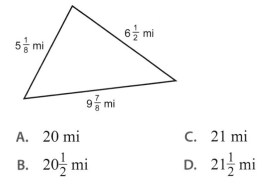

x

$3\frac{3}{4}$ in.

$7\frac{1}{2}$ in.

$P =$ the sum of the side lengths

$$19 = x + 7\frac{1}{2} + 3\frac{3}{4}$$

$$19 = x + 7\frac{2}{4} + 3\frac{3}{4}$$

$$19 = x + 11\frac{\square}{4}$$

$$19 - 11\frac{\square}{4} = x + 11\frac{\square}{4} - 11\frac{\square}{4}$$

$$\square = x$$

The unknown side length is $\square$ in.

17. $P = 71\frac{7}{8}$ mi

y

$19\frac{1}{2}$ mi

$22\frac{3}{8}$ mi

18. Challenge $P = 344\frac{1}{2}$ mi

$129\frac{1}{16}$ mi

x

$42\frac{3}{8}$ mi

$132\frac{1}{4}$ mi

Solve for the variable.

19. $80 = x + 5\frac{3}{4} + 60\frac{5}{8}$

20. $2\frac{7}{8} + y + 1\frac{3}{4} + 2\frac{3}{4} = 9\frac{1}{4}$

Choose the answer.

21. What is the perimeter of the triangle?

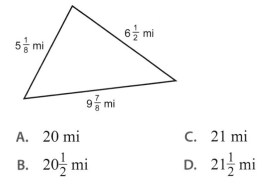

$6\frac{1}{2}$ mi

$5\frac{1}{8}$ mi

$9\frac{7}{8}$ mi

A. 20 mi

B. $20\frac{1}{2}$ mi

C. 21 mi

D. $21\frac{1}{2}$ mi

22. What is the value of y if the perimeter of the triangle is 30 ft?

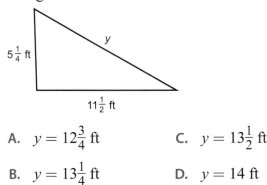

y

$5\frac{1}{4}$ ft

$11\frac{1}{2}$ ft

A. $y = 12\frac{3}{4}$ ft

B. $y = 13\frac{1}{4}$ ft

C. $y = 13\frac{1}{2}$ ft

D. $y = 14$ ft

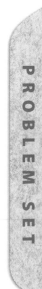

Areas with Fractions

You need to work with fractions to solve some area problems in your everyday situations.

➔ Multiplying Fractions

How to Multiply Fractions

To multiply fractions, multiply the numerators and multiply the denominators. To multiply mixed numbers, either break the mixed numbers into their whole and fractional parts and then use the distributive property or start by converting them to improper fractions.

$$\frac{1}{2} \cdot \frac{3}{4} = \frac{1 \cdot 3}{2 \cdot 4} = \frac{3}{8} \qquad\qquad 2\frac{2}{3} \cdot \frac{7}{8} = \frac{8}{3} \cdot \frac{7}{8} = \frac{8 \cdot 7}{3 \cdot 8} = \frac{7}{3} = 2\frac{1}{3}$$

The commutative and associative properties of multiplication, as well as the distributive property, apply to multiplication with fractions and mixed numbers. Use these properties to reorder or regroup factors to make solving the problem easier.

> **Remember**
>
> The commutative property allows you to multiply numbers in any order.
>
> The associative property allows you to group the factors in any way.

Example

Multiply and simplify.

PROBLEM 1 $\quad \frac{2}{3} \cdot 1\frac{4}{7} \cdot \frac{3}{4}$

SOLUTION

$\frac{2}{3} \cdot 1\frac{4}{7} \cdot \frac{3}{4} = \frac{11}{7} \cdot \frac{2}{3} \cdot \frac{3}{4}$ Convert the mixed number and switch the order of the first two fractions.

$= \frac{11}{7} \cdot \left(\frac{2}{3} \cdot \frac{3}{4} \right)$ Group the factors.

$= \frac{11}{7} \cdot \left(\dfrac{\overset{1}{\cancel{2}} \cdot \overset{1}{\cancel{3}}}{\underset{1}{\cancel{3}} \cdot \underset{2}{\cancel{4}}} \right)$ Multiply.

$= \frac{11}{7} \cdot \frac{1}{2}$ Simplify.

$= \frac{11}{14}$ Simplify.

ANSWER $\quad \frac{2}{3} \cdot 1\frac{4}{7} \cdot \frac{3}{4} = \frac{11}{14}$

Example

Multiply and simplify.

PROBLEM 2 $\frac{2}{5} \cdot \left(\frac{5}{7} + \frac{1}{4} \right)$

SOLUTION

$$\frac{2}{5} \cdot \left(\frac{5}{7} + \frac{1}{4} \right) = \frac{2}{5} \cdot \frac{5}{7} + \frac{2}{5} \cdot \frac{1}{4} \qquad \text{Distribute the factor } \frac{2}{5}.$$

$$= \frac{2 \cdot \overset{1}{\cancel{5}}}{\cancel{5} \cdot 7} + \frac{\overset{1}{\cancel{2}} \cdot 1}{5 \cdot \underset{2}{\cancel{4}}} \qquad \text{Multiply.}$$

$$= \frac{2}{7} + \frac{1}{10} \qquad \text{Simplify.}$$

$$= \frac{20}{70} + \frac{7}{70} = \frac{27}{70} \qquad \text{Simplify.}$$

ANSWER $\frac{2}{5} \cdot \left(\frac{5}{7} + \frac{1}{4} \right) = \frac{27}{70}$

➡ Finding Area with Fractions

Example

PROBLEM 3 Find the area of the rectangle. Explain how each part of the area formula relates to the figure.

$2\frac{1}{6}$ ft

$3\frac{1}{3}$ ft

SOLUTION

$A = lw$

$A = 3\frac{1}{3} \cdot 2\frac{1}{6}$ \qquad Replace l and w with their values.

$= \frac{10}{3} \cdot \frac{13}{6}$ \qquad Write the mixed numbers as fractions.

$= \frac{\overset{5}{\cancel{10}} \cdot 13}{3 \cdot \underset{3}{\cancel{6}}}$ \qquad Simplify.

$= \frac{5 \cdot 13}{3 \cdot 3}$ \qquad Multiply.

$= \frac{65}{9} = 7\frac{2}{9}$ \qquad Convert the fraction to a mixed number.

ANSWER The area is $7\frac{2}{9}$ ft². A represents the area of the rectangle, $7\frac{2}{9}$ ft²; l represents its length, $3\frac{1}{3}$ ft; and w represents its width, $2\frac{1}{6}$ ft.

Problem Set

Multiply and simplify.

1. **Stepping Stones** $5\frac{2}{3} \cdot \frac{3}{4}$

$$5\frac{2}{3} \cdot \frac{3}{4} = \frac{\square}{3} \cdot \frac{3}{4}$$

$$= \frac{\square \cdot 3}{3 \cdot 4}$$

$$= \frac{\square}{12}$$

$$= \square\frac{\square}{\square}$$

2. $2\frac{5}{6} \cdot \frac{1}{7}$

3. $\frac{1}{2} \cdot 4\frac{3}{8}$

4. $6\frac{1}{4} \cdot \frac{4}{5}$

5. $\frac{7}{8} \cdot 7\frac{3}{4}$

6. $\frac{4}{5} \cdot \frac{1}{3} \cdot \frac{5}{8}$

7. $\frac{1}{3} \cdot \left(\frac{1}{4} + \frac{1}{2}\right)$

8. $\frac{1}{2} \cdot \frac{1}{7} \cdot \frac{2}{3}$

9. $\frac{2}{3} \cdot 2\frac{1}{5} \cdot \frac{3}{4}$

10. $1\frac{1}{2} \cdot \left(\frac{1}{2} + \frac{2}{5}\right)$

11. $\frac{1}{2} \cdot \left(2\frac{1}{6} + \frac{7}{8}\right)$

12. $3\frac{1}{5} \cdot \frac{2}{3} \cdot \frac{15}{16}$

13. $1\frac{2}{5} \cdot \frac{16}{17} \cdot \frac{5}{7}$

14. $\frac{2}{3} \cdot \left(\frac{1}{3} + 3\frac{1}{4}\right)$

15. $5\frac{1}{4} \cdot \frac{8}{9} \cdot \frac{8}{21}$

16. $\frac{4}{5} \cdot \left(\frac{9}{11} + 7\frac{1}{2}\right)$

17. **Challenge** $\frac{3}{20} \cdot 3\frac{2}{7} \cdot 3\frac{1}{3}$

18. **Challenge** $2\frac{1}{4} \cdot \left(3\frac{1}{2} + 12\frac{5}{6}\right)$

Find the area of the figure. Explain how each part of the formula relates to the figure.

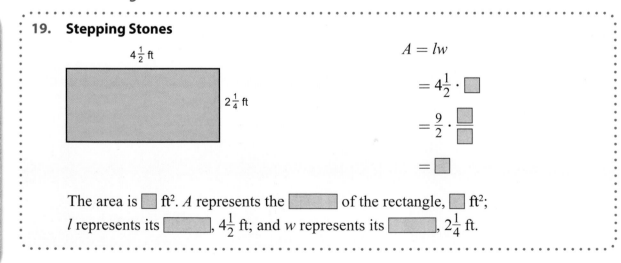

19. **Stepping Stones**

$4\frac{1}{2}$ ft

$2\frac{1}{4}$ ft

$A = lw$

$$= 4\frac{1}{2} \cdot \square$$

$$= \frac{9}{2} \cdot \frac{\square}{\square}$$

$$= \square$$

The area is $\square$ ft². A represents the $\boxed{}$ of the rectangle, $\square$ ft²; l represents its $\boxed{}$, $4\frac{1}{2}$ ft; and w represents its $\boxed{}$, $2\frac{1}{4}$ ft.

Area Formulas
$A = lw$
$A = \frac{1}{2}bh$

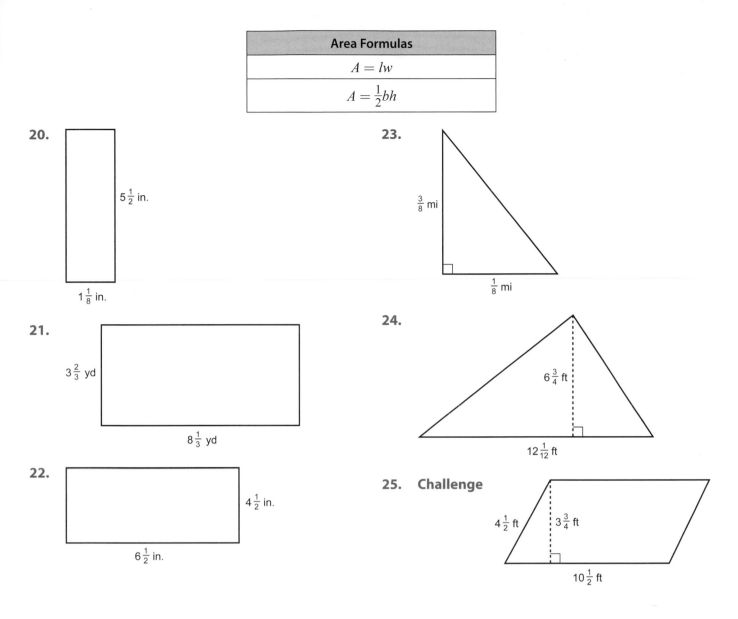

20.

$5\frac{1}{2}$ in.

$1\frac{1}{8}$ in.

21.

$3\frac{2}{3}$ yd

$8\frac{1}{3}$ yd

22.

$4\frac{1}{2}$ in.

$6\frac{1}{2}$ in.

23.

$\frac{3}{8}$ mi

$\frac{1}{8}$ mi

24.

$6\frac{3}{4}$ ft

$12\frac{1}{12}$ ft

25. Challenge

$4\frac{1}{2}$ ft $3\frac{3}{4}$ ft

$10\frac{1}{2}$ ft

Choose the answer.

26. What is the product?

$$\frac{3}{5} \cdot \frac{1}{2} \cdot \frac{5}{6}$$

A. $\frac{1}{4}$ C. $\frac{9}{13}$

B. $\frac{1}{2}$ D. 4

27. What is the area of the rectangle?

$1\frac{1}{2}$ in.

$2\frac{1}{4}$ in.

A. $1\frac{1}{2}$ in^2 C. $3\frac{3}{8}$ in^2

B. $2\frac{1}{4}$ in^2 D. $7\frac{1}{2}$ in^2

Dividing Fractions

You can use reciprocals to change division to multiplication.

➡ Finding Reciprocals

> **Definition**
>
> **Reciprocals**, or multiplicative inverses, are two numbers whose product is 1.
>
> For example, $\frac{3}{4}$ and $\frac{4}{3}$ are reciprocals, since $\frac{3}{4} \cdot \frac{4}{3} = 1$. And the reciprocal of 7 is $\frac{1}{7}$, since $7 \cdot \frac{1}{7} = 1$.

The easiest way to find a reciprocal of a number is first to write the number as a fraction (if the number isn't already a fraction). Then switch the numerator and the denominator.

Example

Find the reciprocal of the number. Multiply to check your answer.

PROBLEM 1 $\frac{2}{5}$

SOLUTION Switch the numerator, 2, with the denominator, 5.

ANSWER The reciprocal of $\frac{2}{5}$ is $\frac{5}{2}$.

CHECK Multiply the fraction by its reciprocal to check.

$$\frac{2}{5} \cdot \frac{5}{2} = \frac{2 \cdot 5}{5 \cdot 2} = \frac{10}{10} = 1 \checkmark$$

PROBLEM 2 $2\frac{1}{4}$

SOLUTION Convert the mixed number to an improper fraction.

$$2\frac{1}{4} = 2 + \frac{1}{4} = 2 \cdot \frac{4}{4} + \frac{1}{4} = \frac{8}{4} + \frac{1}{4} = \frac{9}{4}$$

Switch the numerator, 9, with the denominator, 4.

ANSWER The reciprocal of $2\frac{1}{4}$ is $\frac{4}{9}$.

CHECK Multiply the improper fraction form of the mixed number by its reciprocal to check if their product is 1.

$$\frac{9}{4} \cdot \frac{4}{9} = \frac{9 \cdot 4}{4 \cdot 9} = \frac{36}{36} = 1 \checkmark$$

Think About It

When you multiply the fractions in these examples to check your answer, you don't need to find the products of the numerator and the denominator. The commutative property tells you they are equal.

➡ Dividing of Fractions

How to Divide Fractions

Divide two fractions by multiplying the dividend by the reciprocal of the divisor.

For example:

$$\frac{2}{3} \div \frac{4}{5} = \frac{2}{3} \cdot \frac{5}{4} = \frac{2 \cdot 5}{3 \cdot 4} = \frac{10}{12} = \frac{5}{6}$$

Example

PROBLEM 3 Divide: $5\frac{1}{4} \div 7$

SOLUTION

$5\frac{1}{4} \div 7 = \frac{21}{4} \div \frac{7}{1}$ Write both the dividend and the divisor as fractions.

$= \frac{21}{4} \cdot \frac{1}{7}$ Rewrite as a multiplication problem using a reciprocal.

$= \frac{21 \cdot 1}{4 \cdot 7}$ Multiply.

$= \frac{21}{28} = \frac{3}{4}$ Simplify.

ANSWER $5\frac{1}{4} \div 7 = \frac{3}{4}$

> ### Tip
> If the dividend or divisor is a whole or mixed number, first convert it to a fraction. Then find the reciprocal of the divisor.

➡ Relating Fraction Division Problem Situations

Example

Explain how the division sentence relates to the diagram showing a wooden board that is being cut.

PROBLEM 4 $4\frac{1}{2} \div \frac{3}{4} = 6$

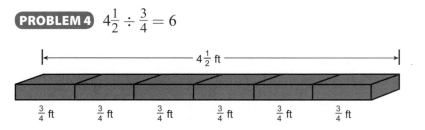

$4\frac{1}{2}$ ft

$\frac{3}{4}$ ft $\frac{3}{4}$ ft $\frac{3}{4}$ ft $\frac{3}{4}$ ft $\frac{3}{4}$ ft $\frac{3}{4}$ ft

SOLUTION The board that is $4\frac{1}{2}$ ft long is being cut into smaller boards that are $\frac{3}{4}$ ft long each.

ANSWER The division sentence $4\frac{1}{2} \div \frac{3}{4} = 6$ shows that a board $4\frac{1}{2}$ ft long can be cut into 6 equal pieces that are $\frac{3}{4}$ ft long each.

TOPIC

Problem Set

Find the reciprocal of the number. Multiply to check your answer.

1. **Stepping Stones** $\frac{2}{3}$

    The reciprocal of $\frac{2}{3}$ is $\frac{3}{\square}$.

    $\frac{2}{3} \cdot \frac{3}{\square} = \frac{6}{\square} = \square$

2. $\frac{5}{7}$

3. $\frac{8}{3}$

4. $\frac{5}{4}$

5. $\frac{12}{11}$

6. $\frac{9}{4}$

7. $\frac{3}{4}$

8. 9

9. $\frac{1}{2}$

10. $\frac{1}{4}$

11. 6

12. $1\frac{1}{2}$

13. $2\frac{3}{4}$

14. **Challenge** $5\frac{7}{12}$

Divide.

15. **Stepping Stones** $\frac{3}{4} \div \frac{1}{3}$

    $\frac{3}{4} \div \frac{1}{3} = \frac{3}{4} \cdot \frac{3}{\square} = \frac{9}{\square} = \square\frac{\square}{\square}$

16. $\frac{5}{6} \div \frac{1}{2}$

17. $\frac{2}{3} \div \frac{1}{3}$

18. $\frac{7}{8} \div \frac{2}{3}$

19. $12 \div \frac{3}{4}$

20. $14 \div \frac{5}{8}$

21. $\frac{1}{2} \div 3$

22. $2\frac{1}{3} \div \frac{4}{9}$

23. $3\frac{1}{3} \div \frac{3}{8}$

24. $6 \div 1\frac{1}{4}$

25. $1\frac{6}{7} \div \frac{4}{7}$

26. $\frac{11}{12} \div 2\frac{1}{2}$

27. $1\frac{1}{2} \div 2\frac{1}{2}$

28. $4\frac{2}{3} \div 1\frac{3}{8}$

29. **Challenge** $2\frac{1}{2} \div 8\frac{5}{6}$

30. **Challenge** $8\frac{3}{4} \div 2\frac{1}{4}$

Explain how the division sentence relates to the diagram.

31. **Stepping Stones** $9 \div 2\frac{1}{4} = 4$

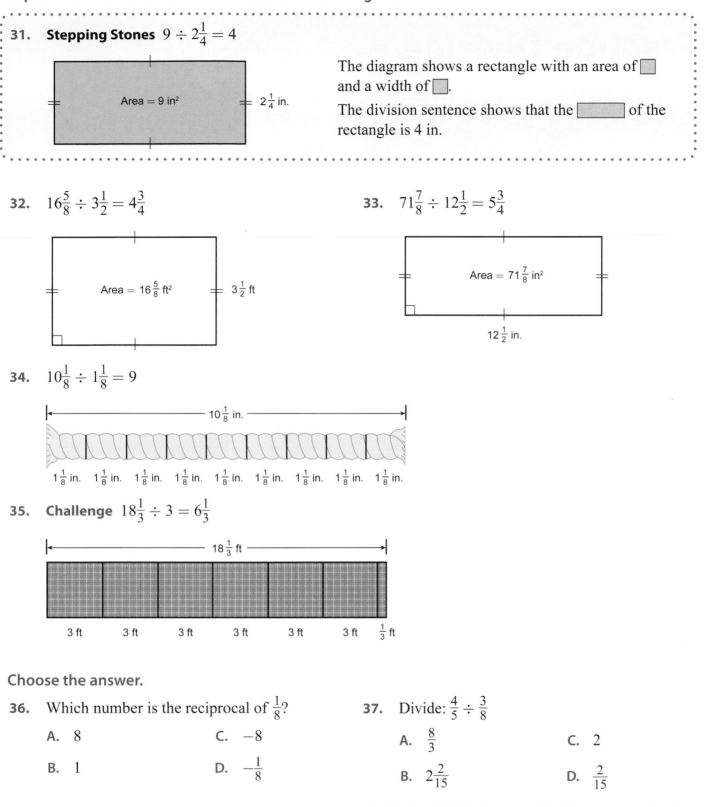

Area = 9 in² $2\frac{1}{4}$ in.

The diagram shows a rectangle with an area of ☐ and a width of ☐.

The division sentence shows that the ☐☐☐ of the rectangle is 4 in.

32. $16\frac{5}{8} \div 3\frac{1}{2} = 4\frac{3}{4}$

Area = $16\frac{5}{8}$ ft² $3\frac{1}{2}$ ft

33. $71\frac{7}{8} \div 12\frac{1}{2} = 5\frac{3}{4}$

Area = $71\frac{7}{8}$ in²

$12\frac{1}{2}$ in.

34. $10\frac{1}{8} \div 1\frac{1}{8} = 9$

$10\frac{1}{8}$ in.

$1\frac{1}{8}$ in. $1\frac{1}{8}$ in. $1\frac{1}{8}$ in. $1\frac{1}{8}$ in. $1\frac{1}{8}$ in. $1\frac{1}{8}$ in. $1\frac{1}{8}$ in. $1\frac{1}{8}$ in. $1\frac{1}{8}$ in.

35. **Challenge** $18\frac{1}{3} \div 3 = 6\frac{1}{3}$

$18\frac{1}{3}$ ft

3 ft   3 ft   3 ft   3 ft   3 ft   3 ft $\frac{1}{3}$ ft

Choose the answer.

36. Which number is the reciprocal of $\frac{1}{8}$?

A. 8

B. 1

C. −8

D. $-\frac{1}{8}$

37. Divide: $\frac{4}{5} \div \frac{3}{8}$

A. $\frac{8}{3}$

B. $2\frac{2}{15}$

C. 2

D. $\frac{2}{15}$

PROBLEM SET

Solving Problems with Fraction Division

Fractions are often used in problems involving English units of measurement.

➔ Solving Multiplication and Division Equations

Use the multiplication and division properties of equality to isolate the variable on one side of the equation. Check your solution by substituting the value for the variable and confirming that the equation remains true.

Example

Solve and check.

PROBLEM 1 $\frac{2}{3}x = 12$

SOLUTION

$\frac{2}{3}x \cdot \frac{3}{2} = 12 \cdot \frac{3}{2}$ Multiply both sides by the reciprocal of $\frac{2}{3}$.

$x \cdot \frac{2}{3} \cdot \frac{3}{2} = 12 \cdot \frac{3}{2}$ Commute.

$x \cdot 1 = \frac{36}{2}$ Simplify.

$x = 18$ Apply the identity property of multiplication and simplify.

ANSWER $x = 18$

CHECK

$\frac{2}{3}x = 12$

$\frac{2}{3} \cdot 18 \overset{?}{=} 12$

$\frac{36}{3} = 12 \checkmark$

> **Tip**
> *Commute* is a short way of saying *apply the commutative property*.

TOPIC

Example

Solve and check.

PROBLEM 2 $\frac{y}{3} = 6\frac{4}{5}$

SOLUTION

$\frac{y}{3} \cdot 3 = 6\frac{4}{5} \cdot 3$ Multiply both sides by the reciprocal of $\frac{1}{3}$ because $\frac{y}{3}$ is the same as $y \cdot \frac{1}{3}$.

$y = 6\frac{4}{5} \cdot 3$ Simplify to isolate y.

$= \frac{34}{5} \cdot \frac{3}{1}$ Convert both factors to fractions.

$= \frac{102}{5} = 20\frac{2}{5}$ Multiply and simplify.

ANSWER $y = 20\frac{2}{5}$

CHECK

$\frac{y}{3} = 6\frac{4}{5}$

$20\frac{2}{5} \div 3 \overset{?}{=} 6\frac{4}{5}$

$\frac{102}{5} \div 3 = \frac{102}{5} \cdot \frac{1}{3} = \frac{102}{15} = \frac{34}{5} = 6\frac{4}{5} \checkmark$

> **Remember**
>
> The multiplication property of equality states that you can multiply both sides of an equation by the same number and the equation remains true.

➡ Application: Cooking

Example

PROBLEM 3 Kate mixes some cake batter that she pours into 26 cupcake tins that hold $\frac{1}{4}$ cup each. How much cake batter does Kate mix?

SOLUTION

$k \div 26 = \frac{1}{4}$ Write an equation that represents the situation.

$(k \div 26) \cdot 26 = \frac{1}{4} \cdot 26$ Apply the multiplication property of equality.

$k = \frac{1}{4} \cdot 26$ Simplify to isolate k.

$= \frac{26}{4} = 6\frac{2}{4} = 6\frac{1}{2}$ Multiply and simplify.

ANSWER Kate mixes $6\frac{1}{2}$ cups of cake batter.

Problem Set

Solve for the variable and check.

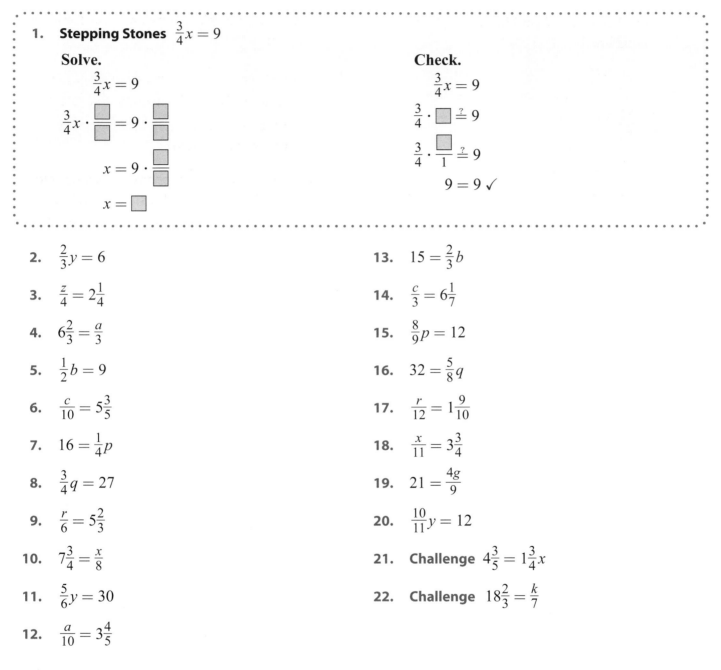

1. **Stepping Stones** $\frac{3}{4}x = 9$

    Solve.

    $$\frac{3}{4}x = 9$$

    $$\frac{3}{4}x \cdot \frac{\square}{\square} = 9 \cdot \frac{\square}{\square}$$

    $$x = 9 \cdot \frac{\square}{\square}$$

    $$x = \square$$

    Check.

    $$\frac{3}{4}x = 9$$

    $$\frac{3}{4} \cdot \square \overset{?}{=} 9$$

    $$\frac{3}{4} \cdot \frac{\square}{1} \overset{?}{=} 9$$

    $$9 = 9 \checkmark$$

2. $\frac{2}{3}y = 6$

3. $\frac{z}{4} = 2\frac{1}{4}$

4. $6\frac{2}{3} = \frac{a}{3}$

5. $\frac{1}{2}b = 9$

6. $\frac{c}{10} = 5\frac{3}{5}$

7. $16 = \frac{1}{4}p$

8. $\frac{3}{4}q = 27$

9. $\frac{r}{6} = 5\frac{2}{3}$

10. $7\frac{3}{4} = \frac{x}{8}$

11. $\frac{5}{6}y = 30$

12. $\frac{a}{10} = 3\frac{4}{5}$

13. $15 = \frac{2}{3}b$

14. $\frac{c}{3} = 6\frac{1}{7}$

15. $\frac{8}{9}p = 12$

16. $32 = \frac{5}{8}q$

17. $\frac{r}{12} = 1\frac{9}{10}$

18. $\frac{x}{11} = 3\frac{3}{4}$

19. $21 = \frac{4g}{9}$

20. $\frac{10}{11}y = 12$

21. **Challenge** $4\frac{3}{5} = 1\frac{3}{4}x$

22. **Challenge** $18\frac{2}{3} = \frac{k}{7}$

Write a multiplication or division equation to solve.

23. **Stepping Stones** Renaldo gave $\frac{2}{3}$ of his baseball cards to his brother. How many baseball cards did Renaldo start with, if he gave his brother 36 cards?

$$\frac{2}{3}x = \square$$

$$\frac{2}{3}x \cdot \frac{\square}{\square} = \square \cdot \frac{\square}{\square}$$

$$x = \square \cdot \frac{\square}{\square}$$

$$= \square$$

Renaldo had $\square$ baseball cards.

24. Grant cuts a ribbon into six $5\frac{3}{4}$ in. pieces. How long was the original piece of ribbon before it was cut?

25. Liu Ha divides the pizzas she orders for her party and puts them on 8 tables. She puts $2\frac{3}{4}$ pizzas on each table. How many pizzas did Liu Ha order for her party?

26. Reem divides the bread dough she makes into 6 pieces that weigh $2\frac{1}{3}$ lb each. How much dough did Reem make?

27. Leslie spent $\frac{3}{4}$ of her time at the gym on the stair machine. She spent a total of $21\frac{3}{4}$ min on the stair machine. How long was Leslie at the gym?

28. Juanita pours $41\frac{1}{4}$ oz of water from a large pitcher into a bottle. That amount is $\frac{2}{5}$ of the water that was in the pitcher. How much water was in the pitcher?

29. Rochelle separates her penny collection into 13 bags. When she has finished, each bag weighs $17\frac{3}{8}$ lb. What is the total weight of Rochelle's penny collection?

30. Lucas cooks $5\frac{1}{3}$ lb of chicken. Each serving of the chicken is $\frac{2}{3}$ lb. How many servings of chicken does Lucas cook?

31. **Challenge** Karen can run at an average speed of $9\frac{1}{2}$ min/mi. How long would it take her to run $26\frac{1}{5}$ mi at that speed?

32. **Challenge** Jerome sold 20 of his paintings on the first day of the art show. That number was $\frac{1}{8}$ of his collection. On the second day of the show, he sold $\frac{2}{5}$ of his remaining paintings. How many paintings did he sell in all?

Choose the answer.

33. What is the value of x in the equation $\frac{3}{5}x = 12$?

   A. $x = \frac{5}{3}$ C. $x = 20$

   B. $x = 7\frac{1}{5}$ D. $x = 40$

34. Sharifa cut a piece of string into eight $4\frac{5}{8}$ in. pieces. How long was the original piece of string?

   A. 37 in.   C. $6\frac{2}{5}$ in.

   B. 27 in.   D. $3\frac{7}{8}$ in.

Chapter 4 Review

Choose the answer.

1. Which fraction is equivalent to $\frac{3}{4}$?

   A. $\frac{4}{3}$ C. $\frac{4}{5}$

   B. $\frac{6}{8}$ D. $\frac{9}{16}$

2. Which improper fraction is equal to $4\frac{2}{3}$?

   A. $\frac{8}{3}$ C. $\frac{6}{3}$

   B. $\frac{42}{3}$ D. $\frac{14}{3}$

3. Which mixed number is equal to $\frac{37}{6}$?

   A. $6\frac{1}{6}$ C. $5\frac{5}{6}$

   B. $7\frac{1}{6}$ D. $6\frac{5}{6}$

4. Which decimal is equivalent to $4\frac{3}{5}$?

   A. 4.3 C. 4.6

   B. 6.4 D. 6.6

5. Which list of numbers is in order from least to greatest?

   A. $0.4, \frac{5}{12}, \frac{9}{20}$ C. $\frac{5}{12}, 0.4, \frac{9}{20}$

   B. $\frac{9}{20}, 0.4, \frac{5}{12}$ D. $\frac{9}{20}, \frac{5}{12}, 0.4$

6. What is the perimeter of the triangle?

   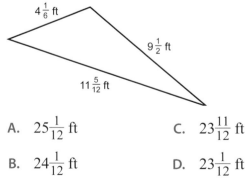

   A. $25\frac{1}{12}$ ft C. $23\frac{11}{12}$ ft

   B. $24\frac{1}{12}$ ft D. $23\frac{1}{12}$ ft

7. What is the area of the rectangle? Use the formula $A = lw$.

   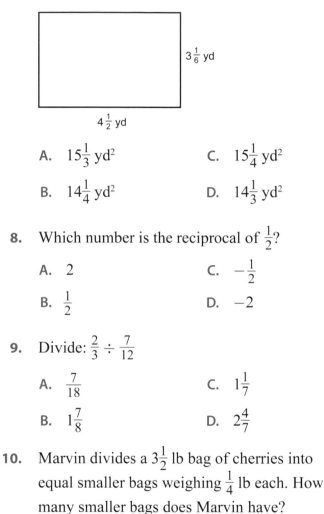

   A. $15\frac{1}{3}$ yd² C. $15\frac{1}{4}$ yd²

   B. $14\frac{1}{4}$ yd² D. $14\frac{1}{3}$ yd²

8. Which number is the reciprocal of $\frac{1}{2}$?

   A. 2 C. $-\frac{1}{2}$

   B. $\frac{1}{2}$ D. -2

9. Divide: $\frac{2}{3} \div \frac{7}{12}$

   A. $\frac{7}{18}$ C. $1\frac{1}{7}$

   B. $1\frac{7}{8}$ D. $2\frac{4}{7}$

10. Marvin divides a $3\frac{1}{2}$ lb bag of cherries into equal smaller bags weighing $\frac{1}{4}$ lb each. How many smaller bags does Marvin have?

    A. 14 C. 7

    B. 21 D. 28

11. A fence is made up of twelve $8\frac{1}{3}$ ft sections. How long is the fence?

    A. 96 ft C. 100 ft

    B. $98\frac{2}{3}$ ft D. $96\frac{2}{3}$ ft

Write the missing number to make equivalent fractions.

12. $\frac{3}{4} = \frac{\square}{16}$

13. $\frac{4}{7} = \frac{\square}{21}$

Convert the mixed number to an improper fraction.

14. $2\frac{3}{4}$

15. $4\frac{1}{7}$

Convert the improper fraction to a mixed number.

16. $\frac{32}{3}$

17. $\frac{17}{8}$

Write $<$, $>$, or $=$ to compare the numbers.

18. $0.70 \;\square\; \frac{3}{4}$

19. $\frac{5}{6} \;\square\; 0.83$

Add.

20. $\frac{1}{6} + \frac{7}{8} + 1\frac{5}{6}$

21. $3\frac{3}{4} + 1\frac{3}{4} + 2\frac{1}{2}$

Find the unknown side length.

22. $P = 24\frac{1}{2}$ ft

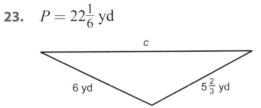

23. $P = 22\frac{1}{6}$ yd

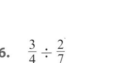

Multiply or divide and simplify.

24. $\frac{3}{4} \cdot 5\frac{1}{2}$

26. $\frac{3}{4} \div \frac{2}{7}$

25. $\frac{2}{3} \cdot \left(\frac{3}{4} + \frac{5}{6} \right)$

27. $3\frac{1}{6} \div \frac{1}{3}$

Solve.

28. A rectangle has an area of $7\frac{7}{8}$ in² and a length of $3\frac{1}{2}$ in. What is the rectangle's width?

29. A painter has $6\frac{1}{2}$ gal of paint for the doors in a new apartment building. It will take $\frac{1}{5}$ gal of paint to paint each door. How many doors can the painter complete?

Problem	Topic Lookup
1, 12–13	Equivalent Fractions
2–3, 14–17	Representing Rational Numbers
4–5, 18–19	Comparing Rational Numbers
6, 11, 20–23	Perimeters with Fractions

Problem	Topic Lookup
7, 24–25	Areas with Fractions
8–9, 26–27	Dividing Fractions
10, 28–29	Solving Problems with Fraction Division

5 Solids

Rectangular containers can be used to move cargo on trains or trucks from a factory to a shipping port. From the port, a container ship can carry hundreds of containers across oceans to other trains and trucks. The amount of cargo a container can hold depends on its volume.

In This Chapter

You will learn how to find the volume and surface area of shapes such as prisms and pyramids. You will also find out how a cube root connects the volume of a cube to its side length.

Chapter Topics

- ► Foundations for Chapter 5
- ► Cubes and Cube Roots
- ► Volumes of Prisms
- ► Nets of Solids
- ► Surface Area: Prisms and Pyramids
- ► Properties of Volume and Surface Area
- ► Chapter 5 Review

Container ships carry tons of cargo.

PORT OF OAKLAND

Foundations for Chapter 5

➤ Finding the Cube of a Number

Definition

The **cube** of a number is the third power of the number. A cube is shown as a power of the number with an exponent of 3.

$$a^3 = a \cdot a \cdot a$$

For example:
$6^3 = 6 \cdot 6 \cdot 6 = 216$

To find the cube of a number, multiply that number as a factor three times.

Example A

Find the cube of the number.

PROBLEM A-1 8

SOLUTION To cube a number, write it as a power and then as a product. Then multiply.

$8^3 = 8 \cdot 8 \cdot 8$
$ = (8 \cdot 8) \cdot 8$
$ = 64 \cdot 8$
$ = 512$

ANSWER $8^3 = 512$

PROBLEM A-2 1.1

SOLUTION

$1.1^3 = 1.1 \cdot 1.1 \cdot 1.1$
$ = (1.1 \cdot 1.1) \cdot 1.1$
$ = 1.21 \cdot 1.1$
$ = 1.331$

ANSWER $(1.1)^3 = 1.331$

Problem Set A

Find the cube of the number.

1. 4
2. 6
3. 9

4. 11
5. 12
6. 20

7. 0.5
8. 1.2
9. 1000

➤ Finding the Volume of a Cube

You can find the volume of a cube by determining the number of unit cubes needed to fill it. Volume is measured in cubic units.

Fill the cube with unit cubes.

  Place 4 rows of 4 cubes on the bottom.
$4 \cdot 4 = 16$
The first layer holds 16 unit cubes.

Make 4 layers of 16 cubes.
$4 \cdot 16 = 64$
The figure holds 64 unit cubes.

You also can use a formula to find the volume of a cube.

Volume of a Cube

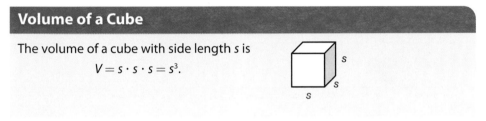

The volume of a cube with side length s is
$$V = s \cdot s \cdot s = s^3.$$

Example B

PROBLEM B-1 Find the volume of a cube with side length of 6 units.

SOLUTION
$$V = s \cdot s \cdot s$$
$$= 6 \cdot 6 \cdot 6$$
$$= 216$$

ANSWER The volume of the cube is 216 cubic units.

Problem Set B

Find the volume of a cube with the given side length.

1. 2 units
2. 3 units
3. 5 units
4. 7 units
5. 8 units
6. 9 units
7. 10 units
8. 12 units
9. 100 units

⇥ Finding the Volume of a Figure Made Up of Cubes

You can break apart, or decompose, some complex figures into smaller cubes. Then you can use the formula to find the volume of each cube. Add the volumes of the cubes to find the total volume of the complex figure.

Example C

PROBLEM C-1 Find the volume of the figure.

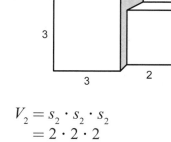

SOLUTION Break the figure into 2 cubes:
The big cube has side length of 3 units.
The small cube has side length of 2 units.

Find the volume of each cube:

$$V_1 = s_1 \cdot s_1 \cdot s_1$$
$$= 3 \cdot 3 \cdot 3$$
$$= 27$$

$$V_2 = s_2 \cdot s_2 \cdot s_2$$
$$= 2 \cdot 2 \cdot 2$$
$$= 8$$

Add the volumes of the cubes:
$27 + 8 = 35$

ANSWER The volume of the figure is 35 cubic units.

Problem Set C

Find the number of 1 by 1 cubes, or unit cubes, that would equal the volume of the figure.

1.

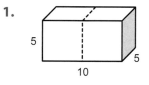

2.

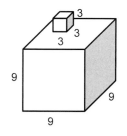

Find the volume of the figure.

3.

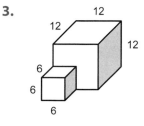

5.

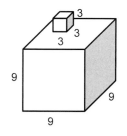

4.

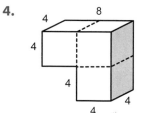

6.

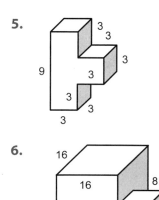

Container ships carry tons of cargo.

Planting the Seed

Solid figures have both surface area and volume. Surface area is a measure of the amount of surface a solid figure has. For example, how much paint will be needed to cover it? Volume measures the amount of space inside a solid figure. For example, how much stuff can it hold?

Cubes and Cube Roots

The cube and cube root of a number can be related to the volume and side length of a cube.

➔ Finding the Cube Root of a Number

Definition

A **cube root** is a number that when multiplied as a factor three times equals a given number. The symbol for cube root is $\sqrt[3]{\ \ }$.

$$\text{If } a^3 = b, \text{ then } a = \sqrt[3]{b}.$$

For example:
$$64 = 4 \cdot 4 \cdot 4 = 4^3, \text{ so } \sqrt[3]{64} = 4$$

Tip

$\sqrt[3]{64} = 4$ is read "the cube root of 64 equals 4."

To find a cube root of a number, think of what number can be cubed to give you that number. You can use a calculator to estimate cube roots that are not whole numbers or simple decimals.

Example

Find the value. Round to the nearest hundredth if necessary.

PROBLEM 1 $\sqrt[3]{8}$

SOLUTION $8 = 2 \cdot 2 \cdot 2 = 2^3$

ANSWER $\sqrt[3]{8} = 2$

PROBLEM 2 $\sqrt[3]{0.001}$

SOLUTION

$0.001 = 0.1 \cdot 0.1 \cdot 0.1 = (0.1)^3$

ANSWER $\sqrt[3]{0.001} = 0.1$

PROBLEM 3 $\sqrt[3]{9}$

SOLUTION No rational number can be multiplied 3 times and result in 9.

Use the calculator to estimate $\sqrt[3]{9}$.

ANSWER $\sqrt[3]{9} \approx 2.08$

CHECK Find the value of $(2.08)^3$.

$2.08 \cdot 2.08 \cdot 2.08 \approx 9 \checkmark$

➔ Finding the Side Length of a Cube

Look at the cube at the right. Its dimensions relate to the cube root found in Problem 1.

$$V = s^3 = 2^3 \qquad\qquad s = \sqrt[3]{V} = \sqrt[3]{8} = 2$$

The side length of a cube is the cube root of the volume.

If you are given a cube's volume, you can take the cube root of the volume to find the side length.

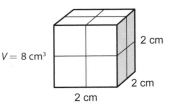
$V = 8 \text{ cm}^3$
2 cm
2 cm
2 cm

Example

PROBLEM 4 Find the side length of a cube with volume 27 m³.

SOLUTION

$V = s^3$

$27 = s^3$ Substitute 27 for V.

$27 = 3 \cdot 3 \cdot 3$ **Think:** What number multiplied three times equals 27?

ANSWER The side length of the cube is 3 m.

➔ Converting Between Cubic Units

Use the table to help you convert between cubic units of measure.

Cubic Unit Conversions	
1 ft³ = 1728 in³	1 cm³ = 1000 mm³
1 yd³ = 27 ft³	1 m³ = 1,000,000 cm³

Example

Convert to the given unit.

PROBLEM 5 4 ft³ = ▢ in³

SOLUTION Since a foot is a larger unit than an inch, multiply by 1728.

$4 \cdot 1728 = 6912$

ANSWER 4 ft³ = 6912 in³

PROBLEM 6

8,000,000 cm³ = ▢ m³

SOLUTION Since a centimeter is a smaller unit than a meter, divide by 1,000,000.

$8,000,000 \div 1,000,000 = 8$

ANSWER

8,000,000 cm³ = 8 m³

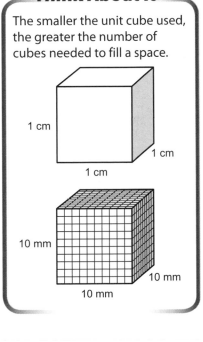
TOPIC

Problem Set

Find the value. Round to the nearest hundredth if necessary.

1. **Stepping Stones** $\sqrt[3]{0.008}$

   $0.008 = \boxed{} \cdot \boxed{} \cdot \boxed{}$

   $\sqrt[3]{0.008} = \boxed{}$

2. $\sqrt[3]{1}$

3. $\sqrt[3]{64}$

4. $\sqrt[3]{216}$

5. $\sqrt[3]{343}$

6. $\sqrt[3]{125}$

7. $\sqrt[3]{512}$

8. $\sqrt[3]{0.064}$

9. $\sqrt[3]{0.027}$

10. $\sqrt[3]{0.001}$

11. $\sqrt[3]{0.36}$

12. $\sqrt[3]{12}$

13. $\sqrt[3]{25}$

14. **Challenge**

    $\sqrt[3]{0.729}$

Find the side length of the cube with the given volume.

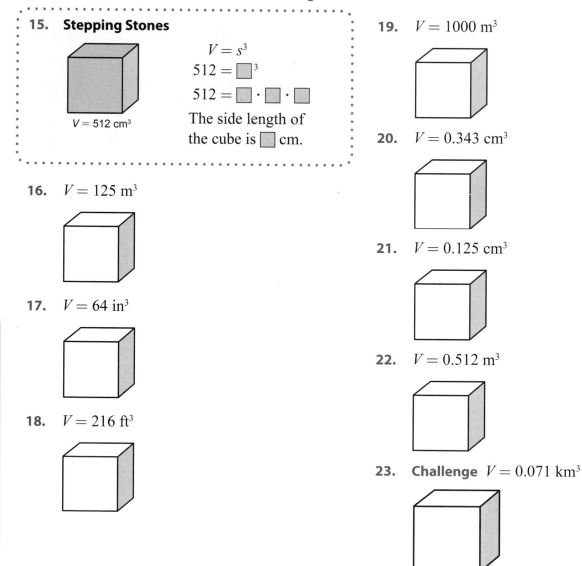

15. **Stepping Stones**

    $V = 512 \text{ cm}^3$

    $V = s^3$

    $512 = \boxed{}^3$

    $512 = \boxed{} \cdot \boxed{} \cdot \boxed{}$

    The side length of the cube is $\boxed{}$ cm.

16. $V = 125 \text{ m}^3$

17. $V = 64 \text{ in}^3$

18. $V = 216 \text{ ft}^3$

19. $V = 1000 \text{ m}^3$

20. $V = 0.343 \text{ cm}^3$

21. $V = 0.125 \text{ cm}^3$

22. $V = 0.512 \text{ m}^3$

23. **Challenge** $V = 0.071 \text{ km}^3$

Convert to the given unit.

24. **Stepping Stones** $12{,}096 \text{ in}^3 = \boxed{} \text{ ft}^3$

   An inch is a smaller unit than a foot, so $\boxed{}$ by the conversion factor.

   $12{,}096 \boxed{} 1728 = \boxed{}$

   $12{,}096 \text{ in}^3 = \boxed{} \text{ ft}^3$

25. $2 \text{ m}^3 = \boxed{} \text{ cm}^3$

26. $8 \text{ yd}^3 = \boxed{} \text{ ft}^3$

27. $5 \text{ ft}^3 = \boxed{} \text{ in}^3$

28. $12 \text{ cm}^3 = \boxed{} \text{ mm}^3$

29. $4374 \text{ ft}^3 = \boxed{} \text{ yd}^3$

30. $15{,}000{,}000 \text{ cm}^3 = \boxed{} \text{ m}^3$

31. $2500 \text{ mm}^3 = \boxed{} \text{ cm}^3$

32. $13.7 \text{ m}^3 = \boxed{} \text{ cm}^3$

33. $4556.25 \text{ ft}^3 = \boxed{} \text{ yd}^3$

34. $8{,}190{,}000 \text{ cm}^3 = \boxed{} \text{ m}^3$

35. $37.75 \text{ yd}^3 = \boxed{} \text{ ft}^3$

36. $5.375 \text{ m}^3 = \boxed{} \text{ cm}^3$

37. **Challenge** $78{,}912 \text{ in}^3 = \boxed{} \text{ yd}^3$

Choose the answer.

38. What is the value of $\sqrt[3]{216}$?

   A. 6

   B. 72

   C. 648

   D. 10,077,696

39. Which measure is equivalent to 12 ft^3?

   A. 12 in^3

   B. 144 in^3

   C. 1728 in^3

   D. $20{,}736 \text{ in}^3$

40. What is the side length of a cube with a volume of 729 m^3?

   A. 9 m

   B. 18 m

   C. 81 m

   D. 243 m

Volumes of Prisms

You know how to find the volume of a cube. You can find volumes of other prisms by using a formula.

➔ Finding the Volume of a Rectangular Prism

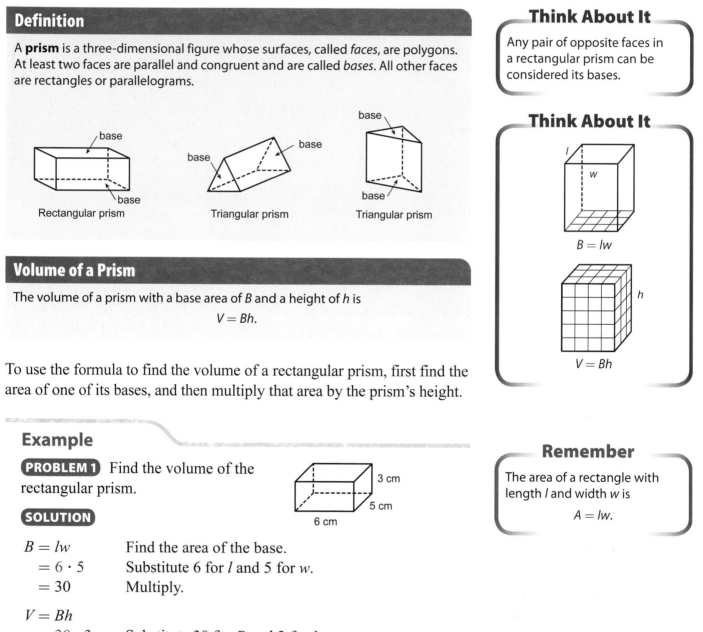

Definition

A **prism** is a three-dimensional figure whose surfaces, called *faces*, are polygons. At least two faces are parallel and congruent and are called *bases*. All other faces are rectangles or parallelograms.

base
Rectangular prism

base   base
Triangular prism

base
base
Triangular prism

Think About It

Any pair of opposite faces in a rectangular prism can be considered its bases.

Think About It

l
w

$B = lw$

h

$V = Bh$

Volume of a Prism

The volume of a prism with a base area of B and a height of h is
$$V = Bh.$$

To use the formula to find the volume of a rectangular prism, first find the area of one of its bases, and then multiply that area by the prism's height.

Example

PROBLEM 1 Find the volume of the rectangular prism.

3 cm
5 cm
6 cm

SOLUTION

$B = lw$ Find the area of the base.
   $= 6 \cdot 5$ Substitute 6 for l and 5 for w.
   $= 30$ Multiply.

$V = Bh$
   $= 30 \cdot 3$ Substitute 30 for B and 3 for h.
   $= 90$ Multiply.

ANSWER The volume of the rectangular prism is 90 cm³.

Remember

The area of a rectangle with length l and width w is
$$A = lw.$$

TOPIC

→ Finding the Volume of a Triangular Prism

Use the same formula to find the volume of a triangular prism. The first step is to find the area of one of the triangular bases.

Example

PROBLEM 2 Find the volume of the triangular prism.

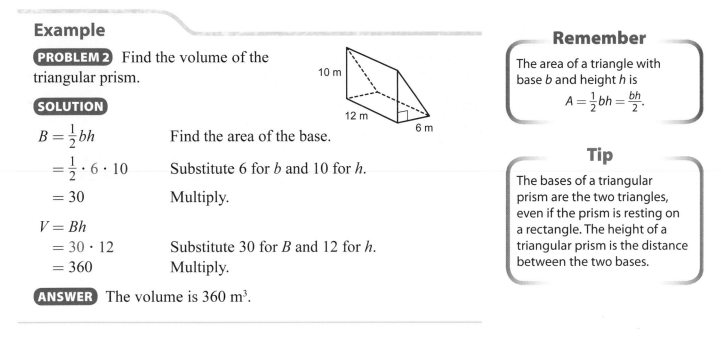

SOLUTION

$B = \frac{1}{2}bh$ Find the area of the base.

$= \frac{1}{2} \cdot 6 \cdot 10$ Substitute 6 for b and 10 for h.

$= 30$ Multiply.

$V = Bh$

$= 30 \cdot 12$ Substitute 30 for B and 12 for h.

$= 360$ Multiply.

ANSWER The volume is 360 m³.

> **Remember**
>
> The area of a triangle with base b and height h is
> $$A = \frac{1}{2}bh = \frac{bh}{2}.$$

> **Tip**
>
> The bases of a triangular prism are the two triangles, even if the prism is resting on a rectangle. The height of a triangular prism is the distance between the two bases.

→ Application: Gardening

Example

PROBLEM 3 Brendan has a compost bin in the shape of a rectangular prism. The bin is $4\frac{1}{2}$ ft high, 3 ft wide, and 3 ft long. How much compost can Brendan's bin hold?

SOLUTION Use the formula for the volume of a prism.

$B = lw$ Find the area of the base.

$= 3 \cdot 3$ Substitute 3 for l and 3 for w.

$= 9$ Multiply.

$V = Bh$

$= 9 \cdot 4\frac{1}{2}$ Substitute 9 for B and $4\frac{1}{2}$ for h.

$= 40\frac{1}{2}$ Multiply.

ANSWER The bin can hold $40\frac{1}{2}$ ft³ of compost.

Problem Set

Find the volume of the prism.

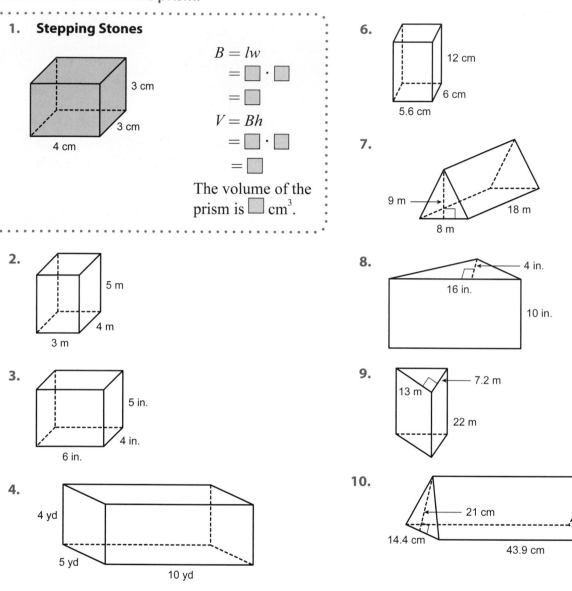

1. **Stepping Stones**

3 cm
3 cm
4 cm

$B = lw$
$= \square \cdot \square$
$= \square$
$V = Bh$
$= \square \cdot \square$
$= \square$

The volume of the prism is $\square$ cm^3.

2.
5 m
4 m
3 m

3.
5 in.
4 in.
6 in.

4.
4 yd
5 yd
10 yd

5.
6 m
3 m
8 m

6.
12 cm
6 cm
5.6 cm

7.
9 m
18 m
8 m

8.
4 in.
16 in.
10 in.

9.
13 m
7.2 m
22 m

10.
21 cm
14.4 cm
43.9 cm

Solve.

11. Stepping Stones A game box is in the shape of a rectangular prism. The box is 18 in. long, 12 in. wide, and 3 in. high. What is the volume of the game box?

$B = lw$

$= \boxed{} \cdot \boxed{}$

$= \boxed{}$

$V = Bh$

$= \boxed{} \cdot \boxed{}$

$= \boxed{}$

The volume of the game box is $\boxed{}$ in^3.

12. A cereal box measures 5 cm by 19 cm by 27 cm. What is the volume of the cereal box?

13. A candy bar comes in a box in the shape of a triangular prism. The area of the base of the prism is 3.5 cm^2. The box is 18 cm long. What is the volume of the box?

14. A tent is in the shape of a triangular prism. The base of the triangular end of the tent is 6 ft long. The height of the triangular end is 4 ft. The tent is $7\frac{1}{2}$ ft long. What is the volume of the tent?

15. The end of a square-prism shipping carton is a square with a side length of 0.1 m. The carton is 0.72 m long. What is the volume of the shipping carton?

16. Challenge Mr. Robinson's and Mrs. Smith's garages are both in the shape of rectangular prisms. Mr. Robinson's garage measures 15 ft by 20 ft by 12.5 ft. Mrs. Smith's garage measures 14 ft by 22.75 ft by 10 ft. How many more cubic feet is Mr. Robinson's garage than Mrs. Smith's garage?

17. Challenge Ricardo needs a box in the shape of a triangular prism with a volume of 200 in^3. He finds a box whose triangular base has a height of 3.5 in. and a base length of 4 in. The height of the box is 28.75 in. Can Ricardo use this box? Explain.

18. Challenge Carlos has a box in the shape of a rectangular prism that is 12 cm wide, 12 cm long, and 6 cm high. Lisa has a box in the shape of a triangular prism that has the same volume as Carlos's box. The base of Lisa's box has an area of 24 cm^2. How tall is Lisa's box?

Choose the answer.

19. What is the volume of the rectangular prism?

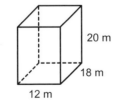

20 m
18 m
12 m

A. 50 m^3

B. 216 m^3

C. 360 m^3

D. 4320 m^3

20. What is the volume of the triangular prism?

14 yd
30 yd
12 yd

A. 5040 yd^3

B. 2520 yd^3

C. 84 yd^3

D. 56 yd^3

Nets of Solids

You can form a solid figure by folding a two-dimensional shape made of connected polygons.

➡ Using Nets to Represent Solids

Definition

The **net** of a solid figure is a pattern of polygons that can be folded to form that solid figure.

To match a net to a solid figure, compare the polygons that make up the net to the faces of the solid figure.

Example

PROBLEM 1 Match the net to the solid figure.

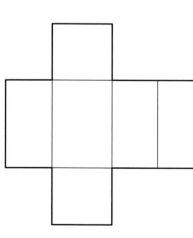

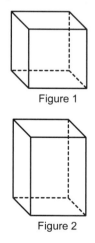

Figure 1

Figure 2

SOLUTION The net is made up of 4 rectangles and 2 squares.

Figure 1 is a cube, so its faces are all squares. The faces do not match the polygons in the net.

Figure 2 is a rectangular prism, and its faces are 4 rectangles and 2 squares. The faces match the polygons in the net.

ANSWER The net can be folded into Figure 2.

TOPIC

➔ Using Nets to Solve Problems

You can draw a net of a solid figure to help solve a problem about the figure.

Example

Solve. Use the net of the pyramid.

PROBLEM 2 What is the surface area of a triangular pyramid that has faces with areas of 5 cm² each?

SOLUTION There are 4 faces.

$4 \cdot 5 = 20$

ANSWER The surface area is 20 cm².

PROBLEM 3 What is the area of 1 face of a triangular pyramid if the pyramid's total surface area is 24 mm²?

SOLUTION $24 \div 4 = 6$

ANSWER The area of 1 face is 6 mm².

➔ Choosing Surface Area or Volume

Definition

The **surface** of a solid figure is made up of the polygons that are its faces.

Surface area problems involve how much is needed to cover a surface. Volume problems involve the measure of the amount of space inside a solid figure.

Example

Explain whether the situation involves *surface area* or *volume*.

PROBLEM 4 A factory needs to ship 50 new games to one of its customers. Each game takes up 1000 cm³ of space. How many 25,000 cm³ boxes will the factory need to be able to ship all the games?

SOLUTION The problem is asking for the amount of space available in boxes to hold the games.

ANSWER The situation involves volume because it is about the amount of space needed inside a box, **not** the area covering the box.

Problem Set

Match the net to the solid figure.

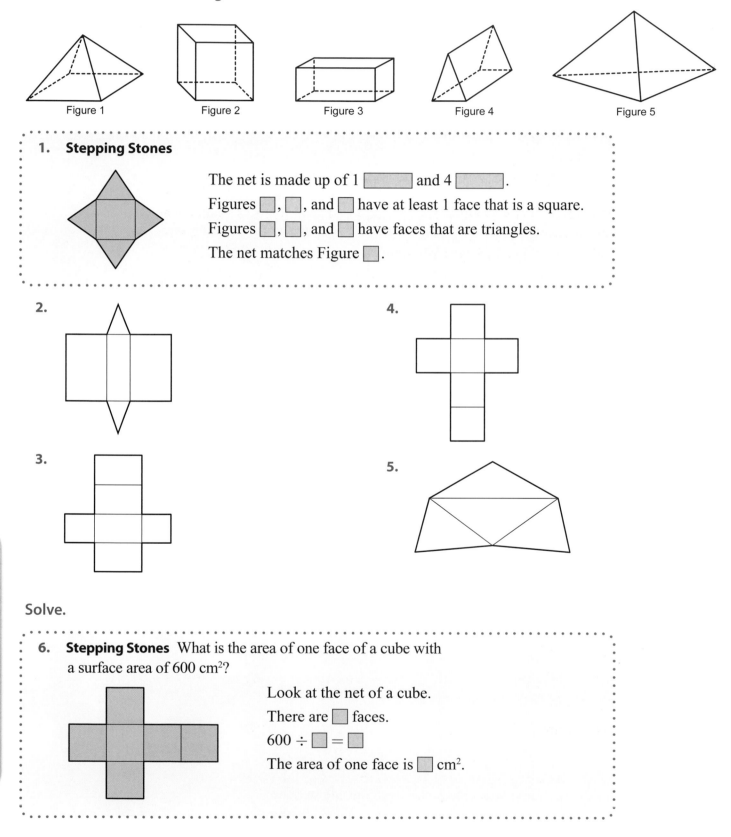

Figure 1 Figure 2 Figure 3 Figure 4 Figure 5

1. **Stepping Stones**

The net is made up of 1 ☐ and 4 ☐.

Figures ☐, ☐, and ☐ have at least 1 face that is a square.

Figures ☐, ☐, and ☐ have faces that are triangles.

The net matches Figure ☐.

2.

3.

4.

5.

Solve.

6. **Stepping Stones** What is the area of one face of a cube with a surface area of 600 cm²?

Look at the net of a cube.

There are ☐ faces.

$600 \div ☐ = ☐$

The area of one face is ☐ cm².

7. What is the surface area of a triangular pyramid if each face has an area of 25 mm²?

8. What is the surface area of a cube with faces that have an area of 6 cm² each?

9. What is the area of 1 face of a cube with a surface area of 24 m²?

10. A square pyramid has a base area of 16 cm². The pyramid's total surface area is 80 cm². What is the area of each triangular face?

11. **Challenge** Which has a greater surface area, a cube with faces that each have an area of 5 in², or a triangular pyramid with faces that each have an area of 7 in²? Explain.

12. **Challenge** What is the surface area of a cube with a volume of 8 cm³?

Explain whether the problem involves *surface area* or *volume*.

13. **Stepping Stones** Regina is going to put wallpaper on the walls of her room. She needs to find the number of square feet of wall space she needs to cover.

The problem is about the amount needed to cover a surface. The situation involves [   ].

14. The captain of a cargo ship needs to know how many cubic feet of space his shipping containers can hold.

15. Enrique is wrapping a present. He needs enough wrapping paper to cover all the sides of the box that is holding the present.

16. Marina is going to paint the inside of her garage. She needs to know how much paint to buy so she can finish the job.

17. **Challenge** Melissa has dug out an area in her backyard for a garden that is 10 ft long, 5 ft wide, and 6 in. deep. She needs to buy enough planting soil to fill it.

Choose the answer.

18. What figure can be formed from the net?

A. rectangular prism

B. triangular prism

C. square pyramid

D. triangular pyramid

19. What is the surface area of a square pyramid that has a base area of 36 cm² and triangular faces with areas of 12 cm² each?

A. 84 cm²

B. 96 cm²

C. 72 cm²

D. 108 cm²

Surface Area: Prisms and Pyramids

Finding surface area will help you find how much wrapping paper you need to wrap a present.

➔ Finding Surface Area of a Prism

Definition

The **surface area** of a solid figure is the sum of the areas of all the figure's faces.

You can find the surface area SA of a solid figure by adding the areas of all its faces. A net can help you see the figure's faces.

Think About It

Opposite faces of a rectangular prism have equal areas.

Example

PROBLEM 1 Find the surface area of the prism.

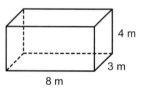

SOLUTION Draw and label a net for the rectangular prism. Then find the areas of the rectangles.

Find the areas of the faces.

Faces A and C: $A = 8 \cdot 4 = 32$

Faces B and D: $A = 8 \cdot 3 = 24$

Faces E and F: $A = 4 \cdot 3 = 12$

Find the sum of the areas of the faces.
$SA = 32 + 32 + 24 + 24 + 12 + 12 = 136$

ANSWER The surface area is 136 m².

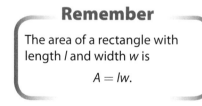

Remember

The area of a rectangle with length l and width w is

$$A = lw.$$

TOPIC

Finding Surface Area of a Pyramid

Definition

A **pyramid** is a solid figure with one base that is a polygon and all other faces that are triangles that meet at a single vertex. A pyramid is named according to the shape of its base.

You can find the surface area of a pyramid by adding the areas of all its faces, just as you did with prisms.

Example

PROBLEM 2 Find the surface area of the pyramid.

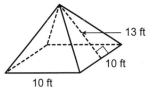

SOLUTION Draw and label a net for the square pyramid. Then find the areas of the square and the triangles.

The base of the pyramid is a square with side lengths of 10 ft.

$A = s^2$
$= 10^2$
$= 100$

All four of the triangles have a base length of 10 ft and a height of 13 ft.

$A = \frac{1}{2}bh$

$= \frac{1}{2} \cdot 10 \cdot 13$

$= 65$

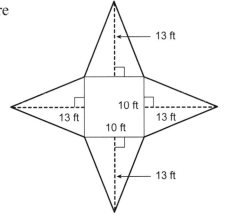

Find the sum of the areas of the faces.
$SA = 100 + 65 + 65 + 65 + 65 = 360$

ANSWER The surface area is 360 ft².

> **Tip**
> The triangular faces of a square pyramid are all the same size and shape.

> **Remember**
> The area of a square with side length s is
> $$A = s^2.$$
> The area of a triangle with base b and height h is
> $$A = \frac{1}{2}bh.$$

Problem Set

Find the surface area of the prism.

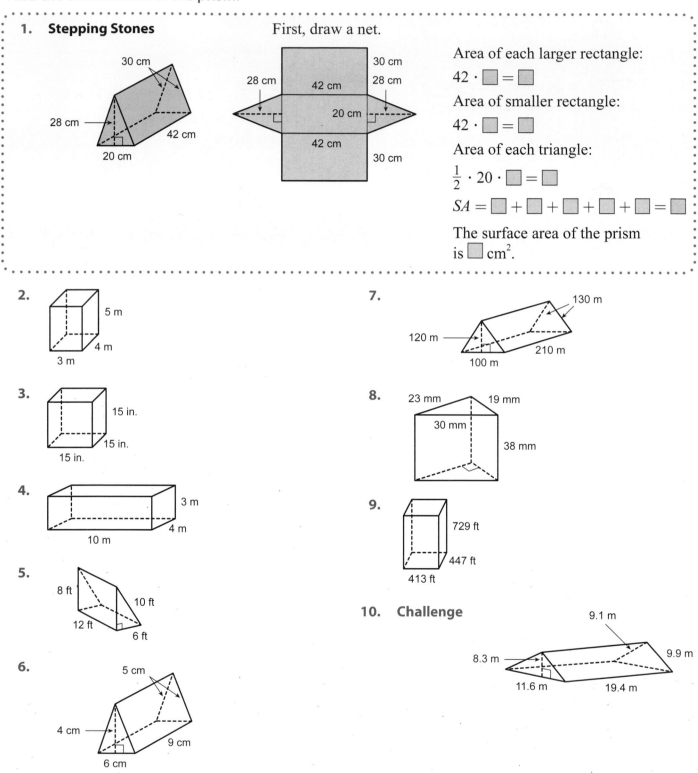

1. Stepping Stones

First, draw a net.

30 cm

28 cm

28 cm   42 cm   30 cm

20 cm   28 cm

42 cm

20 cm

30 cm

Area of each larger rectangle:

$42 \cdot \square = \square$

Area of smaller rectangle:

$42 \cdot \square = \square$

Area of each triangle:

$\frac{1}{2} \cdot 20 \cdot \square = \square$

$SA = \square + \square + \square + \square + \square = \square$

The surface area of the prism is $\square$ cm^2.

2.
5 m
4 m
3 m

3.
15 in.
15 in.
15 in.

4.
3 m
4 m
10 m

5.
8 ft
10 ft
12 ft
6 ft

6.
5 cm
4 cm
9 cm
6 cm

7.
130 m
120 m
100 m
210 m

8.
23 mm   19 mm
30 mm
38 mm

9.
729 ft
447 ft
413 ft

10. Challenge
9.1 m
8.3 m
9.9 m
11.6 m
19.4 m

Find the surface area of the square pyramid.

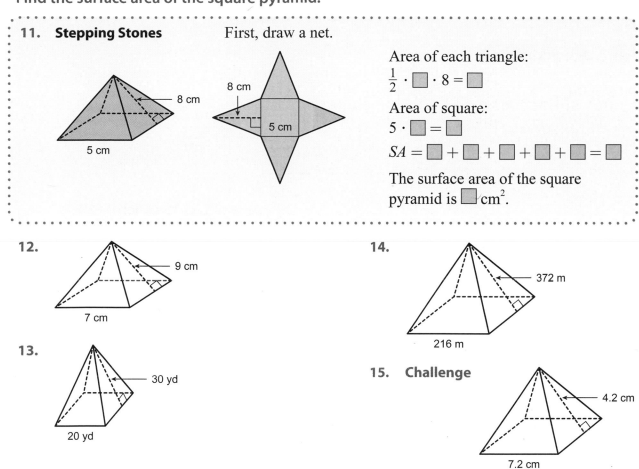

11. Stepping Stones

First, draw a net.

8 cm

8 cm

5 cm

5 cm

Area of each triangle:

$\frac{1}{2} \cdot \square \cdot 8 = \square$

Area of square:

$5 \cdot \square = \square$

$SA = \square + \square + \square + \square + \square = \square$

The surface area of the square pyramid is $\square$ cm².

12.

9 cm

7 cm

13.

30 yd

20 yd

14.

372 m

216 m

15. Challenge

4.2 cm

7.2 cm

Choose the answer.

16. What is the surface area of the prism?

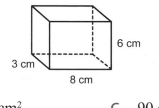

6 cm

3 cm

8 cm

A. 180 cm²   C. 90 cm²

B. 144 cm²   D. 17 cm²

17. What is the surface area of the square pyramid?

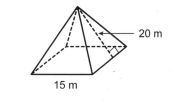

20 m

15 m

A. 225 m²   C. 825 m²

B. 600 m²   D. 4500 m²

Properties of Volume and Surface Area

A solid figure's surface area and volume change when the figure's dimensions change.

➔ Measuring Figures with Different Units

Example

PROBLEM 1 The surface area of a cube is 150 cm². What would change if the surface area of the cube were measured in square meters?

SOLUTION The surface area does not change. A square meter is larger than a square centimeter, so the number would decrease.

ANSWER The number representing the surface area would decrease.

PROBLEM 2 The volume of a cube is 125 cm³. What would change if the volume of the cube were measured in cubic millimeters?

SOLUTION The volume does not change. A cubic millimeter is smaller than a cubic centimeter, so the number would increase.

ANSWER The number representing the volume would increase.

Think About It

The length of a rope does not change when the length is measured with different units. But the number does change.

A rope 1 m long also is 100 cm long.

1 m = 100 cm

➔ Finding Surface Area with Scaled Figures

If you know the surface area or volume of a figure and the scale factor between it and its scaled image, you can use a formula to find the surface area or volume of the scaled image.

Tip

A scaled image is an enlarged or a reduced image of a figure.

Definition

A **scale factor** is a ratio of one measure to another. A scale factor greater than 1 enlarges a figure, and a scale factor less than 1 reduces a figure.

Formula

If SA_F is the surface area of a figure that is enlarged or reduced with a scale factor, then the surface area of the scaled image SA_I is

$$SA_I = (\text{scale factor})^2 \cdot SA_F.$$

Tip

The capital I in SA_I is a subscript. So SA_I is read "SA sub I."

SA_F is read "SA sub F."

V_I is read "V sub I."

V_F is read "V sub F."

TOPIC

Example

PROBLEM 3 Find the surface area of a figure that is an enlargement of a prism with surface area of 160 cm². Use a scale factor of 2.

SOLUTION Use the formula.

$SA_I = (\text{scale factor})^2 \cdot SA_F$
$\quad = 2^2 \cdot 160 \qquad$ Replace *scale factor* with 2 and SA_F with 160.
$\quad = 640 \qquad\qquad$ Simplify.

ANSWER The surface area of the enlargement is 640 cm².

CHECK The figure is an enlargement. The figure's surface area should be greater than the original prism's surface area.
$640 > 160 \checkmark$

➔ Finding Figures with the Same Volume but Different Surface Areas

You can use factoring and multiplication properties to find figures that have the same volume but different surface areas.

Example

PROBLEM 4 Find the dimensions of two rectangular prisms, each with a volume of 48 m³ but each with a different surface area.

SOLUTION Write the volume 48 as the product of three numbers two different ways. Use the factors as dimensions of the prisms. Then find the surface areas.

$$V = 48 = 6 \cdot 4 \cdot 2 \qquad\qquad V = 48 = 2 \cdot 3 \cdot 8$$
$$\quad = l_1 w_1 h_1 \qquad\qquad\qquad = l_2 w_2 h_2$$

$SA_1 = (6 \cdot 2) + (4 \cdot 2) + (6 \cdot 4) + (6 \cdot 2) + (4 \cdot 2) + (6 \cdot 4)$
$\quad = 12 + 8 + 24 + 12 + 8 + 24$
$\quad = 88$

$SA_2 = (2 \cdot 8) + (3 \cdot 8) + (2 \cdot 3) + (2 \cdot 8) + (3 \cdot 8) + (2 \cdot 3)$
$\quad = 16 + 24 + 6 + 16 + 24 + 6$
$\quad = 92$

ANSWER Rectangular prisms with dimensions of 6 m by 4 m by 2 m and 2 m by 3 m by 8 m have the same volume of 48 m³ but different surface areas.

> **Remember**
>
> The volume of a rectangular prism with dimensions *l*, *w*, and *h* is
> $$V = lwh.$$
> The surface area of a rectangular prism is the sum of the areas of the faces.

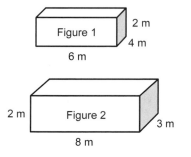

TOPIC

Problem Set

Solve.

1. The surface area of a prism is 1400 mm². What would change if the surface area of the prism were measured in square centimeters?

2. The volume of a prism is 45 yd³. What would change if the volume of the prism were measured in cubic feet?

3. The surface area of a triangular pyramid is 375.2 m². What would change if the surface area were measured in square centimeters?

4. The volume of a cube is 512 cm³. What would change if the volume of the cube were measured in cubic meters?

Find the surface area or volume of the scaled image by using the original figure's measurement and the given scale factor.

5. **Stepping Stones** Prism with $SA = 108$ in²; scale factor $= 3$

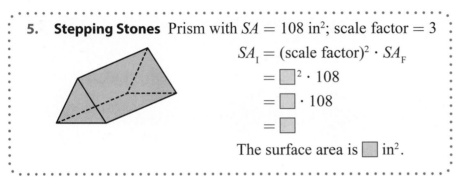

$$SA_I = (\text{scale factor})^2 \cdot SA_F$$
$$= \boxed{}^2 \cdot 108$$
$$= \boxed{} \cdot 108$$
$$= \boxed{}$$

The surface area is $\boxed{}$ in².

6. Prism with $V = 288$ cm³; scale factor $= 2$

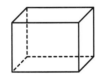

7. Pyramid with $SA = 300$ yd²; scale factor $= 5$

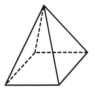

8. Pyramid with $V = 648$ m³; scale factor $= 3$

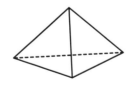

9. Prism with $V = 2592$ ft³; scale factor $= \frac{1}{6}$

10. Prism with $V = 3375$ cm³; scale factor $= \frac{1}{5}$

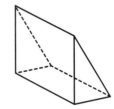

11. Prism with $SA = 1104$ m²; scale factor $= 4$

Solve.

12. **Challenge** The entrance to the Louvre museum in Paris, France, is a large square pyramid with a surface area of 1950 m². Regina bought a $\frac{1}{300}$ scale model of the Louvre museum entrance. To the nearest tenth, what is the surface area of the scale model Regina bought?

Find the dimensions of two rectangular prisms that have the given volume but have different surface areas.

13. **Stepping Stones** $V = 24 \text{ m}^3$

    Prism 1   Prism 2

    $24 = 3 \cdot \square \cdot \square$ $24 = 2 \cdot \square \cdot \square$

    Prism 1: 3 m by $\square$ m by $\square$ m

    Prism 2: 2 m by $\square$ m by $\square$ m

14. $V = 36 \text{ cm}^3$

15. $V = 32 \text{ mm}^3$

16. $V = 60 \text{ m}^3$

17. $V = 80 \text{ ft}^3$

18. $V = 72 \text{ in}^3$

19. $V = 40 \text{ m}^3$

20. $V = 64 \text{ cm}^3$

21. $V = 54 \text{ cm}^3$

22. $V = 56 \text{ mm}^3$

23. $V = 162 \text{ m}^3$

24. $V = 250 \text{ in}^3$

25. $V = 225 \text{ cm}^3$

26. **Challenge** $V = 189 \text{ mm}^3$

27. **Challenge** $V = 536 \text{ cm}^3$

Choose the answer.

28. A prism has a surface area of 100 cm². Which sentence describes the effect of measuring the surface area in square millimeters?

    A. The surface area increases.

    B. The surface area decreases.

    C. The surface area stays the same, but the number representing the surface area increases.

    D. The surface area stays the same, but the number representing the surface area decreases.

29. An image is created of a triangular prism using a scale factor of 3. What is the surface area of the scaled image if the surface area of the original triangular prism is 45 cm²?

    A. 9 cm²   C. 135 cm²

    B. 15 cm²   D. 405 cm²

30. Which dimensions of two rectangular prisms have volumes of 100 m³ but different surface areas?

    A. 25 m by 2 m by 2 m; 4 m by 2 m by 5 m

    B. 5 m by 5 m by 2 m; 2 m by 10 m by 5 m

    C. 2 m by 2 m by 25 m; 2 m by 2 m by 5 m

    D. 2 m by 10 m by 5 m; 4 m by 5 m by 5 m

Chapter 5 Review

Choose the answer.

1. What is the side length of a cube with a volume of 216 m³?

   A. $\sqrt{216}$ m   C. 12 m

   B. $\sqrt[3]{216}$ m   D. 36 m

2. What is the volume of the rectangular prism?

   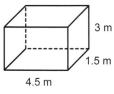

   A. 9 m³   C. 17 m³

   B. 49.5 m³   D. 20.25 m³

3. What is the volume of the triangular prism?

   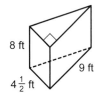

   A. 162 ft³   C. 81 ft³

   B. 324 ft³   D. 220.5 ft³

4. What figure can be formed by folding the net?

   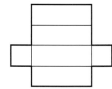

   A. rectangular prism

   B. square pyramid

   C. triangular prism

   D. triangular pyramid

5. What is the surface area of the prism?

   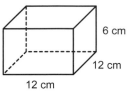

   A. 288 cm²   C. 1152 cm²

   B. 576 cm²   D. 864 cm²

6. What is the surface area of the pyramid?

   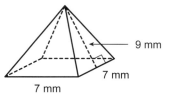

   A. 301 mm²   C. 175 mm²

   B. 350 mm²   D. 602 mm²

7. An image of a rectangular prism is created by using a scale factor of 4. What is the surface area of the scaled image if the surface area of the rectangular prism is 64 yd²?

   A. 256 yd²   C. 512 yd²

   B. 4096 yd²   D. 1024 yd²

8. A square pyramid has a volume of 450 cm³. Which sentence describes the effect of measuring the volume in cubic meters?

   A. The volume increases.

   B. The volume decreases.

   C. The volume stays the same, but the number representing the volume increases.

   D. The volume stays the same, but the number representing the volume decreases.

Find the side length of the cube with the given volume.

9. $V = 64 \text{ m}^3$

10. $V = 512 \text{ m}^3$

Convert to the given unit.

11. $1000 \text{ cm}^3 = \boxed{} \text{ m}^3$

13. $64{,}000 \text{ mm}^3 = \boxed{} \text{ cm}^3$

12. $8 \text{ ft}^3 = \boxed{} \text{ in}^3$

14. $27 \text{ m}^3 = \boxed{} \text{ cm}^3$

Find the volume of the prism.

15.

24 cm
16 cm
16 cm

16.

20 mm
15 mm
25 mm
18 mm

Draw a net for the solid figure and use it to find the figure's surface area.

17.

6.5 m
9 m
13 m

18.

6 m
8 m
8 m

Find the surface area or volume of the image with the given scale factor.

19. Prism with $V = 96 \text{ cm}^3$; scale factor $= 2$

20. Prism with $SA = 108 \text{ m}^2$; scale factor $= 3$

Find the dimensions of two rectangular prisms that have the given volume but different surface areas.

21. $V = 48 \text{ m}^3$

23. $V = 120 \text{ cm}^3$

22. $V = 64 \text{ mm}^3$

24. $V = 72 \text{ ft}^3$

Problem	Topic Lookup	Problem	Topic Lookup
1, 9–14	Cubes and Cube Roots	5–6, 17–18	Surface Area: Prisms and Pyramids
2–3, 15–16	Volumes of Prisms	7–8, 19–24	Properties of Volume and Surface Area
4, 17–18	Nets of Solids		

6 Comparisons: Ratios

In southern Asia and South America, some mosquitoes carry a disease called malaria. How can you compare how efforts to fight the disease are progressing in various countries? Scientists and doctors use ratios to understand many problems.

In This Chapter

You will use ratios and proportions to solve many different problems. For instance, you will compute interest on loans, as well as calculate taxes, tips, and discounts.

Chapter Topics

- ▶ Foundations for Chapter 6
- ▶ Ratios as Comparisons
- ▶ Percent
- ▶ Finding Percents of Numbers
- ▶ Discount
- ▶ Tax and Tip
- ▶ Simple Interest
- ▶ Proportions
- ▶ Solving Proportions
- ▶ Reducing and Enlarging
- ▶ Chapter 6 Review

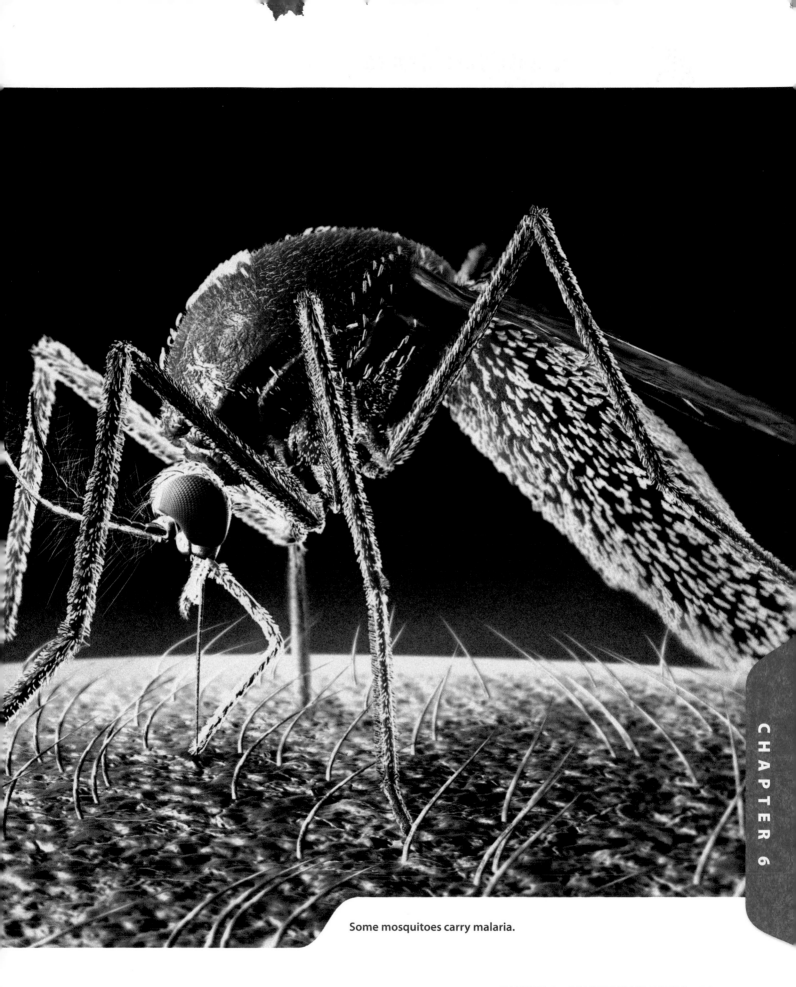

Some mosquitoes carry malaria.

Foundations for Chapter 6

➤ **Writing Mixed Numbers as Improper Fractions**

> **Definition**
>
> A **rational number** is any number that can be expressed as a ratio $\left(\frac{a}{b}\right)$, where a and b are integers and $b \neq 0$. A rational number can be written as a fraction, a decimal, or a percent.

You can write a mixed number as an improper fraction. One way is to convert the whole-number part to an improper fraction that has the same denominator as the fraction part. Then add the fractions' numerators. A simpler way is to multiply the whole-number part by the denominator and then add that product to the numerator.

Example A

Convert the mixed number to an improper fraction.

PROBLEM A-1 $5\frac{3}{4}$

SOLUTION There are $5 \cdot 4$ fourths in 5 wholes, so $5\frac{3}{4} = \frac{5 \cdot 4 + 3}{4} = \frac{20 + 3}{4} = \frac{23}{4}$.

ANSWER $5\frac{3}{4} = \frac{23}{4}$

PROBLEM A-2 $4\frac{1}{3}$

SOLUTION There are $4 \cdot 3$ thirds in 4 wholes, so $4\frac{1}{3} = \frac{4 \cdot 3 + 1}{3} = \frac{12 + 1}{3} = \frac{13}{3}$.

ANSWER $4\frac{1}{3} = \frac{13}{3}$

Problem Set A

Convert the mixed number to an improper fraction.

1. $1\frac{1}{2}$

2. $3\frac{5}{6}$

3. $2\frac{3}{8}$

4. $5\frac{4}{7}$

5. $6\frac{2}{3}$

6. $5\frac{1}{5}$

7. $4\frac{7}{8}$

8. $7\frac{1}{3}$

9. $3\frac{1}{4}$

Writing Decimals as Mixed Numbers

You can use place value to convert decimals to mixed numbers. The whole-number part of the decimal will be the whole-number part of the mixed number. Write the number of tenths or hundredths as the numerator over a denominator of 10 or 100. Simplify the fraction if possible.

Example B

Convert the decimal to a mixed number.

PROBLEM B-1 3.6

SOLUTION There are 3 wholes and 6 tenths. Write the fraction part as a fraction with a denominator of 10. Then simplify.

$$3.6 = 3\frac{6}{10} = 3\frac{3}{5}$$

ANSWER $3.6 = 3\frac{3}{5}$

PROBLEM B-2 2.08

SOLUTION There are 8 hundredths. Write the fraction part as a fraction with a denominator of 100. Then simplify.

$$2.08 = 2\frac{8}{100} = 2\frac{2}{25}$$

ANSWER $2.08 = 2\frac{2}{25}$

Problem Set B

Convert the decimal to a mixed number.

1. 5.3
2. 4.17
3. 7.4
4. 8.8

5. 2.02
6. 4.25
7. 9.1
8. 12.44

9. 18.65
10. 22.14
11. 165.58
12. 300.09

➥ Writing Ratios

Ratios can be used to describe a comparison of one amount to another.
Write a ratio with a fraction bar or as a decimal.

Example C

Use the figure to solve the problem.

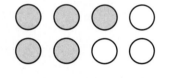

PROBLEM C-1 Write a fraction and a decimal to describe the ratio of shaded circles to white circles.

SOLUTION There are 5 shaded circles and 3 white circles.

Write the ratio with a fraction bar.

$$\frac{\text{shaded circles}}{\text{white circles}} = \frac{5}{3}$$

Convert to a decimal.

$$\frac{5}{3} = 1\frac{2}{3} \approx 1.67$$

ANSWER The ratio of shaded circles to white circles can be written as $\frac{5}{3}$ or about 1.67.

PROBLEM C-2 Write a fraction and a decimal to describe the ratio of shaded circles to all the circles.

SOLUTION There are 5 shaded circles and 8 total circles.

$$\frac{\text{shaded circles}}{\text{all circles}} = \frac{5}{8}$$

$$\frac{5}{8} = 0.625$$

ANSWER The ratio of shaded circles to all circles can be written as $\frac{5}{8}$ or 0.625.

Problem Set C

Write a ratio with a fraction bar and as a decimal for each comparison.
Use the figure to solve the problem.

1. shaded stars to white stars

2. squares to stars

3. shaded stars to all figures

4. white figures to all figures

5. shaded squares to white stars

6. shaded squares to all figures

7. white figures to shaded figures

8. shaded squares to white squares

9. stars to squares

10. shaded stars to white squares

11. squares to all figures

12. stars to white figures

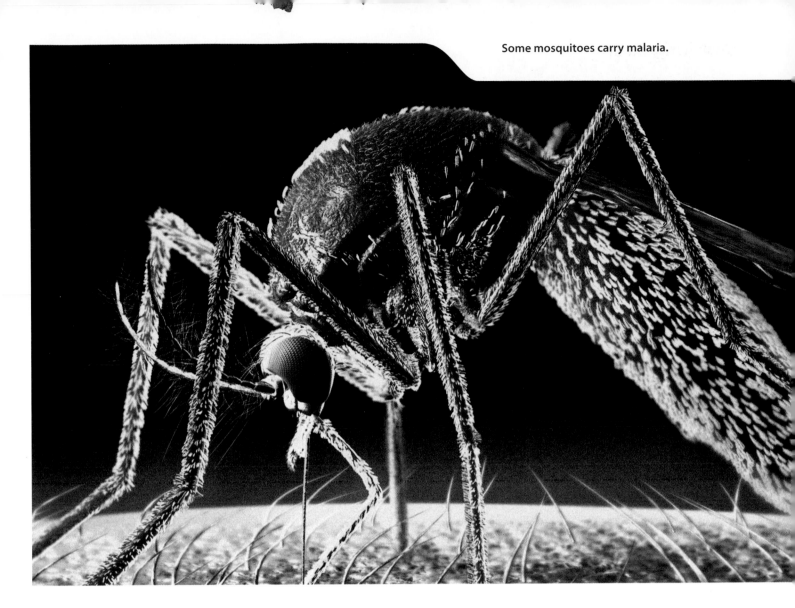

Some mosquitoes carry malaria.

Planting a Seed

A ratio is a way of using division to compare two values. A rational number can be written as a fraction, a decimal, or a percent. The choice of form depends on what you want to do with the number. For instance, when describing disease rates, scientists often use percentages.

Ratios as Comparisons

You use ratios to compare related quantities, such as the ingredients of a recipe.

➡ Writing Ratios

> **Definition**
>
> A **ratio** is a way of using division to compare two values.
> The ratio of a to b can be written in three ways.
>
> $$a \text{ to } b \qquad a:b \qquad \frac{a}{b}$$

You can write a ratio to compare different quantities or different parts of the same whole. When you use a fraction bar, the first value that you are comparing goes on top and the second value goes on the bottom. Simplify the ratio, if possible.

Example

Write the ratio in three different ways.

PROBLEM 1 There are 16 fiction books and 13 nonfiction books on the shelf. Write the ratio of nonfiction to fiction books.

SOLUTION $\dfrac{\text{nonfiction}}{\text{fiction}} = \dfrac{13}{16}$

Also: 13 to 16 *or* 13 : 16

ANSWER The ratio of nonfiction to fiction books can be written as $\frac{13}{16}$, 13 to 16, or 13 : 16.

PROBLEM 2 An 8-acre park has 6 acres of forest. Write the ratio of the acres of forest to the total acres of the park.

SOLUTION $\dfrac{\text{acres of forest}}{\text{total acres}} = \dfrac{6}{8} = \dfrac{6 \div 2}{8 \div 2} = \dfrac{3}{4}$

Also: 3 to 4 *or* 3 : 4

ANSWER The ratio of acres of forest to total acres can be written as $\frac{3}{4}$, 3 to 4, or 3 : 4.

> **Tip**
>
> The order of the terms is important when you write a ratio. In Problem 1, nonfiction to fiction is 13 to 16, but fiction to nonfiction is 16 to 13.

TOPIC

⇥ Writing Ratios for Values with Different Units

It often is a good idea to write both values being compared in a ratio with the same units.

Example

PROBLEM 3 Write a ratio comparing 50 cm to 2 m.

SOLUTION Convert meters to centimeters so that the units are the same.

$1 \text{ m} = 100 \text{ cm}; 2 \text{ m} = 2 \cdot 100 \text{ cm} = 200 \text{ cm}$

$$\frac{50 \text{ cm}}{2 \text{ m}} = \frac{50 \text{ cm}}{200 \text{ cm}}$$

$$= \frac{50 \div 50}{200 \div 50} = \frac{1}{4}$$

ANSWER The ratio of 50 cm to 2 m is $\frac{1}{4}$ or 1 to 4. Because the units for the first and second number are the same, you can drop the units completely. If they were different, you would need to include the units in the answer.

Think About It

The ratio will be the same, regardless of which unit you choose to convert to the other. In Problem 3, you also could convert centimeters to meters and get the same ratio.

⇥ Application: A Recipe

When you increase or decrease one amount in a recipe, the ratios among different ingredients need to stay the same.

Example

PROBLEM 4 A bread recipe calls for 2 teaspoons of baking soda and 4 cups of flour. How much flour is needed if the recipe is increased to use 6 teaspoons of baking soda?

SOLUTION Write the ratio of the amount of baking soda used to the amount in the original recipe.

$$\frac{\text{baking soda used}}{\text{baking soda in recipe}} = \frac{6}{2} = \frac{3}{1} = 3$$

Use the ratio to find the amount of flour to be used.
$3 \cdot 4 \text{ cups} = 12 \text{ cups}$

ANSWER With 6 teaspoons of baking soda, the recipe requires 12 cups of flour.

TOPIC

Problem Set

Write the ratio in three different formats: a to b, $a:b$, and $\frac{a}{b}$.

1. **Stepping Stones** Jesse has 4 white shirts and 3 blue shirts. Write the ratio of white shirts to blue shirts.

   $\dfrac{\text{white shirts}}{\text{blue shirts}} = \dfrac{4}{\boxed{}}$

   The ratio can be written as 4 to $\boxed{}$ or 4 : $\boxed{}$ or $\dfrac{4}{\boxed{}}$.

2. There are 5 dogs and 8 cats at the pet shelter. Write the ratio of dogs to cats.

3. There are 8 children and 6 adults at the park. Write the ratio of the number of children to the total number of people at the park.

4. A store sold 5 sports games and 5 adventure games. Write the ratio of sports games to adventure games.

5. Sarah read 12 pages out of the 20 pages in the chapter. Write the ratio of pages Sarah read to the total pages.

6. Carlos biked 24 miles and ran 6 miles. Write the ratio of the distance Carlos biked to the total distance.

7. The team spent 20 minutes on passing drills and 40 minutes on shooting drills. Write the ratio of time spent on shooting drills to time spent on passing drills.

8. A rectangle is 45 cm long and 15 cm wide. Write the ratio comparing the rectangle's length to its width.

9. In a year, there are 4 months that have 30 days. Write the ratio of the months with 30 days to the months with other than 30 days.

10. Juan has toy cars and trucks. The ratio of cars to trucks is 2 to 3. Write three possible pairs of numbers describing the numbers of cars and trucks.

11. On a soccer team, $\frac{2}{3}$ of the players are boys and the rest are girls. What is the ratio of boys to girls on the team?

12. **Challenge** A bag holds 3 blue marbles, 5 orange marbles, and 4 white marbles. Write the ratio comparing the number of marbles that are either blue or orange to the number of white marbles.

Write a ratio to compare the values. Simplify the ratio.

13. **Stepping Stones** 5 days to 4 weeks

    1 week = $\boxed{}$ days, so 4 weeks = $\boxed{}$ days

    $\dfrac{5 \text{ days}}{4 \text{ weeks}} = \dfrac{5 \text{ days}}{\boxed{} \text{ days}} = \dfrac{5}{\boxed{}}$

14. 5 m to 100 cm

15. 30 in. to 2 ft

16. 8 cm to 20 mm

17. 12 yd to 20 ft

18. 400 m to 1 km

19. 3 years to 6 months

20. 3600 s to 4 min

21. 0.5 ft to 24 in.

22. **Challenge** 12,000 mm to 1.5 m

Solve.

23. **Stepping Stones** Cho reads the first 15 pages in her book in 12 minutes. How long will it take her to read the next 60 pages?

$$\frac{\text{pages to read}}{\text{pages already read}} = \frac{60}{\boxed{}} = \frac{\boxed{}}{1}$$

$$12 \cdot \boxed{} \text{ minutes} = \boxed{} \text{ minutes}$$

It will take her $\boxed{}$ minutes.

24. A 3-pack of notebooks costs $4. How much do 6 notebooks cost?

25. A car travels 63 miles on 3 gallons of gas. How far can the car travel on 15 gallons of gas?

26. Margaret stores 400 photos in 8 equal-sized albums. How many photos does she have in 3 albums?

Complete the table.

Punch Recipe			
Number of Servings	Apple Juice	Cranberry Juice	Soda
6	2 c	3 c	1 c
27. 12	4 c	$\boxed{}$	2 c
28. 18	6 c	9 c	$\boxed{}$
29. 30	$\boxed{}$	15 c	5 c
30. $\boxed{}$	12 c	18 c	6 c

Choose the answer.

31. Jeff bought 7 T-shirts. Four of them were white and the rest were blue. What is the ratio of white shirts to blue shirts?

   A. $3:4$ C. $4:3$

   B. $3:7$ D. $4:7$

32. In a group of 40 children, there were 24 girls. Which fraction, written in simplest form, is the ratio of girls to boys?

   A. $\frac{3}{5}$ C. $\frac{3}{2}$

   B. $\frac{2}{3}$ D. $\frac{5}{3}$

33. The baseball coach wanted $\frac{1}{4}$ of the new bats to be wooden, and the rest to be aluminum. Which ratio compares wooden bats to aluminum bats?

   A. 1 to 3   C. 3 to 4

   B. 1 to 4   D. 4 to 1

34. Stephanie noticed that $\frac{7}{10}$ of the children playing soccer were girls. Which numbers could show the girls and boys in this group?

   A. 7 girls and 10 boys

   B. 7 girls and 17 boys

   C. 10 girls and 7 boys

   D. 14 girls and 6 boys

Percent

The percent sign shows that a ratio is being represented as a comparison to 100.

➥ Converting Percents and Decimals

Definition

A **percent** is a ratio that compares a number to 100.

Because a percent compares a number to 100, you can convert a percent to a decimal by dividing by 100. Show division by 100 by moving the decimal point 2 places to the left. To convert a decimal to a percent, multiply by 100, or move the decimal point 2 places to the right.

Example

PROBLEM 1 Convert 0.2% to a decimal.

SOLUTION $0.2 = 00.2$ Move the decimal point 2 places to the left.

ANSWER $0.2\% = 0.002$

PROBLEM 2 Convert 43% to a decimal.

SOLUTION $43\% = 043. = 0.43$

ANSWER $43\% = 0.43$

PROBLEM 3 Convert 2.5 to a percent.

SOLUTION $2.5 = 2.50$ Write an equivalent decimal.
$2.5 = 2.50$ Move the decimal point 2 places to the right.

ANSWER $2.5 = 250\%$

PROBLEM 4 Convert 0.16 to a percent.

SOLUTION $0.16 = 0.16 = 16\%$

ANSWER $0.16 = 16\%$

Think About It

A percent greater than 100 represents a number greater than one whole.

A percent less than 100 represents a number less than one whole.

A percent less than 1 represents a number less than one hundredth.

→ Converting Percents and Fractions

To convert a fraction to a percent, first divide to convert the fraction to a decimal. Then convert the decimal to a percent. To convert a percent to a fraction, write the percent as a fraction with a denominator of 100, and then simplify.

Example

PROBLEM 5 Convert $\frac{3}{5}$ to a percent.

SOLUTION $\frac{3}{5} = 3 \div 5 = 0.6$ Convert $\frac{3}{5}$ to a decimal.

$0.6 = 60\%$ Convert 0.6 to a percent.

ANSWER $\frac{3}{5} = 60\%$

PROBLEM 6 Convert 18% to a fraction.

SOLUTION $18\% = \frac{18}{100}$ Write the percent as a fraction with a denominator of 100.

$\frac{18 \div 2}{100 \div 2} = \frac{9}{50}$ Simplify.

ANSWER $18\% = \frac{9}{50}$

→ Writing Fractions and Percents

You can use a fraction and a percent to write a ratio describing a problem situation. First write the ratio as a fraction, and then convert the fraction to a percent.

Example

PROBLEM 7 Last month, Polly's Pet Store sold 85 birds. Of these, 15 were parakeets. Write a simplified fraction and a percent to describe what part of the total pets sold were parakeets.

SOLUTION Write a simplified fraction to compare parakeets to the whole.

$\frac{15}{85} = \frac{3}{17}$

Divide to convert the fraction to a decimal.

$\frac{3}{17} = 3 \div 17 \approx 0.176$

Convert the decimal to a percent.

$0.176 = 17.6\%$

ANSWER Last month, $\frac{3}{17}$ or about 17.6% of the birds sold were parakeets.

TOPIC

Problem Set

Convert the decimal to a percent.

1. **Stepping Stones** 0.03

    $0.03 = 0\underset{\frown\frown}{.03} = \blacksquare$

    $0.03 = \blacksquare\%$

2. 0.4

3. 0.05

4. 0.9

5. 0.78

6. 2.6

7. 0.085

8. 0.007

9. 3.45

10. 6.70

11. 3.0

12. **Challenge** 5.006

Convert the percent to a decimal.

13. **Stepping Stones** 80%

    $80\% = 0\underset{\frown\frown}{80}. = \blacksquare$

14. 6%

15. 23%

16. 100%

17. 12.5%

18. 0.3%

19. 173%

20. 200%

21. 1493%

22. **Challenge** 264.05%

Convert the fraction to a percent.

23. **Stepping Stones** $\frac{4}{5}$

    $\frac{4}{5} = 4 \div \blacksquare = \blacksquare$

    $\blacksquare = \blacksquare\%$

24. $\frac{1}{2}$

25. $\frac{3}{4}$

26. $\frac{3}{20}$

27. $\frac{31}{50}$

28. $\frac{5}{7}$

29. $1\frac{3}{4}$

30. $4\frac{5}{8}$

31. $2\frac{7}{12}$

32. **Challenge** $4\frac{13}{200}$

Convert the percent to a fraction or a mixed number.

33. **Stepping Stones** 70%

$$70\% = \frac{70}{\square}$$

$$= \frac{70 \div \square}{\square \div \square} = \frac{\square}{\square}$$

34. 50%

35. 10%

36. 33%

37. 5%

38. 2%

39. 45%

40. 150%

41. 245%

42. **Challenge** 718.5%

Write a fraction and a percent to describe the situation.

43. One afternoon, 18 of the 40 children at a playground are girls. Compare the number of girls to the total number of children.

44. Two out of every five movies rented from a store are action movies. Compare the number of action movies to the total number of movies rented.

45. Morgan has 65 pages to read in her book. So far she has read 30 pages. Compare the number of pages she has read to the total number of pages in the book.

46. **Challenge** There are 17 adult dogs and 3 puppies playing at the park. Compare the number of puppies to the total number of dogs.

Choose the answer.

47. Which decimal is equivalent to 4.5%?

    A. 0.045

    B. 0.405

    C. 0.45

    D. 4.5

48. Which percent is equivalent to $\frac{3}{20}$?

    A. 30%

    B. 3%

    C. 15%

    D. 1.5%

Finding Percents of Numbers

You can use percent to find a part if you know the whole. You can also use percent to find a whole if you know the part.

➡ Finding the Percent of a Number

You can find a given percent of a whole number by first converting the percent to a decimal or a fraction. Then multiply the decimal or the fraction by the whole number.

Example

Find the percent of the number.

PROBLEM 1 18% of 70

SOLUTION It probably is easier to use the decimal than the fraction form.

$18\% = 0.18$ Convert the percent to a decimal.

$0.18 \cdot 70 = 12.6$ Multiply.

ANSWER 18% of 70 is 12.6.

CHECK Use mental math and benchmarks, such as 10% and 20%. When you figure that 10% of 70 is 7, and 20% of 70 is 14, you know that the answer of 12.6 is reasonable.

PROBLEM 2 25% of 440

SOLUTION The percent equals the fraction $\frac{1}{4}$, and using $\frac{1}{4}$ is probably easier than multiplying by 0.25.

$25\% = \frac{1}{4}$ Convert the percent to a fraction.

$\frac{1}{4} \cdot 440 = 440 \div 4$ Write an equivalent division problem.

$= 110$ Divide.

ANSWER 25% of 440 is 110.

Remember

Convert a percent to a decimal by moving the decimal point 2 places to the left.

Convert a percent to a fraction by writing a fraction with a denominator of 100. Then simplify if possible.

TOPIC

➔ Finding the Whole from a Percent

Percent problems often describe a part of a whole. If you are given a percent and a part, you can find the whole by writing a multiplication equation that uses a decimal or a fraction.

Example

PROBLEM 3 20% of what number is 45?

SOLUTION Translate the problem into an equation.

20%	of	what number	is	45
↓	↓	↓	↓	↓
20%	·	n	=	45

$$0.2 \cdot n = 45 \qquad \text{Convert the percent to a decimal.}$$
$$(0.2 \cdot n) \div 0.2 = 45 \div 0.2 \qquad \text{Divide both sides by 0.2.}$$
$$n = 225 \qquad \text{Simplify.}$$

ANSWER 20% of 225 is 45.

Think About It

You also could have converted 20% to the fraction $\frac{1}{5}$.

Look at all the numbers in the problem to see whether working with a fraction or a decimal would be easier.

➔ Application: A Survey

Example

PROBLEM 4 Twenty people in a survey said the library needs more bike racks. That number was 5% of the total number of people in the survey. How many people were in the survey?

SOLUTION Translate the situation into a percent problem, and then into an equation. Let p = the total number of people in the survey.

20	is	5%	of	what number?
↓	↓	↓	↓	↓
20	=	5%	·	p

$$20 = 0.05 \cdot p \qquad \text{Convert the percent to a decimal.}$$
$$20 \div 0.05 = (0.05 \cdot p) \div 0.05 \qquad \text{Divide both sides by 0.05.}$$
$$400 = p \qquad \text{Simplify.}$$

ANSWER There were 400 people in the survey.

TOPIC

Problem Set

Find the percent of the number.

1. **Stepping Stones** 45% of 600

   $45\% \text{ of } 600 = \boxed{} \cdot 600 = \boxed{}$

2. 60% of 400

3. 90% of 240

4. 5% of 800

5. 20% of 75

6. 35% of 60

7. 47% of 2000

8. 113% of 140

9. 522% of 85

10. 11.3% of 700

11. 2.3% of 80

12. 4.15% of 6000

13. **Challenge** 7.5% of 4.6

Find the unknown number.

14. **Stepping Stones** 18 is 45% of what number?

   $18 = 45\% \cdot n$

   $18 = \boxed{} \cdot n$

   $18 \div \boxed{} = (\boxed{} \cdot n) \div \boxed{}$

   $\boxed{} = n$

15. 26 is 40% of what number?

16. 24 is 25% of what number?

17. 45 is 3% of what number?

18. 117 is 15% of what number?

19. 42 is 35% of what number?

20. 64% of what number is 192?

21. 71% of what number is 2840?

22. 10% of what number is 1.25?

23. 150% of what number is 132?

24. 0.5% of what number is 2.4?

Solve. Describe why you chose either a decimal or a fraction to represent the percent.

25. **Stepping Stones** On Saturday, 42% of the 300 people visiting the museum saw the butterfly exhibit. How many people saw the butterfly exhibit?

    ▭ · 300 = ▭

    ▭ people saw the exhibit.

26. A road repair crew has fixed 42 miles of roadway. That number is 30% of the total miles that need repair. How many total miles of road need to be repaired?

27. Of every 5000 people who visit a website, 95% stay more than 2 minutes. How many people out of 5000 visitors stay more than 2 minutes at this website?

28. Of a shipment of 450 flowerpots, 8% arrived broken. How many of the flowerpots broke before they were delivered?

29. At a video rental store, 434 movies were returned in less than 2 days. That number is 62% of the total rented last week. How many movies did the store rent last week?

30. Marcus answered 15, or 60%, of the trivia questions correctly. Deon answered 80% of the questions correctly. How many trivia questions did Deon answer correctly?

31. If 30% of a number is 27, what is 50% of the same number?

32. If 40% of a number is 8, what is 75% of the same number?

33. **Challenge** Which quantity is greater: 35% of 180 or 65% of 90? Explain how you know.

Choose the answer.

34. Which number is 15% of 90?

    A. 6   C. 60

    B. 13.5   D. 135

35. 44 is 80% of what number?

    A. 5.5   C. 55

    B. 35.2   D. 181.8

36. 26% of what number is 39?

    A. 10.14   C. 66.67

    B. 65   D. 150

37. If 20% of a number is 16, what is 70% of the same number?

    A. 14   C. 56

    B. 28   D. 112

Discount

When you buy items on sale, you can save money.
Discounts tell you how much you save.

➔ Finding the Discount

Definitions

A **discount** is a decrease in the price of an item. An item's **sale price** is the price
of the item after a discount.

Discount Rate

The discount rate for an item is

$$\text{discount rate} = \frac{\text{discount}}{\text{regular price}}.$$

> **Tip**
>
> Discount rates are often written
> as fractions or percents. When
> converting a discount rate to a
> percent, write the discount rate
> as a decimal, and then convert
> the decimal to a percent.

To find the amount of discount, multiply the regular price of the item by
the discount rate (expressed as a decimal or a fraction).

> **Remember**
>
> To convert a percent to a
> decimal, move the decimal
> point 2 places to the left.

Example

Find the discount amount.

PROBLEM 1 regular price = $80; discount rate = 15%

SOLUTION Convert the discount rate to a decimal.
$15\% = 0.15$

Multiply.
$0.15 \cdot \$80 = \$12$

ANSWER The discount is $12.

PROBLEM 2 regular price = $65; discount rate: $\frac{1}{4}$ off

SOLUTION $\frac{1}{4} \cdot \$65 = \$65 \div 4 = \$16.25$

ANSWER The discount is $16.25.

➔ Finding the Sale Price

You can find the sale price by subtracting the discount from the
regular price.

Example

Find the sale price.

PROBLEM 3 regular price = $300; discount rate = 20%

SOLUTION Convert the discount rate to a decimal.
20% = 0.2

Multiply the decimal by the regular price to find the discount.
0.2 · $300 = $60

Subtract the discount from the regular price.
$300 − $60 = $240

ANSWER The sale price is $240.

Think About It

You also could solve Problem 3 by subtracting the percent of the discount from 100% and then finding that percent of the regular price.

100% − 20% = 80%

0.8 · $300 = $240

➔ Finding the Discount Rate

If you are given the regular price and the sale price, first subtract to find the discount.

Example

Find the discount rate as a percent.

PROBLEM 4 regular price = $160; discount = $48

SOLUTION discount rate = $\frac{\text{discount}}{\text{regular price}}$

$= \frac{48}{160}$

$= 0.3 = 30\%$

ANSWER The discount rate is 30%.

PROBLEM 5 regular price = $270; sale price = $243

SOLUTION Subtract to find the discount.
270 − 243 = 27

Find the discount rate.

discount rate = $\frac{\text{discount}}{\text{regular price}}$

$= \frac{27}{270}$

$= 0.1 = 10\%$

ANSWER The discount rate is 10%.

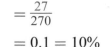

$\frac{22.5}{187.50} = \frac{x}{100}$

2250

70 67.5

Problem Set

Find the discount amount.

1. **Stepping Stones** regular price = $610; discount rate = 10%

   10% = [ ]

   [ ] · $610 = [ ]

2. regular price = $100; discount rate = 35%

3. regular price = $360; discount rate = 40%

4. regular price = $420; discount rate = $\frac{1}{4}$

5. regular price = $8; discount rate = 75%

6. regular price = $75; discount rate = 12%

7. regular price = $349; discount rate = $\frac{1}{10}$

8. regular price = $168; discount rate = 30%

9. regular price = $508; discount rate = 17%

10. **Challenge** regular price = $49.69; discount rate = $\frac{2}{3}$

Find the sale price.

11. **Stepping Stones** regular price = $240; discount rate = 30%

    Write the percent as a decimal.

    30% = [ ]

    Find the discount amount.

    [ ] · $240 = [ ]

    Subtract to find the sale price.

    $240 − [ ] = [ ]

12. regular price = $200; discount rate = 15%

13. regular price = $680; discount rate = 20%

14. regular price = $48; discount rate = 25%

15. regular price = $36; discount rate = $\frac{1}{2}$

16. regular price = $132; discount rate = $\frac{1}{4}$

17. regular price = $570; discount rate = 40%

18. regular price = $712; discount rate = $\frac{1}{5}$

19. regular price = $2316; discount rate = 21%

20. **Challenge** regular price = $19.99; discount rate = $\frac{1}{3}$

Find the discount rate as a percent.

21. **Stepping Stones** regular price = $43; discount = $7

    discount rate = $\dfrac{\boxed{}}{43}$

    $= \boxed{}$

    $= \boxed{}\%$

22. regular price = $275; discount = $15

23. regular price = $85; discount = $22

24. regular price = $720; sale price = $630

25. regular price = $19; sale price = $17

26. regular price = $26; discount = $10

27. regular price = $129; discount = $65

28. regular price = $35.59; sale price = $31

29. regular price = $187.69; sale price = $145

30. regular price = $459.95; sale price = $410.95

Solve.

31. **Challenge** Store A is offering a $15 discount on a jacket that regularly costs $65. Store B regularly sells the same jacket for $70 but now is offering a 15% discount. At which store does the jacket cost less? How much less?

32. **Challenge** Pam bought a television for 30% off its regular price of $325. Steve bought a similar television at another store on sale for $\frac{1}{3}$ off its regular price of $330. Who paid more for the television? How much more?

Choose the answer.

33. A store is having a 20%-off sale on its video games. How much of a discount is there on a game that regularly costs $25?

    A. $5
    B. $20
    C. $22.50
    D. $30

34. What is the discount rate for a $70 table on sale for $55?

    A. 15%
    B. 21.4%
    C. 27.3%
    D. 78.6%

35. A computer with a regular price of $650 is on sale for 25% off. What is the sale price?

    A. $812.50
    B. $625
    C. $487.50
    D. $162.50

36. What is the discount rate for a $264 bicycle that is on sale for $79.20 off?

    A. 3%
    B. 13%
    C. 30%
    D. 33%

Tax and Tip

Use what you know about finding a percent of a number to figure tax or tip.

➜ Finding Tax on a Purchase

Definitions

A **tax** is a sum of money collected by a government. A **sales tax** is a percent of the price of an item paid to a government when the item is sold.

You can find the amount of sales tax on a purchase by multiplying the purchase price by the tax rate, expressed in decimal form. To find the total cost of an item, you can add the tax to the item's purchase price.

Think About It

Another way to find a total cost that includes sales tax is to add the decimal form of the tax to 1, and then multiply that sum times the purchase price.

Example

PROBLEM 1 Find the sales tax: purchase price = $35; tax rate = 5%

SOLUTION 5% = 0.05

Multiply: $0.05 \cdot \$35 = \$1.75$

ANSWER The sales tax is $1.75.

PROBLEM 2 Find the total cost: purchase price = $74; tax rate = 8%

SOLUTION 8% = 0.08

Multiply: $0.08 \cdot \$74 = \$5.92$

Add the tax to the price: $\$74 + \$5.92 = \$79.92$

ANSWER The total cost is $79.92.

PROBLEM 3 Find the total cost: purchase price = $129; tax rate = 7%

SOLUTION 7% = 0.07

Multiply: $0.07 \cdot \$129 = \$9.03$

Add the tax to the price: $\$129 + \$9.03 = \$138.03$

ANSWER The total cost is $138.03.

➔ Finding the Tip for a Bill

Definition

A **tip** is an amount of money given to someone who provides a service. A tip generally is computed as a percent of a bill for service.

A customary tip for restaurant service is 15–20% of the bill. You can find the tip by multiplying the bill by the tip rate, expressed in decimal form. To find the total bill, you can add the tip to the original bill.

Example

PROBLEM 4 Find the tip: bill = $30; tip rate = 15%

SOLUTION 15% = 0.15

Multiply: $0.15 \cdot \$30 = \$4.50$

ANSWER The tip is $4.50.

PROBLEM 5 Find the tip: bill = $85; tip rate = 17.5%

SOLUTION 17.5% = 0.175

Multiply: $0.175 \cdot \$85 = \$14.875$

Round to the nearest cent: $14.875 rounds to $14.88

ANSWER The tip is $14.88.

PROBLEM 6 Find the total bill: bill = $42; tip rate = 20%

SOLUTION 20% = 0.2

Multiply: $0.2 \cdot \$42 = \$8.40$

Add the tip to the bill: $42 + $8.40 = $50.40

ANSWER The total bill is $50.40.

Think About It

Another way to find 20% of a bill is to find 10% by moving the decimal point one place to the left, and then double that number. To find 15% of the bill, find 10%, and then add half.

Think About It

Because tax and tip problems deal with money, rounding any decimal answer to the nearest hundredth will give an answer to the nearest cent. Most often, stores round up to the nearest penny, regardless of the digit in the thousandths place.

Problem Set

Find the sales tax.

1. **Stepping Stones** purchase price = \$32; tax rate = 10%

   Convert percent to a decimal: 10% = ☐

   Multiply to find tax amount: ☐ · \$32 = ☐

2. purchase price = \$49; tax rate = 5%

3. purchase price = \$165; tax rate = 2%

4. purchase price = \$78; tax rate = 6%

5. purchase price = \$32; tax rate = 8%

6. purchase price = \$23.50; tax rate = 5%

7. purchase price = \$121.65; tax rate = 11%

8. **Challenge** purchases: \$73.50, \$56.89, and \$12.30; tax rate = 6.5%

Find the total cost.

9. **Stepping Stones** purchase price = \$60; tax rate = 5%

   Convert percent to a decimal: 5% = ☐

   Multiply to find tax amount: ☐ · \$60 = ☐

   Add to find total cost: \$60 + ☐ = ☐

10. purchase price = \$32; tax rate = 8%

11. purchase price = \$184; tax rate = 10%

12. purchase price = \$75; tax rate = 8%

13. purchase price = \$2615; tax rate = 3%

14. purchase price = \$238.95; tax rate = 7%

15. purchase price = \$434.95; tax rate = 4.5%

16. **Challenge** purchases: \$14.85, \$26.99, and \$9.49; tax rate = 8.8%

Find a 15% tip and a 20% tip for the bill.

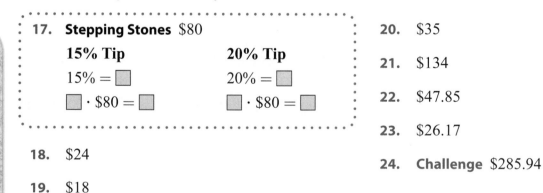

17. **Stepping Stones** \$80

15% Tip	**20% Tip**
15% = ☐	20% = ☐
☐ · \$80 = ☐	☐ · \$80 = ☐

18. \$24

19. \$18

20. \$35

21. \$134

22. \$47.85

23. \$26.17

24. **Challenge** \$285.94

Find the total bill, including a 15% tip.

25. **Stepping Stones** $12

    Convert percent to a decimal: $15\% = \square$

    Multiply to find tax amount: $\square \cdot \$12 = \square$

    Add to find total bill: $\$12 + \square = \square$

26. $36

27. $7

28. $28.49

29. $14.09

30. **Challenge** $178.75

Choose the answer.

31. What is a 15% tip on a $32 taxicab ride?

    A. $1.50

    B. $4.80

    C. $12.50

    D. $13.80

32. Anna's family went out to dinner. If the dinner bill was $76 and her family gave a 20% tip, what was the total cost of the dinner?

    A. $15.20

    B. $60.80

    C. $91.20

    D. $30.40

33. What is a 7% tax on a book that costs $15?

    A. $1.05

    B. $2.10

    C. $13.95

    D. $16.05

34. What is the total cost, including an 8% sales tax, for a computer that sells for $1399?

    A. $1119.20

    B. $1407.00

    C. $2518.20

    D. $1510.92

Simple Interest

You can earn interest on money you keep in the bank. You often pay interest on money you borrow.

→ Finding Simple Interest

Definitions

Interest is the cost to borrow money or the amount earned by lending money.

The **principal** is money that earns interest at a given rate over time. It is the original amount of money on which the interest is based.

Simple interest is the amount of interest earned or paid only on the principal.

An **interest rate** is the percentage of the original amount of money on which the interest will be figured.

Remember

To convert a percent to a decimal, move the decimal point 2 places to the left.

Simple Interest

The interest I paid on principal P with interest rate r and time t is

$$I = Prt.$$

Think About It

The rate and the time must be given using the same units.

Usually rate is given in percent per year and time is given in years.

To find an amount of interest paid or earned, convert the interest rate to a decimal, and then use the simple interest formula.

Example

Find the amount of simple interest.

PROBLEM 1 principal = \$300; rate = 6%; time = 3 years

SOLUTION $I = Prt = \$300 \cdot 0.06 \cdot 3 = \$54$

ANSWER The amount of interest is \$54.

TOPIC

Finding Balance with Interest

You can find the balance, or total amount saved or owed, at the end of a period of time by adding the interest earned or due during that time to the principal.

Example

Find the total amount saved or owed.

PROBLEM 2 principal = $650; rate = 12%; time = 5 years

SOLUTION Find the interest and add it to the principal.

$I = Prt = \$650 \cdot 0.12 \cdot 5 = \$390$

Add to find the total: $\$650 + \$390 = \$1040$

ANSWER The total amount is $1040.

Finding Loan Rates

You can use the formula for simple interest to find the interest rate being paid on a loan if you know the interest payment.

Example

Find the annual interest paid.

PROBLEM 3 Mr. McLeod pays $80 to borrow $400 for 1 year. What annual interest rate did Mr. McLeod pay on the loan?

SOLUTION

$$I = Prt$$
$$80 = 400 \cdot r \cdot 1 \qquad \text{Substitute.}$$
$$80 = 400\,r \qquad \text{Simplify.}$$
$$\frac{80}{400} = r \qquad \text{Divide to solve for } r.$$
$$0.2 = r \qquad \text{Simplify.}$$

Convert the decimal to a percent: $0.2 = 20\%$

ANSWER Mr. McLeod paid 20% interest on the loan.

Problem Set

Find the amount of simple interest.

1. **Stepping Stones** principal = $1000;
    rate = 5%; time = 4 years

    $I = Prt$

    $= \$1000 \cdot \boxed{} \cdot 4$

    $= \boxed{}$

2. principal = $200; rate = 10%;
    time = 4 years

3. principal = $2600; rate = 8%;
    time = 6 years

4. principal = $4500; rate = 6%;
    time = 3 years

5. principal = $750; rate = 14%;
    time = 4.5 years

6. principal = $8100; rate = 17%;
    time = 7 years

7. principal = $10,400; rate = 12.5%;
    time = 11 years

8. principal = $16,600; rate = 4.2%;
    time = 9 years

9. principal = $18,510; rate = 6.55%;
    time = 8.5 years

10. principal = $156,000; rate = 6.25%;
    time = 30 years

11. principal = $3495; rate = 4.5%;
    time = 25 years

12. **Challenge** principal = $11,899;
    rate = 3.875%; time = 66 months

Find the total amount saved or owed.

13. **Stepping Stones** principal = $800; rate = 7%; time = 3 years

    Multiply to find the interest: $I = Prt = \$800 \cdot \boxed{} \cdot 3 = \boxed{}$

    Add interest to principal: $\$800 + \boxed{} = \boxed{}$

14. principal = $1000; rate = 5%;
    time = 2 years

15. principal = $500; rate = 15%;
    time = 3 years

16. principal = $1700; rate = 6%;
    time = 5 years

17. principal = $3000; rate = 12%;
    time = 8 years

18. principal = $1450; rate = 7.5%;
    time = 10 years

19. principal = $10,600; rate = 19.9%;
    time = 14 years

20. principal = $12,300; rate = 25%;
    time = 3.5 years

21. principal = $1056; rate = 3.75%;
    time = 6 years

22. **Challenge** principal = $267,000;
    rate = 5.125%; time = 15 years

Find the annual interest rate paid. Round to the nearest tenth of a percent when neceasary.

23. **Stepping Stones** interest = $675; principal = $3000; time = 1 year

    $$I = Prt$$
    $$\$675 = \$3000 \cdot r \cdot \boxed{}$$
    $$\$675 = \$\boxed{}r$$
    $$\boxed{} = r$$

    Convert the decimal to a percent:
    $$\boxed{} = \boxed{}\%$$

24. interest = $375; principal = $2500; time = 1 year

25. interest = $684; principal = $3600; time = 1 year

26. interest = $90; principal = $6000; time = 1 month

27. interest = $81; principal = $10,800; time = 1 month

28. interest = $540; principal = $1200; time = 6 months

29. interest = $625; principal = $5000; time = 3 months

30. **Challenge** interest = $646.50; principal = $2155; time = 2 months

Choose the answer.

31. Maria borrows $125 from her parents and agrees to pay 3% annual interest. How much will she owe after 4 years, including the initial amount?

    A. $140

    B. $15

    C. $3.75

    D. $1500

32. How much interest will be due on a loan of $5000 at 18% annual interest if the money is borrowed for 1 year?

    A. $900

    B. $5450

    C. $5400

    D. $450

33. Denzel borrows $8000 to buy a car. He will pay 2.75% annual interest. How much will he pay in all if he pays off the loan in 6 years?

    A. $1320

    B. $8220

    C. $9320

    D. $6680

34. Adrian pays $65 to borrow $1200 for 2 months. What annual interest rate does Adrian pay on the loan?

    A. 65%

    B. 6.5%

    C. 3.25%

    D. 32.5%

Proportions

When you increase a recipe, you need to keep the proportion of ingredients the same as in the original recipe.

➔ Using Common Denominators to Find Proportions

Definition

A **proportion** is an equation stating that two ratios are equal.

One way to tell if two ratios form a proportion is to write the ratios with a fraction bar and find common denominators for the ratios. Then compare the numerators.

Example

Use a common denominator to determine whether the ratios form a proportion.

PROBLEM 1 $\frac{5}{6}$ and $\frac{17}{18}$

SOLUTION A common denominator for $\frac{5}{6}$ and $\frac{17}{18}$ is 18.

Convert $\frac{5}{6}$ to a fraction with a denominator of 18:

$$\frac{5}{6} = \frac{5}{6} \cdot \frac{3}{3} = \frac{5 \cdot 3}{6 \cdot 3} = \frac{15}{18}$$

Compare the fractions: $\frac{15}{18} \neq \frac{17}{18}$

ANSWER The ratios $\frac{5}{6}$ and $\frac{17}{18}$ do not form a proportion.

PROBLEM 2 6 to 8 and 9 to 12

SOLUTION Write the ratios with a fraction bar: $\frac{6}{8}$ and $\frac{9}{12}$. The least common denominator (LCD) is 24.

Convert to ratios with denominators of 24 and then compare.

$$\frac{6}{8} = \frac{6}{8} \cdot \frac{3}{3} = \frac{6 \cdot 3}{8 \cdot 3} = \frac{18}{24} \qquad \frac{9}{12} = \frac{9}{12} \cdot \frac{2}{2} = \frac{9 \cdot 2}{12 \cdot 2} = \frac{18}{24}$$

$$\frac{18}{24} = \frac{18}{24}$$

ANSWER The ratios 6 to 8 and 9 to 12 form a proportion.

Think About It

Two ratios written as fractions form a proportion if they are equivalent fractions.

Tip

Check to see if one of the denominators is a multiple of the other. Then use that denominator as the common denominator.

TOPIC

➜ Using Division to Find Proportions

You also can write two ratios as decimals to tell if the ratios form a proportion. If the decimals are equal, the ratios form a proportion.

Example

Use division to determine whether the ratios form a proportion.

PROBLEM 3 $\frac{3}{4}$ and $\frac{6}{8}$

SOLUTION Write the ratios as decimal numbers by dividing the numerator by the denominator.

$$3 \div 4 = 0.75 \qquad 6 \div 8 = 0.75$$

$$0.75 = 0.75$$

ANSWER The ratios $\frac{3}{4}$ and $\frac{6}{8}$ form a proportion.

PROBLEM 4 $\frac{5}{6}$ and $\frac{9}{10}$

SOLUTION Write the ratios as decimal numbers by dividing the numerator by the denominator.

$$5 \div 6 = 0.8\overline{3} \qquad 9 \div 10 = 0.9$$

$$0.8\overline{3} \neq 0.9$$

ANSWER The ratios $\frac{5}{6}$ and $\frac{9}{10}$ do not form a proportion.

➜ Application: Baking

Example

PROBLEM 5 The table shows the amounts of sugar and flour in Rachel's and Miguel's muffin recipes. Do the ratios of sugar to flour in the recipes form a proportion?

Recipe	Sugar	Flour
Rachel	2 c	4 c
Miguel	3 c	6 c

SOLUTION Write the ratios. Then compare them.

Rachel's recipe: $2:4$ Miguel's recipe: $3:6$

$$\frac{2}{4} = \frac{2}{4} \cdot \frac{3}{3} = \frac{2 \cdot 3}{4 \cdot 3} = \frac{6}{12} \qquad \frac{3}{6} = \frac{3}{6} \cdot \frac{2}{2} = \frac{3 \cdot 2}{6 \cdot 2} = \frac{6}{12}$$

$$\frac{6}{12} = \frac{6}{12}$$

ANSWER The ratios of sugar to flour form a proportion.

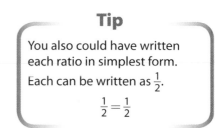

Tip

You also could have written each ratio in simplest form. Each can be written as $\frac{1}{2}$.

$$\frac{1}{2} = \frac{1}{2}$$

Problem Set

Use a common denominator to determine whether the ratios form a proportion.

1. **Stepping Stones** $\frac{2}{5}$ and $\frac{4}{10}$

    Common denominator: ☐

    Convert to the common denominator.

    $\frac{2}{5} = \frac{☐}{☐} = \frac{☐}{10}$

    Compare the fractions.

    $\frac{☐}{10}$ ☐ $\frac{4}{10}$

2. $\frac{1}{7}$ and $\frac{3}{14}$

3. 4 to 8 and 2 to 4

4. $6:9$ and $9:12$

5. $\frac{4}{10}$ and $\frac{3}{5}$

6. $\frac{3}{4}$ and $\frac{16}{20}$

7. 4 to 6 and 8 to 12

8. $3:8$ and $6:6$

9. $\frac{5}{7}$ and $\frac{25}{35}$

10. $5:15$ and $15:45$

11. $\frac{1}{8}$ and $\frac{3}{20}$

12. 16 to 18 and 90 to 140

13. $6:15$ and $30:80$

14. $\frac{63}{81}$ and $\frac{7}{9}$

15. 1 to 6 and 1 to 7

16. $5:9$ and $4:7$

17. $\frac{20}{24}$ and $\frac{20}{36}$

18. 12 to 15 and 84 to 105

19. **Challenge** $42:3$ and $28:2$

20. **Challenge** $\frac{22}{14}$ and $\frac{121}{88}$

Use division to determine whether the ratios form a proportion.

21. **Stepping Stones** $3:5$ and $5:8$

    $3 \div ☐ = 0.6$ $5 \div 8 = \boxed{}$

    Compare: 0.6 ☐ 0.625

22. $5:10$ and $7:14$

23. $\frac{2}{8}$ and $\frac{3}{10}$

24. 4 to 5 and 24 to 30

25. $4:7$ and $20:28$

26. $\frac{1}{4}$ and $\frac{6}{24}$

27. $12:20$ and $24:40$

28. 1 to 3 and 2 to 9

29. $\frac{5}{12}$ and $\frac{6}{24}$

30. $12:44$ and $3:11$

31. $\frac{5}{7}$ and $\frac{30}{42}$

32. 2 to 3 and 5 to 6

33. $75:125$ and $675:1125$

34. **Challenge** $\frac{112}{96}$ and $\frac{224}{192}$

Solve.

35. Stepping Stones The amounts of vanilla and salt in Shalin's cake recipe and in a bakery's recipe are shown in the table.

Recipe	Salt	Vanilla
Shalin	2 t	6 t
Bakery	14 c	42 c

Do the ratio of salt to vanilla in Shalin's recipe and the ratio of salt to vanilla in the bakery's recipe form a proportion?

The ratios are $\frac{2}{6}$ and $\frac{\square}{42}$.

Convert each ratio to use the same denominator:

$\frac{2}{6} = \frac{2}{6} \cdot \frac{7}{7} = \frac{\square}{42}$ $\frac{\square}{42}$

Compare the fractions:

$\frac{\square}{42} \, \square \, \frac{\square}{42}$

36. The amounts of pineapple juice and apple juice in Trent's and Carol's recipes are shown in the table.

Recipe	Pineapple	Apple
Trent	2 qt	7 qt
Carol	6 qt	21 qt

Do the ratio of pineapple juice to apple juice in Trent's recipe and the ratio of pineapple juice to apple juice in Carol's recipe form a proportion?

37. The numbers of red and blue marbles in Ronnie's collection and in Latasha's collection are shown in the table.

Marble	Red	Blue
Ronnie	7	10
Latasha	14	18

Do the ratio of red to blue marbles in Ronnie's collection and the ratio of red to blue marbles in Latasha's collection form a proportion?

38. The numbers of boys and girls in sports leagues in Centerville and West Village are shown in the table.

Town	Boys	Girls
Centerville	280	240
West Village	371	318

Do the ratio of boys to girls in Centerville and the ratio of boys to girls in West Village form a proportion?

39. Challenge Chris made two batches of bread dough. The table shows the cups and tablespoons of some ingredients in each batch.

Batch	Flour	Salt	Water
1	4 c	1 T	2 c
2	12 c	3 T	4 c

Do the ratios of the ingredients form a proportion?

40. Challenge Juan gave a cashier 3 quarters, 5 dimes, and 35 pennies to exchange for nickels. The cashier gave him 33 nickels. Did Juan get the correct number of nickels?

Choose the answer.

41. Which pair of ratios form a proportion?

A. $\frac{1}{5}$ and $\frac{2}{6}$ C. $\frac{5}{8}$ and $\frac{10}{16}$

B. $\frac{3}{4}$ and $\frac{8}{10}$ D. $\frac{7}{10}$ and $\frac{21}{40}$

42. Which pair of ratios form a proportion?

A. $2:8$ and $2:7$ C. $4:8$ and $20:30$

B. $3:5$ and $12:20$ D. $5:20$ and $4:6$

Solving Proportions

If you know that two ratios form a proportion, you can solve the proportion to find a missing number.

➔ Multiplying to Find Proportions

Definitions

In a proportion, the **extremes** are the first and last numbers or variables and the **means** are the second and third numbers or variables.

For the proportion $a : b = c : d$, a and d are the extremes and b and c are the means.

Means-Extremes Property

Two ratios form a proportion if the product of the means equals the product of the extremes.

$$\text{If } ad = bc, \text{ then } \frac{a}{b} = \frac{c}{d}.$$

Using the means-extremes property is often called cross multiplying. You can use this strategy to see if two ratios form a proportion. If the cross products are equal, then the ratios form a proportion.

Tip

Cross multiplying and *cross products* get their names because the multiplications "cross" each other.

$$\frac{a}{b} = \frac{c}{d} \ \rightarrow \ \frac{a}{b} \bowtie \frac{c}{d}$$

Example

State whether the ratios form a proportion.

PROBLEM 1 2 to 3 and 8 to 12

SOLUTION Apply the means-extremes property.

2 to 3 and 8 to 12

$2 \cdot 12 = 24$ $3 \cdot 8 = 24$

Compare the products: $24 = 24$

ANSWER The ratios 2 to 3 and 8 to 12 form a proportion.

PROBLEM 2 $\frac{4}{5}$ and $\frac{5}{7}$

SOLUTION Apply the means-extremes property.

$4 \cdot 7 = 28$ $5 \cdot 5 = 25$

Compare the products: $28 \neq 25$

ANSWER The ratios $\frac{4}{5}$ and $\frac{5}{7}$ do not form a proportion.

Solving Proportions

You can apply the means-extremes property to solve proportions with a missing term. Write an equation with a variable by multiplying the means and the extremes and setting the products equal. Then solve.

Example

Solve for the variable.

PROBLEM 3 $\frac{8}{6} = \frac{4}{x}$

SOLUTION Apply the means-extremes property.

$8 \cdot x = 6 \cdot 4$	Cross multiply.
$8x = 24$	Simplify.
$\frac{8x}{8} = \frac{24}{8}$	Divide by 8.
$x = 3$	Simplify.

ANSWER $x = 3$

PROBLEM 4 $\frac{3}{4} = \frac{n}{12}$

SOLUTION The variable is the numerator, so multiply both sides by that fraction's denominator, 12.

$\frac{3}{4} \cdot 12 = \frac{n}{12} \cdot 12$	Multiply.
$\frac{3 \cdot 12}{4} = n$	Simplify.
$9 = n$	

ANSWER $n = 9$

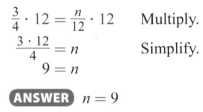

Think About It

If the variable is a numerator, you don't need to use the means-extremes property. Just multiply each side of the equation by the denominator of the fraction that contains the variable.

Application: Painting

Example

PROBLEM 5 Michelle can paint 6 fence sections in 3 hours. How long will it take Michelle to paint 10 fence sections?

SOLUTION Write and solve a proportion.

$\frac{10}{y} = \frac{6}{3}$	Let y represent the time it will take Michelle to paint 10 fence sections.
$10 \cdot 3 = y \cdot 6$	Cross multiply.
$30 = 6y$	Simplify.
$\frac{30}{6} = \frac{6y}{6}$	Divide by 6.
$5 = y$	Simplify.

ANSWER It will take Michelle 5 hours to paint 10 fence sections.

Problem Set

State whether the ratios form a proportion.

1. **Stepping Stones** 3 : 5 and 9 : 15

   The means are 5 and ☐. The extremes are 3 and ☐.

   Cross multiply.

   5 · ☐ = ☐   3 · ☐ = ☐

   Compare the cross products.

   ☐☐☐

   Do the ratios form a proportion? ☐

2. $\frac{1}{4}$ and $\frac{2}{5}$

3. 3 to 4 and 2 to 3

4. 3 : 4 and 6 : 8

5. $\frac{5}{6}$ and $\frac{10}{12}$

6. 4 to 7 and 16 to 28

7. $\frac{2}{6}$ and $\frac{8}{25}$

8. 7 : 9 and 21 : 27

9. $\frac{2}{3}$ and $\frac{6}{9}$

10. $\frac{2}{7}$ and $\frac{10}{35}$

11. 4 to 8 and 5 to 9

12. 10 : 12 and 15 : 18

13. $\frac{12}{15}$ and $\frac{15}{20}$

14. 14 : 28 and 10 : 21

15. 16 to 18 and 24 to 27

16. $\frac{25}{35}$ and $\frac{35}{45}$

17. 14 : 20 and 21 : 30

18. $\frac{12}{16}$ and $\frac{15}{18}$

19. 24 to 36 and 12 to 16

20. 14 : 24 and 28 : 48

21. **Challenge** $\frac{120}{320}$ and $\frac{360}{960}$

22. **Challenge** 124 : 256 and 248 : 502

Solve for the variable.

23. **Stepping Stones** $\frac{2}{y} = \frac{5}{25}$

    $2 \cdot \boxed{} = y \cdot 5$

    $\boxed{} = 5y$

    $\dfrac{\boxed{}}{5} = \dfrac{5y}{5}$

    $\boxed{} = y$

24. $\frac{x}{3} = \frac{8}{12}$

25. $\frac{z}{5} = \frac{6}{30}$

26. $\frac{a}{8} = \frac{2}{4}$

27. $\frac{1}{3} = \frac{7}{b}$

28. $\frac{3}{8} = \frac{6}{c}$

29. $\frac{3}{9} = \frac{p}{24}$

30. $\frac{q}{24} = \frac{12}{36}$

31. $\frac{15}{18} = \frac{40}{r}$

32. $\frac{16}{24} = \frac{x}{72}$

33. $\frac{16}{y} = \frac{32}{48}$

34. **Challenge** $\frac{14}{k} = \frac{6.25}{9}$

Solve.

35. **Stepping Stones** Raul surveys 120 people, asking about their favorite sports. His results show that 30% said basketball. How many people from Raul's survey said basketball is their favorite sport?

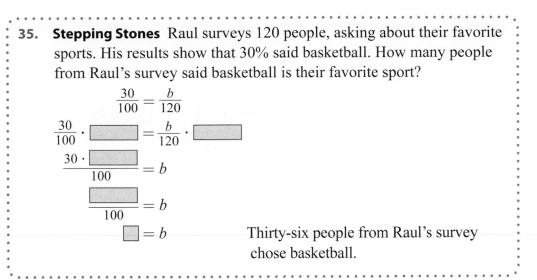

Thirty-six people from Raul's survey chose basketball.

36. The ratio of boys to girls in Megan's club is $\frac{2}{3}$. Anders's club has 12 girls in it and has the same ratio of boys to girls. How many boys are in Anders's club?

37. Usman has a recipe for oatmeal raisin muffins that calls for 3 cups of oats and 4 boxes of raisins. How many boxes of raisins will Usman need if he uses 9 cups of oats?

38. Jerome can read 22 pages of his book in 8 minutes. How many pages of his book can Jerome read in 40 minutes?

39. Rachel works at a company that makes mixed fruit juice. One recipe uses 24 gal of orange juice for every 17 gal of cranberry juice. How many gallons of orange juice are needed if 136 gal of cranberry juice are used?

40. **Challenge** Ricky mixed 5.5 kg of topsoil with every 0.75 kg of fertilizer in his vegetable garden. After he finished, Ricky had used 3.15 kg of fertilizer. How many kilograms of topsoil did Ricky use?

Choose the answer.

41. What pair of ratios form a proportion?

A. $1:4$ and $4:12$

B. $2:3$ and $6:8$

C. $4:5$ and $24:28$

D. $5:8$ and $15:24$

42. What is the value of x?

$$\frac{x}{5} = \frac{12}{15}$$

A. $x = 4$

B. $x = 15$

C. $x = 45$

D. $x = 60$

43. Kate ran a 5-kilometer race in 27 minutes. At the same speed, how far can Kate run in 40.5 minutes?

A. 2.5 km

B. 15 km

C. 7.5 km

D. 25 km

Reducing and Enlarging

When you reduce or enlarge a figure, the dimensions remain proportional.

➥ Finding the Scale Factor

Definition

Two figures are **similar** if they have the same shape, even if they aren't the same size.

Figures are similar when they are reduced or enlarged proportionally by a constant ratio.

Scale Factor

$$\text{scale factor} = \frac{\text{length of side of scaled image}}{\text{length of corresponding side of original figure}}$$

Think About It

A scale factor greater than 1 will give an image that is larger than the original figure.

A scale factor between 0 and 1 will give an image that is smaller than the original figure.

Example

PROBLEM 1 Find the scale factor for the similar figures.

SOLUTION Place the length of the scaled image over the length of the original figure in a ratio. Simplify.

$$\text{scale factor} = \frac{\text{length of side of scaled image}}{\text{length of corresponding side of original figure}} = \frac{1}{3}$$

ANSWER The scale factor is $\frac{1}{3}$.

CHECK The scaled image is smaller than the original figure, so the scale factor should be between 0 and 1.

$$0 < \frac{1}{3} < 1 \checkmark$$

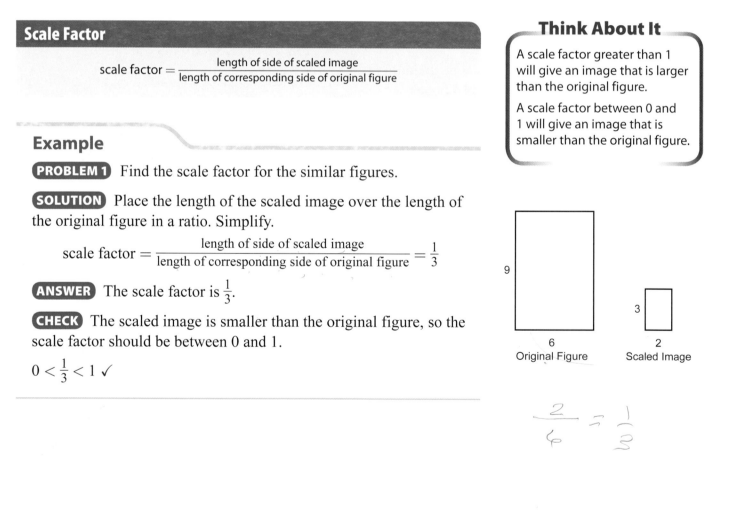

9

3

6
Original Figure

2
Scaled Image

$\frac{2}{6} = \frac{1}{3}$

TOPIC

➤ Solving Reduction and Enlargement Problems

The lengths of corresponding sides of similar figures have the same ratio, so they form a proportion.

Think About It

For similar figures, corresponding angle measures are always equal. Only side lengths change.

Example

PROBLEM 2 Use the scale factor to find the length of the scaled rectangle.

scale factor: 4
length of original rectangle = 12 in.
length of scaled image = ?

SOLUTION Multiply the scale factor by the side length of the figure.

$4 \cdot 12$ in. $= 48$ in.

ANSWER The length of the scaled image is 48 in.

PROBLEM 3 Triangles ABC and DEF are similar. Find the length of side $\overline{EF}$.

SOLUTION Let n stand for the length of side $\overline{EF}$.

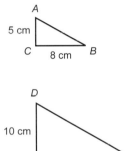

$\dfrac{5}{10} = \dfrac{8}{n}$	Write a proportion.
$5 \cdot n = 10 \cdot 8$	Cross multiply.
$5n = 80$	Simplify.
$\dfrac{5n}{5} = \dfrac{80}{5}$	Divide by 5.
$n = 16$	Simplify.

ANSWER The length of side $\overline{EF}$ is 16 cm.

➤ Application: A Map

Example

PROBLEM 4 On a map, 1 cm represents 8 mi. How many miles does 6 cm represent on the map when you use that scale?

SOLUTION Write a proportion using the map's scale.

$\dfrac{1}{8} = \dfrac{6}{n}$	Use n to represent the actual distance in miles.
$1 \cdot n = 8 \cdot 6$	Multiply.
$n = 48$	Simplify.

ANSWER On the map, 6 cm represents 48 mi.

Problem Set

Find the scale factor for the similar figures.

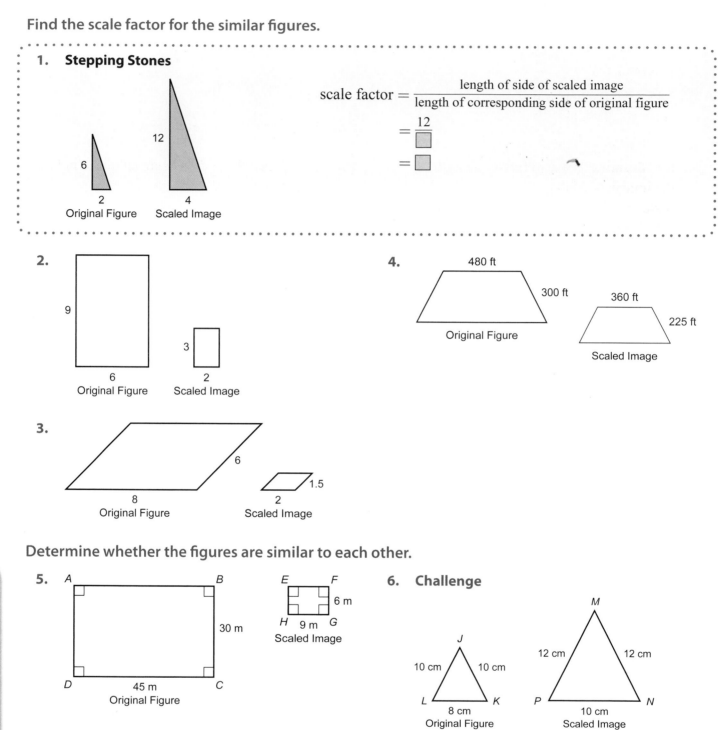

1. Stepping Stones

6   12

2   4

Original Figure   Scaled Image

$$\text{scale factor} = \frac{\text{length of side of scaled image}}{\text{length of corresponding side of original figure}}$$

$$= \frac{12}{\square}$$

$$= \square$$

2.

9

6
Original Figure

3

2
Scaled Image

4.

480 ft

300 ft

Original Figure

360 ft

225 ft

Scaled Image

3.

6

8
Original Figure

1.5

2
Scaled Image

Determine whether the figures are similar to each other.

5.

A   B

30 m

D   45 m   C
Original Figure

E   F

6 m

H 9 m G
Scaled Image

6. Challenge

J

10 cm   10 cm

L   K
   8 cm
Original Figure

M

12 cm   12 cm

P   N
   10 cm
Scaled Image

Use the scale factor to find the unknown side length.

7. **Stepping Stones** Use the scale factor to find the length of the image.

scale factor: 3

length of figure = 14 cm

length of image = ☐

3 · ☐ = ☐

8. Use the scale factor to find the length of the image.
scale factor: 8
length of figure = 10 yd
length of image = ☐

9. Rectangles *PQRS* and *TUVW* are similar. Find the length of side $\overline{UV}$.

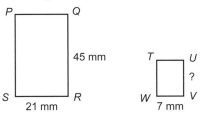

10. Triangles *ABC* and *DEF* are similar. Find the length of side $\overline{DE}$.

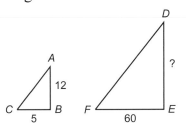

Solve.

11. **Stepping Stones** John sets a copy machine to a scale of $\frac{1}{2}$. By that scale, how many inches long will a copy be if the original is 8 in. long?

scale factor: ☐

☐ · 8 = ☐

12. On a map, 1 cm represents 30 km. Two cities on the map are 2.3 cm apart. How far apart are the actual cities?

13. A photographer enlarges a photo by using a scale of 5. If the length of the original photo is 7 in., what is the length of the enlarged photo?

14. Antoine is drawing a scale map of the park. He uses a scale of 1 cm = 15 paces. A pond is 75 paces from the front gate of the park. How far on the map will the pond be from the gate?

15. **Challenge** Dania uses a scale factor of $\frac{5}{4}$ to enlarge a diagram on her computer screen. If the original diagram is 10.6 cm long, how long is the enlarged diagram?

Choose the answer.

16. What is the scale factor for the similar figures?

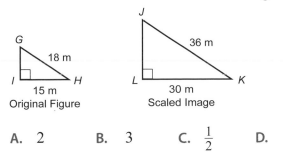

A. 2   B. 3   C. $\frac{1}{2}$ D. $\frac{1}{3}$

17. On a map, 1 in. represents 40 mi. How many miles does 4 in. represent on the map when you use that scale?

A. 4 mi   C. 44 mi

B. 40 mi   D. 160 mi

Chapter 6 Review

Choose the answer.

1. Laurie has 8 volleyballs and 6 soccer balls. What is the ratio of soccer balls to all the balls Laurie has?

   A. $\frac{3}{4}$ C. $\frac{4}{7}$

   B. $\frac{3}{7}$ D. $\frac{4}{3}$

2. What percent is equivalent to $\frac{9}{20}$?

   A. 9%   C. 45%

   B. 55%   D. 20%

3. 72 is 25% of what number?

   A. 35   C. 180

   B. 18   D. 288

4. A skateboard with a regular price of $49 is on sale for 15% off. What is the sale price?

   A. $41.65   C. $34.00

   B. $48.27   D. $47.50

5. Drake's lunch bill was $8.60 and he left a 15% tip. What was the total cost of Drake's lunch?

   A. $8.75   C. $9.89

   B. $10.10   D. $8.73

6. Ella opened a bank account and deposited $275. Her account paid her 4% annual interest. How much did she make in interest after leaving her money in the bank for 3 years?

   A. $11   C. $33

   B. $330   D. $308

7. Which pair of ratios form a proportion?

   A. $\frac{1}{3}$ and $\frac{3}{4}$ C. $\frac{4}{12}$ and $\frac{2}{3}$

   B. $\frac{3}{4}$ and $\frac{4}{12}$ D. $\frac{1}{3}$ and $\frac{4}{12}$

8. What is the value of x?

   $$\frac{7}{x} = \frac{3}{15}$$

   A. $x = 14$ C. $x = 28$

   B. $x = 35$ D. $x = 21$

9. What is the scale factor for the similar figures?

   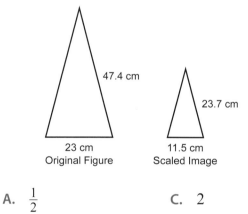

23 cm	11.5 cm
Original Figure	Scaled Image

   A. $\frac{1}{2}$ C. 2

   B. $\frac{1}{4}$ D. 4

10. On a model, 1 cm represents 8 m on a real boat. If the model is 6.5 cm long, how long is the real boat?

    A. 14.5 m   C. 29 m

    B. 26 m   D. 52 m

Write the ratio in three different formats: a to b, $a:b$, **and** $\frac{a}{b}$.

11. There are 8 girls and 12 boys at the playground. Write the ratio of girls to boys.

12. A recipe uses 3 cups of white flour and 2 cups of whole-wheat flour. Write the ratio of whole-wheat flour to total amount of flour.

Convert the fraction to a percent.

13. $\frac{7}{10}$

14. $\frac{23}{8}$

Find the percent of the number.

15. 15% of 48

16. 110% of 35

Find the sale price.

17. regular price = $82; discount rate = 20%

18. regular price = $320; discount rate = $\frac{1}{4}$

Find the total cost.

19. meal price = $52; tip = 20%

20. purchase price = $316; tax = 7%

Find the total amount owed if money is borrowed with simple interest.

21. principal = $500; annual rate = 5%; time = 3 years

22. principal = $1200; annual rate = 3.5%; time = 4 years

State whether the ratios form a proportion.

23. 4 : 5 and 5 : 6

24. 3 to 8 and 12 to 32

Solve for the variable.

25. $\frac{4}{24} = \frac{6}{p}$

26. $\frac{g}{12} = \frac{1}{3}$

Problem	Topic Lookup		Problem	Topic Lookup
1, 11–12	Ratios as Comparisons		6, 21–22	Simple Interest
2, 13–14	Percent		7, 23–24	Proportions
3, 15–16	Finding Percents of Numbers		8, 25–26	Solving Proportions
4, 17–18	Discount		9–10	Reducing and Enlarging
5, 19–20	Tax and Tip			

7 Angles and Circles

Does an artist need to know math? If the artist wants to work with stained glass, then math certainly would help. For centuries, artists have used angles, polygons, and circles to make beautiful stained glass.

In This Chapter

You will learn how to measure and classify angles. You'll also use circles to solve problems.

Chapter Topics

► Foundations for Chapter 7
► Angle Pairs
► Finding Angle Measures
► Regular Polygons
► Parts of a Circle
► Circumference
► Areas of Circles
► Cylinders
► Chapter 7 Review

CHAPTER 7

Stained-glass artwork is made up of polygons and circles.

CHAPTER 7   ANGLES AND CIRCLES   **231**

Foundations for Chapter 7

➜ Naming Lines, Rays, and Angles

Definitions

A **line** is a collection of points arranged in a straight path that extends without end in both directions.

A **ray** is a part of a line that begins from an endpoint and extends without end in one direction.

An **angle** is a figure formed by two rays, called *sides*, that share the same endpoint, called the **vertex**.

Naming Lines, Rays, and Angles

Name a line by using any two points on the line, or by using a lowercase letter that might appear near the line.

Name a ray by using two points. The first point must be the endpoint. The second point can be any other point on the ray.

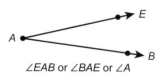

There are three ways to name an angle. You can use three points by naming a point on one side, the vertex, and then a point on the other side. You can use just the vertex point. Or you can use a label, such as a number or a lowercase letter that may be near the vertex, between the sides.

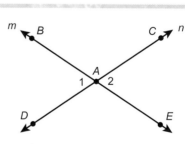

Example A

PROBLEM A-1 Name one line, one ray, and one angle.

SOLUTION

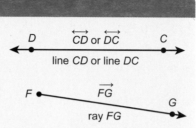

Name a line using any two points along it, such as $\overleftrightarrow{BE}$.
Name a ray using the endpoint and another point, such as $\overrightarrow{AC}$.
Name an angle using three points, such as $\angle BAC$.

ANSWER A line in the figure is $\overleftrightarrow{BE}$, a ray is $\overrightarrow{AC}$, and an angle is $\angle BAC$.

Problem Set A

Give another name for the part of the figure in Problem A-1.

1. $\angle 1$

2. line n

3. $\overrightarrow{EB}$

4. ray AD

5. $\angle CAE$

6. angle DAE

7. $\overrightarrow{BA}$

8. $\overleftrightarrow{DA}$

9. angle BAC

➤ Finding the Measure of an Angle

Using a Protractor

To use a protractor to find the measure of an angle,

1. Place the center hole on the straight edge of the protractor over the vertex of the angle.
2. Line up the zero on the straight edge of the protractor with one side of the angle.
3. Find where the other side of the angle intersects the curved edge of the protractor.
4. Read the angle measure from the correct scale on the protractor.

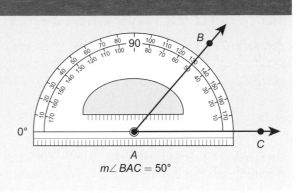

$m\angle BAC = 50°$

You can use a protractor to find the measure of an angle. Copy angles with sides too small to measure and extend their sides until they reach the curved edge of the protractor.

Example B

PROBLEM B-1 Find the measure of $\angle EDF$.

SOLUTION Ray DE intersects the protractor at 70°. Use the notation $m\angle$ to note the angle's measure. The m stands for "measure of."

ANSWER $m\angle EDF = 70°$

CHECK To make sure you used the correct scale, compare the angle to a right angle. The measure is less than a right angle's measure: $70 < 90$ ✓.

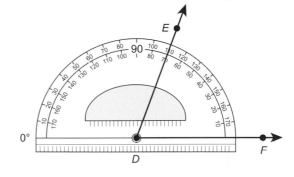

Problem Set B

Use a protractor to find the measure of the angle.

1.

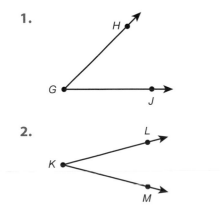

2.

3.

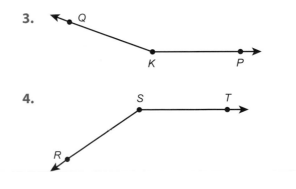

4.

➔ Classifying Angles

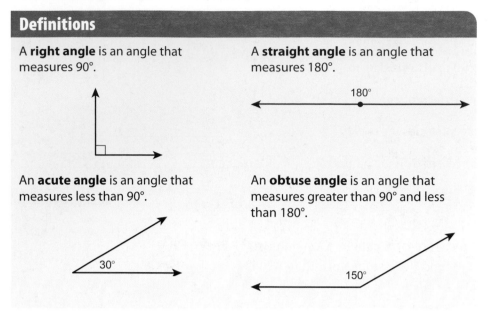

Definitions

A **right angle** is an angle that measures 90°.

A **straight angle** is an angle that measures 180°.

An **acute angle** is an angle that measures less than 90°.

An **obtuse angle** is an angle that measures greater than 90° and less than 180°.

You can compare an angle to the square corner of this page. A square corner represents an angle that measures 90°.

Example C

Classify the angle as *right*, *acute*, *obtuse*, or *straight*.

PROBLEM C-1

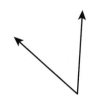

SOLUTION The angle is less than a square corner.

ANSWER The angle is *acute*.

PROBLEM C-2

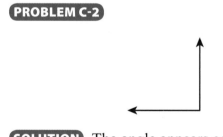

SOLUTION The angle appears equal to a square corner.

ANSWER The angle is *right*.

Problem Set C

Classify the angle as *right*, *acute*, *obtuse*, or *straight*.

Point *B* lies on $\overleftrightarrow{WA}$.

1. ∠*WBR*

2. ∠*RBA*

3. ∠*ABM*

4. ∠*MBW*

5. ∠*MBR*

6. ∠*WBA*

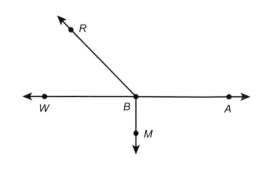

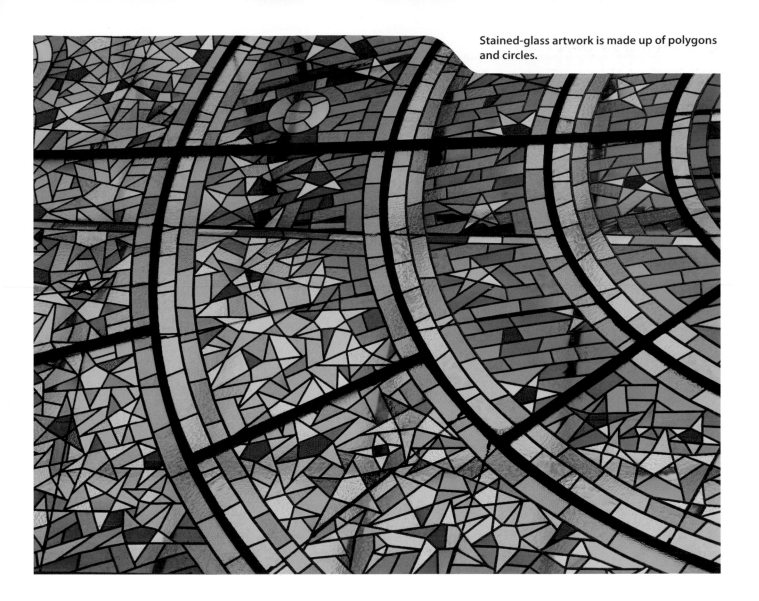

Stained-glass artwork is made up of polygons and circles.

Planting the Seed

Artists and mathematicians use angles to create and understand figures. Angles are measured in degrees.

Angle Pairs

Knowing the relationships between angles in certain pairs can help you solve problems about angles.

➔ Identifying Angle Pairs

Definitions

Adjacent angles are angles that lie in the same plane and have a common vertex and a common side, but have no interior points in common.

Vertical angles are nonadjacent angles formed by two intersecting lines.

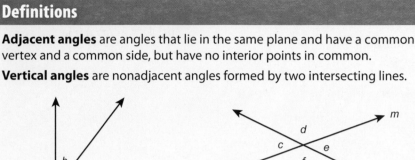

Adjacent angles
∠b and ∠a

Vertical angles
∠c and ∠e, ∠d and∠f

Use the definitions to identify special angle pairs.

Example

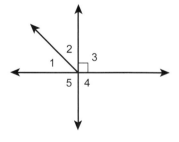

PROBLEM 1 Identify a pair of adjacent and a pair of vertical angles.

SOLUTION
These pairs are next to each other, or adjacent:
1 and 2   2 and 3   3 and 4   4 and 5   5 and 1
Angles 3 and 5 are nonadjacent and formed by intersecting lines.

ANSWER Angles 2 and 3 are adjacent angles; angles 3 and 5 are vertical angles.

➔ Identifying Complements and Supplements

Definitions

The measures of two **complementary angles** have a sum of 90°.
The measures of two **supplementary angles** have a sum of 180°.

Think About It

If two angles are complementary, both must be acute.

If two angles are supplementary, they cannot both be acute.

Example

PROBLEM 2 Identify one pair of complementary angles and two pairs of supplementary angles.

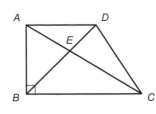

SOLUTION

∠ABE and ∠EBC together form a right angle.
∠AED and ∠DEC together form a straight angle.
∠AEB and ∠BEC together form a straight angle.

ANSWER ∠ABE and ∠EBC are complementary;
∠AED and ∠DEC, and ∠AEB and ∠BEC are supplementary.

Think About It

Intersecting lines form two pairs of vertical angles and at least four pairs of supplementary angles.

PROBLEM 3 Which angles are complementary?
$m\angle H = 35°$, $m\angle J = 145°$, and $m\angle K = 55°$

SOLUTION The measures of complementary angles have a sum of 90°.
$35° + 55° = 90°$

ANSWER ∠H and ∠K are complementary.

➔ Finding Unknown Angle Measures

Angle Sum Property

If point *D* is in the interior of ∠*ABC*, then
$$m\angle ABD + m\angle DBC = m\angle ABC.$$

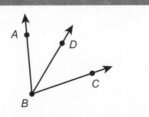

Remember

A *right angle* has a measure of 90°. A *straight angle* has a measure of 180°.

You can use the measures of adjacent angles to help find unknown angle measures.

Example

PROBLEM 4 If $m\angle BAC = 72°$, what is $m\angle DAC$?

SOLUTION Apply the angle sum property.

$m\angle BAD + m\angle DAC = m\angle BAC$
$50° + m\angle DAC = 72°$ Substitute the known values.
$50° + m\angle DAC - 50° = 72° - 50°$ Subtract 50° from both sides.
$m\angle DAC = 22°$ Simplify.

ANSWER $m\angle DAC = 22°$

Problem Set

Identify an angle adjacent to the given angle.

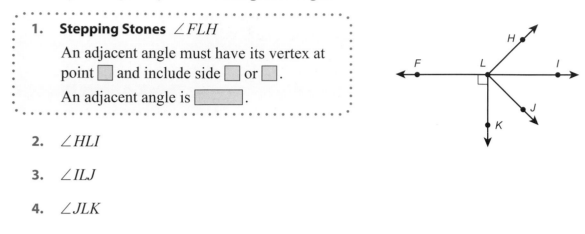

1. **Stepping Stones** ∠*FLH*

   An adjacent angle must have its vertex at point ☐ and include side ☐ or ☐.

   An adjacent angle is ▭.

2. ∠*HLI*

3. ∠*ILJ*

4. ∠*JLK*

State whether the angles are *complementary*, *supplementary*, or *neither*.

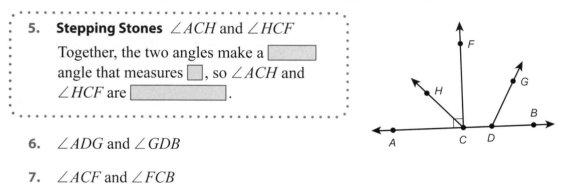

5. **Stepping Stones** ∠*ACH* and ∠*HCF*

   Together, the two angles make a ▭ angle that measures ☐, so ∠*ACH* and ∠*HCF* are ▭.

6. ∠*ADG* and ∠*GDB*

7. ∠*ACF* and ∠*FCB*

8. ∠*HCF* and ∠*FCB*

State whether the angles are *adjacent*, *a vertical pair*, or *neither*.

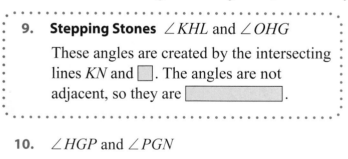
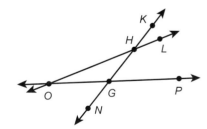

9. **Stepping Stones** ∠*KHL* and ∠*OHG*

   These angles are created by the intersecting lines *KN* and ☐. The angles are not adjacent, so they are ▭.

10. ∠*HGP* and ∠*PGN*

11. ∠*OGH* and ∠*KGP*

12. ∠*OGN* and ∠*HGP*

13. ∠*OGH* and ∠*PGN*

14. ∠*KHO* and ∠*NHO*

15. **Challenge** ∠*HOG* and ∠*LOP*

State whether the angles are *complementary*, *supplementary*, or *neither*.

16. **Stepping Stones** $m\angle P = 35°$ and $m\angle Q = 145°$

    $35° + 145° = $ ▢

    The angles are ▢ .

17. $m\angle C = 64°$ and $m\angle D = 36°$

18. $m\angle H = 108°$ and $m\angle K = 72°$

19. $m\angle X = 27°$ and $m\angle Y = 63°$

20. **Challenge** $m\angle A = 26.4°$ and $m\angle B = 63.6°$

Find the unknown angle measure.

21. **Stepping Stones** If $m\angle KHG = 75°$, find $m\angle FHG$.

    $m\angle KHG = m\angle KHF + m\angle FHG$

    $75° = $ ▢ $+ m\angle FHG$

    $m\angle FHG = $ ▢

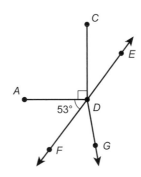

22. If $m\angle EKH = 102°$ and $m\angle FKH = 57°$, find $m\angle EKF$.

23. If $m\angle KFH = 78°$, find $m\angle EFH$.

24. **Challenge** If $m\angle FEK = 90°$, find the sum of the angles in quadrilateral $EFHK$. Show the angle measures you use.

Choose the answer. Point D is on $\overleftrightarrow{EF}$.

25. Which angle is supplementary to $\angle FDG$?

    A. $\angle CDE$ C. $\angle FDA$

    B. $\angle EDG$ D. $\angle GDC$

26. If $m\angle ADE = 127°$, what is the measure of $\angle CDE$?

    A. $37°$ C. $53°$

    B. $47°$ D. $127°$

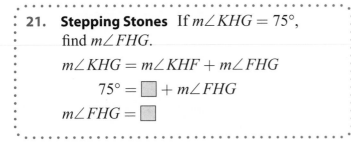

Finding Angle Measures

Finding unknown angle measures is like solving a puzzle. Use properties and known measures as clues.

➔ Using Complementary and Supplementary Angles

Use the properties of complementary and supplementary angles to find unknown angle measures.

Example

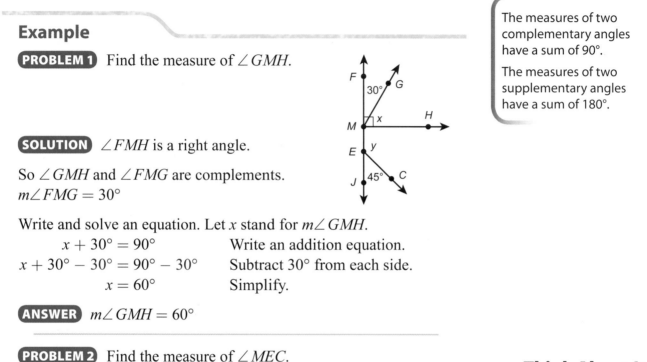

PROBLEM 1   Find the measure of $\angle GMH$.

SOLUTION $\angle FMH$ is a right angle.

So $\angle GMH$ and $\angle FMG$ are complements.
$m\angle FMG = 30°$

Write and solve an equation. Let x stand for $m\angle GMH$.

$$x + 30° = 90°$$ Write an addition equation.
$$x + 30° - 30° = 90° - 30°$$ Subtract 30° from each side.
$$x = 60°$$ Simplify.

ANSWER $m\angle GMH = 60°$

PROBLEM 2   Find the measure of $\angle MEC$.

SOLUTION $\angle JEM$ is a straight angle.

So $\angle MEC$ and $\angle JEC$ are supplements.
$m\angle JEC = 45°$

Write and solve an equation. Let y stand for $m\angle MEC$.

$$y + 45° = 180°$$ Write an addition equation.
$$y + 45° - 45° = 180° - 45°$$ Subtract 45° from each side.
$$y = 135°$$ Simplify.

ANSWER $m\angle MEC = 135°$

TOPIC

➔ Using Angle Sum Properties

You can use an angle sum property to write an equation to find an unknown angle measure in a triangle or quadrilateral.

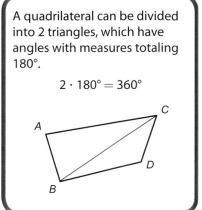

Think About It

A quadrilateral can be divided into 2 triangles, which have angles with measures totaling 180°.

$$2 \cdot 180° = 360°$$

Example

PROBLEM 3 Find the measure of $\angle AEB$.

SOLUTION $\angle AEB$ is one angle in $\triangle ABE$.
$m\angle BAE = 118°$; $m\angle ABE = 22°$

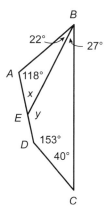

Write and solve an equation. Let x stand for $m\angle AEB$.

$x + 118° + 22° = 180°$	Write an addition equation.
$x + 140° = 180°$	Add.
$x + 140° - 140° - 180° - 140°$	Subtract 140° from each side.
$x = 40°$	Simplify.

ANSWER $m\angle AEB = 40°$

PROBLEM 4 Find the measure of $\angle DEB$.

SOLUTION $\angle DEB$ is one angle in quadrilateral $BCDE$.
$m\angle EBC = 27°$; $m\angle BCD = 40°$; $m\angle CDE = 153°$

Write and solve an equation. Let y stand for $m\angle DEB$.

$y + 27° + 40° + 153° = 360°$	Write an addition equation.
$y + 220° = 360°$	Add.
$y + 220° - 220° = 360° - 220°$	Subtract 220° from each side.
$y = 140°$	Simplify.

ANSWER $m\angle DEB = 140°$

Tip

In Problems 3 and 4, angles x and y are supplementary.

You can check your answers to Problems 3 and 4 by seeing if the sum of the measures is 180°.

$40° + 118° + 22° = 180°$ ✓

$140° + 27° + 40° + 153° = 360°$ ✓

TOPIC

Problem Set

Find the measure of the angle.

1. **Stepping Stones** Angles A and B are supplementary.

   $m\angle A = 24°$

   $m\angle B = \square$

   The sum of the measures of angles A and B must be $\square$.

   $$24° + m\angle B = 180°$$
   $$24° - 24° + m\angle B = 180° - \square$$
   $$m\angle B = \square$$

2. Angles P and Q are complementary.

   $m\angle Q = 12°$

   $m\angle P = \square$

3. **Challenge**

   Angles M and N are supplementary.
   Angles M and N are congruent.

   $m\angle M = \square$

Find the measures of the angles.

4. A. $m\angle x$

   B. $m\angle y$

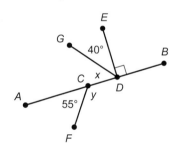

5. A. $m\angle ACD$

   B. $m\angle CED$

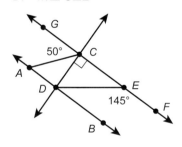

6. A. $m\angle ADE$

   B. $m\angle DEC$

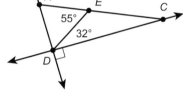

7. **Challenge**

   A. $m\angle KTG$

   B. $m\angle KTJ$

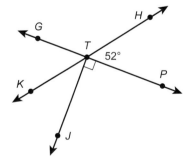

Use an angle sum property to write an equation and solve.

8. **Stepping Stones** Find $m\angle B$.

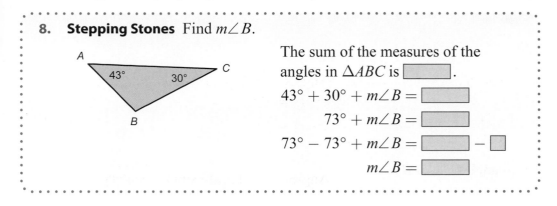

The sum of the measures of the angles in $\triangle ABC$ is $\boxed{}$.

$$43° + 30° + m\angle B = \boxed{}$$
$$73° + m\angle B = \boxed{}$$
$$73° - 73° + m\angle B = \boxed{} - \boxed{}$$
$$m\angle B = \boxed{}$$

9. Two angles of a quadrilateral measure 40° and 110°. The third angle is a right angle. What is the measure of the fourth angle?

10. Two angles in a triangle measure 45° and 60°. What is the measure of the third angle?

11. Angles A and B are congruent.

Find $m\angle D$.

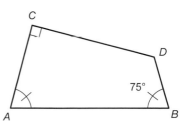

12. A. Find $m\angle x$.
    B. Find $m\angle y$.

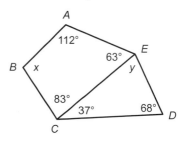

13. A. Find $m\angle x$.
    B. Find $m\angle y$.

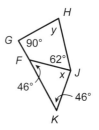

14. Two angles of a quadrilateral measure 60° each. The third angle measures 100°. What is the measure of the fourth angle?

15. **Challenge** The smallest angle in a quadrilateral measures 10°, the largest angle measures 100°, and the other two angles are congruent. List the measures of all the angles.

Choose the answer.

16. Two angles of a triangle measure 30° and 50°. What is the measure of the third angle of the triangle?
    A. 30° C. 100°
    B. 60° D. 160°

17. A quadrilateral has two right angles. The measure of the third angle is 47°. What is the measure of the fourth angle of the quadrilateral?
    A. 133° C. 137°
    B. 43° D. 47°

Regular Polygons

Regular polygons have special properties that help you find their perimeters and side lengths.

➨ Identifying Regular Polygons

Definitions

A **polygon** is a closed figure formed by three or more straight sides in a plane. Each side intersects two other sides only at their endpoints.

In a **regular polygon**, all the sides are congruent and all the angles are congruent.

Think About It

You can't always determine whether a polygon is regular just by the way it looks.

You need to base that decision on what you are told about the polygon or the way its sides and angles are marked.

Example

State whether the polygon is regular. Explain your answer.

PROBLEM 1

SOLUTION The sides are not all the same length.

ANSWER The polygon is not regular because the sides and angles are not congruent.

PROBLEM 2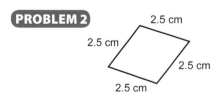
2.5 cm
2.5 cm
2.5 cm
2.5 cm

SOLUTION The sides are all the same length.
The angle measures are not shown to be equal.

ANSWER The polygon is not regular because the angles are not known to be equal.

PROBLEM 3

SOLUTION The sides are all the same length.
The angles all have the same measure.

ANSWER The polygon is regular because the sides and angles are congruent.

PROBLEM 4 square with a side length of 7 cm

SOLUTION Squares have sides that are all the same length. Squares have all right angles.

ANSWER Every square is a regular polygon because its sides and angles are congruent.

Remember

Matching tick marks on a polygon's sides indicate that those sides are congruent.

Matching tick marks in a polygon's angles indicate that those angles are congruent.

TOPIC

➡ Finding Perimeters of Regular Polygons

Perimeter of a Regular Polygon

The perimeter P of a regular polygon with n sides, each with length s, is

$$P = sn.$$

Use the formula to find the perimeter of any regular polygon.

Remember

Polygons can be named by their numbers of sides.

A *pentagon* has 5 sides.

A *hexagon* has 6 sides.

An *octagon* has 8 sides.

Example

Find the perimeter of the regular polygon.

PROBLEM 5

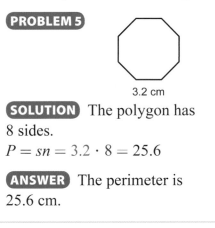

3.2 cm

SOLUTION The polygon has 8 sides.

$P = sn = 3.2 \cdot 8 = 25.6$

ANSWER The perimeter is 25.6 cm.

PROBLEM 6 6 sides; $s = 20$ ft

SOLUTION

$P = sn = 20 \cdot 6 = 120$

ANSWER The perimeter is 120 ft.

Think About It

The angles and side lengths are not marked on the octagon in Problem 5, but you are told that it is a regular polygon.

➡ Finding Side Lengths of Regular Polygons

If you know the perimeter and number of sides, you can use the perimeter formula to find the side length of a regular polygon. Substitute the perimeter and number of sides into the equation and solve for the side length.

Example

PROBLEM 7 A regular pentagon has a perimeter of 45 cm. How long is each side of the pentagon?

SOLUTION A pentagon has 5 sides.

$P = sn$	
$45 = s \cdot 5$	Substitute 45 for P and 5 for n.
$\dfrac{45}{5} = \dfrac{5s}{5}$	Divide both sides by 5.
$9 = s$	Simplify.

ANSWER Each side of the pentagon is 9 cm long.

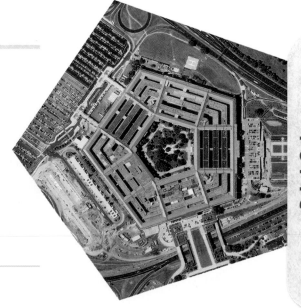

TOPIC

Problem Set

State whether the polygon is regular. Explain your answer.

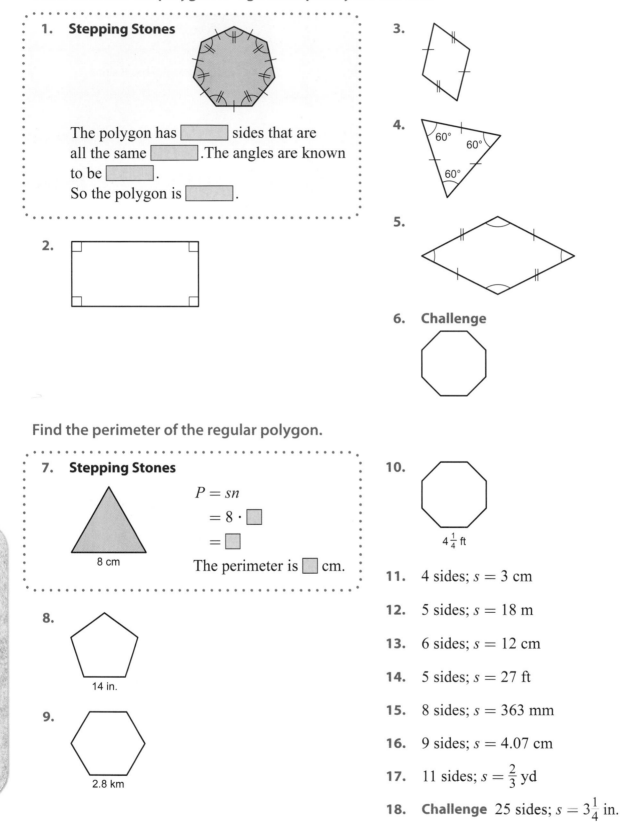

1. Stepping Stones

The polygon has [____] sides that are all the same [____]. The angles are known to be [____].
So the polygon is [____].

2.

3.

4.

5.

6. Challenge

Find the perimeter of the regular polygon.

7. Stepping Stones

8 cm

$P = sn$

$= 8 \cdot \square$

$= \square$

The perimeter is $\square$ cm.

8.

14 in.

9.

2.8 km

10.

$4\frac{1}{4}$ ft

11. 4 sides; $s = 3$ cm

12. 5 sides; $s = 18$ m

13. 6 sides; $s = 12$ cm

14. 5 sides; $s = 27$ ft

15. 8 sides; $s = 363$ mm

16. 9 sides; $s = 4.07$ cm

17. 11 sides; $s = \frac{2}{3}$ yd

18. Challenge 25 sides; $s = 3\frac{1}{4}$ in.

Find the side length of the regular polygon.

19. **Stepping Stones** $P = 24$ cm

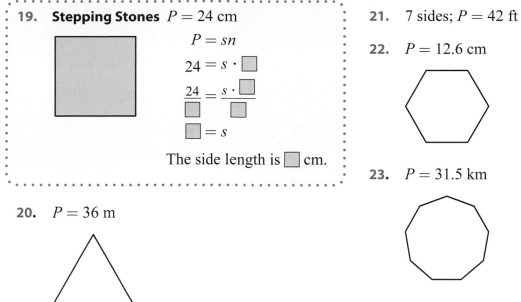

$P = sn$

$24 = s \cdot \boxed{}$

$\dfrac{24}{\boxed{}} = \dfrac{s \cdot \boxed{}}{\boxed{}}$

$\boxed{} = s$

The side length is $\boxed{}$ cm.

20. $P = 36$ m

21. 7 sides; $P = 42$ ft

22. $P = 12.6$ cm

23. $P = 31.5$ km

24. **Challenge** 8 sides; $P = 12\frac{2}{3}$ yd

Choose the answer.

25. A quilt is shaped like a regular octagon with sides 24 in. long. How much ribbon is needed to trim the outside edge of this quilt?

A. 3 in.　　　　C. 144 in.

B. 4 in.　　　　D. 192 in.

26. What is the perimeter of this regular pentagon?

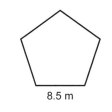

8.5 m

A. 1.7 m　　　　C. 42.5 m

B. 8.5 m　　　　D. 51 m

Parts of a Circle

Knowing the parts of a circle and how they are related
can help you solve problems about circles.

➔ Identifying Parts of a Circle

Definitions

A **circle** is the set of all points in a plane that are the same distance from a given
point in the plane, called the *center*.

A **chord** is a line segment that connects any two points on a circle.

A **radius** of a circle is a segment that connects the center of a circle to a point on
the circle; the length of that segment is also called the radius.

A **diameter** of a circle is a chord that contains the center of the circle; the length
of this chord is also called the diameter.

> **Tip**
> The plural form of *radius* is *radii*.

You can use the definitions to identify parts of a circle.

Example

PROBLEM 1 Name all the chords, radii, and diameters of the circle
with center at O.

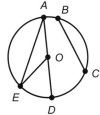

SOLUTION Identify the segments that

- Connect two points on the circle: $\overline{AE}$, $\overline{AD}$, and $\overline{BC}$.
- Connect the center to a point on the circle: $\overline{OA}$, $\overline{OD}$, and $\overline{OE}$.

Then identify the chord that contains the center of the circle: $\overline{AD}$.

ANSWER The chords are $\overline{AE}$, $\overline{AD}$, and $\overline{BC}$; the radii are $\overline{OA}$, $\overline{OD}$,
and $\overline{OE}$; and the diameter is $\overline{AD}$.

TOPIC

➔ Relating Diameter and Radius

Tip

The words *radius* and *diameter* each can be used to mean either the line segment or the length of that segment.

Use the context of the problem to know which meaning is intended.

Diameter and Radius

For any circle with diameter d and radius r,

$$d = 2r \text{ and } r = \frac{d}{2}.$$

A circle's diameter is always twice its radius. Use that relationship to find one measure if you know the other.

Example

Find whichever is missing, the diameter d or radius r of the circle.

PROBLEM 2

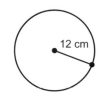
12 cm

SOLUTION You know the radius, so use the formula.

$d = 2r = 2 \cdot 12 = 24$

ANSWER The diameter is 24 cm.

PROBLEM 3 $d = 30$ m

SOLUTION You know the diameter, so use the formula.

$r = \frac{d}{2} = \frac{30}{2} = 15$

ANSWER The radius is 15 m.

➔ Application: Distance

Example

PROBLEM 4 What is the longest distance across a circular swimming pool that has a radius of 26 ft?

SOLUTION The longest distance across a circle is its diameter. Use the formula.

$d = 2r = 2 \cdot 26 = 52$

ANSWER The longest distance across the swimming pool is 52 ft.

TOPIC

Problem Set

Name all the chords, radii, and diameters of the circle.

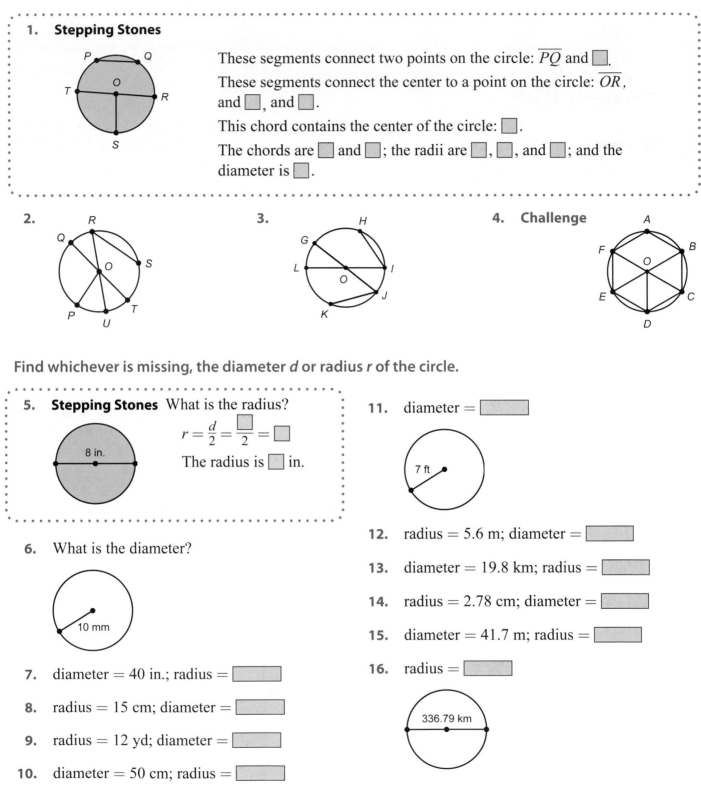

1. **Stepping Stones**

   These segments connect two points on the circle: $\overline{PQ}$ and ☐.

   These segments connect the center to a point on the circle: $\overline{OR}$, and ☐, and ☐.

   This chord contains the center of the circle: ☐.

   The chords are ☐ and ☐; the radii are ☐, ☐, and ☐; and the diameter is ☐.

2.

3.

4. **Challenge**

Find whichever is missing, the diameter _d_ or radius _r_ of the circle.

5. **Stepping Stones** What is the radius?

   8 in.

   $$r = \frac{d}{2} = \frac{\boxed{}}{2} = \boxed{}$$

   The radius is ☐ in.

6. What is the diameter?

   10 mm

7. diameter = 40 in.; radius = ☐

8. radius = 15 cm; diameter = ☐

9. radius = 12 yd; diameter = ☐

10. diameter = 50 cm; radius = ☐

11. diameter = ☐

    7 ft

12. radius = 5.6 m; diameter = ☐

13. diameter = 19.8 km; radius = ☐

14. radius = 2.78 cm; diameter = ☐

15. diameter = 41.7 m; radius = ☐

16. radius = ☐

    336.79 km

Solve.

17. Stepping Stones A circular fountain has a diameter of 20 m. What is the shortest distance from the center of the fountain to its edge?

$$r = \frac{d}{2} = \frac{\boxed{}}{2} = \boxed{}$$

The distance is $\boxed{}$ m.

18. The circular courtyard at a botanical garden has a radius of 16 yd. What is the longest distance across the courtyard?

19. The diameter of the center circle of a basketball court is 12 ft. What is the distance from the center of the circle to its edge?

20. The diameter of a pond is 42.7 m. Ashley was at the center of the pond and swam directly to its edge. How far did Ashley swim?

21. **Challenge** A dog's leash is tied to a stake in a park. The length of the leash is 2.7 m. What is the longest distance the dog can walk in a straight line?

Choose the answer.

22. Which segment is a radius of the circle?

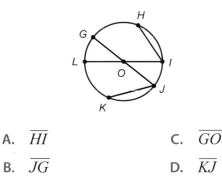

A. $\overline{HI}$ C. $\overline{GO}$

B. $\overline{JG}$ D. $\overline{KJ}$

23. A circle has a radius of 18 m. What is the diameter of the circle?

A. 36 m   C. 9 m

B. 18 m   D. 3 m

Circumference

The distance around a circle is related to its diameter and radius.

➔ Finding Circumference

Definitions

Circumference is the distance around a circle.

The number π, the Greek letter pi, is the ratio of the circumference of any circle to its diameter.

Circumference

The circumference of a circle with diameter d and radius r is
$$C = \pi d \text{ and } C = 2\pi r.$$

You can use a formula and the number π to find the circumference of a circle with a given diameter or radius. The numbers 3.14 and $\frac{22}{7}$ are common estimates of π.

Example

Find the exact circumference. Then find an estimate.

PROBLEM 1

SOLUTION Leave the answer in terms of π to find an exact answer.
$$C = \pi d$$
$$= \pi \cdot 16$$
$$= 16 \cdot \pi = 16\pi$$

16 ft

Substitute 3.14 for π to find an estimate.
$$C \approx 16 \cdot 3.14$$
$$\approx 50.2$$

ANSWER The circumference is exactly 16π ft, or about 50.2 ft.

Think About It

Written as a decimal, the number π never repeats and never ends.

Tip

To give an exact answer for circumference, leave the symbol π in the answer because it represents the exact value.

Think About It

Because you are using an approximation of π with 3 digits, your estimated circumference should be rounded to include at most 3 significant digits.

TOPIC

Example

Find the exact circumference. Then find an estimate.

PROBLEM 2 $r = 3.5$ cm

SOLUTION Leave the answer in terms of π to find an exact answer.

$$C = 2\pi r$$
$$= 2 \cdot \pi \cdot 3.5$$
$$= 2 \cdot 3.5 \cdot \pi = 7\pi$$

Substitute $\frac{22}{7}$ for π to find an estimate.

$$C \approx 7 \cdot \frac{22}{7}$$
$$\approx 22$$

ANSWER The circumference is exactly 7π cm, or about 22 cm.

PROBLEM 3 What is the circumference of a bicycle wheel with a diameter of 29 in.?

SOLUTION Because the diameter is given, use $C = \pi d$.
Use 3.14 for π.
$$C = \pi d = \pi \cdot 29 \approx 3.14 \cdot 29 \approx 91.1$$

ANSWER The circumference is exactly 29π, or about 91.1 in.

➡ Finding Diameter or Radius Given Circumference

Example

PROBLEM 4 Find the diameter of a circle with a circumference of 18π meters.

SOLUTION Use $C = \pi d$, and solve for d.

$18\pi = \pi d$	Replace C with 18π.
$\dfrac{18 \cdot \pi}{\pi} = \dfrac{\pi \cdot d}{\pi}$	Divide both sides by π.
$18 = d$	Simplify.

ANSWER The diameter is 18 m.

> **Tip**
> Look at the number that you will be multiplying by π when you are estimating a circumference.
>
> Think about which estimate, 3.14 or $\frac{22}{7}$, will be easier to multiply.

TOPIC

Problem Set

Find the exact circumference.

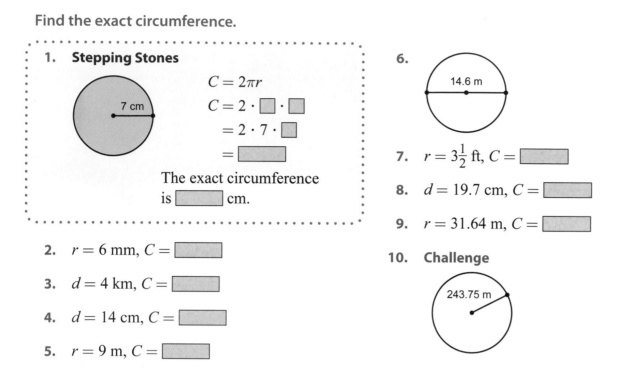

1. **Stepping Stones**

$C = 2\pi r$

$C = 2 \cdot \boxed{} \cdot \boxed{}$

$= 2 \cdot 7 \cdot \boxed{}$

$= \boxed{}$

The exact circumference is $\boxed{}$ cm.

7 cm

2. $r = 6$ mm, $C = \boxed{}$

3. $d = 4$ km, $C = \boxed{}$

4. $d = 14$ cm, $C = \boxed{}$

5. $r = 9$ m, $C = \boxed{}$

6.

14.6 m

7. $r = 3\frac{1}{2}$ ft, $C = \boxed{}$

8. $d = 19.7$ cm, $C = \boxed{}$

9. $r = 31.64$ m, $C = \boxed{}$

10. **Challenge**

243.75 m

Estimate the circumference. Use 3.14 or $\frac{22}{7}$ to approximate π.

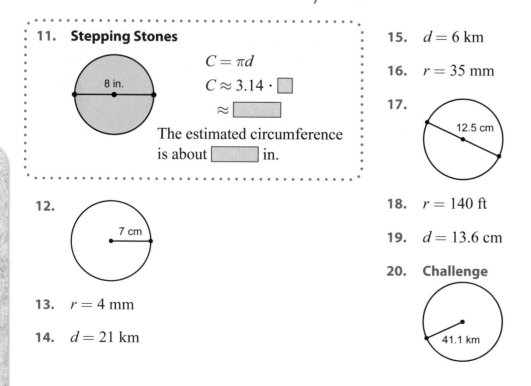

11. **Stepping Stones**

$C = \pi d$

$C \approx 3.14 \cdot \boxed{}$

$\approx \boxed{}$

The estimated circumference is about $\boxed{}$ in.

8 in.

12.

7 cm

13. $r = 4$ mm

14. $d = 21$ km

15. $d = 6$ km

16. $r = 35$ mm

17.

12.5 cm

18. $r = 140$ ft

19. $d = 13.6$ cm

20. **Challenge**

41.1 km

Find the diameter and radius of a circle with the given circumference.

21. **Stepping Stones** $C = 8\pi$ m

$$C = \pi d$$

$$\boxed{} = \pi d$$

$$\frac{\boxed{}}{\pi} = \frac{\pi \cdot d}{\pi}$$

$$\boxed{} = d$$

The diameter is $\boxed{}$ m. Next, find the radius.

$$r = \frac{d}{2}$$

$$= \frac{\boxed{}}{2}$$

$$= \boxed{}$$

The radius is $\boxed{}$ m.

22. $C = 20\pi$ m

23. $C = 36\pi$ cm

24. $C = 14\pi$ mm

25. $C = 35$ yd

26. $C = 31.4$ ft

27. $C = 18.84$ km

28. **Challenge** $C = 144.44$ cm

Solve.

29. What is the circumference of a fountain with a diameter of 9 m?

30. A plate has a diameter of 14 cm. What is the plate's circumference?

31. What is the circumference of a wheel with a radius of 16 inches?

32. What is the circumference of a circular courtyard that is 42 ft in diameter?

33. What is the circumference of a roundabout with a radius of 15 m?

34. **Challenge** A dog is on a leash that is 6 ft long. What is the circumference of the largest circle the dog can make on the leash?

Choose the answer.

35. What is the exact circumference?

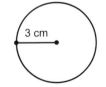
3 cm

A. 3π cm

B. 6π cm

C. 9.42 cm

D. 18.84 cm

36. What is the radius of a circle with a circumference of 24π m?

A. 48 m

C. 12 m

B. 24 m

D. 6 m

Areas of Circles

The area of a circle, like its circumference, is related to its radius and the number π.

➡ Finding Areas of Circles

Area of a Circle

The area of a circle with radius r is

$$A = \pi r^2.$$

You can use the formula and the number π to find the area of a circle with a given diameter or radius.

Think About It

To give an exact answer for the area of a circle, leave the symbol π in the answer since it represents the exact value of pi.

Example

Find the exact area. Then find an estimate.

PROBLEM 1 $r = 4$ cm

SOLUTION Leave the answer in terms of π to find an exact answer.
$A = \pi r^2 = \pi \cdot 4^2 = \pi \cdot 16 = 16\pi$

4 cm

Substitute 3.14 for π to find an estimate.
$A \approx 16 \cdot 3.14 \approx 50.2$

ANSWER The area is exactly 16π cm^2, or about 50.2 cm^2.

Tip

Look at the number that you will be multiplying by π when you are estimating a circumference.

Think about which estimate, 3.14 or $\frac{22}{7}$, will be easier to multiply.

PROBLEM 2 $d = 14$ in.

SOLUTION First find the radius to use in the formula.

$r = \dfrac{d}{2} = \dfrac{14}{2} = 7$

$A = \pi r^2 = \pi \cdot 7^2 = \pi \cdot 49 = 49\pi$

Substitute $\frac{22}{7}$ for π to find an estimate.

$A \approx 49 \cdot \dfrac{22}{7} \approx 154$

ANSWER The area is exactly 49π in^2, or about 154 in^2.

Remember

The diameter of a circle is twice the radius. The radius of a circle is half the diameter.

$$d = 2r$$
$$r = \frac{d}{2}$$

TOPIC

Example

PROBLEM 3 What is the area of a circular bull's eye with a diameter of 10 cm?

SOLUTION Leave the answer in terms of π to find an exact answer.
$$A = \pi r^2$$
$$= \pi \cdot 5^2$$
$$= \pi \cdot 25$$
$$= 25\pi$$

Substitute 3.14 for π to find an estimate.
$$A \approx 25 \cdot 3.14$$
$$\approx 78.5$$

ANSWER The area is exactly 25π cm², or about 78.5 cm².

→ Finding Areas of Parts of Circles

You can find the area of part of a circle by first finding the area of a full circle with the same radius. Then divide to find the area of the part.

Example

PROBLEM 4 Find the area of a semicircle with a radius of 10 cm.

10 cm

SOLUTION Find $\frac{1}{2}$ the area of a circle with a radius of 10 cm.
$$A = \pi r^2$$
$$= \pi \cdot 10^2$$
$$= \pi \cdot 100$$
$$= 100\pi$$

Divide the area by 2.
$$100\pi \div 2 = 50\pi$$

ANSWER The area is exactly 50π cm².

> **Tip**
>
> The prefix *semi–* means "half."
> A semicircle is half of a circle.

TOPIC

Problem Set

Find the exact area of the circle with the given radius or diameter.

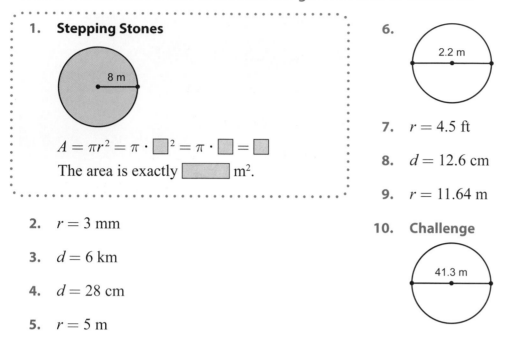

1. **Stepping Stones**

   8 m

   $A = \pi r^2 = \pi \cdot \boxed{}^2 = \pi \cdot \boxed{} = \boxed{}$

   The area is exactly $\boxed{}$ m².

2. $r = 3$ mm

3. $d = 6$ km

4. $d = 28$ cm

5. $r = 5$ m

6.

   2.2 m

7. $r = 4.5$ ft

8. $d = 12.6$ cm

9. $r = 11.64$ m

10. **Challenge**

    41.3 m

Approximate the area of the circle with the given radius or diameter. Use 3.14 or $\frac{22}{7}$ to approximate π.

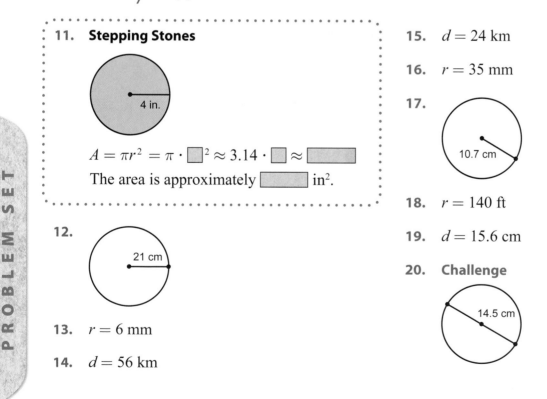

11. **Stepping Stones**

    4 in.

    $A = \pi r^2 = \pi \cdot \boxed{}^2 \approx 3.14 \cdot \boxed{} \approx \boxed{}$

    The area is approximately $\boxed{}$ in².

12.

    21 cm

13. $r = 6$ mm

14. $d = 56$ km

15. $d = 24$ km

16. $r = 35$ mm

17.

    10.7 cm

18. $r = 140$ ft

19. $d = 15.6$ cm

20. **Challenge**

    14.5 cm

Find the area of the figure with the given radius or diameter. Leave the answer in terms of π to find an exact answer.

21. **Stepping Stones** semicircle; $r = 6$ m

    Find the area of a circle with radius 6 m.
    $$A = \pi r^2$$
    $$= \pi \cdot \boxed{}^2$$
    $$= \boxed{}\pi$$

    The semicircle has half the area of the full circle.
    $$36\pi \div \boxed{} = \boxed{}$$
    The area is exactly $\boxed{}$ m².

22. semicircle; $d = 10$ m

23. quarter circle; $r = 2$ cm

24. quarter circle; $d = 7$ mm

25. semicircle; $r = 6$ yd

26. semicircle; $d = 3$ ft

27. quarter circle; $r = 0.8$ km

28. **Challenge** quarter circle; $r = 0.25$ m

Solve.

29. What is the area of a circular pool cover with a radius of 16 ft?

30. What is the area of a pizza with a radius of 40 cm?

31. What is the area of a fountain with a diameter of 11 m?

32. What is the area of a game board with a radius of 16.7 cm?

33. Antoine has raked half of a circular courtyard that has a diameter of 32 m. How much area has Antoine raked?

34. One-quarter of a dartboard is red. If the dartboard has a diameter of 12 in., what is the area of the red part?

Choose the answer.

35. What is the exact area of the circle?

    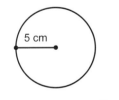

    A. 5π cm² C. 15π cm²

    B. 10π cm² D. 25π cm²

36. Which expression can be used to find the area of a circle with a diameter of 30 cm?

    A. $\pi \cdot 30^2$ C. $\pi \cdot 15^2$

    B. $\pi \cdot 30$ D. $2 \cdot \pi \cdot 15$

Cylinders

You can find the volume of a cylinder in the same way as you find the volume of any prism.

➜ Finding the Volume of a Cylinder

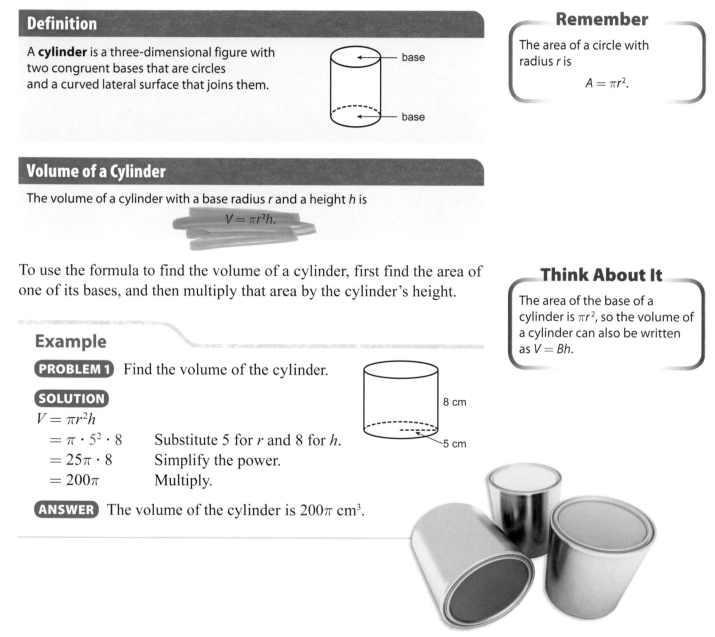

Definition

A **cylinder** is a three-dimensional figure with two congruent bases that are circles and a curved lateral surface that joins them.

base

base

Volume of a Cylinder

The volume of a cylinder with a base radius r and a height h is

$$V = \pi r^2 h.$$

To use the formula to find the volume of a cylinder, first find the area of one of its bases, and then multiply that area by the cylinder's height.

Example

PROBLEM 1 Find the volume of the cylinder.

SOLUTION

$V = \pi r^2 h$

$\quad = \pi \cdot 5^2 \cdot 8$ Substitute 5 for r and 8 for h.

$\quad = 25\pi \cdot 8$ Simplify the power.

$\quad = 200\pi$ Multiply.

8 cm

5 cm

ANSWER The volume of the cylinder is 200π cm³.

TOPIC

Example

PROBLEM 2 Find the volume of a cylinder that is 4 m tall and has a radius of 6 m. Use 3.14 to approximate π.

SOLUTION

$V = \pi r^2 h$
$= \pi \cdot 6^2 \cdot 4$ Substitute 6 for r, 4 for h, and simplify.
$= 144\pi$ Multiply.

Substitute 3.14 for π to approximate the volume.

$V = 144\pi$
$\approx 114 \cdot 3.14$
≈ 452

ANSWER The volume of the cylinder is exactly 144π m³, or approximately 452 m³.

➤ Relating Volumes of Cylinders and Prisms

You can find the volume of a cylinder or prism by multiplying the area of the base by the figure's height. For a rectangular prism, the base is a rectangle. For a cylinder, the base is a circle.

Example

PROBLEM 3 A cylinder and a rectangular prism have the same volume and the same height. The base of the rectangular prism has an area of 144 cm². What is the radius of the cylinder?

SOLUTION Since the volumes and heights are the same, the areas of the bases also are the same. So, $B_{\text{cylinder}} = 144$ cm². Use the formula for the area of a circle.

$A = \pi r^2$
$144 \approx 3.14 \cdot r^2$ Substitute 144 for A and 3.14 for π.
$\dfrac{144}{3.14} \approx \dfrac{3.14 r^2}{3.14}$ Divide by 3.14.
$45.9 \approx r^2$ Simplify.
$6.77 \approx r$ Use the square root property.

ANSWER The radius of the cylinder is approximately 6.77 cm.

T O P I C

Problem Set

Find the exact and approximate volume of the cylinder.
Use 3.14 or $\frac{22}{7}$ to approximate π.

1. Stepping Stones

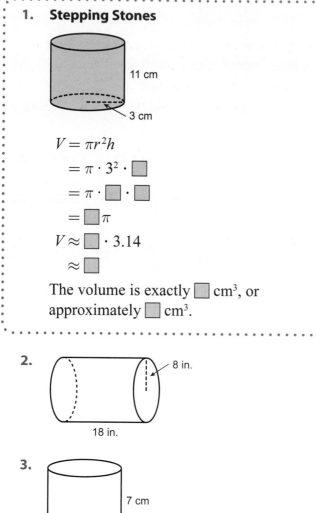

11 cm

3 cm

$$V = \pi r^2 h$$
$$= \pi \cdot 3^2 \cdot \square$$
$$= \pi \cdot \square \cdot \square$$
$$= \square \pi$$
$$V \approx \square \cdot 3.14$$
$$\approx \square$$

The volume is exactly $\square$ cm³, or approximately $\square$ cm³.

2.

8 in.

18 in.

3.

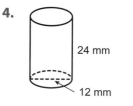

7 cm

6 cm

4.

24 mm

12 mm

5.

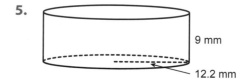

9 mm

12.2 mm

6. Challenge

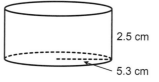

2.5 cm

5.3 cm

7. Challenge

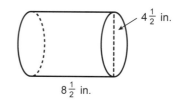

$4\frac{1}{2}$ in.

$8\frac{1}{2}$ in.

8. height = 4 m; radius = 4 m

9. height = 13 cm; radius = 3 cm

10. height = 20.4 mm; radius = 7 mm

11. height = 42 ft; radius = 36 ft

12. height = 100 mm; diameter = 12 mm

13. height = 52.2 cm; diameter = 20 cm

14. height = 6.4 m; diameter = 4.6 m

15. **Challenge** height = 16 in.; diameter = $3\frac{1}{2}$ in.

Use the relationship between the volumes of cylinders and prisms to solve.

16. If a rectangular prism and a cylinder have the same volume and same height, what can you say about the bases of the figures? Explain your answer.

17. If a rectangular prism and a cylinder have the same volume and bases with the same area, what can you say about the heights of the figures? Explain your answer.

18. A cylinder and a rectangular prism have the same volume and the same height. The base of the rectangular prism is a square with side length of 5 cm. What is the radius of the cylinder?

19. A cylinder and a rectangular prism have the same volume and the same height. The radius of the cylinder is 6 m. The base of the rectangular prism is a square. What is the side length of the prism's base?

20. A cylinder and a rectangular prism have the same volume. The base of the rectangular prism is a square with side length of 4 in. The cylinder is 8 in. long and has a radius of 4 in. What is the height of the prism?

21. **Challenge** A cylinder and a rectangular prism have the same height. The cylinder's volume is twice the volume of the prism. The base of the prism has an area of 81 cm². What is the radius of the cylinder?

Solve.

22. A box of oatmeal has the shape of a cylinder. The box is 7 in. high and has a radius of 2 in. What is the volume of the oatmeal box?

23. A cylindrical can of tuna has a radius of 4.25 cm and a height of 4 cm. What is the volume of the can of tuna?

24. A farmer's silo is shaped like a cylinder and has a volume of 18,840 ft³. The silo is 60 ft tall. What is the silo's radius?

25. A cake is shaped like a cylinder with a diameter of 9 in. and a height of 6 in. What is the volume of the cake?

26. A cylindrical soup can has a diameter of 7.5 cm and a height of 11 cm. What is the volume of the soup can?

27. **Challenge** The solid rocket boosters on the space shuttle are 45.46 m long and have a diameter of 3.71 m. What is the volume of each solid rocket booster?

Choose the answer.

28. Which measure is closest to the volume of the cylinder?

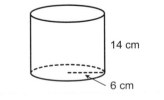

14 cm

6 cm

A. 1580 cm³   C. 3160 cm³

B. 2370 cm³   D. 4740 cm³

29. A cylinder that is 3 yd high has a volume of about 763 yd³. Which measure is closest to the cylinder's diameter?

A. 9 yd   C. 18 yd

B. 15 yd   D. 21 yd

Chapter 7 Review

Choose the answer.

1. Angle 1 and angle 2 are complementary. If $m\angle 1 = 65°$, what is $m\angle 2$?

   A. 25°

   B. 35°

   C. 115°

   D. 125°

2. Which set of measures could be the measures of the angles of a triangle?

   A. 30°, 30°, 30°

   B. 60°, 90°, 60°

   C. 30°, 47°, 103°

   D. 120°, 110°, 130°

3. What is $m\angle ADC$?

   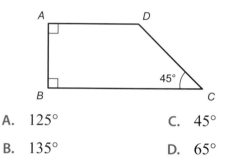

   A. 125°

   B. 135°

   C. 45°

   D. 65°

4. A regular pentagon has a perimeter of 60 cm. What is the length of one side of the pentagon?

   A. 6 cm

   B. 30 cm

   C. 10 cm

   D. 12 cm

5. What is the perimeter of a regular hexagon with a side length of $4\frac{1}{2}$ ft?

   A. 27 ft

   B. $22\frac{1}{2}$ ft

   C. $31\frac{1}{2}$ ft

   D. 36 ft

6. What is the radius of a circle with a diameter of 32 in.?

   A. 8 in.

   B. 16 in.

   C. 8π in.

   D. 64 in.

7. Which measure is closest to the circumference of a circle with a radius of 7 m?

   A. 22 m

   B. 14 m

   C. 44 m

   D. 66 m

8. Which measure is closest to the area of the circle?

   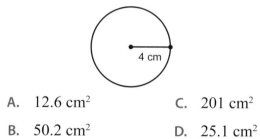

   A. 12.6 cm²

   B. 50.2 cm²

   C. 201 cm²

   D. 25.1 cm²

9. Rita mowed half of a circular yard that has a radius of 12 m. Which measure is closest to the area that Rita mowed?

   A. 226 m²

   B. 113 m²

   C. 452 m²

   D. 5.5 m²

10. A candle that is 11 cm high has a diameter of 10 cm. Which measure is closest to the volume of the candle?

    A. 302 cm³

    B. 3454 cm³

    C. 345 cm³

    D. 864 cm³

State whether the angles are *complementary*, *supplementary*, or *vertical*.

11. $\angle CAD$ and $\angle BAE$

12. $\angle EAF$ and $\angle BAF$

13. $\angle CAD$ and $\angle CAE$

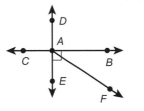

Find the unknown angle measure.

14. Two angles in a triangle measure $100°$ and $35°$. What is the measure of the third angle?

15. Three of a quadrilateral's angles are right angles. What is the measure of the fourth angle?

Find the perimeter of the regular polygon.

16. 5 sides; $s = 13$ m

17. 12 sides; $s = 2\frac{1}{2}$ ft

Find the side length of the regular polygon.

18. 6 sides; $P = 42$ cm

19. 8 sides; $P = 28$ m

Solve.

20. Name a chord of the circle.

21. Name a radius of the circle.

22. Name a diameter of the circle.

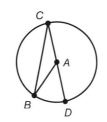

Approximate the circumference of the circle. Use 3.14 or $\frac{22}{7}$ to approximate π.

23. $d = 7$ mm

24. $r = 35$ in.

Approximate the area of the circle. Use 3.14 or $\frac{22}{7}$ to approximate π.

25. $r = 3$ m

26. $d = 18$ cm

Find the volume of the cylinder. Use 3.14 or $\frac{22}{7}$ to approximate π.

27.

5 cm

9 cm

28.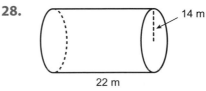

14 m

22 m

Problem	Topic Lookup
1, 11–13	Angle Pairs
2–3, 14–15	Finding Angle Measures
4–5, 16–19	Regular Polygons
6, 20–22	Parts of a Circle

Problem	Topic Lookup
7, 23–24	Circumference
8–9, 25–26	Areas of Circles
10, 27–28	Cylinders

8 Probability

Will the bat hit the ball? If so, will the batter reach base safely? People who play on and coach sports teams, as well as those who follow the teams, deal with uncertainty all the time. Probability provides the tools to understand and communicate this uncertainty.

In This Chapter

You will learn how to use Venn and tree diagrams to count the number of ways a trial can be conducted. You can use a diagram to calculate a theoretical probability. You'll also learn how to use experimental probability and the law of large numbers. Finally, you'll learn about independent, dependent, and complementary events.

Chapter Topics

▶ Foundations for Chapter 8

▶ Counting

▶ Probability and Experiments

▶ Experimental Probability

▶ Theoretical Probability

▶ The Law of Large Numbers

▶ Independent and Dependent Events

▶ Complementary Events

▶ Chapter 8 Review

Getting a hit is not a certain event.

Foundations for Chapter 8

➔ **Determining Likelihood**

Definitions

A result is **impossible** if it can never happen.
A result is **unlikely** if it has a less-than-even chance of happening.
A result is **likely** if it has a better-than-even chance of happening.
A result is **certain** if it will always happen.

Look at the result being considered. Then compare that result to all the other results that are possible.

Example A

State whether the result is *impossible*, *unlikely*, *likely*, or *certain* for one roll of a number cube with faces labeled 1–6.

PROBLEM A-1 a number less than 5

SOLUTION The numbers 1, 2, 3, and 4 are less than 5. Only 5 and 6 are not less than 5. More of the numbers on a number cube are less than 5 than are not.

ANSWER A result less than 5 is *likely*.

PROBLEM A-2 an 8

SOLUTION There is no 8 on the number cube.

ANSWER A result of an 8 is *impossible*.

PROBLEM A-3 a number less than 7

SOLUTION All of the numbers on the number cube are less than 7.

ANSWER A result less than 7 is *certain*.

PROBLEM A-4 a number greater than 4

SOLUTION The numbers 5 and 6 are greater than 4. Fewer of the numbers on a number cube are greater than 4 than are not.

ANSWER A result greater than 4 is *unlikely*.

Problem Set A

State whether the result is *impossible*, *unlikely*, *likely*, or *certain* for one spin of the spinner that has five equal-sized sections. Explain your reasoning.

1. an even number

2. an odd number

3. a number greater than 5

4. a 2

5. a number greater than 1

6. a 2, 4, or 6

7. a number greater than 10

8. an 8, 10, 2, or 4

➥ Expressing Probability

You can express a probability by comparing the number of ways a selected event can occur to all of the possible outcomes. Convert the ratio to give the probability in different forms.

Example B

State the probability of the given event for one toss of a coin. Write the probability in words, as a fraction, as a decimal, and as a percent.

PROBLEM B-1 heads

SOLUTION One of the two sides of a coin is heads.

1 out of $2 = \frac{1}{2} = 0.5 = 50\%$

ANSWER The probability of heads is 1 out of 2, $\frac{1}{2}$, 0.5, or 50%.

PROBLEM B-2 heads or tails

SOLUTION Heads and tails are the only options.

2 out of $2 = \frac{2}{2} = 1 = 100\%$

ANSWER The probability of heads or tails is 2 out of 2, $\frac{2}{2}$, 1, or 100%.

PROBLEM B-3 neither heads nor tails

SOLUTION There are no sides of a coin that are neither heads nor tails.

0 out of $2 = \frac{0}{2} = 0 = 0\%$

ANSWER The probability of neither heads nor tails is 0 out of 2, $\frac{0}{2}$, 0, or 0%.

Problem Set B

State the probability of the given event for one roll of a number cube with faces labeled 1–6. Write the probability in words, as a fraction, as a decimal, and as a percent.

1. an even number

2. a 6

3. a number less than 4

4. a number greater than 6

5. a 2 or 5

6. an odd number

7. a number greater than 5

8. a number less than 3

→ Interpreting Probability

You can interpret probability that is given as a fraction or a percent by relating it to the likelihood of the given event. Remember that the probability ratio is comparing the number of ways the event can occur to the total number of possible different outcomes.

Example C

Explain what the probability means.

PROBLEM C-1 The probability of the event of red on one spin of a 4-section spinner is 0.

SOLUTION A probability of 0 means that the event has no chance of occurring.

ANSWER It's impossible for the spinner to land on red. There are no red sections on the spinner.

PROBLEM C-2 The probability of the event of blue on one spin of a 4-section spinner is $\frac{1}{2}$.

SOLUTION Half the spinner is blue. If each section has equal size, then 2 sections are blue.

ANSWER Half the spinner is blue.

PROBLEM C-3 The probability of the event of orange if you draw 1 marble from a bag of 12 colored marbles is 25%.

SOLUTION 25% is equivalent to $\frac{1}{4}$. If there are 12 marbles, then 3 of them are orange.

ANSWER The bag holds 3 orange marbles.

Problem Set C

Interpret the probability of the event on one spin of a spinner with 6 equal-sized sections.

1. Spinner 1: event: white; probability: $\frac{1}{3}$

2. Spinner 2: event: green; probability: 1

Interpret the probability of the event on one draw of a marble from a bag of 8 marbles. A different bag of marbles is used for each problem.

3. event: purple; probability: 0

4. event: blue or red; probability: $\frac{1}{2}$

5. event: black; probability: 0

6. event: red or white; probability: 75%

7. event: green, blue, or white; probability: $\frac{5}{8}$

8. event: red, white, blue, or green; probability: 1

Getting a hit is not a certain event.

Planting the Seed

Probability helps us make decisions when things aren't certain.

Counting

Diagrams can show how groups of objects are related and make counting certain objects easier.

➡ Using Venn Diagrams to Count

Definition

A **Venn diagram** is a drawing that shows relationships among sets of objects.

You can find the number of objects with one or more characteristics by looking at the objects inside regions of a Venn diagram. Objects in overlapping regions have characteristics of both areas.

Example

Use the Venn diagram to solve.

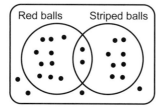

Red balls   Striped balls

PROBLEM 1 State how many balls are red.

SOLUTION Count the dots in both parts of the red region.
$10 + 2 = 12$ Add to find the total.

ANSWER There are 12 red balls.

PROBLEM 2 State how many balls are striped but not red.

SOLUTION Count the dots that are in only the striped region.

ANSWER There are 8 balls that are striped but not red.

PROBLEM 3 State how many balls are both red and striped.

SOLUTION Look at the overlapping region.

ANSWER There are 2 balls that are both red and striped.

Think About It

In the Venn diagram, you can see that 4 balls outside the circles are neither red nor striped.

➡ Using Tree Diagrams to Count

Definition

A **tree diagram** is a drawing that shows all possible combinations of outcomes for multiple events.

TOPIC

You can use a tree diagram to see how different outcomes of different events can be combined. Look at the summary of the outcomes on the right side of a tree diagram.

Example

Solve. Use the tree diagram that shows all possible outcomes of tossing a coin two times.

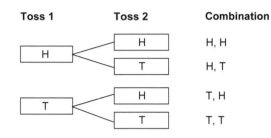

PROBLEM 4 State how many outcomes include one or more heads.

ANSWER There are 3 outcomes that include one or more heads.

PROBLEM 5 State how many outcomes include two tails.

ANSWER There is 1 outcome that includes two tails.

➡ Using Diagrams to Solve Counting Problems

Example

Solve by making a diagram.

PROBLEM 6 Marco has a red shirt and a black shirt. He has blue, brown, and gray pairs of shorts. How many combinations of a shirt and a pair of shorts does Marco have?

SOLUTION Make a tree diagram. Count the outcomes.

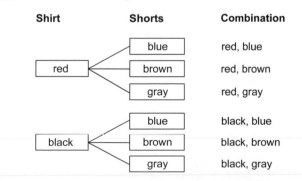

ANSWER Marco has 6 different combinations of a shirt and a pair of shorts.

> **Tip**
>
> Use a Venn diagram for counting possible outcomes of one-step processes.
>
> Use a tree diagram for counting possible outcomes of multistep processes.

Problem Set

Use the Venn diagram about students' pets to solve.

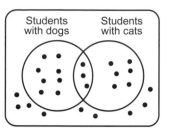

1. **Stepping Stones** How many students have a dog but not a cat?

    Look at the number inside the region for ▭ but outside the region for ▭.

    The number in that region is ▢.

    There are ▢ students with a dog but no cat.

2. How many students have a cat but not a dog?

3. How many students have both a cat and a dog?

4. How many students do not have a cat or a dog?

5. How many more students have a dog than have only a cat?

Use the Venn diagram about camper activities to solve.

6. How many campers participate in hiking and swimming?

7. How many campers participate in hiking but not swimming?

8. How many campers participate in neither hiking nor swimming?

9. How many campers participate in swimming?

10. How many more campers only hike than only swim?

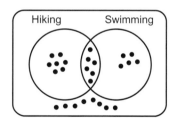

Use the Venn diagram about recipe ingredients to solve.

11. How many recipes include wheat, dairy, and nuts?

12. How many recipes contain only dairy?

13. How many more recipes use only dairy than use only nuts?

14. How many recipes contain wheat and nuts but no dairy?

15. How many recipes contain wheat?

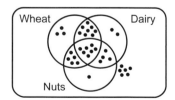

Use the tree diagram about tossing a coin and spinning a spinner to solve.

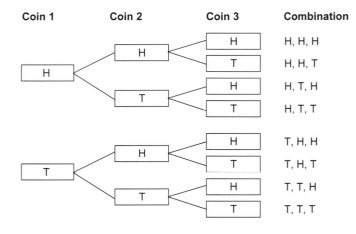

Coin	Spinner	Combination
heads	blue	heads, blue
	orange	heads, orange
	white	heads, white
tails	blue	tails, blue
	orange	tails, orange
	white	tails, white

16. **Stepping Stones** How many outcomes include blue?

    Look for outcomes that include ▭.

    There are ▭ outcomes that include blue.

17. How many outcomes include heads?

18. How many outcomes include white or orange?

Use the tree diagram about tossing 3 coins to solve.

Coin 1	Coin 2	Coin 3	Combination
H	H	H	H, H, H
		T	H, H, T
	T	H	H, T, H
		T	H, T, T
T	H	H	T, H, H
		T	T, H, T
	T	H	T, T, H
		T	T, T, T

19. How many outcomes include two or more heads?

20. How many outcomes are there in all?

21. How many outcomes have one head and two tails?

22. **Challenge** How many more outcomes have both heads and tails than have only one or the other?

Solve. Make a Venn or tree diagram to represent the situation.

23. There are 7 families who visited only New York, 9 families who visited only Florida, and 6 families who visited both states. How many families visited New York?

24. Eight of Ella's friends have skateboards. Of those, 6 also have bikes. Another 3 of Ella's friends have bikes but no skateboards. How many of Ella's friends have a skateboard but no bike?

25. Ishwar can go to either the gym or the library first. Then he can go to the mall, the movies, or the park. How many different combinations of activities does Ishwar have?

26. **Challenge** One bag holds 2 red marbles, 3 blue marbles, and 5 green marbles. Another bag holds 1 black marble, 1 white marble, and 14 purple marbles. Cecil draws one marble from each bag. How many different combinations of marbles could he draw?

Choose the answer.

27. How many more people are there who listen to rock music than people who listen to only country music?

    A. 11

    B. 7

    C. 10

    D. 13

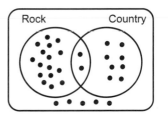

Probability and Experiments

The probability of an event will tell you how likely it is to happen.

➔ Finding Probabilities

Definitions

An **experiment** is any action that has a result.

An **outcome** is a result of an experiment.

The **sample space** is the set of all possible outcomes.

A **favorable outcome** is the outcome you are investigating.

An **event** is a set of outcomes for an experiment.

Remember

Probability is the chance of an event occurring. Probability is a ratio that can be expressed in words, or as a fraction, a decimal, or a percent.

Formula

The probability P of an event is

$$P(\text{event}) = \frac{\text{number of favorable outcomes}}{\text{number of possible outcomes}}.$$

You can use the formula to write a ratio expressing the probability of an event. Compare the number of favorable outcomes to the total number of possible outcomes.

Example

PROBLEM 1 Give the sample space for tossing a coin.

SOLUTION List the two different possible outcomes. Put your list in braces.

ANSWER The sample space for tossing a coin is {heads, tails}.

PROBLEM 2 Find the probability of getting heads on one coin toss.

SOLUTION There is 1 favorable outcome—heads. There are 2 possible outcomes—heads and tails.

$$P(\text{heads}) = \frac{\text{number of heads}}{\text{number of possible outcomes}} = \frac{1}{2} = 0.5 = 50\%$$

ANSWER The probability of tossing heads is $\frac{1}{2} = 0.5 = 50\%$.

Tip

When you write the probability of an event using $P(\text{event})$, replace *event* with the favorable outcome.

In Problem 2, $P(\text{event})$ was replaced with $P(\text{heads})$ because the favorable outcome was heads.

TOPIC

Example

PROBLEM 3 Find the probability of the spinner landing on a 1 or a 2 on one spin.

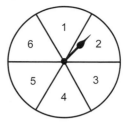

SOLUTION There are 2 favorable outcomes—1 and 2.
There are 6 possible outcomes—1, 2, 3, 4, 5, and 6.

$$P(1 \text{ or } 2) = \frac{\text{number of favorable outcomes}}{\text{number of possible outcomes}} = \frac{2}{6} = \frac{1}{3}$$

ANSWER The probability of the spinner landing on a 1 or a 2 is $\frac{1}{3}$.

➤ Conducting Probability Experiments

You can use a table to record the results of a probability experiment. If the experiment requires drawing an object from a group, be sure to replace the object that is drawn after the outcome is recorded.

> **Think About It**
>
> If an object drawn from a group is not replaced before the next object is drawn, then the number of possible outcomes changes, and the probabilities will be different.

Example

PROBLEM 4 Have a helper place some pennies, nickels, dimes, and quarters in a jar. Conduct an experiment by randomly drawing out one coin from the jar. Record the outcome and repeat the experiment for a total of 24 draws. Report the results.

SOLUTION Make a table to record the outcomes. Draw a coin from the jar and record the result with a tally mark. Return the coin to the jar. Draw another coin.

The table shows a set of possible outcomes.

Coin	Number Drawn
penny	卌
nickel	卌 |||
dime	卌
quarter	卌	

ANSWER Answers will vary, but this table shows that there were 5 pennies, 8 nickels, 5 dimes, and 6 quarters drawn.

Problem Set

Find the probability of the event when a number cube with faces labeled 1–6 is rolled once.

1. **Stepping Stones** an even number

    There are ☐ favorable outcomes.

    There are ☐ possible outcomes.

    $P(\text{even}) = \dfrac{\text{number of favorable outcomes}}{\text{number of possible outcomes}} = \dfrac{☐}{☐}$

2. a 3

3. an odd number

4. a number greater than 4

5. a 2 or a 3

6. a number less than 7

7. a number greater than 6

Find the probability of the event for one spin of the spinner.

8. an odd number

9. a 1

10. a number greater than 2

11. a number less than 4

12. a number greater than 0

13. a 2 or a 4

14. a 1, a 2, or a 3

15. **Challenge** a factor of 8

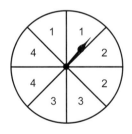

Find the probability of the event for one draw of a coin from a can containing 12 pennies, 28 dimes, 8 nickels, and 2 quarters.

16. a nickel

17. a penny

18. a dime

19. a quarter

20. a dime or a penny

21. **Challenge** a coin that is not a half dollar

Solve. Use the table showing outcomes when one marble is drawn from a bag of colored marbles.

22. How many times was a red marble drawn?

23. How many times was an orange or yellow marble drawn?

24. How many times was a marble drawn?

25. How many times was a marble other than a white marble drawn?

Color	Number Drawn
red	ЖЖ III
orange	III
yellow	ЖЖ II
white	ЖЖ ЖЖ IIII

Conduct the experiment and use a table to report the results.

26. Toss a coin 40 times.

27. Draw one coin from a jar of 5 pennies and 5 nickels. Repeat 20 times.

28. Draw one pen from a box of 3 black pens and 2 blue pens. Repeat 20 times.

29. Roll a number cube with faces labeled 1–6. Repeat 24 times.

30. Draw one letter card from a shuffled deck of letter cards containing 2 Ms, 2 As, 2 Ts, and 2 Hs. Repeat 24 times.

31. Draw one coin from a jar of 10 pennies, 5 dimes, and 5 quarters. Repeat 30 times.

32. Draw one coin from a jar of 3 pennies, 3 nickels, 3 dimes, and 6 quarters. Repeat 30 times.

Choose the answer.

33. What is the probability of rolling a number greater than 2 on a number cube with faces labeled 1–6?

    A. $\frac{2}{3}$ C. $\frac{1}{2}$

    B. $\frac{1}{3}$ D. $\frac{1}{6}$

34. What is the probability of the spinner landing on gray?

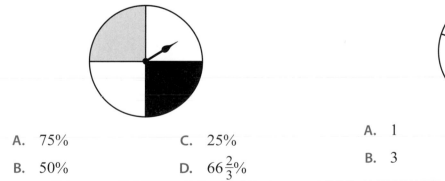

    A. 75%   C. 25%

    B. 50%   D. $66\frac{2}{3}$%

35. What is the probability of drawing a penny from a jar containing 5 pennies, 4 dimes, and 16 nickels?

    A. 0.8   C. 0.6

    B. 0.2   D. 0.5

36. Which number has a probability of 0 being the outcome of one spin of the spinner?

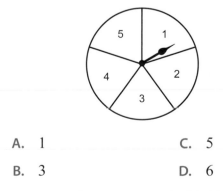

    A. 1   C. 5

    B. 3   D. 6

Experimental Probability

Knowing what has happened in the past can help you predict what might happen in the future.

➜ Using Experimental Probability

Definition and Formula

The **experimental probability** of an event is the ratio of the number of times the event occurs to the total number of trials.

$$P(\text{event}) = \frac{\text{number of times event occurred}}{\text{total number of trials}}$$

Example

PROBLEM 1 Darcy played 20 games of chess in a tournament. She won 16 games and lost the rest. Find the experimental probability she will lose her next game.

SOLUTION Subtract to find the number of losses:
$20 - 16 = 4$
Write and simplify the ratio: $\frac{4}{20} = \frac{1}{5}$

ANSWER According to experimental probability, Darcy has a $\frac{1}{5}$ chance of losing her next game.

➜ Making Predictions from Experiments

You can use experimental probability to make predictions.

Example

PROBLEM 2 Brighter Days Inc. makes flashlights. The company sampled some flashlights and found that 5% were defective. About how many flashlights out of 500 would you expect to be defective?

SOLUTION Change the percent to a decimal: $5\% = 0.05$
Multiply: $0.05 \cdot 500 = 25$

ANSWER One can reasonably expect that about 25 flashlights out of 500 would be defective.

Think About It

A prediction based on experimental probability is just that—a prediction. Predictions are not guarantees that something will occur.

TOPIC

Example

PROBLEM 3 The table shows the results of drawing one marble at a time from a bag of colored marbles. Each marble was replaced after the outcome was recorded. If there are a total of 12 marbles in the bag, about how many of the marbles are red?

SOLUTION

Add to find the total number of draws.
$10 + 2 + 6 + 2 = 20$

Write and simplify the ratio.
$\frac{10}{20} = \frac{1}{2}$

Multiply.
$\frac{1}{2} \cdot 12 = 6$

Color	Number Drawn
red	ЖЖ ЖЖ
yellow	||
blue	ЖЖ	
green	||

ANSWER About 6 of the marbles are red.

Think About It

Another way to solve this problem is to write and solve a proportion.

$$\frac{10}{20} = \frac{n}{12}$$

➡ Conducting Probability Experiments

You can use experimental probability to predict the numbers of different types of coins in a jar.

Example

PROBLEM 4 A jar that contains 40 coins has pennies, nickels, dimes, and quarters. The table shows the results of drawing one coin from the jar. Each coin was replaced after the outcome was recorded. Use the outcomes to predict the number of pennies in the jar.

SOLUTION

Add to find the total number of draws.
$4 + 12 + 10 + 5 = 31$

Write the ratio and divide to convert to a decimal.
$\frac{4}{31} = 4 \div 31 \approx 0.13$

Coin	Number Drawn
penny	||||
nickel	ЖЖ ЖЖ ||
dime	ЖЖ ЖЖ
quarter	ЖЖ

Multiply to find the number of pennies.
$0.13 \cdot 40 = 5.2$

ANSWER About 5 pennies are in the jar.

TOPIC

Problem Set

Find the experimental probability.

1. **Stepping Stones** The Knights won 15 games and lost 10. What are the chances they will win the next game?

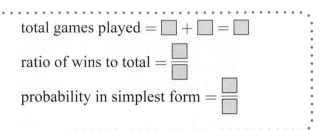

2. Sheila drew single marbles from a bag, recorded the outcome, and replaced the marble. In 50 draws, Sheila drew 20 white marbles and 30 black marbles. What is the experimental probability that the next marble will be black?

3. Dr. Murray is studying the fish in a lake. She captures a fish, records the type, and then releases it. She records 18 fish with spots and 24 fish with no spots. What is the experimental probability that the next fish will have spots?

Use experimental probability to make a prediction.

4. **Stepping Stones** Max drew and replaced single coins from a large jar. He drew 46 pennies, 20 nickels, and 34 dimes. Predict the number of dimes he will draw in the next 50 trials.

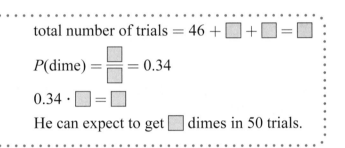

5. Mr. Allen found that 10 out of 80 books were returned late. Predict the number of books out of 2000 that will be returned late.

6. Brahim made 18 free throws and missed 12. Predict the number of free throws he will make in the next 100 tries.

7. Three out of 200 machine parts were found to be defective. About how many parts would you expect to be defective out of 2500 parts?

8. **Challenge** The TrailHound bus company found that 2 out of 25 people have 3 or more pieces of luggage. Predict the number of people in the next 1000 passengers who will have only 1 or 2 pieces of luggage.

Solve. Use the table of results of a spinner.

9. What is the probability that the next outcome of a spin will be black?

10. If the spinner is spun 50 more times, about how many times will the result be red?

11. **Challenge** What fraction of the space of the spinner is colored either blue, black, or red?

Outcome	Number of Times
blue	24
white	49
black	10
red	17

Solve. Use the table of results of letter tiles drawn from a bag.

12. What is the probability that the next tile drawn will be the letter M?

13. What is the probability that the next tile drawn will be a letter other than T?

14. If 40 more tiles are drawn from the bag, about how many times will the letter H be drawn?

15. **Challenge** There are 8 tiles with the letter T in the bag. About how many M tiles are there? A tiles? H tiles?

Outcome	Number of Times
M	11
A	9
T	22
H	8

Have a helper place 20 coins in a jar. The coins can include pennies, nickels, dimes, or quarters. Draw a coin at random from the jar and record the result in the table. Return the coin to the jar. Repeat for 40 trials. Solve using the outcomes.

16. About how many pennies do you predict are in the jar?

17. About how many nickels do you predict are in the jar?

18. About how many dimes do you predict are in the jar?

19. About how many quarters do you predict are in the jar?

Coin	Number Drawn
penny	
nickel	
dime	
quarter	

20. **Challenge** Add the outcomes from another 40 trials to the table. Predict the number of each type of coin in the jar. Which set of data helped you make a better prediction of the number of each type of coin?

Choose the answer.

21. Jakob spun a spinner 40 times and got the outcome of orange 8 times. What is the experimental probability that the next spin will land on orange?

    A. 50%   C. 25%

    B. 20%   D. 15%

22. Lori drew a clear marble from a bag of marbles 14 times out of a total of 56 draws with replacement. If there are 16 marbles in the bag in all, about how many of the marbles are clear?

    A. 4   C. 2

    B. 8   D. 12

Theoretical Probability

Finding theoretical probability will help you find expected outcomes of an event.

➔ Finding the Number of Times an Event Will Occur

Definition and Formula

The **theoretical probability** P of an event is a comparison of the favorable outcomes to the number of possible outcomes. Theoretical probability can be found using the formula

$$P(\text{event}) = \frac{\text{number of favorable outcomes}}{\text{number of possible outcomes}}.$$

Tip

Experimental probability is based on the results of an experiment that has already been performed.

Theoretical probability is based on the known nature of an experiment.

You can predict the number of times an event will occur by multiplying the theoretical probability of the event by the total number of outcomes of an experiment.

Example

PROBLEM 1 A coin is tossed 100 times. About how many times would you expect it to land on tails?

SOLUTION Find the theoretical probability of tossing tails.

$$P(\text{tails}) = \frac{\text{number of favorable outcomes}}{\text{number of possible outcomes}} = \frac{1}{2} = 0.5$$

Multiply by the total number of outcomes of the experiment:

$$0.5 \cdot 100 = 50$$

ANSWER One can reasonably expect about 50 tails.

A prediction doesn't tell you how a particular trial of an experiment will happen, but a prediction does give you an idea of what to expect.

Example

PROBLEM 2 A number cube with faces labeled 1–6 is rolled 72 times. How many times can a result of 4 or 5 be expected?

SOLUTION Find the theoretical probability of rolling a 4 or a 5.

$$P(4 \text{ or } 5) = \frac{\text{number of favorable outcomes}}{\text{number of possible outcomes}} = \frac{2}{6} = \frac{1}{3}$$

Multiply by the total number of outcomes of the experiment.

$$\frac{1}{3} \cdot 72 = \frac{1}{3} \cdot \frac{72}{1} = \frac{72}{3} = 24$$

ANSWER One can reasonably expect that a result of a 4 or a 5 would occur about 24 times.

PROBLEM 3 There are 24 blue, 9 yellow, 12 red, and 15 green marbles in a bag. Regina draws a marble out of the bag, records its color, and replaces the marble. She completes 30 draws from the bag. How many times would you expect Regina to draw a red marble?

SOLUTION Find the theoretical probability of drawing a red marble. The total number of possible outcomes is the total number of marbles.

$$P(\text{red}) = \frac{\text{number of favorable outcomes}}{\text{number of possible outcomes}}$$

$$= \frac{12}{24 + 9 + 12 + 15} = \frac{12}{60} = \frac{1}{5} = 0.2$$

Multiply by the total number of outcomes of the experiment.

$$0.2 \cdot 30 = 6$$

ANSWER One can reasonably expect that Regina will draw a red marble 6 times.

Problem Set

Solve.

1. **Stepping Stones** A number cube with faces labeled 1–6 is rolled 42 times. About how many times would you expect the result to be a 3?

Find the theoretical probability of rolling a 3.

$$P(3) = \frac{\text{number of favorable outcomes}}{\text{number of possible outcomes}} = \frac{\boxed{}}{6}$$

Multiply by the total number of outcomes of the experiment.

2. A coin is tossed 60 times. About how many times would you expect it to land on heads?

3. A number cube with faces labeled 1–6 is rolled 72 times. About how many times would you expect the result to be 4?

4. A spinner has 8 equal-sized sections labeled with letters A–H. If the spinner is spun 80 times, about how many times would you expect a result of B?

5. A bag contains a total of 25 marbles. Five of the marbles are blue, 3 are red, 8 are green, and 9 are white. If a marble is drawn from the bag and then replaced 50 times, about how many times would you expect a green marble to be drawn?

6. Each letter of the word KNIGHTS is written on a card and placed in a bag. Daunte draws one card from the bag, records the letter written on the card, and replaces the card. He will draw a card 56 times. About how many times would you expect Daunte to draw the letter G?

7. Cards numbered 1, 1, 2, 3, 4, 4, 4, 5, 6, 6, 7, 8, 8, 8, and 9 are placed in a bag. If a card is drawn from the bag and then replaced 135 times, about how many times would you expect a 6 to be drawn?

8. A box is filled with 75 different-colored cubes. There are 20 red cubes, 25 blue cubes, 15 purple cubes, 10 yellow cubes, and 5 black cubes in the box. If a cube is drawn from the box and then replaced 150 times, about how many times would you expect a black cube to be drawn?

9. A number cube with faces labeled 1–6 is rolled 90 times. About how many times would you expect the result to be greater than 2?

10. A bag contains 24 blue marbles, 32 yellow marbles, 43 white marbles, and 21 red marbles. If a marble is drawn from the bag and replaced 90 times, about how many times would you expect a yellow marble to be drawn?

11. There are 250 marbles in a large bag. The bag contains 47 silver marbles, 52 purple marbles, 71 red marbles, 26 blue marbles, 13 white marbles, and the rest are either black or gold. If a marble is drawn from the bag and then replaced 2000 times, about how many times would you expect a black or gold marble to be drawn?

Dana spins the spinner 48 times. How many times would you expect the given result?

12. lose a turn

13. forward 1 or forward 2

14. back 1, back 2, or back 3

Choose the answer.

15. If a number cube with faces labeled 1–6 is rolled 60 times, about how many times would you expect the result to be a 1 or a 2?

A. 2   C. 30

B. 20   D. 40

16. The spinner will be spun 80 times. About how many times would you expect a result of B or C?

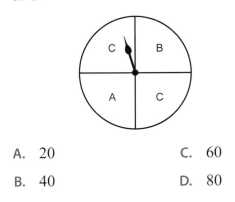

A. 20   C. 60

B. 40   D. 80

PROBLEM SET

The Law of Large Numbers

No matter how many times you toss a coin, you still can't know what the outcome of the next toss will be.

➔ Comparing Theoretical and Experimental Probability

You can use theoretical probability to make a prediction by comparing favorable outcomes to the total number of possible outcomes. You can make a prediction with experimental probability by using earlier results of the experiment.

Example

A number cube has faces labeled 1–6.

PROBLEM 1 Find the theoretical probability of rolling an even number.

SOLUTION Apply the formula for theoretical probability.

$$P(\text{even}) = \frac{\text{number of even-numbered faces}}{\text{number of possible outcomes}} = \frac{3}{6} = \frac{1}{2} = 50\%$$

ANSWER The theoretical probability of rolling an even number is 50%.

PROBLEM 2 The table shows the results of rolling the number cube several times. Find the experimental probability of rolling an even number.

Outcome	1	2	3	4	5	6
Number	15	17	14	16	13	15

SOLUTION Apply the formula for experimental probability.

$$P(\text{even}) = \frac{\text{number of even results}}{\text{total number of trials}}$$

$$= \frac{17 + 16 + 15}{15 + 17 + 14 + 16 + 13 + 15}$$

$$= \frac{48}{90} \approx 0.53 = 53\%$$

ANSWER The experimental probability of rolling an even number is about 53%.

> **Tip**
> Ratios such as probabilities are often more easily compared if they are in percent or decimal form than in fraction form.

TOPIC

➜ Using the Law of Large Numbers

The Law of Large Numbers

As an experiment is repeated more times, the experimental probability of an event gets closer to the theoretical probability of the event.

The law of large numbers explains why theoretical and experimental probabilities for a normal experiment may be different.

Example

A jar contains 5 different colors of marbles, and each color has the same number of marbles. A student draws and replaces one marble and repeats this experiment a total of 100 times. She draws a red marble 17 times.

PROBLEM 3 Find the experimental probability of drawing a red marble. How would you expect this value to change as the student continues to draw marbles?

SOLUTION Find the experimental probability.

$$P(\text{red}) = \frac{\text{number of times result was red}}{\text{total number of trials}} = \frac{17}{100} = 17\%$$

Find the theoretical probability.

$$P(\text{red}) = \frac{\text{number of favorable outcomes}}{\text{number of possible outcomes}} = \frac{1}{5} = 20\%$$

Compare the probabilities.
$17\% < 20\%$

ANSWER As the number of trials increases, you should expect the experimental probability of drawing a red marble to get closer to 20%.

PROBLEM 4 In the problem above, predict the number of red marbles drawn in 2500 trials.

SOLUTION With a large number of trials, the outcome should be closer to that predicted by the theoretical outcome.
Write the probability as a decimal: $20\% = 0.2$
Multiply by the number of trials: $0.2 \cdot 2500 = 500$

ANSWER There will be about 500 red marbles drawn in 2500 trials.

Problem Set

Solve. Identify the resulting probability as theoretical or experimental.

1. **Stepping Stones** A spinner has four sections, but they are not the same size. The spinner lands on red 6 out of 50 times. What is the probability that the next spin will be a color other than red?

   number not red: $50 - 6 = \square$

   probability: $\frac{44}{50} = \square\%$

   The computation is based on an experiment, so the probability is $\boxed{}$.

2. The outcomes for rolling a number cube with faces labeled 1 – 6 are equally likely. Find the probability that the number rolled is at least a 4.

3. There are 2000 tickets in a lottery and two of the tickets are for grand prizes. What is the probability of winning a grand prize?

4. In a survey of people leaving the library, 42 use the library only on weekdays, 26 only on weekends, and 32 during both parts of the week. What is the probability that a library patron chosen at random will visit the library on weekends?

5. Ten people's names are put in a hat. If only 2 of the people are women, what is the probability that a name drawn from the hat is a man's?

6. One-half of the people in a chess club are adults 21 years old or older. The other half are younger. What is the probability that a club member chosen at random will be under 21 years old?

7. A large box contains buttons with pictures of animals. There are four different animals. A button is drawn and replaced. In 100 trials, there were 35 cats. What is the probability that the next button will be a different animal?

8. A student kept track of the prizes won in a contest over several months. What is the probability that someone who won a prize won an audio player in this contest?

Prize	Winners
Audio player	2
Poster of rock star	78
1 song download	125
Video game	33

9. A mall is having a raffle ticket drawing. The table shows the tickets to be drawn. What is the probability of drawing a restaurant coupon?

Prize	Number
50% off at a sports store	25
2 for 1 at a restaurant	50
Paperback book at a bookstore	75
Movie ticket	100

10. **Challenge** Mel has 6 white T-shirts, 4 blue T-shirts, 3 black T-shirts, and 1 red T-shirt in a drawer. He randomly takes out 2 white T-shirts and hangs them in the closet. What is the probability that the next T-shirt he takes out at random will be a white T-shirt?

Solve. Use the table of results of drawing colored marbles from a bag.

Color	Actual Number of Marbles	Number of Times Drawn
red	4	10
blue	8	19
yellow	4	9
green	8	20
orange	8	22

11. Stepping Stones How would you expect the experimental probability of drawing a blue marble to change as the number of trials increases?

experimental probability:

☐ out of 80 outcomes were blue.

$P(\text{blue}) = \dfrac{\Box}{\Box} = \Box\%$

theoretical probability:

$P(\text{blue}) = \dfrac{\Box}{\Box} = \Box\%$

The experimental probability will ☐.

12. How would you expect the experimental probability of drawing an orange marble to change as the number of trials increases?

13. How would you expect the experimental probability of drawing a green marble to change as the number of trials increases?

14. Based on theoretical probability, what is the best prediction of the number of times a red marble will be drawn in 1000 trials?

15. What is the best prediction of the number of times an orange marble will be drawn in 1000 trials?

16. Challenge In 1000 trials, how many more yellow marbles would be drawn according to theoretical probability than would be drawn according to experimental probability?

Choose the answer.

17. A bag contains an equal number each of red, black, and white marbles. A marble is drawn and replaced. The first 5 marbles are red. What are the chances of getting a red marble on the next draw?

A. $\dfrac{1}{3}$

B. more than $\dfrac{1}{3}$

C. It is certain that the next marble will be red.

D. It is certain that the next marble will not be red.

18. A spinner with 4 equal parts has sections that are red, yellow, green, and blue. Out of 200 spins, 18% were yellow. What is likely to happen in 800 spins?

A. The percent of yellow will get closer to 0%.

B. The percent of yellow will get closer to 25%.

C. The spinner will land on yellow exactly 200 times.

D. The spinner will land on yellow exactly 18% of the time.

Independent and Dependent Events

Sometimes we need to know what happened first to know what happens next.

➔ Determining If Events Are Independent or Dependent

Definitions

Two events are **independent events** if the probability of one event is not affected by the outcome of the other event.

Two events are **dependent events** if the probability of one event is affected by the outcome of the other event.

Look to see whether the probability of the second event is affected by the occurrence of the first. If it is, then the events are dependent.

Example

PROBLEM 1 A bag contains 4 red and 6 blue marbles. A red marble is drawn and not replaced. Another red marble is drawn. State if the events are *independent* or *dependent*.

SOLUTION Determine if the probability of the second draw is affected by the first draw.

After the first marble is drawn, there are only 9 marbles in the bag, and there is one fewer red marble. The first draw changed the sample space for the second draw, so the probability of the second event is changed.

ANSWER The events are dependent.

Think About It

If a bag only contains 1 black marble and 1 white marble, and you draw 1 marble at a time without replacing it, the probability that the second marble you draw is black will be either 0% or 100%, depending on the first marble you drew.

TOPIC

Example

Determine whether the outcomes are *dependent* or *independent*.

PROBLEM 2 The spinner is spun two times. Determine whether landing on a shaded section on the first spin and landing on an odd number on the second spin are independent or dependent events.

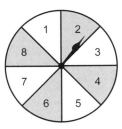

SOLUTION Each spin on a spinner is a "fresh" spin. The second spin is not related to the outcome of the first spin. The probability of an odd number on the second spin is not changed from 50% because the spinner landed on a shaded section with the first spin.

ANSWER The events are independent.

➔ Finding Probability of Independent Events

Probability of Independent Events

If events A and B are independent events, then
$$P(A \text{ and } B) = P(A) \cdot P(B).$$

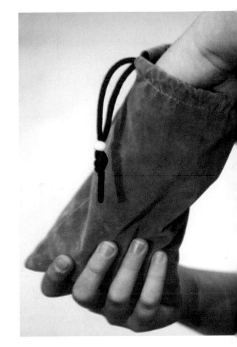

Example

PROBLEM 3 Find the probability of rolling a 5 on a number cube with faces labeled 1–6 and tossing tails with a coin.

SOLUTION The events are independent. Find the probability of each event. Then apply the formula.

Event A: $P(5) = \frac{1}{6}$ $\qquad$ Event B: $P(\text{tails}) = \frac{1}{2}$

$P(A \text{ and } B) = P(A) \cdot P(B)$

$P(5 \text{ and tails}) = P(5) \cdot P(\text{tails})$

$\qquad = \frac{1}{6} \cdot \frac{1}{2}$ $\qquad$ Replace $P(5)$ with $\frac{1}{6}$ and $P(\text{tails})$ with $\frac{1}{2}$.

$\qquad = \frac{1 \cdot 1}{6 \cdot 2} = \frac{1}{12}$ $\quad$ Multiply.

ANSWER The probability of rolling a 5 and tossing tails is $\frac{1}{12}$.

Problem Set

State if the events are *independent* or *dependent*. Explain your reasoning.

1. **Stepping Stones** A tile is drawn from a bag that contains red, blue, and yellow tiles. The tile is not replaced, and then another tile is drawn.

   Event *A*: ▢

   Event *B*: drawing a blue tile with a second draw

   After the first tile is drawn and not replaced, there is ▢ fewer tile in the bag. That event affects the outcome of drawing the ▢ tile.

   The events are ▢ .

2. The result of tossing a coin is heads, and a spinner lands on 8.

3. A red card is drawn from a deck of cards and is not replaced, and then another red card is drawn.

4. A spinner lands on 10. The same spinner is spun again and lands on 10 again.

5. An orange cube is drawn from a bag of different-colored cubes and then the result of tossing a coin is tails.

6. Each letter of the word PROBABILITY is written on a card and placed in a bag. A P is drawn from the bag and it is not replaced. Then a B is drawn.

7. A spinner is spun and lands on 6. A second, identical spinner is spun and lands on 6.

8. A small box is filled with 50 marbles. There are 15 red marbles, 15 blue marbles, 10 purple marbles, 5 yellow marbles, and 5 black marbles in the box. A yellow marble is drawn from the box and is not replaced, and then a black marble is drawn.

9. Mr. O'Leary gets heads on a coin toss and then gets tails by tossing the same coin again.

10. **Challenge** Each letter of the word TOUCHDOWN is written on a card and placed in a bag. A T is drawn from the bag and is replaced, and then the T is drawn again.

Find the probability of the independent events.

11. **Stepping Stones** rolling a 2 with a number cube with faces labeled 1–6, and then a spinner labeled 1–8 landing on a 7

Event A: P(rolling 2) = $\boxed{}$

Event B: P(spinning 8) = $\boxed{}$

$P(A \text{ and } B) = P(A) \cdot P(B)$

$P(\text{rolling 2 and spinning 8}) = \dfrac{\boxed{}}{\boxed{}} \cdot \dfrac{\boxed{}}{\boxed{}} = \dfrac{\boxed{}}{\boxed{}}$

12. tossing heads with a coin, and a spinner labeled 1–8 landing on a 4

13. rolling a 6 with a number cube, and then drawing a red marble from a bag of 20 marbles that has 5 red marbles in it

14. a 10-section spinner labeled 1–10 landing on a 5, and then tossing tails with a coin

15. drawing a number less than 8 from a jar containing 25 cards with the numbers 1–25 written on them, and then rolling a 1 or 2 on a number cube labeled 1–6

16. drawing a blue marble from a bag with 3 red, 5 blue, and 6 green marbles in it; and then rolling a 1, 2, or 3 on a number cube with faces labeled 1–6

17. rolling a number greater than 2 on a number cube with faces labeled 1–6, and then a spinner labeled 1–8 landing on an odd number

18. **Challenge** drawing a blue or red marble from a bag of 60 marbles that have 17 orange, 12 yellow, 3 green, and the rest blue or red; and then a spinner labeled 1–10 landing on a multiple of 3

Choose the answer.

19. Which events are dependent?

   A. rolling a 5 on a number cube and tossing heads on a coin

   B. rolling a 3 on a number cube and a spinner landing on blue

   C. drawing a black marble from a bag and not replacing it, and then drawing another black marble

   D. drawing a white marble from a bag and replacing it, and then drawing another white marble

20. What is the probability of rolling a number less than 3 on a number cube with faces labeled 1–6, and then tossing heads with a coin?

   A. $\dfrac{1}{6}$

   B. $\dfrac{1}{3}$

   C. $\dfrac{1}{2}$

   D. $\dfrac{5}{6}$

Complementary Events

Tomorrow for lunch you will either eat a salad or not eat a salad. It will be one or the other.

➔ Finding the Probability of Complementary Events

Definition and Formula

Complementary events are two or more events that together cover all possible outcomes.

If events A and B are complementary, then

$$P(A) + P(B) = 1 \quad \text{and} \quad P(A) = 1 - P(B).$$

You can find the probability of the complement of an event by subtracting the event's probability from 1.

Example

PROBLEM 1 Find the probability of the complement of event E. Event E: the spinner landing on an even number on the spinner

SOLUTION The complement of landing on an even number is landing on an odd number.

$P(\text{odd}) = \frac{3}{5} = 0.6$

ANSWER The probability of the complement of the spinner landing on an even number is 0.6.

PROBLEM 2 The probability of drawing a red marble from a bag of colored marbles is $\frac{3}{8}$. Find the probability of drawing a marble that is not red.

SOLUTION
$$
\begin{aligned}
P(\text{not red}) &= 1 - P(\text{red}) && \text{Start with the formula.} \\
&= 1 - \frac{3}{8} && \text{Substitute } \tfrac{3}{8} \text{ for } P(\text{red}). \\
&= \frac{5}{8} && \text{Subtract.}
\end{aligned}
$$

ANSWER The probability of drawing a marble that is not red is $\frac{5}{8}$.

Think About It

The probability of the complement of an event is the same as the probability that the event does **not** happen.

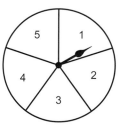

Think About It

Problem 1 can also be solved by first finding $P(\text{even})$ and then subtracting that number from 1 to find $P(\text{odd})$.

TOPIC

➔ Finding the Sum of Probabilities

The sum of the probabilities of two events that do not overlap will always be a number greater than or equal to 0 and less than or equal to 1. If the probabilities are expressed in different forms, then convert one probability to the form of the other before adding.

Example

Find the sum of the probabilities of events that do not overlap. State if the events are complementary.

PROBLEM 3 $P(\text{blue}) = \frac{5}{8}$; $P(\text{orange}) = \frac{3}{8}$

SOLUTION Add the probabilities.

$$\frac{5}{8} + \frac{3}{8} = 1$$

ANSWER The sum is 1. The events are complementary.

PROBLEM 4 $P(\text{blue}) = \frac{1}{4}$; $P(\text{orange}) = 40\%$

SOLUTION Convert the fraction to a percent.

$$\frac{1}{4} = 25\%$$

Add the percents.
$40\% + 25\% = 65\%$

ANSWER The sum is 65%. The events are not complementary.

Problem Set

Find the complementary event of the given event.

1. heads on a coin toss

2. a number less than 5 on a roll of a number cube with faces labeled 1–6

3. an odd number on a spinner with equal-sized sections labeled 1–8

4. a 2, 3, or 4 on a roll of a number cube with faces labeled 1–6

Find the probability of the complementary event of one spin of the spinner.

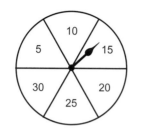

6. a 10

7. a number less than 25

8. a multiple of 10

9. a number greater than 10

10. an odd number

5. **Stepping Stones** Event E: a number greater than 20

   The complementary event is a number ▭ 20.

   $$P(E) = \frac{\text{number of favorable outcomes}}{\text{number of possible outcomes}}$$

   $P(\text{complement of } E) = \dfrac{\square}{6}$

   The probability is ▢.

11. a 5 or a 25

12. an even number

13. a number greater than 25

14. a 10, a 15, or a 20

15. **Challenge** a multiple of 5

16. **Challenge** a number less than 5

Solve.

17. The probability of drawing a green marble from a bag of colored marbles is $\frac{2}{3}$. Find the probability of drawing a marble that is not green.

18. The probability of a spinner landing on an odd number is 75%. Find the probability of the spinner landing on an even number.

19. The probability of drawing a white chip from a bag of white chips and black chips is $\frac{5}{6}$. Find the probability of drawing a black chip.

20. The probability of drawing a girl's name from a hat is 0.37. Find the probability of drawing a boy's name.

21. The probability of drawing a white or a black marble from a bag of colored marbles is $\frac{7}{12}$. Find the probability of drawing a marble that is not white or black.

22. **Challenge** A bag holds some letter tiles. Each tile has a K, an A, or a G on it.
$P(K) = \frac{1}{3}; P(A) = \frac{1}{4}$
Find $P(G)$.

Find the sum of the probabilities. State if the events are complementary.

23. **Stepping Stones** $P(3) = \frac{1}{4}; P(4) = \frac{1}{2}$
$P(3) + P(4) = \square + \square$
$= \square$
Are the events complementary? $\square$

24. $P(\text{black}) = \frac{2}{3}; P(\text{white}) = \frac{1}{3}$

25. $P(\text{red}) = 40\%; P(\text{yellow}) = 40\%$

26. $P(1) = 0.2; P(10) = 0.8$

27. $P(\text{computer}) = 54\%; P(\text{television}) = 46\%$

28. $P(\text{orange}) = \frac{5}{6}; P(\text{green}) = 10\%$

29. $P(\text{New York}) = \frac{3}{8}; P(\text{Maryland}) = 0.625$

30. $P(< 5) = \frac{7}{20}; P(> 5) = 60\%$

31. **Challenge** $P(2) = \frac{3}{8}; P(4) = 25\%;$
$P(6) = 0.125$

Choose the answer.

32. What is the probability of the event that is complementary to the event of rolling an even number on a number cube with faces labeled 1−6?

A. $\frac{1}{4}$ C. $\frac{1}{3}$

B. $\frac{1}{6}$ D. $\frac{1}{2}$

33. What is the probability of the spinner **not** landing on a number greater than 3?

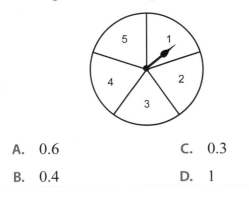

A. 0.6 C. 0.3

B. 0.4 D. 1

34. The probability of drawing a purple tile from a bag of purple tiles and gold tiles is 65%. What is the probability of drawing a gold tile?

A. 25% C. 30%

B. 35% D. 65%

35. What is the sum of the probabilities of drawing a black marble and drawing a white marble from a bag holding these marbles?

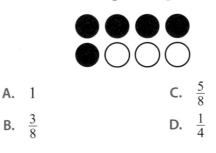

A. 1 C. $\frac{5}{8}$

B. $\frac{3}{8}$ D. $\frac{1}{4}$

Chapter 8 Review

Choose the answer.

1. Marcus tosses a coin and rolls a number cube with faces labeled 1–6. How many different possible outcomes are there?

   A. 8   C. 12

   B. 10   D. 36

2. What is the probability of drawing a nickel from a jar that holds 5 nickels, 3 pennies, 6 dimes, and 1 quarter?

   A. $\frac{1}{5}$ C. $\frac{3}{5}$

   B. $\frac{1}{3}$ D. $\frac{5}{5}$

3. Madeleine spins a spinner 36 times and records the outcome of blue 9 times. What is the experimental probability that the next spin will stop on blue?

   A. 75%   C. 50%

   B. 36%   D. 25%

4. Cedric draws a green marble from a bag of colored marbles 19 times out of a total of 60 draws. If there are 12 marbles in the bag, about how many of the marbles are green?

   A. 2   C. 6

   B. 8   D. 4

5. A number cube with faces labeled 1–6 is rolled 45 times. How many times is the outcome expected to be a number greater than 4?

   A. 0   C. 33

   B. 15   D. 22

6. Paige tosses a coin 10 times and records the outcome of heads 7 times. How would you expect the experimental probability of the outcome of heads to change as Paige increases the number of trials to 100?

   A. The probability will probably decrease.

   B. The probability will probably increase.

   C. The probability will probably stay the same.

   D. The probability will increase and then decrease.

7. What is the probability of rolling an even number on a number cube with faces labeled 1–6 and flipping tails on a coin?

   A. $\frac{1}{6}$ C. $\frac{1}{2}$

   B. $\frac{1}{12}$ D. $\frac{1}{4}$

8. What is the probability of the complementary event of the spinner landing on a 2?

   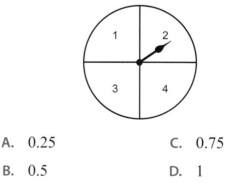

   A. 0.25   C. 0.75

   B. 0.5   D. 1

Use the Venn diagram about siblings children have to solve.

9. How many children have a sister?

10. How many children have a brother but no sister?

11. How many children are represented in the diagram?

Have a sister   Have a brother

Find the probability for one roll of a number cube with faces labeled 1–6.

12. a 1 or a 6

13. a number greater than or equal to 1

Solve.

14. Cho draws a marble from a bag of colored marbles 20 times. She records the outcome of red 8 times. What is the probability that the next marble she draws is not red?

15. A spinner has 5 equal-sized sections labeled 1–5. If the spinner is spun 60 times, how many times can you expect it to land on 1 or 5?

State if the events are *independent* or *dependent*.

16. A green tile is drawn from a bag and not replaced, and then a yellow tile is drawn from the bag.

17. A white block is drawn from a bag and not replaced. Then heads is tossed on a coin.

Find the combined probability of the independent events.

18. tossing heads with a dime and tossing heads with a quarter

19. on a spinner with 4 equal sections labeled 1–4, the spinner landing on a 1, and then the spinner landing on a number greater than 1

Find the complement of the given event for one roll of a number cube with faces labeled 1–6. Then find the probabilities of the event and its complement. Give the sum of the probabilities.

20. an even number

22. a number greater than 2

21. a 5

23. a number less than 7

Problem	Topic Lookup	Problem	Topic Lookup
1, 9–11	Counting	6	The Law of Large Numbers
2, 12–13	Probability and Experiments	7, 16–19	Independent and Dependent Events
3–4, 14	Experimental Probability	8, 20–23	Complementary Events
5, 15	Theoretical Probability		

9 Statistics

Every jelly bean can be described. Each one has color, flavor, mass, and number of calories. The language and tools of statistics help describe buckets full of data.

In This Chapter

You will learn how to create and interpret statistical graphs, including circle graphs, bar graphs, line plots, line graphs, box-and-whisker plots, and histograms. You'll also learn how to calculate and interpret measures of center and variation. Finally you will learn how sampling can help you make decisions about a population.

Chapter Topics

- ▶ Foundations for Chapter 9
- ▶ Circle Graphs
- ▶ More Statistical Graphs
- ▶ Histograms
- ▶ Measures of Center
- ▶ Box-and-Whisker Plots
- ▶ Measures of Variation
- ▶ Outliers
- ▶ Samples and Bias
- ▶ Sampling Strategies
- ▶ Statistical Claims
- ▶ Chapter 9 Review

Jelly beans come in many different colors and flavors.

Foundations for Chapter 9

➔ **Finding Range, Mean, and Median**

Definitions

The **minimum** piece of data, or value, in a data set is the least value, and the **maximum** is the greatest value.

The **range** of a data set is the difference of the maximum and minimum values in the data set.

The **mean** of a data set is the sum of the data divided by the number of values. The mean is also called the average.

The **median** of a data set with an odd number of values is the middle value in the data set after the values have been ordered from least to greatest. If there are an even number of values, the median is the average of the two middle values after the values have been ordered from least to greatest.

Example A

Solve for the set of data about club members' ages.

Ages of Club Members (years)				
11	13	14	14	12
11	11	11	10	12

PROBLEM A-1 Find the minimum, maximum, and range of the data set.

SOLUTION least, 10; greatest, 14
Subtract: $14 - 10 = 4$

ANSWER The minimum is 10 years, the maximum is 14 years, and the range is 4 years.

PROBLEM A-2 Find the mean age.

SOLUTION Add to find the sum of the values.
$11 + 13 + 14 + 14 + 12 + 11 + 11 + 11 + 10 + 12 = 119$
Divide the sum by the number of values.
$119 \div 10 = 11.9$

ANSWER The mean age is 11.9 years.

PROBLEM A-3 Find the median age.

SOLUTION Order from least to greatest.
10, 11, 11, 11, 11, 12, 12, 13, 14, 14
There are an even number of values, and the middle two values are 11 and 12. Add them and divide by 2 to find the average.
$11 + 12 = 23$
$23 \div 2 = 11.5$

ANSWER The median age is 11.5 years.

Problem Set A

Find the minimum, maximum, range, mean, and median for the data set.

1. 1, 2, 4, 5, 5, 5, 6, 7, 9

2. 12, 13, 13, 17, 18, 19, 27

3. 37, 43, 54, 83, 102, 117, 160, 208

4. 2.4, 2.6, 7.2, 5.5, 4.1, 5.5, 6.1, 6.1

FOUNDATIONS

➔ Finding Mode

Ordering the values in a data set from least to greatest can help you find the value or values that occur most often.

Example B

Find the mode for the data set.

PROBLEM B-1

3, 7, 6, 3, 5, 8, 7, 9, 2, 7

SOLUTION Order the values from least to greatest.

2, 3, 3, 5, 6, 7, 7, 7, 8, 9

The value 7 occurs most often.

ANSWER The mode is 7.

PROBLEM B-2

1, 4, 5, 3, 8, 9, 4, 6, 7, 5

SOLUTION Order the values from least to greatest.

1, 3, 4, 4, 5, 5, 6, 7, 8, 9

The values 4 and 5 occur twice each.

ANSWER The modes are 4 and 5.

PROBLEM B-3

3, 7, 5, 2, 0, 6, 9, 1, 8, 4

SOLUTION Order the values from least to greatest.

0, 1, 2, 3, 4, 5, 6, 7, 8, 9

No value appears more than once.

ANSWER There is no mode.

Problem Set B

Find the mode for the data set.

1. 6, 7, 8, 8, 9, 10, 11, 12

2. 8, 9, 11, 14, 15, 17, 18, 22

3. 13, 14, 16, 17, 17, 17, 18, 20

4. 18, 24, 24, 24, 25, 37, 37, 46

5. 119, 190, 145, 146, 133, 119, 147, 104

6. 8.3, 8.7, 4.5, 6.9, 3, 4.2, 11.7, 4

FOUNDATIONS

➔ Selecting Measures of Center and Spread

Definitions

The **measures of center** for a data set, which include the mean, median, and mode, are used to represent the center of the distribution of the values.

The **measures of spread** for a data set, which include the range, are used to represent the extent to which the values of a data set are spread out.

Look at what you are trying to find out about the values in a data set, and identify the measure that will give you that information.

If you are looking for this information:	then find this measure:
average ⟶	mean
middle value ⟶	median
most common value ⟶	mode
spread or variation ⟶	range

Example C

State which measure of center or measure of spread represents the situation.

PROBLEM C-1 A newspaper reports that the middle price of a new home in the community has risen.

SOLUTION The middle value is the median.

ANSWER The *median* represents the middle price.

PROBLEM C-2 A student finds his average grade on math assignments.

SOLUTION The average of the values is the mean.

ANSWER The *mean* represents the average grade.

Problem Set C

State which measure of center or measure of spread represents the situation.

1. Most people who visit the skate park are 13 years old.

2. A company finds the difference between the lightest and the heaviest packages it ships.

3. There are as many employees who earn more than a certain salary as those who learn less than that salary.

4. Alex found the average weight of several fish he caught.

5. A store orders more of the shirt size that it sells most often.

6. A stock's price reached its highest point in March and its lowest point in July.

Planting the Seed

· ·

Statistics help you describe and understand data.

FOUNDATIONS

Circle Graphs

Circle graphs are useful to help you see how data groups are related to each other.

➔ Interpreting Circle Graphs

Definition

A **circle graph** is a circular chart that shows divisions according to how data results are distributed.

Example

Solve by using the circle graph.

PROBLEM 1 How much more of her workout time does Joan spend lifting weights than swimming? Express your answer as a fraction of Joan's time.

SOLUTION Subtract the amount of time spent swimming from the amount of time spent lifting weights.

$30 - 15 = 15$

Divide by the total time to find the part of her workout time.

$$\frac{15}{60 + 30 + 15 + 15} = \frac{15}{120} = \frac{1}{8}$$

ANSWER Joan spends $\frac{1}{8}$ more of her time lifting weights than she does swimming.

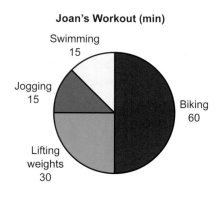

Joan's Workout (min)

Swimming 15
Jogging 15
Biking 60
Lifting weights 30

PROBLEM 2 A total of 400 people were asked if their favorite fruits are apples, oranges, or bananas. What fraction of those surveyed chose bananas?

SOLUTION Find the number who chose bananas.

$400 - (200 + 80) = 400 - 280 = 120$

Write the ratio of the number who chose bananas to the total number surveyed, and simplify.

$$\frac{120}{400} = \frac{3}{10}$$

ANSWER $\frac{3}{10}$ of the people surveyed chose bananas.

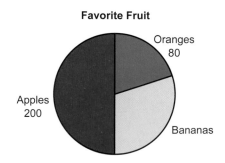

Favorite Fruit

Oranges 80
Apples 200
Bananas

TOPIC

Example

PROBLEM 3 What is the ratio of students who like soccer or baseball best to those who like football best?

SOLUTION Write the ratio and simplify.

$$\frac{\text{soccer or baseball}}{\text{football}} = \frac{75 + 150}{100} = \frac{225}{100} = \frac{9}{4}$$

ANSWER The ratio of students who like soccer or baseball best to those who like football best is $\frac{9}{4}$.

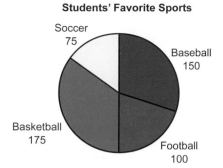

Students' Favorite Sports

Soccer 75
Baseball 150
Basketball 175
Football 100

PROBLEM 4 What is the ratio of students who like basketball best to all of the students surveyed?

SOLUTION Write the ratio and simplify.

$$\frac{\text{basketball}}{\text{all students surveyed}} = \frac{175}{175 + 75 + 150 + 100} = \frac{175}{500} = \frac{7}{20}$$

ANSWER The ratio of students who like basketball best to all the students surveyed is $\frac{7}{20}$.

➡ Drawing Circle Graphs

You can use ratios to draw circle graphs.

Example

PROBLEM 5 Draw a circle graph that represents the data.

SOLUTION Write the ratio of each part to the total.

How Lin Spent His Allowance		
Savings	**Food**	**Fun**
$15	$5	$30

savings: $\frac{15}{50} = \frac{3}{10}$ food: $\frac{5}{50} = \frac{1}{10}$ fun: $\frac{30}{50} = \frac{6}{10}$

A circle measures 360°. Multiply each ratio by 360° to find the angle to use for each section of data.

savings: $\frac{3}{10} \cdot 360° = 108°$ food: $\frac{1}{10} \cdot 360° = 36°$ fun: $\frac{6}{10} \cdot 360° = 216°$

Draw a circle and mark its center. Align a protractor at the center, draw the angles less than 180°, and label the sections.

ANSWER

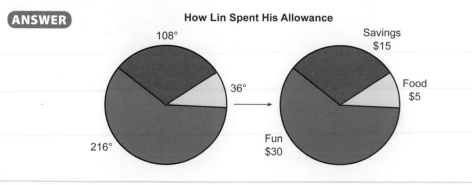

How Lin Spent His Allowance

108°
36°
216°

Savings $15
Food $5
Fun $30

TOPIC

Problem Set

Use the graph of diners' favorite vegetables to solve.

1. **Stepping Stones** What is the ratio of the number of people who prefer carrots to total number of people surveyed?

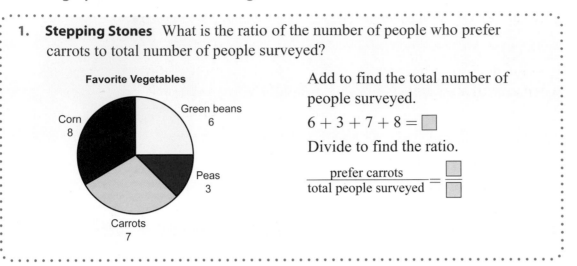

Favorite Vegetables

Corn 8
Green beans 6
Peas 3
Carrots 7

Add to find the total number of people surveyed.

$6 + 3 + 7 + 8 = \Box$

Divide to find the ratio.

$$\frac{\text{prefer carrots}}{\text{total people surveyed}} = \frac{\Box}{\Box}$$

Use the graph of favorite types of movies to solve.

2. What is the ratio of the number of people who prefer mystery movies to drama movies?

3. What is the ratio of the number of people who prefer comedies to all people surveyed?

4. What is the ratio of the number of people surveyed to the number who prefer action movies?

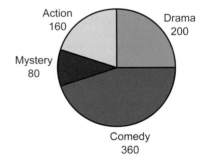

Favorite Types of Movies

Action 160
Drama 200
Mystery 80
Comedy 360

Use the graph of customers' favorite flavors of ice cream to solve.

5. How many more people prefer strawberry ice cream than prefer vanilla?

6. What percent of the customers prefer chocolate?

7. What is the ratio of customers who prefer vanilla to those who prefer chocolate or strawberry?

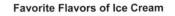
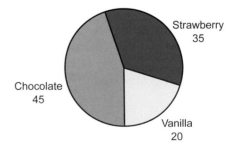

Favorite Flavors of Ice Cream

Strawberry 35
Chocolate 45
Vanilla 20

Use the graph of a student's afternoon activities to solve.

8. What is the ratio of minutes spent doing schoolwork to playing sports or games?

9. What percent of the student's time is spent on the Internet?

10. What is the ratio of the student's time spent playing sports to the time spent playing games?

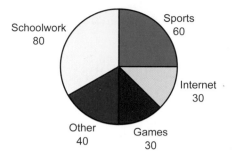

Time Spent in Afternoon Activities (min)

Schoolwork 80
Sports 60
Internet 30
Games 30
Other 40

Use the graph of favorite places to visit to solve.

11. What is the ratio of the number of people who chose an amusement park to all the people surveyed?

12. What percent of the people surveyed prefer visiting a national park?

13. **Challenge** How many people would need to change their response from beach to mountains for the ratio of people who prefer the mountains to national parks to be $\frac{1}{2}$?

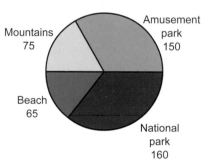

Favorite Places to Visit

Mountains 75
Amusement park 150
Beach 65
National park 160

Draw a circle graph that represents the data.

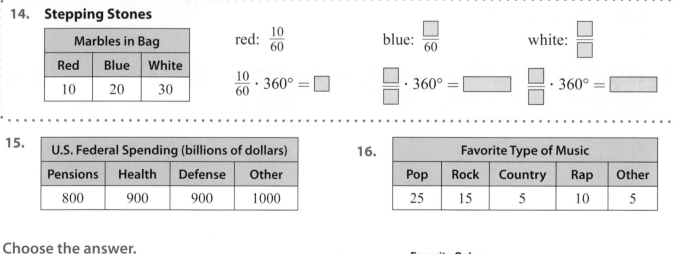

14. **Stepping Stones**

Marbles in Bag		
Red	Blue	White
10	20	30

red: $\frac{10}{60}$

$\frac{10}{60} \cdot 360° = \square$

blue: $\frac{\square}{60}$

$\frac{\square}{\square} \cdot 360° = \boxed{}$

white: $\frac{\square}{\square}$

$\frac{\square}{\square} \cdot 360° = \boxed{}$

15.

U.S. Federal Spending (billions of dollars)			
Pensions	Health	Defense	Other
800	900	900	1000

16.

Favorite Type of Music				
Pop	Rock	Country	Rap	Other
25	15	5	10	5

Choose the answer.

17. What is the ratio of people who chose red or green to those who chose blue?

A. $\frac{9}{8}$

B. $\frac{8}{9}$

C. $\frac{13}{18}$

D. $\frac{5}{18}$

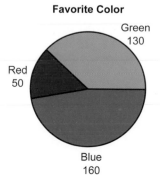

Favorite Color

Green 130
Red 50
Blue 160

More Statistical Graphs

Different types of graphs can be used to display sets of data differently.

➤ Interpreting Statistical Graphs

Definitions

A **bar graph** uses bars to display data.

A **line plot** uses dots to display individual data values with a number line.

A **line graph** displays data values as a series of points connected by straight line segments.

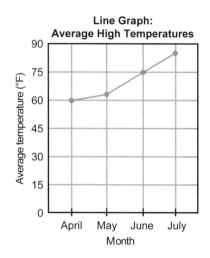

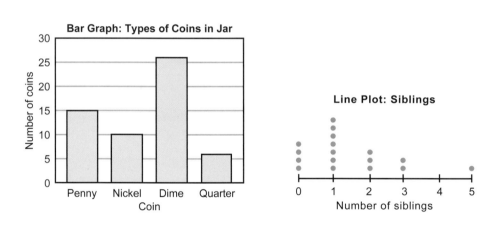

Example

PROBLEM 1 How many more pennies than nickels are shown in the bar graph?

SOLUTION Read the bar for each coin and subtract: $15 - 10 = 5$

ANSWER There are 5 more pennies than nickels.

PROBLEM 2 What is the ratio in the line plot of the number of people with exactly 2 siblings to those with just 1 sibling?

SOLUTION There are 3 people with 2 siblings and 7 with 1 sibling.

ANSWER The ratio is $\frac{3}{7}$.

Example

PROBLEM 3 According to the line graph, what was the temperature difference between April and June?

SOLUTION temperature in April, 60°F; temperature in June, 75°F
Subtract: $75 - 60 = 15$

ANSWER The temperature was 15°F higher in June.

➔ Selecting Statistical Graphs

Definitions

Discrete data have distinct intervals between any values. No intermediate values are possible. Examples: colors, shoe sizes, and ages

Continuous data can be any value within a range. Examples: temperature, time, and weight

Think About It

Think about the data set you are trying to represent with a graph. You should use bar graphs and line plots to represent discrete data. You should use line graphs to represent continuous data.

Example

Explain which type of graph would best display the data.

PROBLEM 4 town residents' votes for each of 4 possible new park sites

SOLUTION Vote numbers are discrete data, best shown in a bar graph or line plot. Bar graphs display larger numbers of data values better.

ANSWER A bar graph would display the discrete data best.

PROBLEM 5 heights of a sunflower recorded each week for a month

SOLUTION Height data are continuous. A line graph displays continuous data best.

ANSWER A line graph would display the continuous height data best.

PROBLEM 6 numbers of books read by 10 people over the summer

SOLUTION Numbers of books are discrete data, so a bar graph or line plot would work best. Line plots display smaller numbers of numeric data values better.

ANSWER A line plot would display the discrete data best.

TOPIC

Problem Set

Use the line graph to solve.

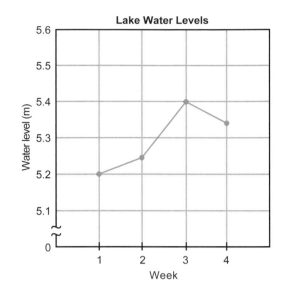
Lake Water Levels

1. **Stepping Stones** What was the difference in water levels between Week 1 and Week 3?

   The water level at Week 1 was ⬚.

   The water level at Week 3 was ⬚.

   ⬚ – ⬚ = ⬚

   The difference in water levels was ⬚ m.

2. What was the difference in water levels between Week 2 and Week 4?

3. Between which two weeks did the water level decrease?

Use the bar graph to solve.

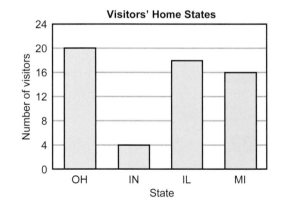
Visitors' Home States

4. How many visitors came from either Indiana or Michigan?

5. Order the home states from greatest to least number of visitors.

6. How many visitors are represented in the graph?

7. What fraction of the visitors are from Ohio or Michigan?

Use the line plot to solve.

8. How many people watched either 2 or
    3 movies last month?

9. How many more people watched exactly
    4 movies than did not watch any movies?

10. **Challenge** How many more people watched
    3 or more movies than watched 2 or fewer
    movies?

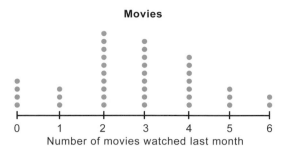

Movies

Number of movies watched last month

Explain which type of graph would best display the data.

11. numbers of sit-ups done each day for a month

12. amounts of time spent doing different drills at
    soccer practice

13. weights of a new puppy from ages 6 months
    to 1 year

14. numbers of votes for a club mascot

15. proportion of ethnicities of a state's residents

16. temperature of a liquid being heated in a
    science experiment

17. distance a train travels along the tracks during
    4 hours

18. food items in a day's diet that are meat, fruit,
    and bread

19. numbers of birds counted each morning for
    2 months

20. height of a melting snowbank during a warm
    spring weekend

21. **Challenge** ages of family members from 3 to
    77 years old at a family reunion

Choose the answer.

22. How many SUVs and trucks were sold?

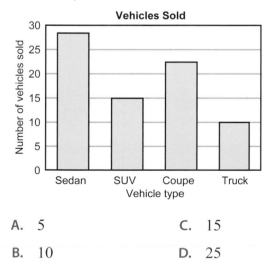

Vehicles Sold

Number of vehicles sold

Sedan   SUV   Coupe   Truck

Vehicle type

A. 5

B. 10

C. 15

D. 25

23. Which type of graph would best display a
    city's average monthly rainfall amounts for
    5 months?

    A. bar graph   C. line graph

    B. line plot   D. circle graph

24. Which type of graph would best display the
    numbers of free throws a basketball player
    took during each game of the season?

    A. bar graph   C. line graph

    B. line plot   D. circle graph

Histograms

You can use a graph to display the numbers of data points that fall within different intervals.

➜ Drawing Histograms

Definition

A **histogram** is a bar graph that displays the frequency of data values that occur within certain intervals. The height of each bar on a histogram gives the frequency for that bar's interval.

Tip
The bars in a histogram touch each other because there are no gaps in the intervals of the data.

Determine the equal-sized numerical intervals you will use, and then find the number of data values that fall within each interval. Be sure to use consecutive intervals, without any gaps. Draw a bar for each interval to show that number.

Example

PROBLEM 1 Draw a histogram to represent the rainfall data.

SOLUTION Select reasonable intervals for the data. The data go from 0 to 7. Use intervals of 0–1, 2–3, 4–5, and 6–7. Count the number of data values in each interval.
0–1, 16 data values
2–3, 8 data values
4–5, 4 data values
6–7, 2 data values
Draw and label the axes. Then draw a bar above each interval.

Daily Rainfall Amounts in June (cm)					
0	1	2	0	0	2
6	3	4	1	0	1
0	0	2	4	3	2
5	1	1	0	1	5
0	2	0	3	7	0

ANSWER

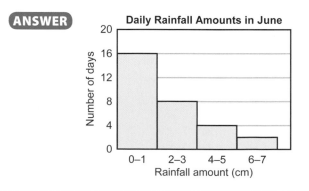

➜ Interpreting Histograms

Read data from a histogram by looking at the heights of the bars and the interval for each.

Example

Solve using the histograms that show heights of basketball players.

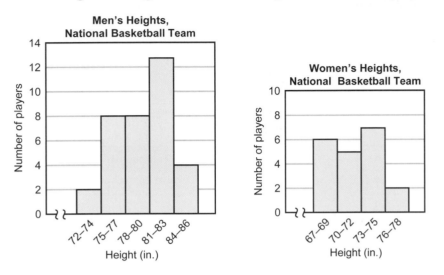

Think About It

Because data are shown only for intervals, histograms do not show specific data values.

You can't tell from the men's histogram, for example, how many players are exactly 82 in. tall.

PROBLEM 2 How many men players are shorter than 81 in.?

SOLUTION Add the values for the intervals with heights less than 81 in.
$2 + 8 + 8 = 18$

ANSWER There are 18 men players shorter than 81 in.

PROBLEM 3 How many women players are 73 in. or taller?

SOLUTION Add the values for the intervals with heights greater than or equal to 73 in.
$7 + 2 = 9$

ANSWER There are 9 women players who are 73 in. or taller.

PROBLEM 4 How many men players are as tall as or taller than the tallest woman player?

SOLUTION Look at the intervals. The tallest woman player could be 78 in. The intervals on the men's graph 78 in. and greater are 78–80, 81–83, and 84–86.
$8 + 13 + 4 = 25$

ANSWER There are 25 men players as tall as or taller than the tallest woman player, if you assume the tallest woman player is 78 in.

Think About It

In Problem 4, the greatest height interval for women players is 76–78 in., so you know that the tallest woman is at least 76 in. tall, and at most 78 in. tall.

Problem Set

Draw a histogram using the given category ranges to represent the data.

1. ranges: 0–1, 2–3, 4–5, 6–7

Numbers of Siblings					
0	1	1	2	2	0
2	0	6	1	0	3
2	1	0	4	1	3

2. ranges: 10–19, 20–29, 30–39, 40–49

Ages of Shoppers					
15	17	30	28	20	26
32	21	13	33	40	37
21	18	18	27	15	23

3. ranges: 30–34, 35–39, 40–44, 45–49, 50–54

Heights of Plants (cm)					
30	38	36	34	43	32
42	49	47	41	44	47
50	33	30	42	48	38
33	50	43	35	31	46

4. ranges: 70–73, 74–77, 78–81, 82–85

Daily High Temperatures (°F)					
72	72	73	75	77	79
79	76	74	70	70	72
72	78	79	81	81	82
78	77	75	75	75	72
73	73	72	74	71	72

Use the histograms to solve.

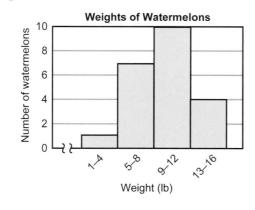

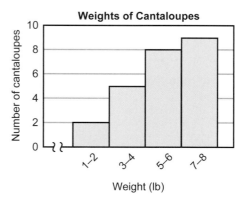

5. **Stepping Stones** How many watermelons weigh more than 4 lb?

Add the values for the weights greater than ☐ lb.

7 + ☐ + ☐ = ☐

There are ☐ watermelons that weigh more than 4 lb.

6. How many watermelons' weights are shown?

7. How many cantaloupes' weights are shown?

8. How many cantaloupes weigh 3 lb to 6 lb?

9. How many more cantaloupes weigh 8 lb or less than watermelons that weigh 8 lb or less?

10. **Challenge** How many watermelons weigh more than any of the cantaloupes?

Use the histogram to solve.

11. In how many games did the Wolverines score between 55 and 64 points?

12. In how many games did the Wolverines score fewer than 70 points?

13. How many games would the Wolverines have won against teams that scored 64 points?

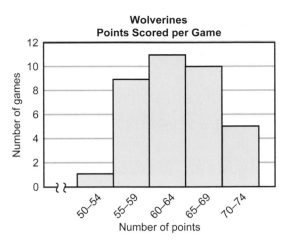

Use the histograms to solve.

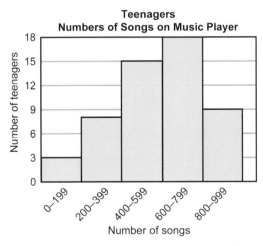

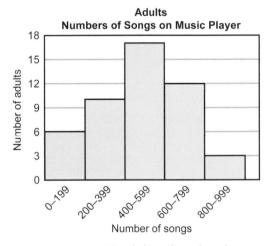

14. Which age group has more members with fewer than 600 songs? How many more members?

15. How many adults have 400 or more songs on their music players?

16. **Challenge** Explain what the shapes of the histograms tell you about how the numbers of songs teenagers have compare to the numbers the adults have.

Choose the answer.

17. How many more campers are 13 or younger than are 14 or older?

    A. 22

    B. 12

    C. 10

    D. 34

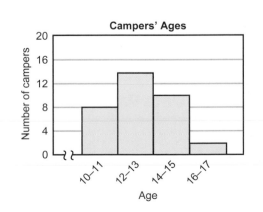

Measures of Center

Measures of center, like mean and median, can help summarize a set of data.

➥ Finding Mean, Median, and Mode

Definition

A **stem-and-leaf plot** is a graph used to organize and display data.

0	0	1	5	
1	5	6	7	7 8
2	0	2	8	9
3	4	4	6	

This line represents 0, 1, and 5.
This line represents 15, 16, 17, 17, and 18.
This line represents 20, 22, 28, and 29.
This line represents 34, 34, and 36.

Key: 2|2 means 22

Data shown in a table or stem-and-leaf plot can make it easier to calculate the mean, median, and mode.

Example

PROBLEM 1 Find the mean, median, and mode of the test scores shown in the stem-and-leaf plot.

7	9 9
8	2 4 6 8 9
9	0 1 2

Key: 8|2 means 82

SOLUTION Use the stem-and-leaf plot.

mean
$$\frac{79 + 79 + 82 + 84 + 86 + 88 + 89 + 90 + 91 + 92}{10} = \frac{860}{10} = 86$$

median   There are 10 test scores. The median is the average of the fifth and sixth test scores.

$$\frac{86 + 88}{2} = \frac{174}{2} = 87$$

mode   The number 79 occurs more than any other number.

ANSWER The mean is 86, the median is 87, and the mode is 79.

Remember

The *mean* is the sum of the values in a data set divided by the number of values.

The *median* is the middle value in a data set, or the average of the two middle numbers.

The *mode* is the value or values that appear most often in a data set.

➥ Adding New Data Values

Adding just one value to a data set may not change a measure of center, or it may have a great effect on the measure.

Example

PROBLEM 2 Michael's test scores were 90, 90, 94, 94, 96, 98, and 100. Find the effect that a new test score of 50 would have on the mean and median scores.

SOLUTION Find the mean and median of the original test scores.
median = 94

$$\text{mean} = \frac{90 + 90 + 94 + 94 + 96 + 98 + 100}{7} = \frac{662}{7} \approx 94.6$$

Find the new median and mode with a score of 50 added.
median = 94

$$\text{mean} = \frac{50 + 90 + 90 + 94 + 94 + 96 + 98 + 100}{7} = \frac{712}{8} = 89$$

ANSWER The median does not change, but the mean drops approximately 5.6 points.

➡ Determining the Best Measure of Center

The larger the group of data, the better a measure of center can summarize the data. Which measure you choose to use depends on the purpose for and shape of the data.

Example

Decide whether the mean or median is the better measure of center to summarize the data.

PROBLEM 3

```
2 | 4  7
3 | 3  3  7  8
4 | 0  1  2  5  7  9
5 | 4  6  8
6 | 1  3
```
Key: 2|4 means 24

SOLUTION There are no outliers and the data are symmetrical.

ANSWER The mean is the better measure of center to summarize the data.

PROBLEM 4 The data about home values in a neighborhood show that most of the values lie between $125,000 and $150,000. There are two homes in the neighborhood with values greater than $500,000.

A realtor wants to give a fair measure of the values of the homes.

SOLUTION There are outliers and the data are not symmetrical.

ANSWER The median is the better measure of center.

> **Remember**
>
> An *outlier* is a value in a data set that is separated from most of the rest of the values in the set.
>
> A value that is an outlier is much greater or much less than the other values.

Problem Set

Find the mean, median, and mode of the data.

1. **Stepping Stones**

   ```
   5 | 2 6 8 9 9
   6 | 0 2
   ```
   Key: 5|6 means 56

   Mean $\dfrac{52 + 56 + 58 + 59 + 59 + 60 + 62}{\boxed{}} = \dfrac{406}{\boxed{}} = \boxed{}$

   Median   Find the ▢ number: 52, 56, 58, ▢, 59, 60, 62

   Mode   The number ▢ occurs more than any other.

   The mean is ▢, the median is ▢, and the mode is ▢.

2.
   ```
   1 | 5 5
   2 | 0 5 5
   3 | 0 0 0 5
   4 | 5
   ```
   Key: 2|5 means 25

3.
   ```
   5 | 1
   6 |
   7 | 5 9
   8 | 1 9
   9 | 0 6 8
   ```
   Key: 8|1 means 81

4.
   ```
   3 | 2
   4 | 1 1
   5 | 0 6 7
   6 | 2
   7 | 0 0 2 2 2 3 4
   8 |
   9 | 1 2 4 4 4 4
   ```
   Key: 7|4 means 74

5. **Challenge**

Miles Driven					
535	129	445	329	657	801
299	549	190	449	535	663
990	375	980	876	678	556

Describe the effect on the mean and the median of adding the value 10 to the data set.

6.
   ```
   0 | 2 4 4 5 7
   1 | 0 0 0 4
   2 | 4 5
   3 | 1 1 2 7 9
   ```
   Key: 2|5 means 25

7.
   ```
   6 | 3 3 7 9
   7 | 2 2 2
   8 | 9
   9 | 0 5 6 7 8
   ```
   Key: 8|9 means 89

Decide whether the mean or median is the better measure of center to summarize the data.

9.
```
5 | 0 0 1 3
6 | 2 2 4 7 9
7 | 0 1 3 8 9 9 9
8 | 2 4 8 8
9 | 3 3 4
```
Key: 5|3 means 53

10.
```
2 | 0
3 | 1 6 7
4 | 2 8 8 9
5 | 0 1 2 5 7 8 8 9 9
```
Key: 4|9 means 49

11. PRG Corp. pays each of its 3 executives a salary of $125,000 per year. It pays each of its 62 production workers a salary of $30,000 per year.

12. The campers at a summer camp are all between 13 and 17 years old. There are about the same number of campers of each age.

13. Antoine received grades of As and Bs on 9 of his 10 assignments. He forgot to turn in one assignment and earned a 0 on it.

14. **Challenge**

Minutes Spent Online					
56	72	65	66	74	61
74	5	50	68	68	50
63	68	55	2	71	70

Choose the answer.

15. Which number is the median of the data?

   A. 56
   B. 57.5
   C. 57
   D. 63

```
4 | 0 8
5 | 2 7 7 8 9
6 | 3 3 3
```
Key: 4|8 means 48

16. How will adding the value 65 affect the mean and median of the data set 3, 3, 7, 8, 9?

   A. The mean increases less than the median increases.

   B. The mean increases more than the median increases.

   C. The mean and the median increase by the same amount.

   D. The mean stays the same and the median increases.

PROBLEM SET

Box-and-Whisker Plots

Box-and-whisker plots allow you to interpret different things about a set of data.

➔ **Interpreting a Box-and-Whisker Plot**

Quartiles are any of the three values that separate an ordered data set into four equal parts; a quartile also refers to the entire set of data in any quarter of the data, such as all the data between Q_2 and Q_3.

A **box-and-whisker plot** shows the distribution or spread of data; it uses the minimum, the maximum, and the three quartiles of the data to split the data into 4 quarters, or quartiles, of data.

The median of the lower half of the data is the first, or lower, quartile (Q_1). The median of the data is the second quartile (Q_2). The median of the upper half of the data is the third, or upper, quartile (Q_3).

Example

PROBLEM 1 What are the highest, lowest, and median test scores? What is the range of each of the four quarters of data?

Test

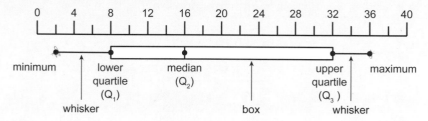

SOLUTION Interpret the box-and-whisker plot.
The maximum is 100, the minimum is 68, and the median is 86.

first quarter: $78 - 68 = 10$ third quarter: $91 - 86 = 5$
second quarter: $86 - 78 = 8$ fourth quarter: $100 - 91 = 9$

ANSWER The highest test score is 100, the lowest is 68, and the median is 86. The first-quarter range is 10, the second-quarter range is 8, the third-quarter range is 5, and the fourth-quarter range is 9.

Example

PROBLEM 2 The box-and-whisker plot was made using the ages of 100 people. In which quarters are the data most concentrated and least concentrated?

Ages of People

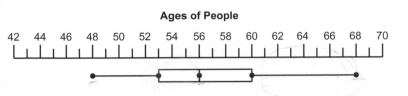

SOLUTION The lower quartile and median are closest together, indicating data are closest together in the second quarter.

The upper quartile and maximum are furthest apart, indicating data are the most spread out in the fourth quarter.

ANSWER The second quarter has the most-concentrated data and the fourth quarter has the least-concentrated data.

➡ Making a Box-and-Whisker Plot

Find the lower and upper extremes and the quartiles to help you make a box-and-whisker plot.

Example

PROBLEM 3 Use the data to make a box-and-whisker plot.

```
2 | 3
3 | 2  2  6  8
4 | 0  1  3  4  9
```
Key: 3|6 means 36

SOLUTION Find the minimum, the maximum, and the quartiles. Then draw the number line, points, box, and whiskers.

minimum: 23   maximum: 49   median: $\dfrac{38 + 40}{2} = 39$

first quartile: 32 (median of lower half of data)
third quartile: 43 (median of upper half of data)

ANSWER

Tip

When drawing the number line, start with a value less than the minimum and a value greater than the maximum. Use a ruler to help draw the number line, box, and whiskers.

TOPIC

Problem Set

Use the temperatures box-and-whisker plot to solve.

> 1. **Stepping Stones** What are the maximum, minimum, and median temperatures?
>
>   The maximum is ☐, the minimum is 12, and the median is ☐.

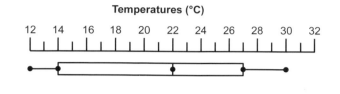

Temperatures (°C)

12 14 16 18 20 22 24 26 28 30 32

2. What are the quartiles of the data?

3. What is the range of each of the four quarters of data?

Use the card collection box-and-whisker plot to solve.

4. What are the maximum, minimum, and median number of cards?

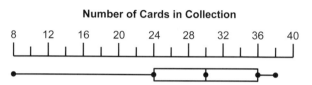

Number of Cards in Collection

8 12 16 20 24 28 32 36 40

5. In which quarter are the data most concentrated?

6. In which quarter are the data least concentrated?

Use the dog weights box-and-whisker plot to solve.

7. What are the maximum, minimum, and median weights?

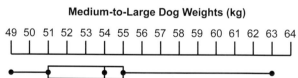

Medium-to-Large Dog Weights (kg)

49 50 51 52 53 54 55 56 57 58 59 60 61 62 63 64

8. What are the quartiles of the data?

9. What is the range of each of the four quarters of data?

Use the finishing times box-and-whisker plot to solve.

10. What are the maximum, minimum, and median times?

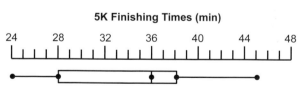

5K Finishing Times (min)

24 28 32 36 40 44 48

11. What are the quartiles of the data?

12. What is the range of each of the four quarters of data?

Use the box-and-whisker plot to solve.

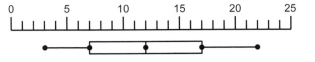

13. What are the maximum, minimum, and median values?

14. **Challenge** In which quarter are the data most concentrated?

15. **Challenge** In which quarter are the data least concentrated?

Use the data to make a box-and-whisker plot.

16. **Stepping Stones**

```
6 | 5  8  8  9
7 | 0  2  4  4
8 | 0  2
```
Key: 7|4 means 74

minimum: ☐   maximum: ☐   first quartile: ☐

median: ☐   third quartile: ☐

60   65   70   75   80   85

17.
```
3 | 0
4 | 0  2  2  3  3  5  6  6
5 | 9
```
Key: 4|6 means 46

18.
```
2 | 6  7  8
3 | 3  3  4  5
4 | 0
5 | 1  2
```
Key: 5|1 means 51

19.
```
4 | 2  3  5  5  8
5 | 0  3  4  8
6 | 3
7 | 3  9
```
Key: 4|8 means 48

20. **Challenge**

```
0 | 4  5  7
1 | 0  1  4  4  5  5  5  8  8
2 |
3 | 1
4 | 3  4  7  9  9
```
Key: 1|5 means 15

Choose the answer.

0   5   10   15   20

21. In what quarter are the data most concentrated?

   A. first quarter
   B. second quarter
   C. third quarter
   D. fourth quarter

22. What is the median of the data?

   A. 2
   B. 5
   C. 8
   D. 15

Measures of Variation

Measures of variation show the spread of a set of data.

➦ Finding Interquartile Range

Definition

A **measure of variation** measures the range or spread of a set of data compared to a measure of center like the mean. Examples of measures of variation are the **interquartile range (IQR)** and the **mean absolute deviation (MAD)**.

Interquartile Range (IQR)

$IQR = Q_3 - Q_1$, where Q_3 is the upper quartile and Q_1 is the lower quartile of a set of data.

Use the formula to find the interquartile range, which is the range between Q_1 and Q_3 and is where half the data lies.

Example

Find the interquartile range of the data.

PROBLEM 1

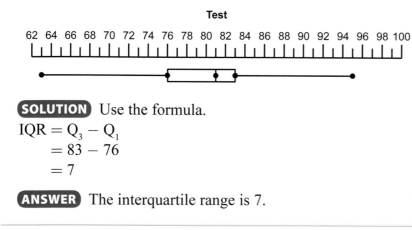

Test

SOLUTION Use the formula.

$$IQR = Q_3 - Q_1$$
$$= 83 - 76$$
$$= 7$$

ANSWER The interquartile range is 7.

Example

PROBLEM 2

```
4 | 6  8  9  9
5 | 1  2  3  6  8  9
6 | 0  2  3  5  7
7 | 1  2  4  7
```
Key: 4|8 means 48

SOLUTION There are 19 data values, so Q_1 is the 5th value, and Q_3 is the 15th value.

$IQR = Q_3 - Q_1 = 67 - 51 = 16$

ANSWER The interquartile range is 16.

→ Finding Mean Absolute Deviation

Mean Absolute Deviation (MAD)

An **absolute deviation** is the absolute value of the difference between a data value and the mean. To find the **MAD**, find the mean of all the absolute deviations.

The mean absolute deviation is the average distance of all data values from the mean of the data.

Example

PROBLEM 3 Find the mean absolute deviation of the data.

```
0 | 3  5
1 | 6
2 | 4  7
```
Key: 2|4 means 24

SOLUTION

First find the mean.

$$\frac{3 + 5 + 16 + 24 + 27}{5} = \frac{75}{5} = 15$$

Add all the absolute deviations.

$|3 - 15| + |5 - 15| + |16 - 15| + |24 - 15| + |27 - 15|$

$= |-12| + |-10| + |1| + |9| + |12| = 12 + 10 + 1 + 9 + 12 = 44$

Divide the sum by the number of data values.

$$\frac{44}{5} = 8.8$$

ANSWER The mean absolute deviation is 8.8.

TOPIC

Problem Set

Find the interquartile range of the data.

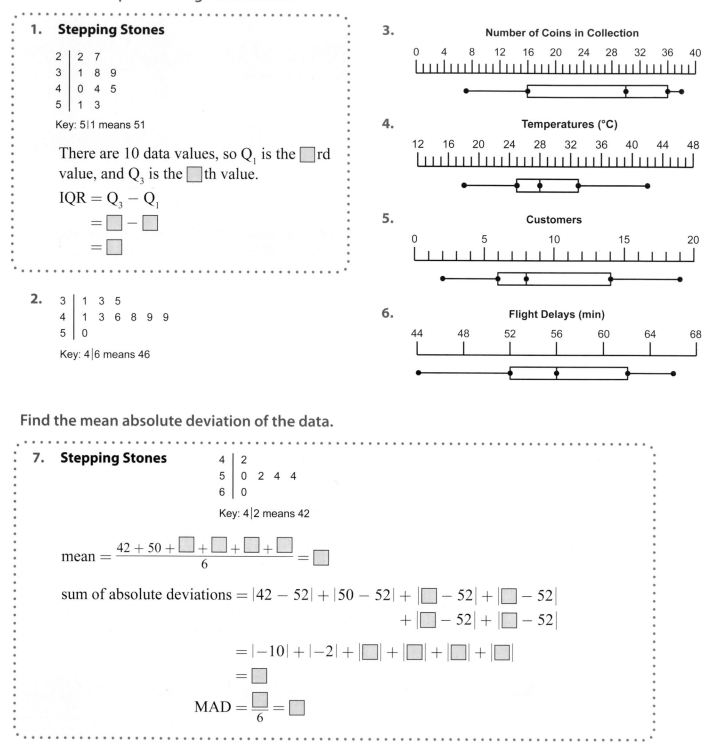

1. Stepping Stones

```
2 | 2  7
3 | 1  8  9
4 | 0  4  5
5 | 1  3
```

Key: 5|1 means 51

There are 10 data values, so Q_1 is the ☐rd value, and Q_3 is the ☐th value.

$$IQR = Q_3 - Q_1$$
$$= \boxed{} - \boxed{}$$
$$= \boxed{}$$

2.

```
3 | 1  3  5
4 | 1  3  6  8  9  9
5 | 0
```

Key: 4|6 means 46

3. Number of Coins in Collection

4. Temperatures (°C)

5. Customers

6. Flight Delays (min)

Find the mean absolute deviation of the data.

7. Stepping Stones

```
4 | 2
5 | 0  2  4  4
6 | 0
```

Key: 4|2 means 42

$$\text{mean} = \frac{42 + 50 + \boxed{} + \boxed{} + \boxed{} + \boxed{}}{6} = \boxed{}$$

$$\text{sum of absolute deviations} = |42 - 52| + |50 - 52| + |\boxed{} - 52| + |\boxed{} - 52|$$
$$+ |\boxed{} - 52| + |\boxed{} - 52|$$

$$= |-10| + |-2| + |\boxed{}| + |\boxed{}| + |\boxed{}| + |\boxed{}|$$

$$= \boxed{}$$

$$MAD = \frac{\boxed{}}{6} = \boxed{}$$

PROBLEM SET

8.

```
1 | 3  5
2 | 1  1
3 | 2  9
```
Key: 3|2 means 32

9.

```
0 | 1
1 | 3  9
2 | 3  5  6
```
Key: 1|3 means 13

10.

```
5 | 5  6  7
6 | 3  3
7 | 3  6  9
```
Key: 6|3 means 63

11.

```
6 | 1  1  1
7 | 0
8 | 3  5  6  9
```
Key: 8|3 means 83

Describe the spread of the data using measures of variation.

12. Stepping Stones

```
3 | 0  1  1  4
4 | 0  1  1  2  2  3  6
5 | 9
```
Key: 4|6 means 46

IQR = 10   MAD = 5.7

The IQR shows that the spread of the middle 50% of the data is ☐.

If this problem were about miles driven, the MAD shows that the average number of miles away from the overall average is ☐.

13.   IQR = 15   MAD ≈ 6.85

14.   IQR = 15   MAD = 6.4

Choose the answer.

15. What is the interquartile range?

```
0        5        10        15        20
└┴┴┴┴┴┴┴┴┴┴┴┴┴┴┴┴┴┴┴┴┴┘
```

A. 2   C. 9

B. 7   D. 17

16. What is the mean absolute deviation?

```
4 | 0  5  5
5 |
6 | 0  5
```
Key: 4|5 means 45

A. 51   C. 9.2

B. 46   D. 0.92

Outliers

In some data sets, there are values that are far from most of the rest of the values.

→ Finding Outliers

Definition

An **outlier** is a value that is unusually small or large compared with the rest of the data.

Numbers called fences can help you identify outliers in a data set.

Lower and Upper Fences

Lower fence $= Q_1 - 1.5 \cdot IQR$, where Q_1 is the lower quartile and IQR is the interquartile range.

Upper fence $= Q_3 + 1.5 \cdot IQR$, where Q_3 is the upper quartile and IQR is the interquartile range.

A data value that is less than the lower fence or greater than the upper fence is an outlier.

Remember

The lower quartile, Q_1, is the median of the lower half of the data. The upper quartile, Q_3, is the median of the upper half of the data. The interquartile range, IQR, is the difference between the upper and lower quartiles.

Example

PROBLEM 1 Find whether there are any outliers in the data set.

SOLUTION Find the lower and upper fences. Note them on the graph.
$$IQR = 76 - 70 = 6$$

lower fence $= 70 - 1.5 \cdot 6$ upper fence $= 76 + 1.5 \cdot 6$
$$= 61 \qquad\qquad\qquad\qquad = 85$$

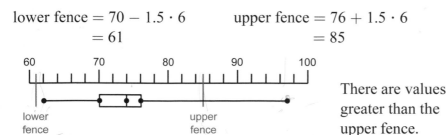

There are values greater than the upper fence.

ANSWER Yes, there are outliers.

Finding How Outliers Affect the Mean and Median

Example

PROBLEM 2 The mean and median of the data are given. Compare how they are affected when the outlier 2 is added to the data.

SOLUTION Find the mean and median ages with the outlier included. Then compare the measures of center.

$$\text{mean} = \frac{2 + 44 + 44 + 52 + 54 + 54 + 56 + 60}{8} = 45.75 \text{ years}$$

$$\text{median} = 53 \text{ years}$$

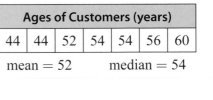

Ages of Customers (years)						
44	44	52	54	54	56	60

mean = 52   median = 54

Compare means: Compare medians:

$52 - 45.75 = 6.25$ $54 - 53 = 1$

The mean with the outlier is 6.25 years less than the mean without the outlier.

The median with the outlier is 1 year less than the median without the outlier.

ANSWER The outlier has a greater effect on the mean, decreasing the average age by 6.25 years, while it decreases the median age by only 1 year.

Identifying Skewed Data

Definitions

A set of data is said to be **skewed left** if the distribution of the data has a longer tail to the left side.

A set of data is said to be **skewed right** if the distribution of the data has a longer tail to the right side.

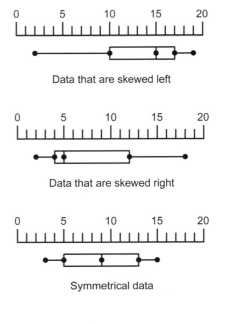

Data that are skewed left

Data that are skewed right

Symmetrical data

Example

PROBLEM 3 Determine if the data are skewed left, skewed right, or not skewed either way.

Months of Exercise

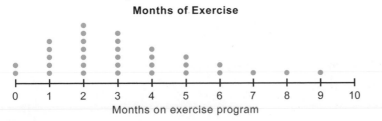

Months on exercise program

SOLUTION The distribution has a longer tail on the right-hand side.

ANSWER The data are skewed right.

Problem Set

State whether the minimum or maximum for either extreme in the data set is an outlier.

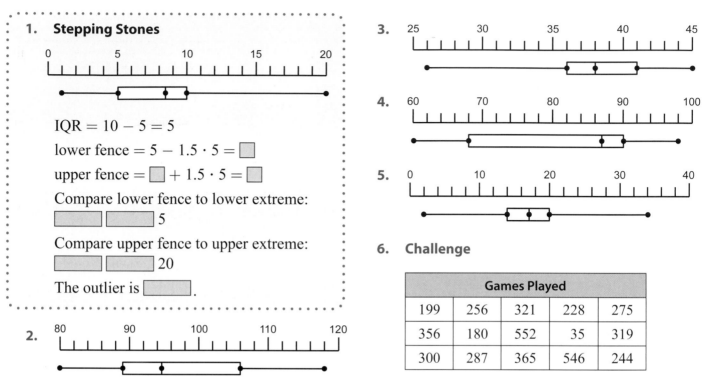

1. Stepping Stones

0   5   10   15   20

IQR $= 10 - 5 = 5$

lower fence $= 5 - 1.5 \cdot 5 = \square$

upper fence $= \square + 1.5 \cdot 5 = \square$

Compare lower fence to lower extreme:

$\square$ $\square$ 5

Compare upper fence to upper extreme:

$\square$ $\square$ 20

The outlier is $\square$.

2.

80   90   100   110   120

3.

25   30   35   40   45

4.

60   70   80   90   100

5.

0   10   20   30   40

6. Challenge

Games Played				
199	256	321	228	275
356	180	552	35	319
300	287	365	546	244

Compare how the mean and median are affected when each outlier is added to the data set.

7. Stepping Stones outliers: 31, 0

Number of Fish Caught				
4	7	11	6	7

mean $= 7$ median $= 7$

mean with outlier $31 = \dfrac{4 + 7 + 11 + 6 + 7 + \square}{6} = \square$

median with outlier $31 = \square$

mean with outlier $0 = \dfrac{4 + 7 + 11 + 6 + 7 + \square}{6} = \square$

median with outlier $0 = \square$

The outlier $\square$ had a greater effect on the mean, increasing it by $\square$, while the median remained the same.

8.

Minutes Spent Studying							
84	84	71	73	90	89	86	79

mean $= 82$ median $= 84$

outliers: 40, 163

9. Challenge

Kilometers Jogged				
18.5	19.6	17.5	18.2	14.7

mean $= 17.7$ median $= 18.2$

outliers: 0, 26.5

Determine if the data are skewed left, skewed right, or not skewed either way.

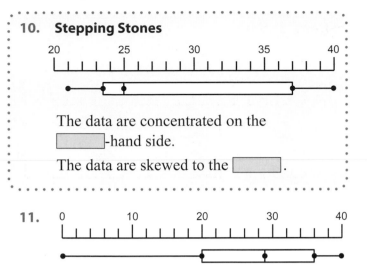
11.

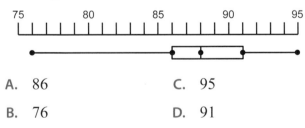

12.

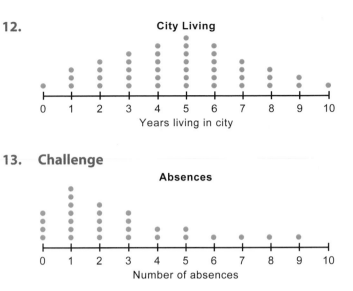

13. Challenge

Absences

Solve.

14. A company paid 5 employees the following salaries: $40,000; $42,000; $88,000; $46,000; $51,000. What salary is an outlier?

15. How does the house price $78,000 affect the mean house price when added to the house prices $249,000; $250,000; $229,000; and $261,000?

Choose the answer.

16. Which grade is an outlier?

A. 86   C. 95

B. 76   D. 91

17. What effect does adding the outlier to the data set have on the mean and median?

Pennies Collected					
56	44	48	51	52	49

mean = 50   median = 50

outlier: 134

A. The median and mean do not change.

B. The median increases and the mean does not change.

C. The mean increases and the median does not change.

D. The median and mean increase.

Samples and Bias

Sometimes you can't survey everyone in a big group. So ask a smaller group that represents the big group.

➜ Finding Sources of Error in Samples

Definitions

A **population** is a group of individuals or objects on which data are collected.

A **sample** is a part of a group or a population.

Bias is the error that can arise when a sample is not representative of the population.

Tip

Samples that include randomly selected members of a population are more likely to be representative of the population as a whole.

When you look at a sample and a population, consider how representative the data from the sample will be of the population.

Example

Explain whether the sample is representative of the population.

PROBLEM 1 A survey seeks to find activities that teenagers in a town enjoy. A sample is taken from teenagers at the town's library.

SOLUTION The population is all teenagers in the town, and the sample is teenagers who use the library. Teenagers using the library might have different interests than other teenagers in the town.

ANSWER The sample is not representative of the population, because it includes only teenagers who might be interested in books or reading.

PROBLEM 2 A survey seeks to find the shopping habits of shoppers at the mall. A sample is taken by surveying every fifth person to enter the mall.

SOLUTION The sample randomly includes some shoppers of all the shoppers at the mall.

ANSWER The sample is representative of the population.

TOPIC

➡ Describing Effects of Bias from a Sample

If a sample is not representative of the population, there can be bias in the data when it is applied from the sample to the population. Think about what data from the population will be left out or overemphasized if a biased sample is used.

Example

Describe the effect of any bias from the sample.

PROBLEM 3 A survey about community members' favorite sports is given to a sample made up of parents of youth baseball league players.

SOLUTION The sample includes members of the population who are involved in baseball, but not any members who do not like baseball.

ANSWER The results from the sample might show bias in favor of baseball.

PROBLEM 4 A survey about computer use is sent to randomly selected e-mail addresses.

SOLUTION The sample is limited to members of the population who have an e-mail account. People with e-mail accounts might be more likely to use computers than those without e-mail accounts.

ANSWER The results from the sample might show bias in favor of people who use computers.

PROBLEM 5 A survey about how much television people in a community watch is taken by calling randomly selected homes in the community between 10:00 a.m. and 2:00 p.m.

SOLUTION Because the survey will poll people who are at home during the day, the sample will include more people who do not work outside the home. These people might have more time during the day to watch television than those who are at work.

ANSWER The results from the sample might show bias in increased times watching television.

Problem Set

Explain whether the sample is representative of the population.

1. **Stepping Stones** population: drivers; sample: drivers who stop to get gas at the local convenience store

   Drivers also can get gas at other gas stations.

   All drivers [   ] be included in the sample.

   The sample [   ] representative.

2. population: football fans; sample: people in randomly selected seats at a football game

3. population: restaurant diners; sample: subscribers to a gourmet food magazine

4. population: parents; sample: shoppers at a baby clothing store

5. population: toll road users; sample: every 10th car passing through a toll booth

6. population: cell phone users; sample: randomly selected phone numbers from the phone book

7. population: swimmers; sample: every fifth person entering the community pool

8. population: shoppers for electronics; sample: every 10th person entering a shopping mall that includes a large electronics store

9. population: chocolate consumers; sample: surveys inside a company's chocolate bar wrappers that are completed and returned to the company

10. population: theme park visitors; sample: every third adult entering the park

Describe the effect of any bias from the sample.

11. **Stepping Stones** survey: amount of weekly exercise; sample: every 10th person entering a gym

    People entering a gym are [   ] likely to exercise than those not entering a gym.

    The survey is likely to find that people exercise [   ] than they actually do.

12. survey: Americans' favorite winter activity; sample: randomly selected residents of Maine

13. survey: number of members in the household; sample: shoppers at a discount warehouse store

14. survey: length of time people keep their cars; sample: every fifth driver through a carwash

15. survey: all-time best basketball player; sample: players in a youth basketball league

16. survey: Americans' favorite fruit; sample: randomly selected residents of Florida

17. survey: favorite type of movie; sample: every 10th person entering a movie theater for a 9:00 p.m. show

18. survey: amount of money spent monthly on yard-care products; sample: randomly selected addresses throughout the county

State whether the sample is representative of the population. If not, describe the effect of any bias from the sample.

19. **Stepping Stones** Alex wants to know children's favorite piece of playground equipment. He asks all the children on the swings and the slide.

    The population is [   ].

    The sample selects from [   ] of the population.

    Samples are more likely to prefer the [   ] or the [   ].

20. Sheila conducts a survey to find the types of shoes teenagers are wearing. She surveys every third teenager she sees entering a sporting goods store.

21. Julio thinks the city needs to build more soccer fields in its sports complex. He surveys randomly selected people at the city's sports complex about their use of the facilities there.

22. Mr. Jenkins wants to order more fiction books for the community center's library. He surveys every fifth person entering the town's public library to find the types of books they like to read.

23. Anderson wants to convince the mayor of his city that the roads throughout the city need to be plowed more often during snowstorms. He surveys every 10th driver stopping at a gas station in the center of town about whether the roads are well maintained.

24. **Challenge** Ella wants to know how many different states other students her age have visited. She surveys randomly selected members of a travel club who are her age.

Choose the answer.

25. Which sample is most representative of a population of pet owners?

    A. visitors to a dog park

    B. customers of a pet-grooming salon

    C. customers of a pet store

    D. subscribers to a magazine about cats and dogs

26. Sahil surveys 50 randomly selected people at the city park to find their favorite activities. How might the sample be biased?

    A. Not everyone in the city lives near the park.

    B. People at the park might be more likely to prefer outdoor activities to indoor activities.

    C. The 50 people he surveyed might not visit the park every week.

    D. People at the park might be less likely to have a favorite activity.

Sampling Strategies

You need to use a sound sampling strategy if you want the sample's data to represent the population.

➡ Identifying Sampling Strategies

Definitions

In a **simple random** sampling, all members of the population have an equal probability of selection.

In a **stratified random** sampling, the population is first organized into separate categories, and then each is sampled as an independent subpopulation.

In a **systematic** sampling, the population is ordered, and then members are selected at regular intervals through that ordered list.

In a **convenience** sampling, members of the population who are close at hand are selected.

Remember

A representative sample will look like the population.

You can use any of the sampling strategies defined above to take a sample from a population.

Example

Identify the type of sample used.

PROBLEM 1 To find out opinions from users of the city's baseball fields, a sample is taken by asking every 10th person entering the field complex.

SOLUTION The sample is taken by selecting members of the population at regular intervals.

ANSWER A *systematic* sampling is used.

PROBLEM 2 A sample of students from a tae kwon do school population is taken by surveying 20 randomly selected students from each belt level.

SOLUTION The population is being broken down by belt levels with students randomly selected from each level.

ANSWER A *stratified random* sampling is used.

Think About It

The smaller the sample size is, the greater the chance that a random sampling will not be representative of the population.

TOPIC

➡ Selecting a Sampling Strategy

Some strategies will be easier to implement, while others might give more representative samples. Look at the population and the purpose of the sample to decide which strategy to use.

Example

Select a sampling strategy that will produce the most representative sample for the situation.

PROBLEM 3 The state keeps records of all licensed drivers and wants to find out their opinions about a new registration process.

SOLUTION The state could use a computer program to select random drivers from its records of all drivers to survey.

ANSWER A *simple random* sample would work best.

PROBLEM 4 A surf shop owner in Daytona Beach wants to find out information about what types of things people buy when they visit Florida beaches.

SOLUTION Florida's beaches cover a large area, so taking a sample from the entire population would not be practical. The shop owner could take a sample of those beach visitors near the shop.

ANSWER A *convenience* sample would work best.

PROBLEM 5 The owners of a new sports stadium want to get opinions about their facilities from season ticket holders. Season tickets can be bought for the lower level of the stadium, for the upper level, and for luxury skyboxes.

SOLUTION Fans in different parts of the arena may have different opinions about the facilities, so a sample that fairly represents each subgroup of the population would work best.

ANSWER A *stratified random* sample would work best.

> ## Think About It
>
> A systematic sampling of drivers also would be effective for Problem 4. Drivers could be ordered alphabetically by name, and then chosen from the list at a given interval.

TOPIC

Problem Set

Identify the type of sample used.

1. **Stepping Stones** Club members' names are written on slips of paper, and 20 names are drawn at random to conduct a survey about club benefits.

   All members of the population have an [ ] probability of selection.

   The sample is a [ ] sample.

2. Coaches pick 20 boys and 20 girls randomly from the basketball league to survey about practice and game times.

3. A store employee surveys every 20th person who enters the store.

4. An electronics store sends out a survey to the people on its mailing list asking them about their favorite brands of televisions.

5. Max surveys the children who live on his street about the types of equipment they want installed at the new city playground.

6. A computer generates a random list of telephone numbers to call to survey people about telephone fees.

7. Ten people are picked at random from each of 15 different theaters at a cinema.

8. **Challenge** Carlos randomly selects a house on the first street of a neighborhood to survey about traffic. Then he stops at every seventh house in the neighborhood to ask the same questions.

Select a sampling strategy that will produce the most representative sample for the situation.

9. **Stepping Stones** Shelby plays on an elite soccer team that travels around the state to play other elite teams. She wants to find out what brands of soccer shoes players at the elite level wear.

   Shelby probably doesn't have access to all elite soccer players, but she does come into contact with some of them. She should use a [ ] sampling.

10. A gym offers four different levels of membership. A trainer at the gym wants to know how likely the gym members would be to pay extra for personal training.

11. A company receives a shipment of 5 tons of coffee beans. The beans are shipped in bags weighing 10 lb each. The company wants to test the quality of the beans.

12. Eli takes her younger brother to the playground every afternoon. She wants to find out what outdoor activities boys enjoy most.

13. A party official has a printed list of all registered voters in a county. She wants to know whom they plan to vote for in the upcoming election.

14. Kyle wants to know how many hours the members of his service club typically spend on volunteer projects throughout the year.

15. A baseball league is made up of five different divisions based on age. The league wants to survey players' parents about league issues.

16. An automobile manufacturer wants to know that the wheels on its cars are balanced when they leave the factory.

17. Marcel wants to find out information about shoppers at a large mall by placing a survey on the car windshields in the parking lot.

18. Mrs. Rowe attends a conference for math educators. She wants to know the most popular method for teaching areas of circles among educators across the country.

19. A librarian wants to get an idea of how old the books in the library are. Books are divided and displayed by type.

20. A marketing company wants to know what times the most residents of a region are watching television.

21. Antoine lives near a state park in Virginia. He wants to find out the types of activities people enjoy most at all of Virginia's state parks.

22. Isabella wants to know which swimming stroke is most popular among all of the swimmers gathered for a large regional swim competition.

23. A grocery store owner wants to know whether his shoppers would use coupons that could be printed from a home computer.

24. **Challenge** An engineer needs to know how many cars pass over a bridge during a year. The number of cars using the bridge varies depending on the time of day and day of the week.

Choose the answer.

25. Which sampling strategy does Lien use if she samples a population of club members by calling every fifth member in the club's phone book?

A. simple random

B. stratified random

C. systematic

D. convenience

26. Which sampling strategy is best to use when not all of the members of a population are easily accessible for a survey?

A. simple random

B. stratified random

C. systematic

D. convenience

Statistical Claims

Be very careful of claims that are backed up by statistics. Things are not always what they seem to be.

➡ Distorting Statistical Claims with Graphs

Look carefully at how statistics are gathered and presented to make sure that the true data points are not being distorted.

Example

PROBLEM 1 Company Y created this bar graph to compare the life spans of its computers and its competitors' computers. Explain how this graph might distort the data.

SOLUTION Because of the bars' heights, the life span of Company Y's computers seems to be much longer than the other companies' computers. But the scale does not start at 0, so the actual difference in life spans is less than 5 months.

ANSWER The graph distorts the data by using a scale that does not start at 0, making the bar height differences exaggerated.

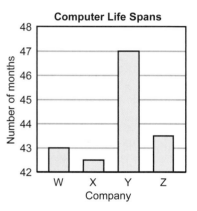

➡ Identifying Survey Bias

Example

PROBLEM 2
This ad appeared in a newspaper. Explain how the claim might distort actual data.

> Our juice is preferred by **99%** of children surveyed!

SOLUTION The ad does not reveal how the sample of the population of children was chosen. The company could have surveyed children that it already knows prefer its product.

ANSWER The sample might not be representative of the population.

T O P I C

➜ Misleading Statistical Measures

Different statistical measures can be selected to emphasize different features of the same data set. Look at the measure being used and what that measure tells you about the data set.

Example

Use this table of salaries paid by a company to solve.

Company Salaries			
$36,000	$41,000	$39,000	$36,000
$32,500	$40,000	$37,000	$450,000

PROBLEM 3 The company is advertising to hire a new employee. It advertises a mean salary of $89,000. Why did the company choose to advertise the mean?

SOLUTION A higher salary would be more attractive to a potential employee. There is an outlier in the data set, $450,000, which will make the mean salary higher than all but one salary.

ANSWER The company chose the mean salary because it would be most attractive.

PROBLEM 4 What measures of the company's salary are closer to what most employees at the company earn?

SOLUTION The mode salary is $36,000. The median salary is the mean of $37,000 and $39,000, which is $38,000. Both of those measures are closer to what most of the employees earn.

ANSWER The median and mode are closer to what most employees earn.

PROBLEM 5 The table shows recent wait times at a clinic. Which measure should the clinic use to advertise that patients there are seen quickly?

Clinic Wait Times (min)			
45	8	20	5
10	15	80	90

SOLUTION Find the measures and compare.

mean = (45 + 8 + 20 + 5 + 10 + 15 + 80 + 90) ÷ 8 = 273 ÷ 8 = 34.1
median = (15 + 20) ÷ 2 = 35 ÷ 2 = 17.5
mode: none

ANSWER The clinic should advertise the median wait time.

T O P I C

Problem Set

Use the graph to solve.

1. **Stepping Stones** Andre says that the graph shows that the number of hurricanes increased each year in the 1990s. Explain how this conclusion might not be valid.

   Look at the horizontal scale.

   The scale includes only years ☐, ☐, ☐, ☐, and ☐.

   The data for years ☐, ☐, and ☐ are missing.

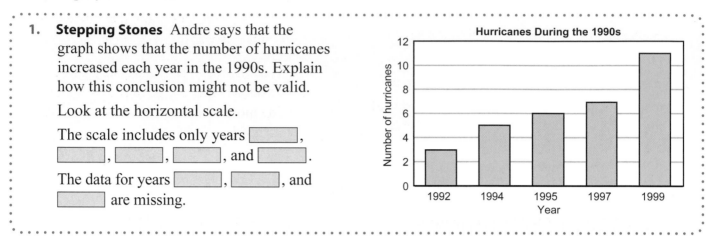

2. Explain how the graph might distort the data to give a false impression about the relative returns on investment.

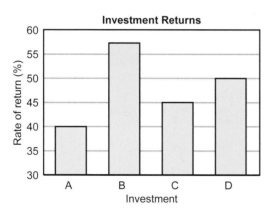

3. A student makes this bar graph to show her math quiz scores. Explain how this graph might distort the data.

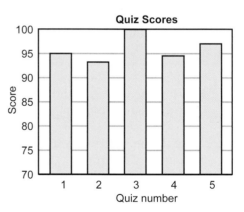

4. Riley uses these graphs to show that average temperatures were higher in July than in August. Explain how the graphs could be misleading.

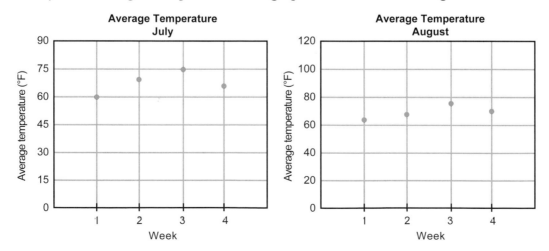

Explain how bias in the survey might have affected the results.

5. A survey of a sample of children about their favorite sports shows that the most popular sports are gymnastics and softball.

6. A survey of drivers shows that most drivers prefer the G300 to any other sports car.

7. A survey asks teens, "Do you, like most teenagers, dislike listening to boring classical music?" The results show that teens dislike classical music.

8. A survey asks, "Don't you think the city should spend more money on trash cans to do something about the overflowing trash in our area?" The results show that citizens want more money spent on trash cans.

9. A survey of residents in a wealthy part of town asks whether the government should provide more low-income housing for the town's residents.

Explain why the measure was selected to report on the data set.

10. The mean price of homes sold in the area is $197,000.

Home Prices		
$124,000	$99,000	$130,000
$122,000	$450,000	$106,000
$114,000	$497,000	$131,000

11. Jerrol jogged a median distance of 7 miles.

Miles Jogged		
6	7	6
8	8	6
7	9	1

12. The mean number of coins used is 30.

Number of Coins		
3	5	25
24	63	70
48	27	5

13. **Challenge** The median pumpkin weight is 34 lb.

Pumpkin Weights (lb)		
34	11	16
12	42	41
38	40	13

Choose the answer.

14. What could cause the graph to be misleading?

A. There are missing values along the horizontal axis.

B. The bars have different labels.

C. The scale does not begin at 0.

D. The titles are misleading.

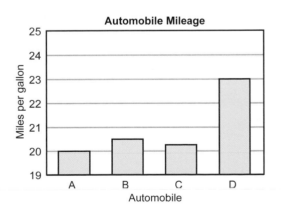

Chapter 9 Review

Choose the answer.

1. What is the ratio of money saved to money spent on clothes?

A. 5 : 6

B. 3 : 10

C. 6 : 5

D. 25 : 100

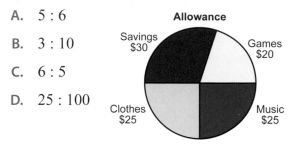

Allowance

Savings $30

Games $20

Music $25

Clothes $25

2. Which type of graph would best display the number of different-colored marbles in a jar?

A. bar graph

C. line graph

B. line plot

D. circle graph

3. How many visitors to the park were less than 31 years old?

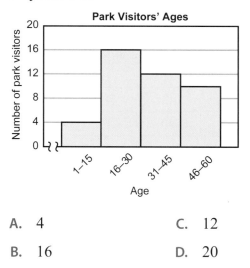

Park Visitors' Ages

Number of park visitors

Age

A. 4

C. 12

B. 16

D. 20

4. What is the mode of the data?

```
2 | 0  0  2  3  8
3 | 6  8  9
4 | 1  1  3  5  7  9
5 | 5  8  8  8  9
```

Key: 4|1 means 41

A. 20

C. 8

B. 41

D. 58

5. What is the median of the data?

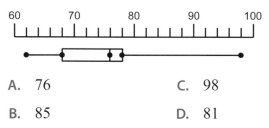

A. 3

C. 9

B. 5

D. 16

6. What is the interquartile range?

A. 7

C. 44

B. 37

D. 14

7. Which score is an outlier?

A. 76

C. 98

B. 85

D. 81

8. Which sample is most representative of a population of mall shoppers?

A. shoppers in the food court

B. shoppers using an automated banking machine

C. shoppers entering through a mall entrance

D. shoppers at the mall's largest store

9. Which sampling strategy does DeShawn use if he surveys 10 people from each street in a neighborhood?

A. simple random

C. systematic

B. stratified random

D. convenience

Use the graph to solve.

10. What is the ratio of yellow to red counters?

11. What percent of the counters are green?

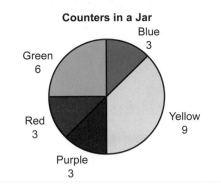

Counters in a Jar

Blue 3
Green 6
Red 3
Purple 3
Yellow 9

Explain which type of graph would best display the data.

12. percentages of International Club members from different countries

13. average number of hours of daylight each month

Use the histogram to solve.

14. How many rock samples are represented in the graph?

15. How many rock samples have a mass greater than 399 g?

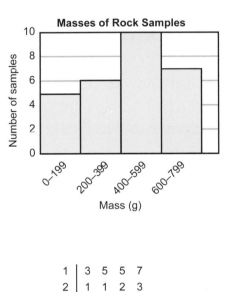

Masses of Rock Samples

Number of samples / Mass (g)
0–199, 200–399, 400–599, 600–799

Use the stem-and-leaf plot to solve.

16. What is the median value?

17. What is the mean value?

18. What is the mode?

19. Decide whether there is an outlier.

1	3 5 5 7
2	1 1 2 3
3	2 9
4	
5	9

Key: 2|1 means 21

Solve.

20. Linus grew 10 pumpkins. Nine of them weigh about 10 pounds and one weighs 100 pounds. If he wants to impress his friends, should he tell them the mean weight or median weight of the pumpkins he grew?

10 The Second Dimension

How can a scientist figure out how tall someone was from a single bone? From looking at lots and lots of data, scientists can find a relationship between the length of the big leg bone (the femur) and a person's height. When you have two variables, such as femur length and overall height, a two-dimensional plot can help you see patterns and make predictions.

In This Chapter

You will learn how to identify and plot points on a coordinate plane. You'll then identify points that are solutions to equations with two variables, and create and interpret scatter plots.

Chapter Topics

- ▶ Foundations for Chapter 10
- ▶ Points on a Coordinate Plane
- ▶ Using Points to Solve Problems
- ▶ Equations with Two Variables
- ▶ Scatter Plots
- ▶ Interpreting Scatter Plots
- ▶ Chapter 10 Review

Archaeologists use a single bone to determine the height of someone who lived centuries ago.

Foundations for Chapter 10

➔ **Representing Variables on a Number Line**

> **Definition**
>
> A **variable** is a symbol used to represent one or more numbers.

You can find the coordinate for a value that is shown on a number line by looking at the scale. The coordinates on a number line increase from left to right.

Example A

Identify the coordinate of the variable shown on the number line.

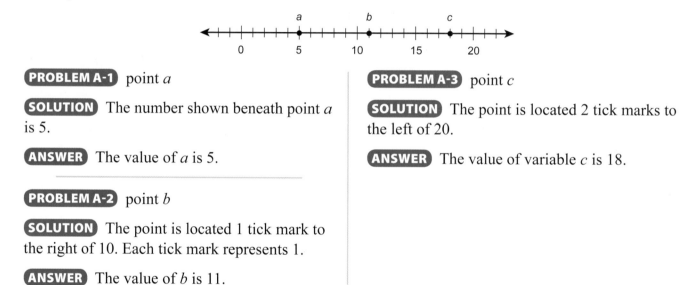

PROBLEM A-1 point a

SOLUTION The number shown beneath point a is 5.

ANSWER The value of a is 5.

PROBLEM A-2 point b

SOLUTION The point is located 1 tick mark to the right of 10. Each tick mark represents 1.

ANSWER The value of b is 11.

PROBLEM A-3 point c

SOLUTION The point is located 2 tick marks to the left of 20.

ANSWER The value of variable c is 18.

Problem Set A

Identify the coordinate of the variable shown on the number line.

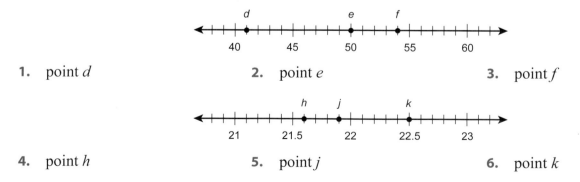

1. point d

2. point e

3. point f

4. point h

5. point j

6. point k

➤ Finding Negative Numbers on a Number Line

Variables can represent positive or negative numbers. Points on the
number line to the left of 0 represent negative values. The values of the
numbers decrease as you move farther to the left.

Example B

Draw a number line from −20 to 20 and graph a point with the given coordinate.

PROBLEM B-1 point *a* with a coordinate of −15

SOLUTION Find the tick mark labeled −15. Graph point *a* at that place on the number line.

ANSWER Point *a* is shown on the number line.

PROBLEM B-2 point *b* with a coordinate of −9

SOLUTION Find the tick mark labeled −10. Move 1 unit to the right. Graph point *b* at that
place on the number line.

ANSWER Point *b* is shown on the number line.

PROBLEM B-3 point *c* with a coordinate of −13

SOLUTION Find the tick mark labeled −15. Move 2 units to the right. Or find the tick mark
labeled −10 and move 3 units to the left. Graph point *c* at that place on the number line.

ANSWER Point *c* is shown on the number line.

Problem Set B

Draw a number line from −20 to 20 and graph a point with the given coordinate.

1. point *d* with a coordinate of −10

2. point *e* with a coordinate of −12

3. point *f* with a coordinate of −1

4. point *g* with a coordinate of −7

Draw a number line from −200 to 200 and graph a point with the given coordinate.

5. point *h* with a coordinate of −200

6. point *j* with a coordinate of −180

7. point *k* with a coordinate of −190

8. point *m* with a coordinate of −170

Draw a number line from −2 to 2 and graph a point with the given coordinate.

9. point *n* with a coordinate of −1.5

10. point *p* with a coordinate of −0.2

11. point *q* with a coordinate of −1.1

12. point *r* with a coordinate of −1.8

→ Converting Fractions and Decimals on a Number Line

Points on a number line can be described by both a fraction and a decimal. To convert a fraction to a decimal, divide the numerator by the denominator. Use place value to convert a decimal to a fraction.

Example C

PROBLEM C-1 Write a decimal equivalent to the fraction plotted on the number line.

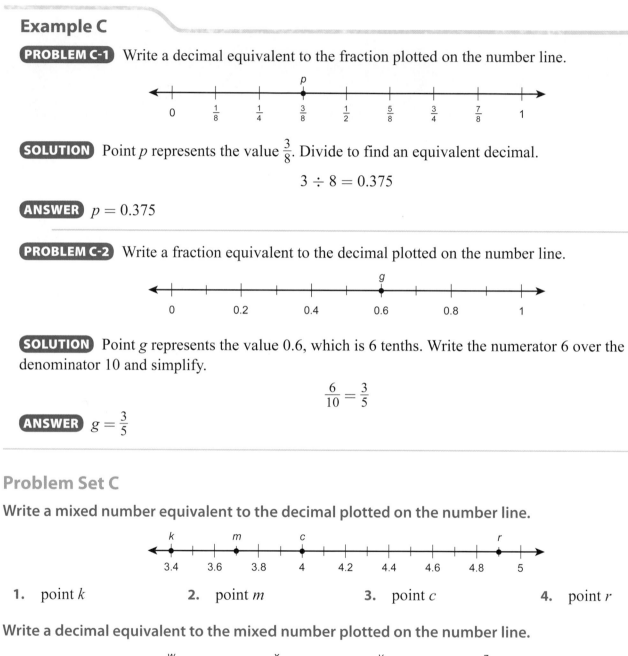

SOLUTION Point p represents the value $\frac{3}{8}$. Divide to find an equivalent decimal.

$$3 \div 8 = 0.375$$

ANSWER $p = 0.375$

PROBLEM C-2 Write a fraction equivalent to the decimal plotted on the number line.

SOLUTION Point g represents the value 0.6, which is 6 tenths. Write the numerator 6 over the denominator 10 and simplify.

$$\frac{6}{10} = \frac{3}{5}$$

ANSWER $g = \frac{3}{5}$

Problem Set C

Write a mixed number equivalent to the decimal plotted on the number line.

1. point k 2. point m 3. point c 4. point r

Write a decimal equivalent to the mixed number plotted on the number line.

5. point w 6. point x 7. point y 8. point z

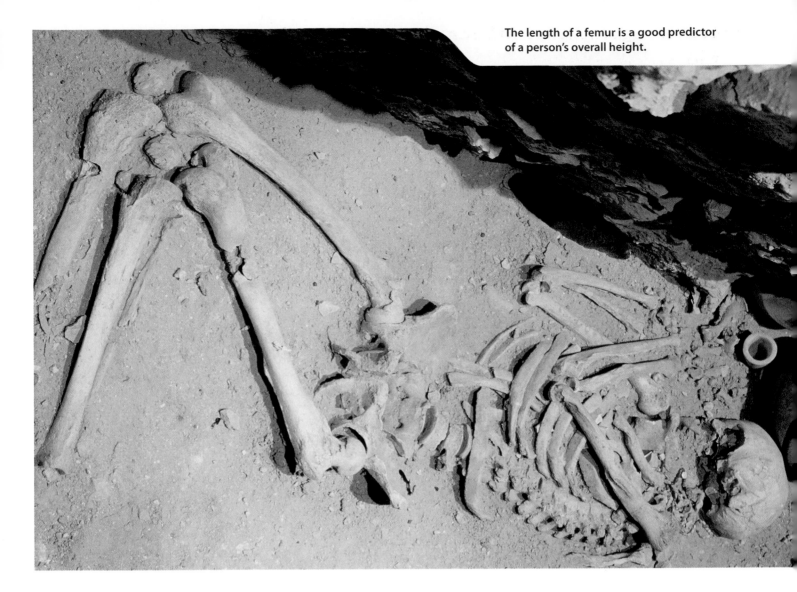

The length of a femur is a good predictor of a person's overall height.

Planting the Seed

Any point in a coordinate plane can be described by an ordered pair of coordinates.

Points on a Coordinate Plane

A grid on a map can show locations. That kind of grid is one example of a coordinate plane.

➤ Plotting Points on a Coordinate Plane

The location of a point on a number line is named with one number. The location of a point on a plane is named with two numbers.

Definitions

The **coordinate plane** is a plane that has an **x-axis** and a **y-axis** perpendicular to each other on which points can be located.

An **ordered pair** (x, y) shows the location of each point. The first number is the **x-coordinate**. The second number is the **y-coordinate**.

The pair $(0, 0)$ is the **origin**. It is the point where the two number lines intersect.

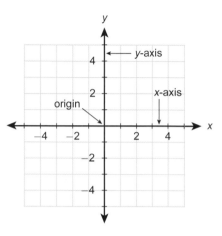

To plot a point, start at the origin. Use the x-coordinate to move left or right. Then use the y-coordinate to move up or down.

Example

Plot the point on a coordinate plane.

PROBLEM 1 point A at $(2, 4)$

SOLUTION Start at the origin. The x-coordinate is 2, so move 2 units to the right on the x-axis. The y-coordinate is 4, so move 4 units up. Write A next to the point.

ANSWER Point A is shown on the coordinate plane.

PROBLEM 2 point B at $(-4, -3)$

SOLUTION Start at the origin. Move 4 units to the left. Then move 3 units down. Write B next to the point.

ANSWER Point B is shown on the coordinate plane.

Tip

The order of the numbers in an ordered pair is important: $(2, 5)$ is not the same point as $(5, 2)$.

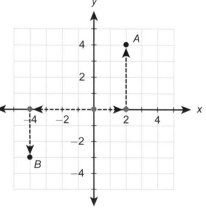

➔ Describing the Locations of Points

Example

Find the coordinates of the point in the figure.

PROBLEM 3 point P

SOLUTION Start at point P.
Look down to the x-axis. Point P is above -4.
Look right from point P to the y-axis. Point P is across from 3.

ANSWER The coordinates for point P are $(-4, 3)$.

PROBLEM 4 point Q

SOLUTION Start at point Q.
Look up to the x-axis. Point Q is below 2.
Look left from point Q to the y-axis. Point Q is across from -5.

ANSWER The coordinates for point Q are $(2, -5)$.

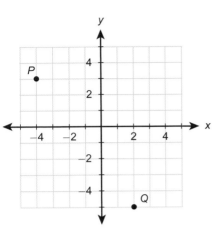

➔ Identifying Quadrants on a Coordinate Plane

Definition

The coordinate plane is divided into four regions called **quadrants**.

If the y-coordinate of a point is 0, the point is on the x-axis. If its x-coordinate is 0, the point is on the y-axis.

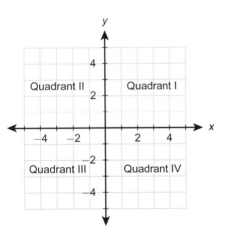

Example

State whether the point is on the x-axis or the y-axis. If the point is not on an axis, state which quadrant it is in.

PROBLEM 5 $(-18, 25)$

SOLUTION The first number is negative, so the point is left of the y-axis. The second number is positive. The point is above the x-axis.

ANSWER $(-18, 25)$ is in Quadrant II.

CHECK Plot the point to check that you have the correct quadrant. ✓

Think About It

You can tell which quadrant a point is in from the signs of its x- and y-coordinates.

Coordinates	Quadrant
both $+$	I
both $-$	III
different signs	II or IV

Problem Set

Plot the point on a coordinate plane.

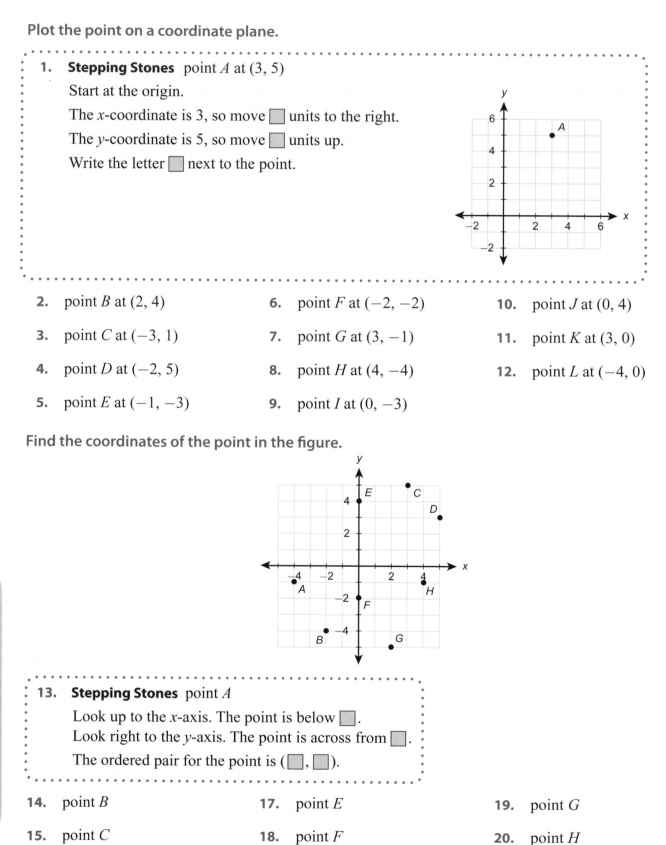

1. **Stepping Stones** point A at $(3, 5)$

   Start at the origin.

   The x-coordinate is 3, so move ☐ units to the right.

   The y-coordinate is 5, so move ☐ units up.

   Write the letter ☐ next to the point.

2. point B at $(2, 4)$

3. point C at $(-3, 1)$

4. point D at $(-2, 5)$

5. point E at $(-1, -3)$

6. point F at $(-2, -2)$

7. point G at $(3, -1)$

8. point H at $(4, -4)$

9. point I at $(0, -3)$

10. point J at $(0, 4)$

11. point K at $(3, 0)$

12. point L at $(-4, 0)$

Find the coordinates of the point in the figure.

13. **Stepping Stones** point A

   Look up to the x-axis. The point is below ☐.

   Look right to the y-axis. The point is across from ☐.

   The ordered pair for the point is (☐, ☐).

14. point B

15. point C

16. point D

17. point E

18. point F

19. point G

20. point H

State whether the point is on the *x*-axis or the *y*-axis. If the point is not on an axis, state which quadrant it is in.

21. $(-13, 13)$

22. $(-8, 8)$

23. $(0, -2)$

24. $(0, 5)$

25. $(-2, -11)$

26. $(-15, -20)$

27. $(6, 14)$

28. $(11, 8)$

29. $(6, 0)$

30. $(-8, 0)$

31. $(10, -7)$

32. $(14, -9)$

Use the figure to solve.

33. Which two points are on the same vertical line? Name their coordinates. Find another point on this same line and give its coordinates.

34. Which two points are on the same horizontal line? Name their coordinates. Find another point on this same line and give its coordinates.

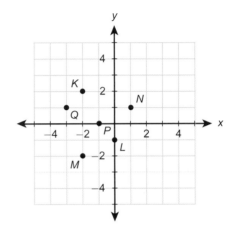

Solve.

35. **Challenge** Plot two points that are each exactly 3 units to the right of the *y*-axis. Draw a straight line through these points. Describe the line you drew.

36. **Challenge** Plot the points $A\,(-2, 2)$, $B\,(2, 5)$, and $C\,(5, 1)$. Connect the points in order. Describe the figure you get.

37. **Challenge** Plot five points that have *x*- and *y*-coordinates that are equal to each other. Describe what you see.

Choose the answer.

38. Which ordered pair describes point T?

    A. $(-2, 0)$ **C.** $(0, -2)$

    B. $(-2, -2)$ **D.** $(0, -3)$

39. Which point is at $(-3, 1)$?

    A. point Z **C.** point V

    B. point U **D.** point W

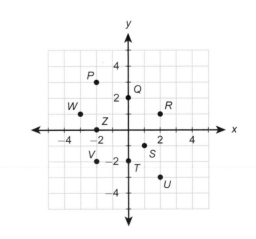

PROBLEM SET

Using Points to Solve Problems

You can find the distance between two points on a plane just as you did with two points on a line.

➡ Finding Distances Between Points on a Coordinate Plane

You can use the formulas below to find the vertical or horizontal distance between two points on a coordinate plane.

Vertical and Horizontal Distance Between Two Points

The vertical and horizontal distance between two points on a coordinate plane that have the same x- or y-value can be found using one of the following formulas:

same x-value (vertical distance): $d = |y_2 - y_1|$

same y-value (horizontal distance): $d = |x_2 - x_1|$

Think About It

Different points with the same x-value lie on a vertical line.

Different points with the same y-value lie on a horizontal line.

Example

PROBLEM 1 Find the distance between points on the coordinate plane.

SOLUTION Find the coordinates for each point.

(3, 1), (3, 5)

The ordered pairs have the same x-value, so use the vertical distance formula.

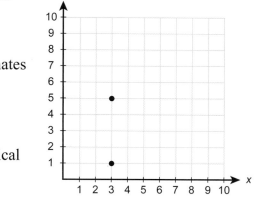

$$d = |y_2 - y_1|$$
$$= |5 - 1| \qquad \text{Replace } y_2 \text{ with 5 and } y_1 \text{ with 1.}$$
$$= |4| \qquad \text{Simplify.}$$
$$= 4$$

ANSWER The distance between the two points is 4 units.

CHECK Count the number of units on the graph. The points are 4 units apart. ✓

Think About It

It doesn't matter which point you select for y_1 and which you select for y_2.

The answer is the same:

$|1 - 5| = |-4| = 4$.

TOPIC

➔ Applications: Figures on a Coordinate Plane

You can use the horizontal and vertical distance formulas to solve problems about figures that are graphed on a coordinate plane.

Remember

Opposite sides of a rectangle have the same length.

Example

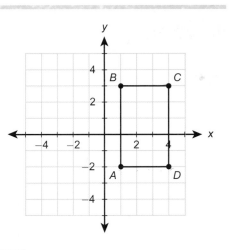

PROBLEM 2 Find the perimeter of rectangle $ABCD$.

SOLUTION Find the coordinates for each point.

A $(1, -2)$
B $(1, 3)$
C $(4, 3)$
D $(4, -2)$

Use the formulas to find the lengths of $\overline{AB}$ and $\overline{BC}$.

$\overline{AB}$:

$d = |y_2 - y_1|$
$\quad = |3 - (-2)|$
$\quad = |5|$
$\quad = 5$

$\overline{BC}$:

$d = |x_2 - x_1|$
$\quad = |4 - 1|$
$\quad = |3|$
$\quad = 3$

Use the perimeter formula.
$P = 2l + 2w = 2 \cdot 5 + 2 \cdot 3 = 16$

ANSWER The perimeter of rectangle $ABCD$ is 16 units.

PROBLEM 3 Find the coordinates of point Z that could be connected to points W $(-2, 1)$, X $(1, 1)$, and Y $(-2, -2)$ to form a square with side length 3. Then graph the figure.

SOLUTION Point Z will be located 3 units to the right of point Y and 3 units below point X.
Three units to the right of point Y is $(1, -2)$. Also, 3 units below point X is $(1, -2)$. However you look at it, the other corner of the square must be at $(1, -2)$.

ANSWER The coordinates of point Z are $(1, -2)$.

TOPIC

Problem Set

Find the distance between points on the coordinate plane.

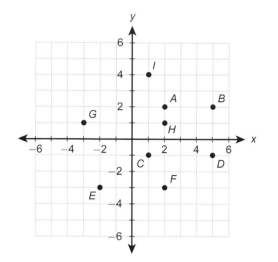

1. **Stepping Stones** points A and B

   The points have the same ▨-values.
   Use the formula.

   $d = |x_2 - x_1|$

   $= |\boxed{} - \boxed{}| = |\boxed{}| = \boxed{}$

2. points C and D

3. points A and F

4. points B and D

5. points E and F

6. points I and C

7. points G and H

8. points A and $(2, -2)$

9. points B and $(-1, 2)$

10. points $(1, -4)$ and $(1, 0)$

11. points $(3, -2)$ and $(-2, -2)$

12. points $(-1, -2)$ and $(-1, 2)$

Use the figure to solve.

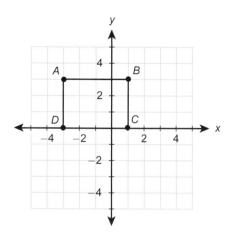

13. **Stepping Stones** Find the length of $\overline{BC}$.

    Use the formula.

    $d = |y_2 - y_1|$

    $= |\boxed{} - \boxed{}| = \boxed{}$

14. Find the length of $\overline{DC}$.

15. Find the length of $\overline{DA}$.

16. **Challenge** Find the perimeter of rectangle $ABCD$.

Find the coordinates of the fourth point that could be connected with the three given points to form a rectangle. Then graph the figure.

17. Stepping Stones $(1, 1), (1, 4),$ and $(3, 4)$

The first two points share the same ▢-coordinate.

The second and third points share the same ▢-coordinate.

The fourth point will share the x-coordinate with the ▢▢▢▢ point.

The fourth point will share the y-coordinate with the ▢▢▢▢ point.

The coordinates of the fourth point are (▢, ▢).

18. $(4, 1), (0, 1),$ and $(4, 4)$

19. $(-1, 1), (-1, 4),$ and $(1, 4)$

20. $(0, 0), (3, 0),$ and $(3, 6)$

21. $(-2, 3), (1, -2),$ and $(1, 3)$

22. $(-2, -2), (-1, -1),$ and $(-1, -2)$

23. $(-3, 4), (3, 4),$ and $(3, 1)$

24. $(2, -1), (-3, -1),$ and $(-3, -2)$

25. $(-1, 5), (-1, -4),$ and $(1, -4)$

26. $(5, 5), (5, -3),$ and $(-4, -3)$

27. $(-2, 4), (1, 4),$ and $(-2, 1)$

Choose the answer.

28. Which point is 4 units from $(2, 0)$ on a coordinate plane?

A. $(2, 6)$

B. $(2, -2)$

C. $(-2, 0)$

D. $(6, 2)$

29. What are the coordinates of the fourth point that could be connected with $(-4, 2), (1, 2),$ and $(1, -2)$ to form a rectangle?

A. $(2, -4)$

B. $(4, -2)$

C. $(-4, -2)$

D. $(-2, -4)$

Equations with Two Variables

You can show solutions to a two-variable equation as a list of ordered pairs, a table, or a graph.

➡ Identifying Solutions on Graphed Lines

Definition

If x and y in an ordered pair (x, y) are substituted into a two-variable equation and the equation is then true, the ordered pair is a **solution**, or an answer, to the equation.

Some equations have two variables. For example, $x + y = 10$ has the variables x and y. A single solution to this kind of equation is an ordered pair.

Example

PROBLEM 1 State whether the graph shows the solutions of the equation $2x + y = -3$. Explain why or why not.

SOLUTION Choose two points on the line and find out if they make the equation true.

$(0, -3) \longrightarrow 2 \cdot \underline{0} + (-3) \stackrel{?}{=} -3 \longrightarrow -3 \stackrel{?}{=} -3 \longrightarrow$ Yes

$(1, -5) \longrightarrow 2 \cdot 1 + (-5) \stackrel{?}{=} -3 \longrightarrow -3 \stackrel{?}{=} -3 \longrightarrow$ Yes

ANSWER Yes; the line shows the solutions of $2x + y = -3$.

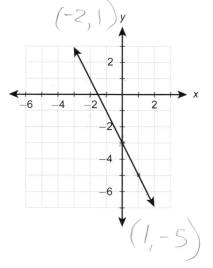

➡ Finding Ordered-Pair Solutions

An equation in two variables has ordered pairs of numbers as solutions. To find solutions, substitute a number for one variable and solve for the other.

When an equation has y alone on one side, then you can simply substitute values for x and find corresponding y-values.

Definition

The **domain** of an equation is the set of allowable x-values, or inputs, of the equation.

TOPIC

Example

PROBLEM 2 Find three ordered-pair solutions of the equation $y = 2x + 1$. Use the values 0, 1, and 2 for x.

SOLUTION Substitute each x-value. Solve for y.

For $x = 0$ For $x = 1$ For $x = 2$

$y = 2 \cdot 0 + 1$ $y = 2 \cdot 1 + 1$ $y = 2 \cdot 2 + 1$

$y = 0 + 1$ $y = 2 + 1$ $y = 4 + 1$

$y = 1$ $y = 3$ $y = 5$

ANSWER $(0, 1), (1, 3), (2, 5)$

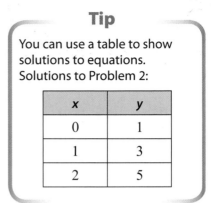
➜ Graphing Solutions

You can find some solutions to a two-variable equation by substituting. To show all the solutions, make a graph.

Example

PROBLEM 3 Graph the solution to the equation $y = 3x + 2$.

SOLUTION Substitute some x-values into the equation and find each y-value.

x	3x + 2	y	(x, y)
−2	$3(-2) + 2 = -4$	−4	$(-2, -4)$
−1	$3(-1) + 2 = -1$	−1	$(-1, -1)$
0	$3 \cdot 0 + 2 = 2$	2	$(0, 2)$
1	$3 \cdot 1 + 2 = 5$	5	$(1, 5)$
2	$3 \cdot 2 + 2 = 8$	8	$(2, 8)$

Plot the ordered pairs. Draw a line to connect them.

ANSWER The graph shows the solutions to the equation $y = 3x + 2$.

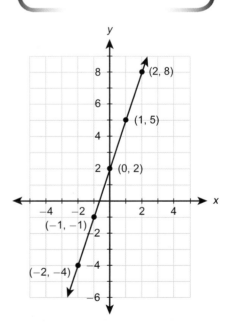

Problem Set

State whether every point on the graph is a solution of the equation.
Explain why or why not.

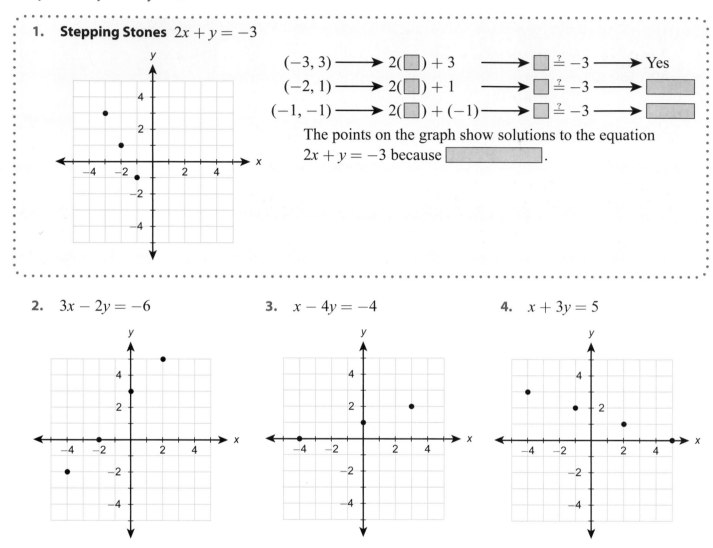

1. **Stepping Stones** $2x + y = -3$

$$(-3, 3) \longrightarrow 2(\boxed{}) + 3 \longrightarrow \boxed{} \overset{?}{=} -3 \longrightarrow \text{Yes}$$
$$(-2, 1) \longrightarrow 2(\boxed{}) + 1 \longrightarrow \boxed{} \overset{?}{=} -3 \longrightarrow \boxed{}$$
$$(-1, -1) \longrightarrow 2(\boxed{}) + (-1) \longrightarrow \boxed{} \overset{?}{=} -3 \longrightarrow \boxed{}$$

The points on the graph show solutions to the equation
$2x + y = -3$ because $\boxed{}$.

2. $3x - 2y = -6$

3. $x - 4y = -4$

4. $x + 3y = 5$

Solve.

5. **Challenge** Three points on a graph are
    $(-1, 4)$, $(0, 3)$, and $(2, 7)$. Do those points
    show solutions to the equation $y = x^2 + 3$?
    State why or why not.

6. How many solutions are there to the equation
    $y = 14x - 9$? Explain your answer.

Use the values for *x*. Find three ordered-pair solutions for the equation.

---

7. **Stepping Stones** $x = 0, 2, 5; y = -2x$

$y = -2 \cdot \boxed{} = \boxed{}$

$y = -2 \cdot \boxed{} = \boxed{}$

$y = -2 \cdot \boxed{} = \boxed{}$

The ordered pairs are $(0, \boxed{})$, $(2, \boxed{})$,
and $(\boxed{}, \boxed{})$.

---

8. $x = 1, 3, 4; y = 5 + x$

9. $x = 0, 1, 2; y = 3x - 1$

10. **Challenge** $x = 0, 1, 2; 5x + 2y = -8$

Complete the table to find three ordered-pair solutions for the equation.

11. $y = x + 4$

x	x + 4	y	(x, y)
0			
1			
2			

13. $y = -3x$

x	−3x	y	(x, y)
−2			
0			
2			

12. $y = x - 2$

x	x − 2	y	(x, y)
−1			
0			
1			

14. $y = 6x$

x	6x	y	(x, y)
−5			
0			
5			

Graph the equation.

15. $y = x + 4$

16. $y = -4x$

17. $y = 3x$

18. $y = -\dfrac{3x}{2}$

19. $y = \dfrac{5x}{4}$

20. **Challenge** $2x - 5y = 12$

Choose the answer.

21. Which equation is shown on the graph?

   A. $y = -2x - 4$

   B. $y = -2x + 4$

   C. $y = \dfrac{x}{2} - 2$

   D. $y = \dfrac{x}{2} + 2$

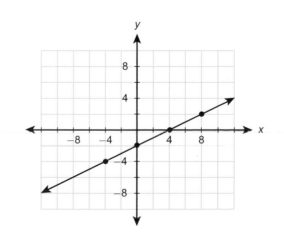

Scatter Plots

When you use scatter plots, you can see patterns in statistical data with pairs of values.

➡ Creating Scatter Plots

Definition

A **scatter plot** is a graph that displays two sets of data as ordered pairs.

To create a scatter plot, graph points as you would on the coordinate plane. Label the horizontal axis with one variable and the vertical axis with the other variable.

Example

PROBLEM 1 Use the data to create a scatter plot.

SOLUTION Identify the variables. Label the axes and graph the points.

The money Travis earns as tips depends on the hours he works.

ANSWER

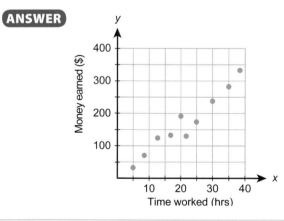

Hours Travis Works	Money Earned as Tips ($)
30	248
13	135
5	30
35	280
25	175
38	342
17	136
20	198
22	132
8	64

TOPIC

➡ Identifying Independent and Dependent Variables

Independent and dependent variables are related to each other. The independent variable can be changed and, as a result, the dependent variable changes.

Example

Identify the independent and dependent variables.

PROBLEM 2 The more time Tucker spends driving, the farther he will travel.

SOLUTION Identify the variables in the problem. Then determine which of them depends on the other.

Variables   time spent driving
distance traveled

The distance Tucker travels changes depending on the time he spends driving.

ANSWER The independent variable is the time spent driving and the dependent variable is the distance traveled.

PROBLEM 3 The more times Julie practices fielding ground balls while playing softball, the fewer errors she will make in the games.

SOLUTION Identify the variables in the problem. Then determine which of them depends on the other.

Variables   number of times Julie practices fielding ground balls
number of errors Julie will make

The number of errors she makes changes depending on the number of times she practices.

ANSWER The independent variable is the number of times Julie practices fielding ground balls and the dependent variable is the number of errors she will make.

> ### Tip
> When you read the problem, think of what can be controlled. That amount is usually the independent variable. Then think of what will be affected by the change. That amount is the dependent variable.

Problem Set

Use the data to create a scatter plot.

1. Stepping Stones

Time (min)	Distance (km)
2	121
12	624
3	210
7	434
9	367
6.5	318.5
4	283
10	675
8	400
3.5	224

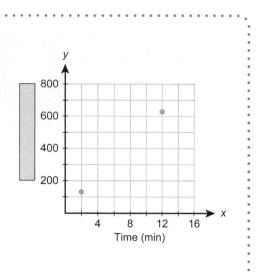

The independent variable is [   ].
The dependent variable is [   ].

2.

Customers	Profit ($)
76	2812
64	2880
48	1824
79	2844
144	5616
189	7749
180	5760
112	4256
132	6336
98	2940

3.

Time (min)	Calories
14	336
30	930
45	990
28	700
19	532
60	1501
53	1166
48	1248
27	729
36	1008

4.

Elevation (m)	Temp. (°C)
460	19
501	18.6
1223	14.6
2239	5
1504	9.2
1322	9.9
1456	6
775	17.2
821	13.7
2000	4.8
1156	10.1

Identify the independent and dependent variables.

5. **Stepping Stones** As the football team plays more games, the money earned at the concession stand will increase.

   Variables: number of football games played and [   ]

   The [   ] changes depending on [   ].

   The independent variable is [   ] and the dependent variable is [   ].

6. The number of campers decreased, so fewer counselors are needed.

7. As time increased, the distance the plane flew increased.

8. As the time Rita spent exercising every day decreased, the time she went to bed became earlier.

9. The more water that is flowing into the pool, the greater the water depth is in the pool.

10. When more fertilizer is added to the soil around a plant, the plant grows more.

11. Bill wants to see how a person's age affects how much time the person spends on the Internet.

12. Eman is conducting an experiment to see how much sugar will dissolve in water as the temperature of the water is increased.

13. The amount of yearly profit made at the bike rental store is compared to the number of sunny days during the year.

14. **Challenge** Caitlin was jogging and noticed that her heart rate would increase when she increased her running rate.

Choose the answer.

15. What is the independent variable?
    The number of students at a soccer camp increased, so more coaches are needed.

    A. number of coaches

    B. number of students

    C. type of school

    D. size of school

16. What is the dependent variable?
    The more time David spent playing video games, the lower his grades became.

    A. number of video games owned

    B. points earned playing video games

    C. David's time playing video games

    D. David's grades

Interpreting Scatter Plots

A scatter plot can be interpreted by looking at the relationship it shows.

➔ Identifying the Type of Correlation

Definitions

A **positive correlation** is shown in a scatter plot when the values of both variables increase or decrease together. The data points form a pattern that slants up.

A **negative correlation** is shown in a scatter plot when the value of one variable increases while the other value decreases. The data points form a pattern that slants down.

A scatter plot shows **no correlation** when the data points don't show a consistent upward or downward trend.

Look at the trend of the data points while thinking about the definitions of the different types of correlations.

Example

Identify the type of correlation shown in the scatter plot, if any.

PROBLEM 1

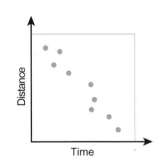

SOLUTION As time increases, distance decreases.

ANSWER The scatter plot shows a negative correlation.

PROBLEM 2

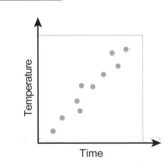

SOLUTION As time increases, temperature increases.

ANSWER The scatter plot shows a positive correlation.

Tip

In Problem 1, the data points slant **downward**, which shows a **negative** correlation.

In Problem 2, the data points slant **upward**, which shows a **positive** correlation.

TOPIC

→ Using Scatter Plots to Make Conjectures

Observe the relationship between the independent and dependent variables on a scatter plot to help you make a conjecture about the data. Sketch a line that best fits the data so you can see the relationship.

Example

Make a conjecture about the data shown in the scatter plot.

PROBLEM 3

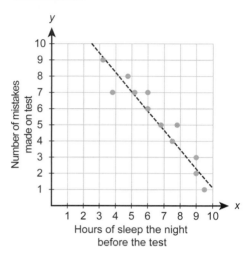

SOLUTION

As the number of hours of sleep increased, the mistakes made on the test decreased.

ANSWER

According to these data, the more hours of sleep a person gets the night before a test, the fewer mistakes the person will make on the test.

PROBLEM 4

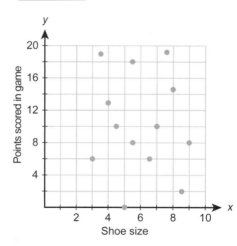

SOLUTION

There is no consistent increasing or decreasing pattern in the scatter plot.

ANSWER

According to these data, a person's shoe size has nothing to do with the number of points the person will score in a game.

Problem Set

Identify the type of correlation shown in the scatter plot, if any.

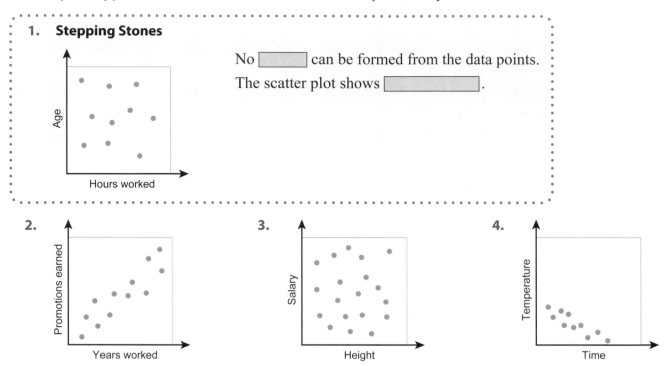

1. Stepping Stones

Age / Hours worked

No [＿＿＿] can be formed from the data points.
The scatter plot shows [＿＿＿＿＿＿].

2. Promotions earned / Years worked

3. Salary / Height

4. Temperature / Time

Make a conjecture about the data shown in the scatter plot. If there is a correlation, draw a line to best fit the data.

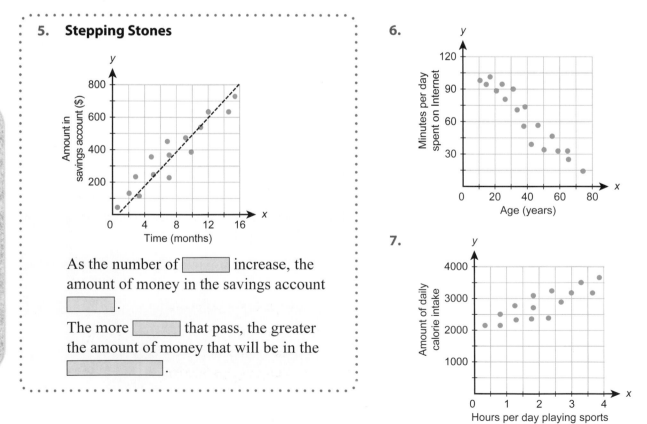

5. Stepping Stones

Amount in savings account ($) / Time (months)

As the number of [＿＿＿＿] increase, the amount of money in the savings account [＿＿＿＿].

The more [＿＿＿＿] that pass, the greater the amount of money that will be in the [＿＿＿＿＿＿].

6. Minutes per day spent on Internet / Age (years)

7. Amount of daily calorie intake / Hours per day playing sports

8.

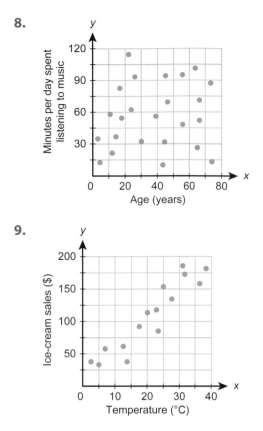

9.

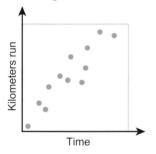

10.

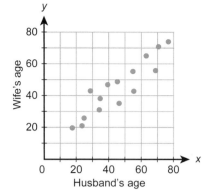

11. Challenge

Choose the answer.

12. What type of correlation is shown in the scatter plot?

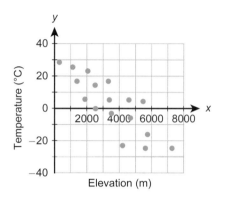

A. positive correlation

B. negative correlation

C. no correlation

D. random correlation

13. Which conjecture about the data shown in the scatter plot is most reasonable?

A. The more time people spent at the mall, the more money they had in their savings account.

B. The more time people spent at the mall, the less money they had in their savings account.

C. The less time people spent at the mall, the less money they had in their savings account.

D. There is no relation between money and time spent at the mall.

Chapter 10 Review

Choose the answer.

1. What are the coordinates of point P?

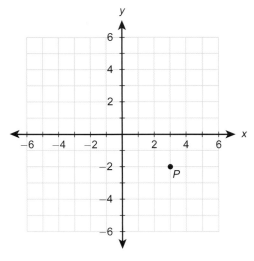

A. $(3, 2)$ C. $(-3, 2)$

B. $(3, -2)$ D. $(-2, 3)$

2. Point C is a solution to which equation?

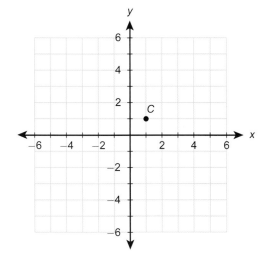

A. $y = 3x - 4$ C. $y = 4x - 3$

B. $y = 3x + 4$ D. $y = 4x + 3$

3. Which ordered pair is a solution of the equation $y = x - 6$?

A. $(2, -4)$ C. $(2, 4)$

B. $(-2, 4)$ D. $(-2, -4)$

4. What are the coordinates of the fourth point that could be connected with $(1, 2)$, $(-2, 2)$, and $(-2, -3)$ to form a rectangle?

A. $(-1, -3)$ C. $(1, 3)$

B. $(-1, 3)$ D. $(1, -3)$

5. What is the independent variable?

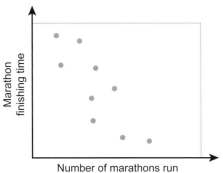

A. marathon finishing time

B. number of marathons run

C. runner's age

D. distance of the marathon

6. What type of correlation is shown in the scatter plot?

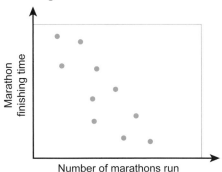

A. positive correlation

B. negative correlation

C. no correlation

D. random correlation

Use the graph to solve.

7. Find the coordinates of point A.

8. Find the coordinates of point B.

9. Find the coordinates of point C.

10. Find the coordinates of point D.

11. Find the coordinates of point E.

12. Find the distance between points A and $(2, -2)$.

13. Find the distance between points D and $(2, 3)$.

14. Find the distance between points $(-2, 1)$ and $(-2, -2)$.

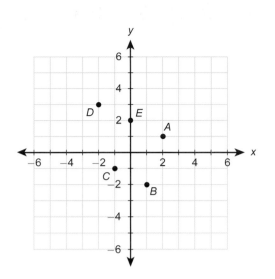

State whether the graph shows solutions of the equation. Explain why or why not.

15. $y = 2x$

16. $x + y = 3$

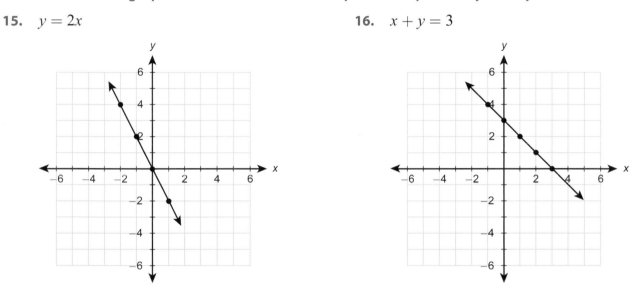

Find three ordered-pair solutions for the equation. Use the values for *x*.

17. $x = 8, 12, 14; y = x - 9$

18. $x = -7, -6, 3; y = 2x + 16$

Use the data to create a scatter plot.

19.

Plants' Age (wk)	3	4	5	6	4	2	6	5
Plants' Height (cm)	2	3	3	5	4	1	4	4

11 Rates

On average, about 1088 cubic meters of water flow over southern Africa's Victoria Falls every second. That's more than 1,000,000 liters, or enough to fill 26 Olympic-sized swimming pools every minute!

In This Chapter

You will calculate and use rates to solve many types of problems, including pricing, speed, and work problems. You'll also use direct variation and see how rates affect graphs of relationships.

Chapter Topics

Victoria Falls is on the Zambezi River between Zambia and Zimbabwe.

Foundations for Chapter 11

⇒ The Meanings of Rates

Definition

A **rate** is a ratio comparing quantities that have different units.

Rates are often expressed with words such as *per*, *in*, and *each*. Look at the units used and how they are being related. When one term in a rate changes, the other term also changes by the same factor.

Example A

Describe the meaning of the rate.

PROBLEM A-1 8 km per hour

ANSWER The rate *8 km per hour* means that something travels a distance of 8 km for each hour of travel time.

PROBLEM A-2 24 pages each day

ANSWER The rate *24 pages each day* means that 24 pages can be read for each day of reading.

PROBLEM A-3 3 cups of rice in 2 servings

ANSWER The rate *3 cups of rice in 2 servings* means that 3 cups of rice are needed to make 2 servings of a dish.

PROBLEM A-4 1 table for every 6 people

ANSWER The rate *1 table for every 6 people* means that there are enough tables so that 6 people can sit at each table.

Problem Set A

Describe the meaning of the rate.

1. 55 miles per hour

2. 6 days each month

3. 9 apples in 10 minutes

4. 2 spoonfuls each morning

5. 4 scoops per load

6. 17 minutes per item

7. 3 balls for 22 players

8. 3 countries in 8 days

➜ Relating Distance, Rate, and Time

Distance-Rate-Time

The distance d traveled by an object moving at a constant rate r for a time t is
$$d = rt.$$

Use the formula to solve problems involving distance, rate, and time.

Example B

Solve.

PROBLEM B-1 A green sea turtle travels at a speed of 2 km per hour. How far does the turtle travel in 4 hours?

SOLUTION

$d = rt$

$\quad = 2\,\dfrac{\text{km}}{\text{h}} \cdot 4\,\text{h}$ Substitute 2 for r and 4 for t.

$\quad = 8\text{ km}$ Multiply.

ANSWER The turtle travels 8 km in 4 hours.

PROBLEM B-2 Carlton's family drove for 3.5 hours at an average rate of 60 miles per hour. How far did Carlton's family drive?

SOLUTION

$d = rt$

$\quad = 60\,\dfrac{\text{mi}}{\text{h}} \cdot 3.5\,\text{h}$ Substitute 60 for r and 3.5 for t.

$\quad = 210\text{ mi}$ Multiply.

ANSWER Carlton's family drove 210 miles.

Problem Set B

Solve.

1. If Paulina can ride her bicycle 25 km in 1 hour, how far can she ride in 6 hours?

2. An airplane travels at an average speed of 250 mph for 3 hours. How far does the airplane travel?

3. The orbiting space shuttle travels 465 km each minute. How far does the space shuttle travel in 1 hour?

4. Manny walks for 30 min at a speed of 5 km/h. How far does Manny walk?

➔ Relating Work, Rate, and Time

Work-Rate-Time

The work w performed at rate r for time t is

$$w = rt.$$

Use the formula to solve problems involving work, rate, and time.

Example C

Solve.

PROBLEM C-1 Lin can stack 5 boxes per minute. How many boxes can she stack in 1 hour?

SOLUTION The rate is given in minutes, so first convert the time to minutes.

$1\ h = 60\ min$

$w = rt$

$\quad = 5\ \dfrac{boxes}{\cancel{min}} \cdot 60\ \cancel{min}$ Substitute 5 for r and 60 for t.

$\quad = 300\ boxes$ Multiply.

ANSWER Lin can stack 300 boxes in 1 hour.

PROBLEM C-2 Alejandro can read 40 pages per hour. How many pages can he read in 3 hours?

SOLUTION

$w = rt$

$\quad = 40\ \dfrac{pages}{\cancel{h}} \cdot 3\ \cancel{h}$ Substitute 40 for r and 3 for t.

$\quad = 120\ pages$ Multiply.

ANSWER Alejandro can read 120 pages in 3 hours.

Problem Set C

Solve.

1. Rita can pack 8 boxes in 1 hour. How many boxes can she pack in 8 hours?

2. A road crew can lay 25 m of new road in 4 hours. How much new road can the crew lay in 40 hours?

3. A carpenter can install 7 doors per day in an apartment building. How many doors can he install in 12 days?

4. Nelson can peel 6 potatoes each minute. How many potatoes can he peel in 45 minutes?

Planting the Seed

You can use rates to describe how one quantity changes compared to another. For instance, you can compare distance to time (speed is a rate), dollars to hours (salary is a rate), or cubic liters to seconds (water flow is a rate).

Rates as Comparisons

Rates help you solve problems that involve comparing different measures.

➨ Choosing the Correct Representation for Rates

When writing an expression to represent a rate situation, make sure that the quantities you are comparing appear on the correct side of the comparison.

Example

Write an expression that could be used to solve the problem.

PROBLEM 1 Jeremy earns $8 per hour in his pet-sitting business. Last month, he earned $200. How many hours did he work?

SOLUTION If you wanted to find the number of dollars earned, you would multiply the rate by the time.

$$\frac{\text{dollars}}{\text{hours}} \cdot \text{hours} = \text{dollars}$$

$$\frac{\$8}{1 \text{ h}} \cdot t \text{ hours} = \$200$$

To find t hours, you divide both sides of the equation by $\frac{\$8}{1 \text{ h}}$.

$$t \text{ hours} = \$200 \div \frac{\$8}{1 \text{ h}}$$

ANSWER The expression $\$200 \div \frac{\$8}{1 \text{ h}}$ could be used to solve the problem.

> **Remember**
>
> A **rate** is a ratio comparing quantities that have different units.

PROBLEM 2 On a trip, Ramon drove his car 288 miles and used 12 gallons of gasoline. How many miles per gallon did Ramon's car get?

SOLUTION

$$\frac{\text{miles}}{\text{gallon}} = \text{miles} \div \text{gallons}$$

$$= 288 \text{ miles} \div 12 \text{ gallons}$$

ANSWER The expression 288 miles ÷ 12 gallons could be used to solve the problem.

> **Think About It**
>
> A rate that is miles per gallon indicates how many miles can be traveled using 1 gallon of gas.

➜ Using Rates to Solve Problems

When writing equations that use rates, carefully consider what rate will help solve the problem.

Example

Write an equation using a rate and solve the problem.

PROBLEM 3 Rebecca spent $48 downloading songs from the Internet. Each song cost $2. How many songs did she download from the Internet?

SOLUTION To find the number of songs downloaded, multiply the per-song rate times the number of songs.

$$\frac{\text{dollars}}{\text{song}} \cdot \text{songs} = \text{dollars}$$

Write a related equation for the multiplication equation. Use a related equation that has songs alone on one side.

$$\text{songs} = \text{dollars} \div \frac{\text{dollars}}{\text{song}}$$

Let s represent the number of songs.

$$s = \$48 \div \frac{\$2}{1 \text{ song}}$$
$$= 48 \div 2$$
$$= \frac{48}{2} = 24$$

ANSWER Rebecca downloaded 24 songs.

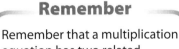

Remember

Remember that a multiplication equation has two related division equations:

$a \cdot b = c$

is equivalent to

$a = c \div b$ and $b = c \div a$.

PROBLEM 4 Juanita jogged at a constant rate of 9 km/h for 2 hours. How far did she jog?

SOLUTION Let $d =$ the distance jogged.

$$\text{kilometers} = \frac{\text{km}}{\text{hour}} \cdot \text{hours}$$
$$d = \frac{9 \text{ km}}{1 \text{ hour}} \cdot 2 \text{ hours}$$
$$= 18 \text{ km}$$

ANSWER Juanita jogged 18 km.

T O P I C

Problem Set

Write an expression that could be used to solve the problem.

1. **Stepping Stones** Lin bought 30 pens that came in 5 packages with the same number of pens in each package. How many pens were in each package?

   $$\frac{\text{pens}}{\text{package}} = \text{pens} \cdot \frac{1}{\boxed{}} = \text{pens} \div \boxed{}$$
   $$= \frac{30}{\boxed{}}$$

   The expression $\dfrac{30}{\boxed{}}$ could be used to solve the problem.

2. Luiza saved $189 in 7 weeks. If she saved the same amount every week, how much did Luiza save each week?

3. It took Elliot 190 seconds to do 38 sit-ups. He took the same amount of time for each sit-up. How long did it take Elliot to do each sit-up?

4. Gem counted 54 wheels on 3 semitrucks. The same number of wheels were on each semitruck. How many wheels were on each semitruck?

5. During practice, it took Shawn 27 min to swim 81 laps. If Shawn swam at a constant rate, how long did it take him to complete each lap?

6. While preparing a recipe, Chris noticed that 4 cans held a total of 34 oz of tomato sauce. The cans were all the same size. How many ounces did each can hold?

7. Ricardo read 160 pages of a book over a period of 8 days. He followed a schedule in which he read the same number of pages each day. How many pages did Ricardo read each day?

8. **Challenge** Jennifer paid $7.80 for 2 dozen eggs. What was the cost for each egg?

Write an equation using a rate that could be used to solve the problem.

9. **Stepping Stones** Brendon spent $180 on 12 footballs for the team. What was the cost of each football?

   Write the basic rate equation.

   $$\text{total dollars} = \frac{\text{dollars}}{\text{football}} \cdot \text{total footballs}$$

   Write a related equation.

   $$\frac{\text{dollars}}{\text{football}} = \text{total dollars} \div \text{total footballs} = \frac{180}{\boxed{}}$$

   If you let p represent the cost of each football, then you can use the equation $p = \dfrac{180}{\boxed{}}$ to solve the problem.

10. Rohit traveled 285 mi in 5 h. If he traveled at a constant rate, how far did he travel each hour?

11. Ricky paid $24 for 12 lb of apples. What was the price per pound of apples?

12. Tamika paid $20.88 for 9.5 gallons of milk. How much did Tamika pay per gallon?

13. While exercising, Ipek burned 280.5 calories in 4.25 h. How many calories did she burn per hour?

14. **Challenge** Gwen has 110 of the same items to pack in 12 boxes. Will Gwen be able to pack the same number of items in each box?

Solve.

15. Stepping Stones Enrique spent $10 for 5 oz of cologne. How much did he pay per ounce?

Write the basic rate equation.

$$\text{total cost} = \frac{\text{dollars}}{\text{ounce}} \cdot \text{ounces}$$

Write a related equation.

$$\frac{\text{dollars}}{\text{ounce}} = \text{total cost} \div \text{ounces} = \frac{10}{\square} = \square$$

Enrique paid $\square$ per ounce for the cologne.

16. Amanda bought 192 trading cards and 12 cards came in each pack. How many packs did she buy?

17. Larry is on a train that travels 62 mi in 1 h. At this rate, how far will the train travel in 5 h?

18. Belynda climbed 47 ft in 30 min. At this rate, how far will Belynda climb in 120 min?

19. On the football team, there are 11 players for every 2 coaches. There are 12 coaches for the team. How many players are on the team?

20. The ratio of miles traveled per hour on a trip is 121.5 to 4. At this rate, how many miles will be traveled in 16 hours?

21. Challenge Caroline is in charge of buying furniture for a new hotel lobby. She spends $1472 on 5 chairs for the lobby. Her boss tells her that he needs a total of 19 chairs. If Caroline buys the same type of chairs as before, how much will she pay for the additional chairs?

Choose the answer.

22. Which equation could be used to solve the problem?

David did 40 push-ups in 80 seconds. How many push-ups, p, did he do per second?

A. $p = \dfrac{80 \text{ seconds}}{40 \text{ push-ups}}$

B. $p = \dfrac{40 \text{ push-ups}}{80 \text{ seconds}}$

C. $p = 80 \text{ seconds} \cdot 40 \text{ push-ups}$

D. $p = 80 \text{ seconds} - 40 \text{ push-ups}$

23. Jane ran 12 mi in 1 h. At this rate, how many miles will she run in 3 h?

A. 1 mi   C. 15 mi

B. 4 mi   D. 36 mi

Unit Rates

Unit rates help you solve problems involving distance, work, and price.

➡ Finding the Unit Rate

Definition
A **unit rate** is a rate that has a second term of 1 unit.

To find a unit rate, divide the first term of the rate by the second term of the rate.

Example

Find the unit rate.

PROBLEM 1 12 servings for 6 people

SOLUTION Write the rate. Divide the first term by the second term.

$$\frac{12 \text{ servings}}{6 \text{ people}} = \frac{12}{6} \text{ servings/person} = \frac{2}{1} \text{ servings/person}$$
$$= 2 \text{ servings/person}$$

ANSWER The unit rate is $\frac{2 \text{ servings}}{1 \text{ person}}$ or 2 servings/person.

PROBLEM 2 10 km in 4 h

SOLUTION Write the rate. Divide the first term by the second term.

$$\frac{10 \text{ km}}{4 \text{ h}} = \frac{10}{4} \text{ km/h} = 2\frac{1}{2} \text{ km/h} = 2.5 \text{ km/h}$$

ANSWER The unit rate is $\frac{2.5 \text{ km}}{1 \text{ h}}$, or 2.5 km/h, or $2\frac{1}{2}$ km/h.

➔ Using Unit Rates to Solve Problems

Many times, it is easier to use the unit rate rather than the given rate to solve a problem.

Example

PROBLEM 3 Miguel can ride his bike 3 mi in 15 min. If he rides at the same speed, how long will it take him to ride 12 mi?

SOLUTION Find the unit rate. Use it to help find the answer.

$\frac{15 \text{ min}}{3 \text{ mi}} = \frac{15}{3}$ min/mi = 5 min/mi   It takes Miguel 5 min to ride 1 mi.

Use the unit rate to find the total time.

$\text{minutes} = \frac{\text{minutes}}{\text{mile}} \cdot \text{miles}$

$\qquad = (5 \text{ min/mi}) \cdot (12 \text{ mi})$ Multiply the unit rate by 12 mi.

$\qquad = 60 \text{ min}$

ANSWER It will take Miguel 60 min to ride 12 mi.

PROBLEM 4 Denzel makes crafts to sell at art shows. He times himself and finds he can make 12 crafts in 4 hours. How long will it take Denzel to make 48 crafts?

SOLUTION Find the unit rate. Use it to help find the answer.

$\frac{12 \text{ crafts}}{4 \text{ h}} = \frac{12}{4}$ crafts/h = 3 crafts/h   He can make 3 crafts in 1 hour.

Use the unit rate to find the total time. The simple rate equation is total crafts = rate · time.

You want to know the time, so write an equivalent equation with time alone on one side.

time = total crafts ÷ rate

Substitute and simplify.

$\text{hours} = 48 \text{ crafts} \div \frac{3 \text{ crafts}}{1 \text{ h}}$ Divide 48 by the unit rate.

$\text{hours} = 48 \text{ crafts} \cdot \frac{1 \text{ h}}{3 \text{ crafts}} = 16 \text{ hours}$ Multiply by the reciprocal of the unit rate.

ANSWER It will take Denzel 16 hours to make 48 crafts.

Problem Set

Find the unit rate with the second given unit in the denominator.

1. **Stepping Stones** 200 pages in 12 days

   $\dfrac{\boxed{}\text{ pages}}{12\text{ days}} = \dfrac{\boxed{}}{12}$ pages/days $= \boxed{}$ pages/day

   The unit rate is $\boxed{}$.

2. 42 baseballs in 7 boxes

3. 36 pencils in 12 packs

4. 40 trading cards on 8 pages

5. 600 m in 12 h

6. 540 calories in 90 min

7. $76\frac{1}{2}$ mi in 9 min

8. $67.50 for 9 pizzas

9. 12 girls for every 5 boys

10. 49 students for every 2 teachers

11. $8907.25 for 11 couches

12. 91 min to paint 3 walls

13. 4600 words in 60 min

14. 5700 people voted for Smith for every 600 people who voted for Jones

15. 13,500 m in 250 s

16. $57,256 for 586 color printers

17. 1090 heartbeats in 15 min

18. 567 dog owners for every 142 cat owners

19. 3645 people living within $5\frac{1}{2}$ square kilometers

20. **Challenge** The space shuttle traveled 421,920 mi in 24 h.

Solve.

21. **Stepping Stones** Greg bought 8 cheeseburgers for $32. How much did he pay for each cheeseburger?

    $\dfrac{32\text{ dollars}}{\boxed{}\text{ cheeseburgers}} = \dfrac{32}{\boxed{}}$ dollars/cheeseburgers

    $= \boxed{}$ dollars/cheeseburger

    Greg paid $\boxed{}$ for each cheeseburger.

22. Tanisha paid $35 for 7 movie tickets. How much would 15 movie tickets cost?

23. Marian packed 60 softballs in 5 boxes. How many softballs can she pack in 11 boxes?

24. Jonathon can jog 5 km in 40 min. At this rate, how far can he jog in 64 min?

25. Ricardo can do 14 box jumps in 2 min. At this rate, how many box jumps could he do in 21 min?

26. Clarice walked 720 m in 9 min. At that rate, how many meters could she walk in 13 min?

27. Tonya can swim 5 laps in 10 min. At that rate, how many laps could she swim in 36 min?

28. Clint baked 14 cakes in 2 h. How many cakes can Clint bake in 3 h?

29. Paige covered 5 walls with wallpaper in 15 h. At this rate, how many walls could she cover in 40 h?

30. Sharon paid $90 for 6 CDs. How much would 10 CDs cost?

31. Renee was able to plant 15 flowers in 5 min. At this rate, how many flowers could she plant in 45 min?

32. The copy machine is able to make 4986 copies in 18 min. How many copies can it make in 37 min?

33. Johnny earned $168 detailing 6 cars. How much could he earn detailing 38 cars?

34. Homer can stack 261 cups in 3 min. At this rate, how many cups could he stack in 14 min?

35. Molina rode 4 mi in 16 min on her bicycle. At this rate, how far could she ride her bike in 1 h?

36. A car factory can produce 362 cars every 8 h. How many cars could the factory produce in 44 h?

37. The baseball league paid $629 for 17 uniforms. How much would the league have to pay for 2035 uniforms?

38. **Challenge** In 2 weeks, a charity group raised $12,548. At that rate, how long will it take the group to raise $213,316?

Choose the answer.

39. What is the unit rate?

70 ft in 10 s

A. 7 ft/s   C. 700 ft/s

B. 70 ft/s   D. 17 ft/s

40. Jane biked 34 mi in 2 h. At this rate, how far could she bike in 5 h?

A. 13.6 mi   C. 76 mi

B. 37 mi   D. 85 mi

Solving Unit-Rate Problems

Although some unit rates involve only whole numbers, unit rates can also include decimals.

➔ Finding Both Unit Rates

You can find two different unit rates for any given pair of measures. Divide the first measure by the second to find one unit rate. Then divide the second measure by the first to find the other unit rate.

Example

Find both unit rates for the pair of measures.

PROBLEM 1 $11.16 for 4 gallons of gas

SOLUTION Divide dollars by gallons.

$$\frac{\$11.16}{4 \text{ gallons}} = \frac{11.16}{4} \text{ dollars/gallons} = 2.79 \text{ dollars/gallon}$$

Divide gallons by dollars.

$$\frac{4 \text{ gallons}}{\$11.16} = \frac{4}{11.16} \text{ gallons/dollars} \approx 0.358 \text{ gallon/dollar}$$

ANSWER The unit rates are $2.79/gallon and 0.358 gallon/dollar.

PROBLEM 2 499.2 mi in 8 h

SOLUTION Divide miles by hours.

$$\frac{499.2 \text{ mi}}{8 \text{ h}} = \frac{499.2}{8} \text{ mi/h} = 62.4 \text{ mi/h}$$

Divide hours by miles.

$$\frac{8 \text{ h}}{499.2 \text{ mi}} = \frac{8}{499.2} \text{ h/mi} \approx 0.016 \text{ h/mi}$$

ANSWER The unit rates are 62.4 mi/h and 0.016 h/mi.

Think About It

The two unit rates will be reciprocals.

TOPIC

➦ Using Unit Rates to Solve Problems

Unit rates can help you find the best price when items are packaged differently.

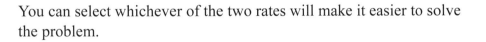

Example

PROBLEM 3 Marco can buy 3 bottles of olive oil for a total of $36.30 or a case of 12 bottles for $118.80. Which is the better deal?

SOLUTION Find and compare the unit prices.

unit price for 3 bottles:

$$\frac{\$36.30}{3 \text{ bottles}} = \frac{36.30}{3} \text{ dollars/bottles} = 12.10 \text{ dollars/bottle}$$

unit price for case of 12 bottles:

$$\frac{\$118.80}{12 \text{ bottles}} = \frac{118.80}{12} \text{ dollars/bottles} = 9.90 \text{ dollars/bottle}$$

$9.90/bottle is less than $12.10/bottle.

ANSWER The better deal is the case with 12 bottles for $118.80.

You can select whichever of the two rates will make it easier to solve the problem.

Example

PROBLEM 4 Paul drove his car 268.2 miles in 6 hours. Which unit rate is better to use to find how far Paul could drive in 11 hours?

SOLUTION Decide whether you will need to multiply or divide with each unit rate.

If the rate is in mi/h, multiply to find the distance.

$$\text{miles} = \text{hours} \cdot \frac{\text{miles}}{\text{hour}}$$

If the rate is in h/mi, divide to find the distance.

$$\text{miles} = \text{hours} \div \frac{\text{hours}}{\text{mile}}$$

Multiplication is easier than division, so choose the unit rate that allows you to do that.

ANSWER Use the unit rate for mi/h to solve the problem.

TOPIC

Problem Set

Find both unit rates.

1. **Stepping Stones** $143.88 for 12 footballs

   Divide dollars by footballs.

   $$\frac{\$143.88}{12 \text{ footballs}} = \frac{143.88}{12} \text{ dollars/footballs} = 11.99 \text{ dollars/football}$$

   Divide footballs by dollars.

   $$\frac{12 \text{ footballs}}{\$143.88} = \frac{12}{143.88} \text{ footballs/dollar} = 0.083 \text{ footballs/dollar}$$

   The unit rates are $☐/football and ☐ footballs/dollar.

2. 14 min to walk around the block 4 times

3. $7.84 for 8 kg

4. 65 pictures on 10 pages

5. 144 calories in 15 min

6. $96.88 for 8 pizzas

7. 30 white cars for every 12 red cars

8. 544 m in 20 s

9. 374 students for every 20 teachers

10. $2.16 for 8 hot dogs

11. 1435 points scored in 25 games

12. 691.12 ft in 21.2 s

13. $100.33 for 12.7 kg

14. 2885.75 m in 87.5 s

15. 4543.08 km in 52.4 h

16. **Challenge** $460,460.84 for 29 cars

Solve.

17. **Stepping Stones** Greg bought 8 songs for $7.92 and Beaula bought 12 songs for $12.36. Who got a better deal?

    Greg:

    $$\frac{\$7.92}{8 \text{ songs}} = \frac{7.92}{8} \text{ dollars/songs} = \boxed{} \text{ dollars/song}$$

    $\boxed{}$/song is less than $\boxed{}$/song.

    $\boxed{}$ got a better deal.

    Beaula:

    $$\frac{\$12.36}{\boxed{} \text{ songs}} = \frac{12.36}{\boxed{}} \text{ dollars/song}$$

    $$= \boxed{} \text{ dollars/song}$$

18. Claire walked 733.5 m in 9 min and Jean walked 636.8 m in 8 min. Who walked at the greater rate of speed?

19. Tony can buy a 6-pack of baseballs for $22.74 or a 10-pack for $42.10. Which is the better deal?

20. Sharifa's white ball rolled 143 cm in 4 s and her green ball rolled 112 cm in 3 s. Which ball rolled at a greater rate of speed?

21. Renaldo can buy 3 lb of Brand A turkey for $17.97 or 2 lb of Brand B turkey for $11.58. Which is the better deal?

22. Orchard owner Joe sells 1.5 kg of apples for $3.95 and orchard owner Jane sells 3.5 kg of apples for $6.24. Which person offers the better deal for apples?

23. Raul ran 1260 m in 100 s. Rebecca ran 2640 m in 200 s. Which of them ran at the greater rate of speed?

24. Brand X copy machine made 9571 copies in 85 min. Brand Y copy machine made 12,903 copies in 115 minutes. Which copy machine makes copies faster?

25. Johnny earned $165 mowing 6 lawns. Melinda made $345 mowing 12 lawns. Who has a better rate of pay?

26. George was able to solve 36 math problems in 15 minutes. Urban was able to solve 42 math problems in 20 minutes. Who was able to solve math problems at a greater rate?

27. Regina spent $55.13 on 18.5 gal of gas. Ingrid spent $62.78 on 21.5 gal of gas. Who got the better deal?

28. **Challenge** Ricky bought 8.5 oz of peanut butter for $2.72, Colin bought 12.75 oz for $4.21, and Shirley bought 15.8 oz for $5.53. Who got the best deal?

State which rate would be better to use to solve the problem.

29. **Stepping Stones** Celia paid $299 for a 4-night stay at a hotel. How much would a 5-night stay cost?

$$\text{dollars} = \text{nights} \cdot \frac{\text{dollars}}{\text{night}}$$

$$\text{dollars} = \text{nights} \; \boxed{} \; \frac{\text{nights}}{\text{dollars}}$$

The rate of $\boxed{}/\boxed{}$ would be better to use to solve the problem.

30. Jose picked 3 bushels of apples in 20 minutes. How many bushels could Jose pick in 90 minutes?

31. A 2-kilogram bag of oranges costs $9.50. How many kilograms of oranges can be bought for $20.00?

32. A painting crew can paint 5 apartments in 3 days. How long will it take the crew to paint 32 apartments?

Choose the answer.

33. What is the unit rate?

263.5 m in 31 s

A. 8.5 m/s   C. 263.5 m/s

B. 31 m/s   D. 8168.5 m/s

34. Which is the best deal for a jar of jelly?

A. $1.26 for 6 oz

B. $1.52 for 8 oz

C. $2.30 for 10 oz

D. $2.40 for 12 oz

Average-Speed Problems

Unit rates can help you solve problems about distance, time, and speed.

➔ Using Rate Tables to Show Speed

One special type of unit rate is speed. The first quantity in the rate is a distance. The second quantity is a time. For example, a speed of 50 miles per hour can be written as the unit rate 50 mi/1 h, or 50 mi/h, or 50 mph.

Definition
Speed is the ratio of distance traveled to time.

Tip

The word *per* is often used to describe speed.

Example

PROBLEM 1 This rate table shows Akira's hiking at 4 miles per hour. Complete the table to show equivalent speeds. Then use it to find the distance covered in 10 hours.

Distance (miles)	4				
Time (hours)	1	2	3	6	10

SOLUTION The rate for the speed is $4 : 1$. Multiply both terms of the rate by 2, then by 3, and so on.

$$4 \cdot 2 \qquad 4 \cdot 3 \qquad 4 \cdot 6 \qquad 4 \cdot 10$$
$$\downarrow \qquad\quad \downarrow \qquad\quad \downarrow \qquad\quad \downarrow$$

Distance (miles)	4	8	12	24	40
Time (hours)	1	2	3	6	10

$$\uparrow \qquad\quad \uparrow \qquad\quad \uparrow \qquad\quad \uparrow$$
$$1 \cdot 2 \qquad 1 \cdot 3 \qquad 1 \cdot 6 \qquad 1 \cdot 10$$

ANSWER Akira will hike 40 miles in 10 hours.

➔ Using the Distance Formula

The formula $r = \dfrac{d}{t}$ shows that speed is the ratio of distance to time.

The Distance Formula
For a moving object traveling a distance d at speed r for time t:
$$d = rt \qquad r = \frac{d}{t} \qquad t = \frac{d}{r}$$

Think About It

The variable r can be used for speed. The r reminds you that speed is a rate.

TOPIC

Example

Write and evaluate an expression to find the time or the speed.

PROBLEM 2 $r = 35$ mi/h, $d = 175$ mi

SOLUTION You are given the speed and the distance. Use $t = \frac{d}{r}$ to find the time.

$t = \frac{d}{r}$ Write the formula.

$\quad = 175$ mi $\div$ 35 mi/h   Substitute.

$\quad = 5$ h   Divide.

ANSWER 5 h

> **Tip**
>
> Instead of memorizing three formulas, you can always use $d = rt$ and solve for the distance, rate, or time.

PROBLEM 3 $t = 10$ min, $d = 3.2$ m

SOLUTION You are given the time and the distance. Use $r = \frac{d}{t}$ to find the speed.

$r = \frac{d}{t}$ Write the formula.

$\quad = \frac{3.2 \text{ m}}{10 \text{ min}}$ Substitute.

$\quad = 0.32$ m/min   Divide.

ANSWER 0.32 m/min

➥ Application: Average Speed

To find average speed, divide the total distance by the total time.

Example

PROBLEM 4 The Changs sailed 30 km in 6 hours, stopped for lunch, and then sailed 15 km in 5 hours. Find their average sailing speed.

SOLUTION

Find the total distance: $30 + 15 = 45$

Find the total time: $6 + 5 = 11$

Use $r = \frac{d}{t}$ to find the speed. $r = \frac{45 \text{ km}}{11 \text{ h}}$ Substitute.

                                       $r \approx 4.1$ km/h   Divide.

ANSWER The average speed was about 4.1 km/h.

TOPIC

Problem Set

Complete the rate table. Then use it to solve the problem.

1. **Stepping Stones** Charlotte rides her bicycle 15 km in 30 minutes. Complete the table to find how far she travels in 3 hours and 45 minutes at this speed.

Distance (km)	15				
Time (h)	0.5	1	2	3	3.75

Multiply 0.5 by ☐ for a product of 1, by 4 for a product of 2, by ☐ for a product of 3, and by ☐ for a product of 3.75.

Fill in the top row by multiplying by the same numbers that you used to multiply by 0.5: $15 \cdot$ ☐ $= 30$, $15 \cdot 4 =$ ☐, $15 \cdot$ ☐ $= 90$, and $15 \cdot 7.5 =$ ☐.

The distance for 3.75 hours is ☐.

Charlotte rides her bicycle ☐ km in 3 hours and 45 minutes.

2. A sailboat averages 8 km per hour. Find the distance covered in 20 hours at that speed.

Distance (km)	8				
Time (h)	1	2	5	10	20

3. A toy car in a science experiment covers 1.6 meters in half a second. If the car travels at a steady speed, how far will it go in 10 seconds?

Distance (m)	1.6				
Time (s)	0.5	1	1.5	4	10

4. A train travels 42 kilometers in 15 minutes. How far will the train travel in 3 hours at that speed?

Distance (km)	42				
Time (h)	0.25	1	1.5	2	3

Write and evaluate an expression to find the speed or the time.

5. **Stepping Stones** distance = 80 miles, time = 2 hours

   Use the formula $r =$ ☐.

   $r = \dfrac{80 \text{ mi}}{\boxed{} \text{ h}}$

   The speed is ☐.

6. $d = 40$ meters, $t = 10$ seconds

7. $d = 38$ miles, $r = 2$ miles/hour

8. $d = 140$ miles, $r = 70$ miles/hour

9. $d = 100$ m, $t = 20$ s

10. $d = 165$ km, $t = 5$ h

11. $d = 450$ mi, $r = 45$ mi/h

12. $d = 375$ mi, $r = 50$ mi/h

13. $d = 25$ mi, $t = 4$ h

14. $d = 90$ km, $t = 3$ h

15. $d = 75$ m, $r = 5$ m/s

16. $d = 160$ m, $r = 16$ m/s

17. $d = 450$ km, $r = 30$ km/h

18. $d = 780$ mi, $r = 40$ mi/h

19. **Challenge** $t = 15$ min, $r = 2.3$ km/h

20. **Challenge** $t = 23$ min, $d = 1250$ m

Solve.

21. A bicyclist rode 70 miles at 20 mi/h, and then another 75 miles at 15 mi/h. How long did the bike ride last?

22. A train heading north covered 240 km at 96 km/h. On the return journey heading south, the train averaged 120 km/h. How long did both trips take?

23. A group hiked 21 km in 8 hours on Saturday. On Sunday, the group hiked 4 hours and covered 40 km. Find the group's average hiking speed.

24. A boat traveled 3 hours and covered 96 km. Later that day, the boat went another 80 km in 2.5 hours. Find the average speed of the boat.

25. **Challenge** Edna Kiplagat ran the New York City marathon (42.19 km) in 2:28:20. What was her average speed in km/h? What was her pace in min/km?

26. **Challenge** On the way to work in the morning, Sally drove 42 mi in 1 h and 15 min. On the way home, she took a different route and drove 58 mi in 84 min. Which trip had the greater average speed, and what was the difference?

Choose the answer.

27. How long does it take to travel 250 miles at an average speed of 20 mi/h?

   A. 10.5 h   C. 23 h

   B. 12.5 h   D. 25 h

28. What is the average speed in kilometers per hour of a runner who covers 10 km in 30 minutes?

   A. 0.15 km/h   C. 20 km/h

   B. 0.33 km/h   D. 30 km/h

Constant-Rate Problems

Problems about constant rates can be solved with tables or equations.

➨ Using Rate Tables

A speed such as miles/hour is one kind of rate. Many other types of rates exist. Rates that don't change over time are called constant.

> **Definition**
>
> A rate is a **constant rate** if it does not change over time.

Tip

To use a rate table for problems with constant rates, multiply both terms of the rate by the same number.

Example

PROBLEM 1 This rate table shows a factory machine that fills bottles at a constant rate. Find the number of bottles filled in 60 minutes.

Number of Bottles	40				
Time (min)	1	5	10	20	60

SOLUTION The production rate for the machine is 40 bottles per minute. Multiply each time by 40 to complete the top row of the table.

Number of Bottles	40	200	400	800	2400
Time (min)	1	5	10	20	60

ANSWER The machine will fill 2400 bottles in 60 minutes.

PROBLEM 2 Another machine at the bottle factory fills 300 bottles in 5 minutes. How many bottles does it fill in 8 minutes?

SOLUTION Find the unit rate, and then multiply by 8 minutes. Divide to find the unit rate:
(300 bottles) ÷ (5 minutes) = 60 bottles/minute

Multiply the rate by time:
(60 bottles/minute) · (8 minutes) = 480 bottles

ANSWER This machine fills 480 bottles in 8 minutes.

Think About It

The machine in Problem 2 is faster because it has a greater unit rate.

➜ Using the Work Formula

Many problems involve finding how long it takes to do a task at a constant rate of work. To solve these problems, use the work formula.

> ### The Work Formula
>
> If w is the amount of work done, r is the constant rate, and t is the time worked, then
>
> $$w = rt.$$

To solve work problems, translate to an equation. Look at the units to make sure you are using the correct form of the equation. Then solve.

Example

Use the work formula to find the work done, the rate of work, or the time worked.

PROBLEM 3 rate = 6 miles of road paved per day, time = 5 days

SOLUTION You are given the rate and the time. Find the work.

$$\text{miles of road} = \frac{\text{miles of road}}{\text{day}} \cdot \text{days}$$

$w = rt$	Write the formula.
$= \dfrac{6 \text{ miles}}{\text{day}} \cdot 5 \text{ days}$	Substitute.
$= 30 \text{ miles}$	Multiply.

ANSWER The work was the paving of 30 miles of road.

PROBLEM 4 A pipe can fill a 3000-gallon tank in 12 hours.

SOLUTION You are given the time and the work. Find the rate.

$$\text{gallons} = \frac{\text{gallons}}{\text{hour}} \cdot \text{hours}$$

$w = rt$	Write the formula.
$3000 \text{ gal} = r \cdot 12 \text{ h}$	Substitute.
$\dfrac{3000 \text{ gal}}{12 \text{ h}} = \dfrac{r \cdot 12 \text{ h}}{12 \text{ h}}$	Divide both sides of the equation by 12 hours.
$\dfrac{250 \text{ gal}}{1 \text{ h}} = r$	Simplify.

ANSWER The rate for the pipe filling the tank is 250 gallons per hour.

Problem Set

Complete the rate table. Then use it to solve the problem.

1. **Stepping Stones** Marianne can decorate 3 cakes per hour. How many cakes can she decorate in 8 hours?

Number of Cakes	3				
Time (h)	1	2	5	8	10

The constant rate is ☐ cakes per hour.

Multiply each number in the bottom row by ☐ to fill in the top row.

Find 8 in the bottom row. The number of cakes for 8 hours is ☐.

2. A pipe fills a water tank at the rate of 200 gallons per minute. What size water tank can the pipe fill in 10 minutes?

Number of Gallons	200				
Time (min)	1	2	3	5	10

3. A window-washing crew can wash 10 windows per hour. How long will it take the crew to complete a building with 200 windows?

Number of Windows	10	20	50	100	200
Time (h)	1				

4. Carlos can read 30 pages per hour in the 270-page book he is reading. At this rate, how long will it take him to finish the book?

Number of Pages	30	60	120	180	270
Time (h)	1				

Find the unit rate, and then use it to solve the problem.

5. A machine can sew on 15 buttons in 3 minutes. How many buttons can it sew in 60 minutes?

6. Some students washed 24 cars in 2 hours. How many cars can they wash in 15 hours?

7. A gardening company plants 10 trees in 2 hours. How long will it take to plant 150 trees?

8. A trucking company makes 50 deliveries in 5 days. How long will it take for 400 deliveries?

Use the work formula to find the work done, the rate of work, or the time worked.

9. **Stepping Stones** time = 12 minutes, rate = 120 boxes sealed per minute

   Use the formula $w = rt$.

   $$w = \frac{\boxed{} \text{ boxes}}{\text{minute}} \cdot \boxed{} \text{ minutes}$$

   $w = \boxed{}$ boxes

   Work: A total of $\boxed{}$ boxes were sealed.

10. time = 10 hours, rate = 50 square yards of carpet laid per hour

11. work = 150 trees trimmed, time = 5 days

12. work = 200 tote bags sewed, time = 4 hours

13. rate = 120 square yards per hour, work = 6000 square yards of crops to be tilled

14. rate = 5 dozen per hour, work = 200 dozen cookies to be baked

Solve.

15. At the rate of 60 units per second, how long will it take to make 30,000 units?

16. At the rate of 45 boxes per minute, how long will it take to make 11,250 boxes?

17. A basket factory made 300 baskets in 5 days. What is the factory's production rate per day?

18. A mining company produced 2000 tons of iron ore in 10 days. What is the company's production rate?

19. A company manufactures 80 tons of steel per hour. How many tons can be manufactured in three 8-hour days?

20. A company produces natural gas at the rate of 80 million cubic feet per day. How many million cubic feet can be produced in ten 5-day weeks?

21. **Challenge** An oil rig pumps 75,000 barrels of oil per day. How many days will it take to pump a million barrels?

Choose the answer.

22. A machine in a factory can make 35 toy cars per hour. How many hours will it take to make 700 toy cars?

    A. 20   C. 200

    B. 24.5   D. 245

23. An airplane factory made 36 airplanes per month. At this rate, how many airplanes can the factory make per year?

    A. 3   C. 144

    B. 12   D. 432

Direct Variation

Unit rates will help you find and graph direct variation equations.

➔ Using Tables

Two quantities can be related in a special way. As one quantity increases, the other does, too. That relationship is called direct variation.

Definition

A **direct variation** shows that one quantity increases in proportion to another. In a direct variation, the ratio between values is a constant.

Tip

A unit rate has a denominator of 1. Find the unit rate and you will have the constant of variation.

Example

PROBLEM 1 The tables show the number of computers assembled each hour at two different factories. Identfy which factory's data show a direct variation.

Factory A		Factory B	
Hours	Computers Assembled	Hours	Computers Assembled
1	8	1	14
4	16	4	56
7	32	7	98

SOLUTION Find the ratios for each factory for each time period. The ratio will be a constant for a direct variation.

Factory A:
$8 \div 1 = 8$
$16 \div 4 = 4$
$32 \div 7 = 4.6$
The ratios are not the same.

Factory B:
$14 \div 1 = 14$
$56 \div 4 = 14$
$98 \div 7 = 14$
The ratios are the same.

ANSWER Factory B's data show a direct variation.

Direct Variations

A direct variation equation has the form $y = kx$. The variable k is the **constant of variation**.

Example

PROBLEM 2 Marcy runs 6 miles every day. Write the direct variation equation. Use it to complete the table.

x	y
1	
2	
3	

SOLUTION The variable x represents days, and y represents miles. Use the unit rate as k, the constant of variation. Write the equation.

$y = 6x$

Substitute each x-value. Solve for y.

x	$y = 6x$
1	$y = 6 \cdot 1 = 6$
2	$y = 6 \cdot 2 = 12$
3	$y = 6 \cdot 3 = 18$

ANSWER

x	y
1	6
2	12
3	18

➡ Graphing Direct Variation

Graphs are a good way to show direct variation. When you connect the points of a direct variation graph, you see a linear relationship

Tip

The point (0, 0) is on all direct variation graphs.

Example

PROBLEM 3 The direct variation equation $y = 50x$ shows a car moving at 50 miles per hour. Identify the constant of variation and draw the graph.

SOLUTION The equation is in the form $y = kx$. So $k = 50$.

Choose some values for x.
Substitute to find the values for y.

x	0	1	2	3
y	0	50	100	150

Look at the y-values to decide how to number the vertical scale. Number by 25 or 50 on the y-axis. Plot the ordered pairs. Start at (0, 0) and draw the line.

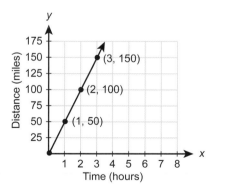

Problem Set

Identify which table shows a direct variation.

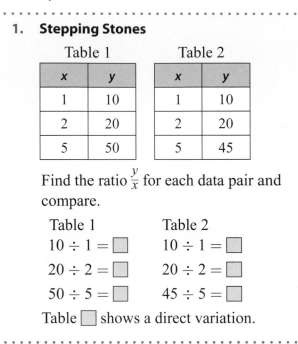

1. Stepping Stones

Table 1

x	y
1	10
2	20
5	50

Table 2

x	y
1	10
2	20
5	45

Find the ratio $\frac{y}{x}$ for each data pair and compare.

Table 1
$10 \div 1 = \square$
$20 \div 2 = \square$
$50 \div 5 = \square$

Table 2
$10 \div 1 = \square$
$20 \div 2 = \square$
$45 \div 5 = \square$

Table $\square$ shows a direct variation.

2.

Table 1

x	y
2	2
6	12
9	18

Table 2

x	y
2	14
6	42
9	63

3.

Table 1

x	y
1	19
2	38
3	57

Table 2

x	y
5	48
6	72
7	84

4.

Table 1

x	y
2	$4\frac{1}{2}$
4	9
6	$12\frac{1}{2}$

Table 2

x	y
3	4
5	$6\frac{2}{3}$
7	$9\frac{1}{3}$

5.

Table 1

x	y
3	7.5
4.5	11.25
7	17.5

Table 2

x	y
1.5	3
8	12
13	19.5

Complete the table to show the direct variation.

6. Stepping Stones A bicyclist rides at a speed of 30 miles per hour.

Hours	Miles	
0	$\square$	$\leftarrow \square \cdot 30$
1	$\square$	$\leftarrow \square \cdot 30$
5	$\square$	$\leftarrow \square \cdot 30$
10	$\square$	$\leftarrow \square \cdot 30$

7. A company makes 200 chairs per week.

Weeks	Chairs
0	
1	
10	
52	

8. $y = 12x$

x	y
0	
1	
2	
3	

9. A construction crew paves 3.5 miles of road per day.

Days	Miles
0	
1	
7	
30	

10. A spaceship travels 800 kilometers per second.

Seconds	Kilometers
0	
1	
2	
3	

11. $y = 5.2x$

x	y
0	
1	
10	
20	

Make a table of ordered pairs to graph the linear relationship of the direct variation.

12. Stepping Stones The equation $y = 15x$ shows that a pipe can fill a water storage tank at the rate of 15 liters per minute.

x	y
0	☐
1	☐
2	30
4	☐

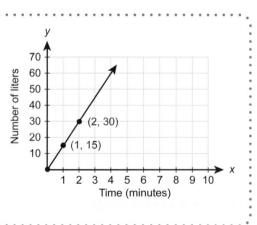

13. The equation $y = 25x$ shows that a musician practices 25 minutes per day.

14. The equation $y = 120x$ shows that 120 people per hour can ride a roller-coaster.

15. The equation $y = 75x$ shows that a train travels 75 miles per hour.

16. The equation $y = 9x$ shows that a boat travels 9 kilometers per hour.

Choose the answer.

17. Which equation is shown on the graph?

   A. $y = 5x$

   B. $y = x + 5$

   C. $y = x + 10$

   D. $y = 10x$

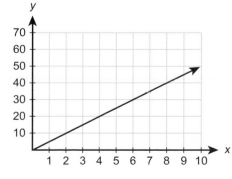

Interpreting Direct Variation

The steepness of a direct variation graph shows you how quickly a quantity increases.

➡ Using Graphs to Show Rate of Increase

The steepness of a direct variation graph is connected to its unit rate.

Example

PROBLEM 1 The graphs show two direct variations of cost per hour. Find the unit rate for each. Then compare each graph's unit rate to the slope of the line.

SOLUTION The ordered pair (4, 60) is shown on Graph 1, and the ordered pair (5, 30) is shown on Graph 2. Divide to find each unit rate.

Graph 1: $60 \div 4 = 15$ Graph 2: $30 \div 5 = 6$

ANSWER The unit rates are $15 per hour and $6 per hour. The greater the unit rate, the steeper the line.

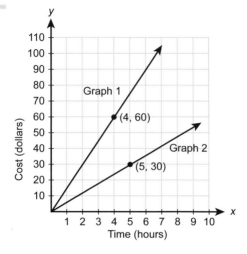

PROBLEM 2 Graph these two rates on one grid.

Rate 1: $25/month   Rate 2: $125/3 months

SOLUTION The ordered pair (3, 75) matches the first rate. Choose the ordered pair (3, 125) for the second rate.

ANSWER The graphs are shown on the grid.

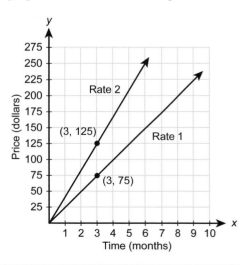

Tip

To check your work on problems like Problem 1, pick another point that lies on the line and find the ratio of the values. If the ratio is the same, then the points are on the same line.

➔ Solving Problems with Direct Variation Graphs

You can compare direct variation graphs on the same grid. The line that is steeper shows the faster rate or speed.

Example

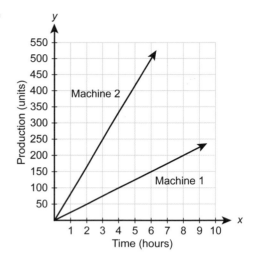

PROBLEM 3 The graph shows two machines at a factory. Compare the production rates of the two machines. Which machine is faster?

SOLUTION Compare the steepness of the two lines.

ANSWER The line for Machine 2 rises more quickly. Machine 2 has a faster production rate.

PROBLEM 4 Trish and Kathy run a 50-meter race. The equations relate the time in seconds to their distance in meters in the race.

Trish: $y = 5x$ Kathy: $y = \dfrac{25x}{6}$

Graph the equations on the same grid. Who ran faster?

SOLUTION Select an x-value for each equation and find the corresponding y-value. Graph the ordered pairs and connect the points with $(0, 0)$.

Trish:
For $x = 5$:

$y = 5 \cdot 5 = 25$

ordered pair: $(5, 25)$

Kathy:
For $x = 6$:

$y = \dfrac{25 \cdot 6}{6} = 25$

ordered pair: $(6, 25)$

ANSWER The slope of the graph for Trish is greater than the slope for Kathy, so Trish's rate is greater, and she ran faster.

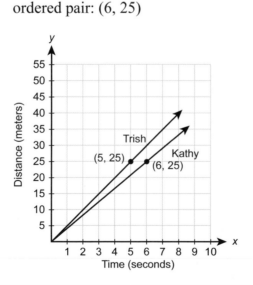

Tip

When you are comparing two direct variation graphs, draw them both on the same grid. If they are on different grids, make sure the scales on the axes are the same.

TOPIC

Problem Set

Find each unit rate. Compare the rates.

1. **Stepping Stones** Josh earned $40 in 5 hours, and Clay earned $30 in 2 hours.

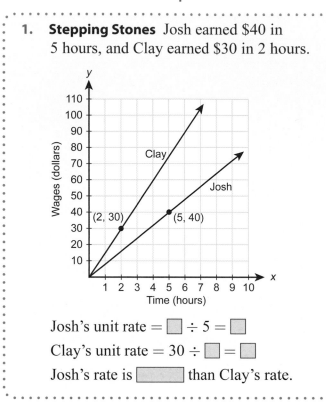

Josh's unit rate = ☐ ÷ 5 = ☐

Clay's unit rate = 30 ÷ ☐ = ☐

Josh's rate is ☐ than Clay's rate.

2. Brahim earned $3000 in 6 weeks, and Amanda earned $2500 in 7 weeks.

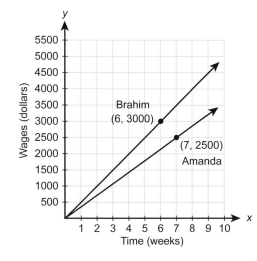

3. Fiona read 45 pages in 3 hours, and Albert read 30 pages in 6 hours.

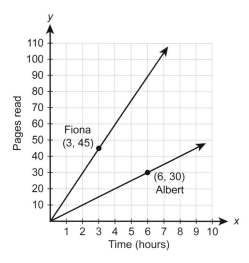

4. Machine 1 packs 75 boxes in 3 minutes, and Machine 2 packs 75 boxes in 5 minutes.

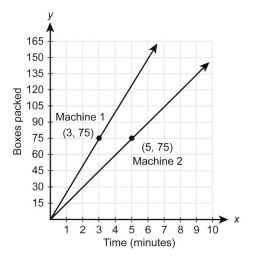

Graph both rates on the same grid.

5. 6 apples per pound; 8 pears per pound

6. 12 L in 4 min; 15 L in 6 min

7. 36 riders per hour; 52 riders in 2 hours

8. 8 m in 14 s; 12 m in 20 s

9. 78 cars in 20 min; 180 cars in 1 h

10. 4.5 mm for 6 layers; 2.3 mm for 4 layers

Solve.

11. Who saved money at a greater rate?

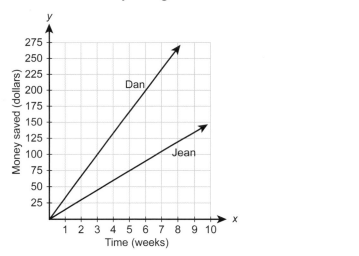

12. Who reads books at a slower rate?

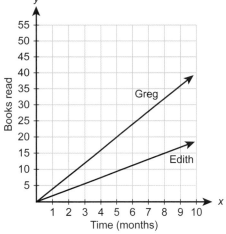

The equations show cars driving at different speeds, in kilometers per hour. Graph the equations on the same grid. State which car is driving faster.

13. Car 1: $y = 60x$

Car 2: $y = 90x$

14. Car 1: $y = 90x$

Car 2: $y = 70x$

The graph shows the distances covered by two runners in 2 hours. Choose the answer.

15. Which comparison is shown by the graph?

   A. The runners are moving at the same speed.

   B. Runner 2 has run farther than Runner 1.

   C. Runner 2 is faster than Runner 1.

   D. Runner 1 is faster than Runner 2.

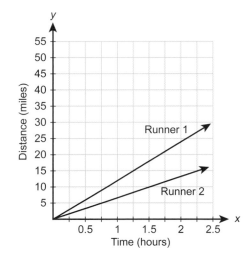

16. A third runner goes 10 miles in 1 hour. How does this runner compare with Runner 1 and Runner 2?

   A. The third runner is faster than both.

   B. The third runner is slower than both.

   C. The third runner is faster than Runner 2, but slower than Runner 1.

   D. The third runner is faster than Runner 1, but slower than Runner 2.

Chapter 11 Review

Choose the answer.

1. Which equation could be used to solve the problem?

   Raffle tickets cost $3 each. The math club sells $153 in raffle tickets. How many raffle tickets, t, does the math club sell?

   A. $t = \dfrac{\$3}{1 \text{ ticket}} + \$153$

   B. $t = \$153 \cdot \dfrac{\$3}{1 \text{ ticket}}$

   C. $t = \$153 \div \dfrac{\$3}{1 \text{ ticket}}$

   D. $t = \dfrac{\$3}{1 \text{ ticket}} \div \$153$

2. Ellen buys 8 picture frames for $72. How much does each frame cost?

   A. $64   C. $80

   B. $9   D. $7

3. A 3-pound bag of grapes costs $2.07. How much does a 5-pound bag of grapes cost?

   A. $0.69   C. $3.45

   B. $4.14   D. $1.38

4. A store sells 3 CDs for $27.99. How much do 2 CDs cost?

   A. $18.66   C. $9.33

   B. $55.98   D. $26.99

5. Shelby rides his bicycle 72 km in 3 hours. What is Shelby's average speed?

   A. 69 km/h   C. 21 km/h

   B. 75 km/h   D. 24 km/h

6. It takes Anna 8 hours to mow 5 lawns belonging to her neighbors. What is her rate in hours per lawn?

   A. 0.625   C. 3

   B. 1.6   D. 11

7. Which equation matches the table of values?

x	y
2	26
3	39
5	65
7	91

   A. $y = 24 + x$ C. $x = y - 36$

   B. $x = 13y$ D. $y = 13x$

8. The table shows 2 runners in a 50-yard dash. The line for Runner 3 on the same graph is steeper than the lines for both Runner 1 and Runner 2.

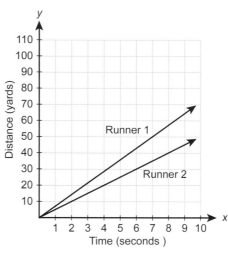

   Which conclusion can be drawn about the runners' speeds?

   A. Runner 1 was faster than Runner 3.

   B. Runner 2 was faster than Runner 3.

   C. Runner 3 was faster than Runner 1.

   D. Runner 3 was slower than Runner 1, but faster than Runner 2.

Write an equation that could be used to solve the problem.

9. Antoinette read the same number of pages in her book each day for 13 days. She read a total of 312 pages. How many pages did Antoinette read each day?

10. Marcus finished the 5 km race in 25 minutes. What was Marcus's average pace in minutes per kilometer?

Find the unit rate with the second unit as the denominator.

11. $27 for 3 books

12. 425 kilometers in 5 hours

Use a unit rate to solve.

13. It took Arturo 24 minutes to wrap 3 presents. How long will it take Arturo to wrap 7 presents?

14. A store sells 5 T-shirts for $37.50. How much do 3 shirts cost?

Write and evaluate an expression to find the speed or the time.

15. distance = 32 km; time = 2 h

16. distance = 800 mi; speed = 40 mi/h

Solve the constant rate problem.

17. A student can solve 25 math problems in 5 minutes. How long will it take her to solve 80 math problems?

18. Lance can swim 20 laps in the pool in 14 minutes. How long will it take him to swim 15 laps?

Use the graph to solve.

19. Write an equation that is shown by line *a* on the graph.

20. Write an equation that is shown by line *b* on the graph.

21. Describe the steepness of a line that shows a rate slower than line *b* but faster than line *a*.

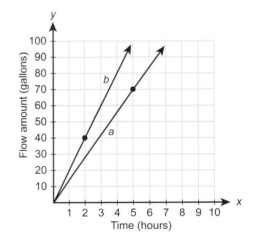

Graph both rates on the same grid.

22. 5 km in 45 min; 10 km in 80 min

23. 14 pages in 4 days; 3 pages in 1 day

12 Working with Positives and Negatives

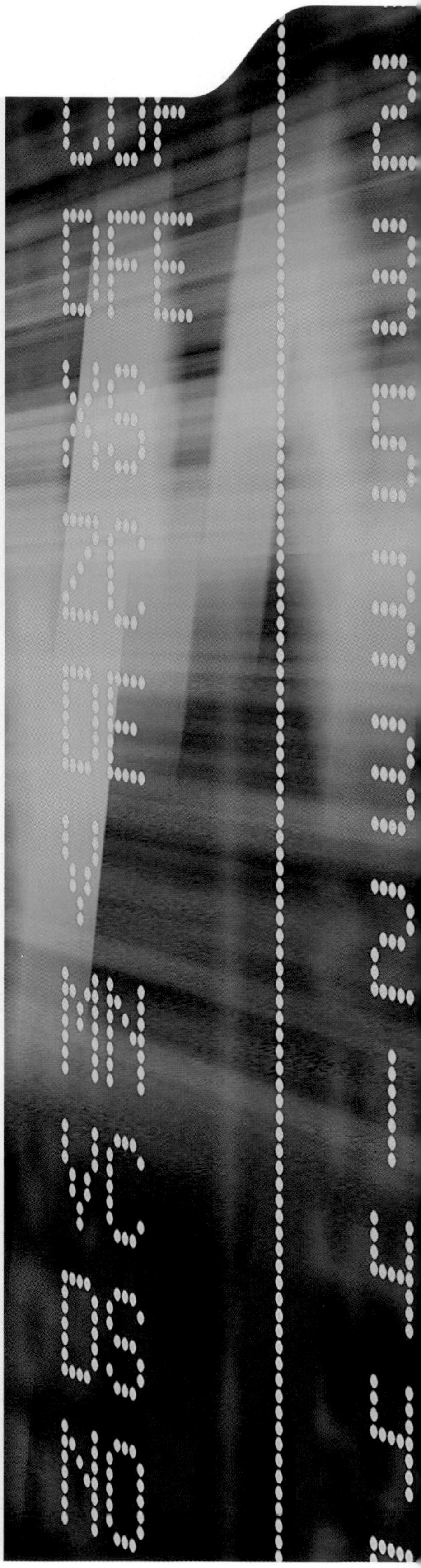

Businesspeople really care about positive and negative numbers. The difference between positive and negative is the difference between profit and loss. When you want to figure out how well a business is operating, positives and negatives will help.

In This Chapter

You will learn how to add, subtract, multiply, and divide positive and negative numbers, including decimals. You'll also work with inequalities.

Chapter Topics

▶ Foundations for Chapter 12

▶ Adding and Subtracting Signed Numbers

▶ Net Gains and Losses

▶ Multiplying Signed Numbers

▶ Dividing Signed Numbers

▶ Properties of Signed Numbers

▶ Inequalities

▶ Chapter 12 Review

Financial companies use positive and negative numbers to describe increases and decreases in value.

Foundations for Chapter 12

➔ Showing Numbers on a Number Line

Positive and negative numbers, including integers, decimals, fractions, and mixed numbers, can be shown on a number line.

Example A

Draw a number line from -3 to 3 and put tick marks at fourths. Graph a point with the given coordinate.

PROBLEM A-1 point a, coordinate of $-\frac{1}{2}$

SOLUTION Find the tick mark labeled $-\frac{1}{2}$. Graph point a at that place on the number line.

ANSWER Point a is shown on the number line.

PROBLEM A-2 point b, coordinate of $-1\frac{3}{4}$

SOLUTION Find the tick mark labeled -2. Move one-fourth of a whole unit to the right. Or find the tick mark labeled $-1\frac{1}{2}$ and move one-fourth of a whole unit to the left. Graph point b at that place on the number line.

ANSWER Point b is shown on the number line.

PROBLEM A-3 point c, coordinate of 2.5

SOLUTION Convert 2.5 to a mixed number.

$$2.5 = 2\frac{1}{2}$$

Find the tick mark labeled $2\frac{1}{2}$. Graph point c at that place on the number line.

ANSWER Point c is shown on the number line.

Problem Set A

Graph a point with the given coordinate.

Draw a number line from -10 to 10. Put tick marks at fourths.

1. point d, coordinate of $-3\frac{1}{2}$

2. point e, coordinate of $1\frac{1}{4}$

3. point f, coordinate of -7

4. point g, coordinate of $-8\frac{3}{4}$

Draw a number line from -1 to 1. Put tick marks at eighths.

5. point h, coordinate of $-\frac{7}{8}$

6. point j, coordinate of $-\frac{1}{4}$

7. point k, coordinate of $\frac{3}{4}$

8. point m, coordinate of $-\frac{1}{8}$

Draw a number line from -2 to 2. Put tick marks at tenths.

9. point n, coordinate of -1.7

10. point p, coordinate of -0.3

11. point q, coordinate of 1.1

12. point r, coordinate of -1.2

Finding Opposites and Reciprocals

Definitions

Opposites are pairs of numbers that are the same distance from 0.
Reciprocals are two numbers that have a product of 1.

To find the opposite of a number, change the number's sign. To find the reciprocal of a number, first write the number as a fraction (if the number isn't already a fraction). Then switch the numerator and the denominator.

Example B

PROBLEM B-1 Find the opposite of $2\frac{3}{8}$.

SOLUTION The number $2\frac{3}{8}$ is positive, so change its sign to a negative to find its opposite.

ANSWER The opposite of $2\frac{3}{8}$ is $-2\frac{3}{8}$.

PROBLEM B-2 Find the reciprocal of $\frac{1}{3}$.

SOLUTION Switch the numerator and the denominator. Then simplify.

$$\frac{3}{1} = 3$$

ANSWER The reciprocal of $\frac{1}{3}$ is 3.

Problem Set B

Find the opposite of the number.

1. -7

2. $-\frac{5}{8}$

3. $1\frac{2}{3}$

4. -3.75

5. 4.01

6. $-11\frac{5}{6}$

7. $\frac{1}{12}$

8. $-\frac{11}{7}$

9. $-4\frac{1}{4}$

Find the reciprocal of the number.

10. $\frac{3}{4}$

11. $2\frac{1}{2}$

12. 9

13. $-\frac{5}{3}$

14. $4\frac{2}{5}$

15. -3

16. $\frac{2}{3}$

17. $-3\frac{1}{8}$

18. 2

→ Adding and Subtracting Integers

Rules for Adding and Subtracting Integers

For addends with the same sign, add their absolute values. The sum has the same sign as the addends.

$-3 + (-4)$
$|-3| + |-4| = 3 + 4 = 7$
$-3 + (-4) = -7$

For addends with different signs, subtract the lesser absolute value from the greater absolute value. The sum has the same sign as the addend with the greater absolute value.

$-8 + 5$
$|-8| - |5| = 8 - 5 = 3$
$|-8| > |5|$, so
$-8 + 5 = -3$

To subtract a number, add its opposite.

$-6 - (-7)$
$-6 + 7 = 1$

Look at the integers' signs and use the rules to add or subtract absolute values.

Example C

PROBLEM C-1 Add: $8 + (-10)$

SOLUTION The signs of the addends are different, so subtract the absolute values. The negative value has greater absolute value, so the sum is negative.

$8 + (-10) = -(|-10| - |8|) = -(10 - 8) = -2$

ANSWER $8 + (-10) = -2$

PROBLEM C-2 Subtract: $-5 - (-9)$

SOLUTION The opposite of -9 is 9.
$-5 - (-9) = -5 + 9$
Subtract the absolute values. The positive number has greater absolute value, so the difference is positive.

$-5 + 9 = +(|9| - |-5|) = +(9 - 5) = +4$

ANSWER $-5 - (-9) = 4$

Problem Set C

Add or subtract.

1. $-5 + 11$

2. $6 + (-4)$

3. $-4 - 7$

4. $8 - (-9)$

5. $-8 + (-12)$

6. $7 + 14$

7. $-20 + (-32)$

8. $-17 - (-12)$

9. $13 - 29$

10. $18 + (-63)$

11. $-45 + 45$

12. $-34 - (-41)$

13. $51 - 78$

14. $66 + (-118)$

15. $-70 - 82$

FOUNDATIONS

Positives and negatives can represent profit and loss.

Planting the Seed

Positive and negative numbers obey the rules of arithmetic just as whole numbers do.

Adding and Subtracting Signed Numbers

Use what you know about working with integers to add and subtract other numbers that have positive and negative signs.

➡ Adding Signed Numbers

If two numbers have the same sign, the sum also will have the same sign. If the signs of two numbers are different, subtract the lesser absolute value from the greater absolute value. The sum has the sign of the number with the greater absolute value.

Example

PROBLEM 1 Add: $3.6 + 0.08$

SOLUTION Both addends are positive, so the sum is positive.
$3.6 + 0.08 = 3.68$

ANSWER $3.6 + 0.08 = 3.68$

PROBLEM 2 Add: $-1.2 + (-6.05)$

SOLUTION Both addends are negative, so the sum is negative.

$-1.2 + (-6.05) = -(|-1.2| + |-6.05|) = -|7.25| = -7.25$

ANSWER $-1.2 + (-6.05) = -7.25$

PROBLEM 3 Add: $-8.2 + 3$

SOLUTION The signs are different, so subtract the absolute values. $|-8.2| > |3|$, so the sum is negative.

$-8.2 + 3 = -(|-8.2| - |3|) = -|5.2| = -5.2$

ANSWER $-8.2 + 3 = -5.2$

PROBLEM 4 Add: $13 + (-6.5)$

SOLUTION The signs are different, so subtract the absolute values. $|13| > |-6.5|$, so the sum is positive.

$|13| - |-6.5| = 13 - 6.5 = 6.5$

ANSWER $13 + (-6.5) = 6.5$

TOPIC

➦ Subtracting Signed Numbers

Subtraction is the same as adding the opposite.

Example

PROBLEM 5 Subtract: $3 - 8$

SOLUTION Rewrite as addition. Add.

$3 - 8 = 3 + (-8) = -5$

ANSWER $3 - 8 = -5$

PROBLEM 6 Subtract: $-25 - (-10.3)$

SOLUTION Rewrite as addition. Add.

$-25 - (-10.3) = -25 + 10.3 = -14.7$

ANSWER $-25 - (-10.3) = -14.7$

PROBLEM 7 Subtract: $-2.5 - 0.7$

SOLUTION Rewrite as addition. Add.

$-2.5 - 0.7 = -2.5 + (-0.7) = -3.2$

ANSWER $-2.5 - 0.7 = -3.2$

When you're working with more than two numbers, work from left to right, adding or subtracting pairs of numbers.

Example

PROBLEM 8 Find the value of $-5 + 6 - 2.4 + 10.6 - 15$.

SOLUTION

$-5 + 6 - 2.4 + 10.6 - 15$ Add.
$\downarrow$
$1 - 2.4 + 10.6 - 15$ Subtract.
$\downarrow$
$-1.4 + 10.6 - 15$ Add.
$\downarrow$
$9.2 - 15$ Subtract.
$\downarrow$
-5.8

ANSWER $-5 + 6 - 2.4 + 10.6 - 15 = -5.8$

T O P I C

Problem Set

Add.

1. Stepping Stones $-18 + 10.9$

The signs are different. Subtract the absolute values.

The absolute value of -18 is greater, so the sum will be [____].

$-18 + 10.9 = -(|-18| - |\boxed{}|)$
$= -(18 - \boxed{})$
$= \boxed{}$

2. $-26.8 + 7$

3. $9 + (-5.2)$

4. $13.3 + (-7)$

5. $-6 + 12.9$

6. $-11 + 2.57$

7. $-9 + (-14.11)$

8. $-12.05 + (-5)$

9. $-7.1 + 3.6$

10. $-5.2 + 1.9$

11. $0.08 + (-3.4)$

12. $1.6 + (-7.25)$

13. $-0.03 + 1.7$

14. $-3.4 + 5.84$

15. $-6.25 + (-4.7)$

16. $-8.03 + (-6.8)$

17. Challenge $\frac{3}{8} + \left(-\frac{13}{16}\right)$

Subtract.

18. Stepping Stones $15 - 22$

Rewrite as addition: $15 - 22 = 15 + \boxed{}$
The absolute value of $\boxed{}$ is greater, so the sum will be $\boxed{}$.

$15 + (-22) = -(|\boxed{}| - |15|)$
$= -(\boxed{} - 15)$
$= \boxed{}$

19. $35.1 - 40$

20. $-12 - 6.7$

21. $-23 - 7.2$

22. $14.4 - (-8)$

23. $23 - (-9.12)$

24. $-36.45 - (-14)$

25. $-56 - (-27.07)$

26. $3.5 - 7.42$

27. $6.04 - 9.1$

28. $-4.5 - 7.12$

29. $-9.3 - 17.05$

30. $1.2 - (-7.8)$

31. $3.5 - (-9.1)$

32. $-0.09 - (-1.2)$

33. $-3.05 - (-5.8)$

34. Challenge $-\frac{7}{12} - \left(-\frac{1}{6}\right)$

Simplify.

35. **Stepping Stones** $-14 + 28 - 6 - (-30)$

    Add or subtract numbers from left to right in pairs.

    $$-14 + 28 - 6 - (-30) = \boxed{} - 6 + 30$$
    $$= \boxed{} + 30$$
    $$= \boxed{}$$

36. $18 - 5 - (-7) + 16$

37. $1.2 - 6.2 - (-4.9)$

38. $-7.5 - (-3.6) + 8.2$

39. $0.056 - 1.2 - (-0.048)$

40. $-1.03 + 6.8 - (-2.057)$

Solve.

41. **Stepping Stones** Carly's scores for five rounds of a game were $-4, 6, -2, -3,$ and 8. What was her final score?

    Add or subtract numbers from left to right in pairs.

    $$-4 + 6 - 2 - 3 + 8 = \boxed{} - 2 - 3 + 8$$
    $$= \boxed{} - 3 + 8$$
    $$= \boxed{} + 8$$
    $$= \boxed{}$$

    Carly's final score was $\boxed{}$.

42. Bart's scores for five rounds of a game were $7, -1, 6, 0,$ and -8. What was his final score?

43. At the beginning of an experiment, the temperature of a substance was $-2.5°C$. During the experiment, the temperature rose $5.2°C$ and then fell $8.4°C$. What was the final temperature?

44. The temperature of a substance in a science experiment was $1.4°C$. During the experiment, the temperature fell $3.5°C$ and then rose $2.8°C$. What was the final temperature?

Choose the answer.

45. What is the sum?
    $$-6.4 + 3.75$$

    A. -10.15 C. 2.65

    B. -2.65 D. 10.15

46. What is the difference?
    $$-2.03 - (-1.6)$$

    A. -3.63 C. 0.43

    B. -0.43 D. 3.63

47. Marlon's scores for four rounds of a game were $34, -17, -56,$ and 78. What was his final score?

    A. 185 C. 73

    B. 151 D. 39

Net Gains and Losses

Signed numbers can help you solve problems about gains and losses.

➔ Calculating Net Gain or Loss

A loss can be written with a negative number. A gain can be written with a positive number.

Definition
When a situation includes several gains and losses, the **net gain** or the **net loss** is the sum of the individual values.

Think About It

Other practical problems that use integers are those about debts and payments, profits and expenses, and values of investment accounts.

Example

PROBLEM 1 A football team loses 3 yards on one play, gains 5 yards on the next play, and then loses 7 yards on the third play. What is the net gain or loss?

SOLUTION Write the losses and gains as signed numbers. Then add.

loses 3 yards	gains 5 yards	loses 7 yards
↓	↓	↓
-3	$+5$	-7

$$-3 + 5 + (-7) = -5$$

ANSWER The result -5 represents a net loss of 5 yards.

PROBLEM 2 In one day, Potty Training Inc.'s stock value increased 2.65 points and then went down 8.85 points. How many more points must it gain or lose to have a net gain of 8 points at the end of the day?

SOLUTION Write an equation and solve for the missing value.

$2.65 + (-8.85) + n = 8$	Write the equation.
$-6.2 + n = 8$	Simplify on the left side.
$6.2 + (-6.2) + n = 8 + 6.2$	Add 6.2 to both sides.
$n = 14.2$	Simplify.

ANSWER PTI's stock must gain 14.2 points to have a net gain of 8 points.

TOPIC

➔ Solving Problems Shown with Tables

Example

Janine has started a home business. The table shows the profit or loss for each month of the first 6 months that her business existed.

Janine's Home Business					
Jan.	Feb.	Mar.	Apr.	May	June
−$575	+$84	−$173	+$367	+$184	+$682

PROBLEM 3 What is the net profit or loss through the end of April?

SOLUTION Find the sum of the signed numbers from January through April. Add pairs of numbers from left to right.

$$-575 + 84 + (-173) + 367$$
$$-491 \quad + (-173) + 367$$
$$-664 \qquad + 367$$
$$-297$$

ANSWER Through the end of April, the net loss was $297.

PROBLEM 4 What is the net profit or loss for all 6 months?

SOLUTION Add the profits from May and June to the net loss through April.

$$-297 + 184 + 682$$
$$-113 \quad + 682$$
$$569$$

ANSWER In the first 6 months, her business had a net profit of $569.

Example

PROBLEM 5 The table shows part of Manuel's checking account activity. If Manuel's starting account balance was $462.18, what was his ending balance?

SOLUTION Start with the beginning balance. Add the deposits and withdrawals in pairs from left to right.

$$462.18 + 75 + (-48.65) + 250 + 180 + (-645)$$
$$537.18 \quad + (-48.65) + 250 + 180 + (-645)$$
$$488.53 \qquad\quad + 250 + 180 + (-645)$$
$$738.53 \qquad\qquad + 180 + (-645)$$
$$918.53 \qquad\qquad\quad + (-645)$$
$$273.53$$

Manuel's Account		
Date	Deposit	Withdrawl
4/2	$75	
4/4		−$48.65
4/7	$250	
4/14	$180	
4/15		−$645

ANSWER The ending balance in Manuel's account was $273.53.

T O P I C

Problem Set

Use signed numbers to solve.

1. **Stepping Stones** In the past 3 months, Red Shoe Company had one monthly loss of $1800 and two monthly profits of $4500 and $5600. What was the net profit or loss for the 3 months?

   $4500 + 5600 + \boxed{} = \boxed{}$

   The Red Shoe Company had a net $\boxed{}$ of $\$\boxed{}$.

2. In the past 3 months, Pet Tenders had two monthly losses of $8750 and $6200 and one monthly profit of $13,750. What was the net profit or loss?

Write an equation, and then solve the problem.

6. **Stepping Stones** A football team gained 8 yards on first down, lost 12 yards on second down, and gained 6 yards on third down. How many yards does the team need to gain on fourth down to have a 10-yard gain from its starting position?

   $8 + (-12) + \boxed{} + n = 10$

   $n = \boxed{}$

   The team needs to gain $\boxed{}$ yards.

7. A football team lost 9 yards on first down and 4 yards on second down. It gained 5 yards on third down. How many yards does it need to gain on fourth down to have a 10-yard gain from its starting position?

3. A helicopter descended 1200 feet, rose 800 feet, and then descended 450 feet. What was the net gain or loss in altitude?

4. A helicopter rose 2400 feet, descended 1650 feet, and then descended another 725 feet. What was the net gain or loss in altitude?

5. **Challenge** A stock price with an initial value of $42.25 rose $6.18 and then decreased 10% in value. What was the net gain or loss?

8. Vick's Vitamins had start-up expenses of $85,000 for research and $125,000 for the first year's inventory. So far, the sales are $45,000. What do the sales have to be for the rest of the year for the company to break even?

9. During a period of 6 months, MegaCorp had monthly profits of $3.2 million, $1.8 million, and $6.4 million. Two months had losses of $4.5 million and $2.7 million. The net profit was $7.5 million. What happened in the month that is not included in the problem data?

10. **Challenge** Ming checked her account balance yesterday and saw it was $417.50. She checked it again today and saw a balance of $340.18. What can you tell about what happened between yesterday and today?

Use the table showing monthly profits and losses for Ted's Woodworking to write an equation, and then solve the problem.

Ted's Woodworking Business					
Jan.	Feb.	Mar.	Apr.	May	June
$873	−$456	−$329	$610	$532	−$795

11. Find the net profit or loss at the end of March.

12. Find the net profit or loss for all 6 months.

Use the table showing monthly profits and losses for Desiree's Design Studio to write an equation, and then solve the problem.

Desiree's Design Studio					
Sept.	Oct.	Nov.	Dec.	Jan.	Feb.
−$126	$345	−$280	−$164	$375	$293

13. Find the net profit or loss at the end of December.

14. Find the net profit or loss for all 6 months.

Use the table to write an equation, and then solve the problem.

15. The table shows part of Stella's checking account activity. If Stella's starting account balance was $925.62, what was her ending balance?

Stella's Account		
Date	Deposit	Withdrawal
7/8		−$75.60
7/14		−$450
7/30	$750	
8/11	$875	
8/31		−$35.25

16. The table shows part of Tom's checking account activity. If Tom's starting account balance was $1345.74, what was his ending balance?

Tom's Account		
Date	Deposit	Withdrawal
2/2	$925	
2/16		−$648
3/2		−$59.85
3/16	$485	
3/30	$700	

Choose the answer.

17. What is the net gain or loss in yardage for a football team that gains 6 yards, loses 12 yards, and then gains back 15 yards?

A. −21 yards   C. 9 yards

B. −9 yards   D. 21 yards

18. The first and second year's sales for We-Sell-Cellular were $125,000 and $470,000. The expenses for the second year were $165,000. If the company had a net profit of $50,000 after two years, what were the expenses for the first year?

A. $380,000   C. $560,000

B. $480,000   D. $810,000

Multiplying Signed Numbers

When you multiply signed numbers, you can follow rules to find the sign of the product.

➔ Using Rules to Multiply Signed Numbers

Look at this pattern of products:

$$3 \cdot 3 = 9 \qquad 3 \cdot 2 = 6 \qquad 3 \cdot 1 = 3 \qquad 3 \cdot 0 = 0$$

As the second factor is decreased by 1 each time, the product decreases by 3. Continue the pattern.

$$3 \cdot (-1) = -3 \qquad 3 \cdot (-2) = -6 \qquad 3 \cdot (-3) = -9$$

Now look at a pattern of products where the first factor is negative:

$$-4 \cdot 3 = -12 \qquad -4 \cdot 2 = -8 \qquad -4 \cdot 1 = -4 \qquad -4 \cdot 0 = 0$$

As the second factor is decreased each time by 1, the product increases by 4. Continue the pattern.

$$-4 \cdot (-1) = 4 \qquad -4 \cdot (-2) = 8 \qquad -4 \cdot (-3) = 12$$

Multiplying Two Signed Numbers

The product of two numbers with like signs is positive.

$$2 \cdot 4 = 8 \qquad -8 \cdot \left(-\frac{1}{2}\right) = 4$$

The product of two numbers with unlike signs is negative.

$$-6 \cdot 2 = -12 \qquad \frac{2}{3} \cdot \left(-\frac{1}{5}\right) = -\frac{2}{15}$$

Use the rules to find the product. Remember that when you make something negative, you are finding its opposite. So two negatives is the opposite of the opposite, or the original.

Example

Find the product. Use the rules for multiplying signed numbers.

PROBLEM 1 $-8 \cdot 4$

SOLUTION The signs are unlike, so the product is negative.

$$-8 \cdot 4 = -(8 \cdot 4) = -(32)$$

ANSWER $-8 \cdot 4 = -32$

PROBLEM 2 $-\frac{1}{3} \cdot (-6)$

SOLUTION The signs are alike, so the product is positive.

$$-\frac{1}{3} \cdot (-6) = +\left(\frac{1}{3} \cdot \frac{6}{1}\right)$$
$$= +\left(\frac{6}{3}\right) = +2$$

ANSWER $-\frac{1}{3} \cdot (-6) = 2$

TOPIC

➡ Finding the Products of Multiple Signed Numbers

Look at the pattern of these products and the number of negative factors:

Three negative factors: $-4 \cdot (-2) \cdot (-3) = -4 \cdot 6 = -24$

Four negative factors: $-2 \cdot (-3) \cdot (-2) \cdot (-3) = (2 \cdot 3) \cdot (2 \cdot 3) = 6 \cdot 6 = 36$

Five negative factors:
$$-4 \cdot (-2) \cdot (-4) \cdot (-2) \cdot (-4) = (4 \cdot 2) \cdot (4 \cdot 2) \cdot (-4)$$
$$= (8 \cdot 8) \cdot (-4)$$
$$= 64 \cdot (-4)$$
$$= -256$$

The pattern above leads to the following rules for multiplying multiple signed numbers.

Multiplying Multiple Signed Numbers

If there are an odd number of negative factors, then the product is negative.
If there are an even number of negative factors, then the product is positive.

See if the number of negative factors is odd or even to find the product's sign. Rewrite with all-positive factors. Write the product's sign.

Example

Find the product.

PROBLEM 3 $-2 \cdot (-7) \cdot (-3)$

SOLUTION There are an odd number of negative factors, so the product is negative.
$$-2 \cdot (-7) \cdot (-3) = -(2 \cdot 7 \cdot 3)$$
$$= -(14 \cdot 3)$$
$$= -42$$

ANSWER $-2 \cdot (-7) \cdot (-3) = -42$

PROBLEM 4 $-4 \cdot 6 \cdot 2 \cdot (-0.25)$

SOLUTION There are an even number of negative factors, so the product is positive.
$$-4 \cdot 6 \cdot 2 \cdot (-0.25) = +(4 \cdot 6 \cdot 2 \cdot 0.25)$$
$$= 24 \cdot 2 \cdot 0.25$$
$$= 48 \cdot 0.25$$
$$= 12$$

ANSWER $-4 \cdot 6 \cdot 2 \cdot (-0.25) = 12$

Think About It

You can use the commutative property of multiplication to reorder the factors so you can multiply any pairs of negative factors to get a positive product.

Tip

After you determine the sign of the product, write it down before you begin to multiply so you don't forget to place it in the answer.

Problem Set

Find the product. Use the rules for multiplying signed numbers.

1. **Stepping Stones** $3 \cdot (-8)$

   The first number is positive and the second is ☐. The signs are ☐, so the product is ☐.

   $3 \cdot (-8) = $ ☐

2. $-6 \cdot (-4)$

3. $-9 \cdot 5$

4. $-12 \cdot (-2)$

5. $8 \cdot 8$

6. $4 \cdot (-9)$

7. $-11 \cdot (-4)$

8. $15 \cdot 2$

9. $7 \cdot (-12)$

10. $3 \cdot (-10)$

11. $-\frac{1}{2} \cdot (-8)$

12. $-0.75 \cdot 24$

13. $20 \cdot \left(-\frac{1}{5}\right)$

14. $-\frac{1}{3} \cdot (-15)$

15. $\frac{2}{3} \cdot \left(-\frac{1}{2}\right)$

16. $0.3 \cdot 1.5$

17. $-\frac{2}{7} \cdot \left(-\frac{5}{8}\right)$

18. $-320 \cdot \frac{7}{16}$

19. $42.78 \cdot (-8.3)$

20. **Challenge** $-\frac{9}{10} \cdot (-3.5)$

Find the product. Use the rules for multiplying multiple signed numbers.

21. **Stepping Stones** $-8 \cdot (-4) \cdot 6$

    There are two negative factors, so the product is ☐.

    $-8 \cdot (-4) \cdot 6 = +(\boxed{} \cdot \boxed{}) \cdot 6 = \boxed{} \cdot 6$

    $ = \boxed{}$

22. $3 \cdot (-7) \cdot (-9)$

23. $-5 \cdot 2 \cdot 10$

24. $-7 \cdot (-3) \cdot (-8)$

25. $12 \cdot 14 \cdot \frac{1}{2}$

26. $0.8 \cdot (-0.4) \cdot 5$

27. $-\frac{1}{4} \cdot 12 \cdot \left(-\frac{1}{2}\right)$

28. $-2 \cdot (-4) \cdot 6 \cdot (-8)$

29. $-9 \cdot (-1) \cdot (-7) \cdot (-4)$

30. $12 \cdot \frac{2}{3} \cdot (-1) \cdot (-8)$

31. $0.5 \cdot (-4) \cdot 3 \cdot (-2) \cdot 1$

32. $2.6 \cdot (-2) \cdot (-3) \cdot (-1) \cdot 1.1$

33. $-2 \cdot (-3) \cdot 7 \cdot (-4) \cdot \left(-\frac{1}{4}\right)$

34. $-\frac{1}{5} \cdot (-20) \cdot \left(-\frac{3}{5}\right) \cdot (-40) \cdot (-10)$

35. $4 \cdot (-2) \cdot 5 \cdot (-2) \cdot (-1) \cdot 4$

36. $-7 \cdot (-8) \cdot (-2) \cdot (-3) \cdot (-9) \cdot (-0.5)$

37. $12 \cdot (-42) \cdot (-3) \cdot 2 \cdot (-25) \cdot 1$

38. **Challenge** $-\frac{1}{3} \cdot (-0.12) \cdot \frac{2}{5} \cdot (-3.5)$

Solve.

39. A multiplication problem has 6 positive factors and 7 negative factors. What is the sign of the product?

40. Alfonso finds four factors that multiply to −120. Two of the first three factors are negative. What is the sign of the fourth factor?

41. A positive number is written as a product with one more negative factor than positive factors. What is the least number of factors?

42. Jane is scuba diving 8 m below the surface of the water. Regina is 12 times as deep as Jane. At what depth is Regina?

43. **Challenge** A hiker starts at an elevation of 317 m and hikes down 3 m every minute. After 4 minutes, at what elevation is he?

Choose the answer.

44. What is the product?
$$-9 \cdot (-4)$$

A. 36

B. 13

C. −13

D. −36

45. What is the product?
$$3 \cdot (-1) \cdot (-4) \cdot (-6)$$

A. −72

B. −14

C. 14

D. 72

Dividing Signed Numbers

The rules for dividing signed numbers are similar to the rules for multiplying signed numbers.

➔ Using Rules to Divide Signed Numbers

Look at this pattern of quotients:

$9 \div 3 = 3 \qquad 6 \div 3 = 2 \qquad 3 \div 3 = 1 \qquad 0 \div 3 = 0$

As the dividend is decreased by 3 each time, the quotient decreases by 1. Continue the pattern.

$-3 \div 3 = -1 \qquad -6 \div 3 = -2 \qquad -9 \div 3 = -3$

Now look at a pattern of quotients where the divisor is negative:

$9 \div (-3) = -3 \qquad 6 \div (-3) = -2 \qquad 3 \div (-3) = -1 \qquad 0 \div (-3) = 0$

As the dividend is decreased by 3 each time, the quotient increases by 1. Continue the pattern.

$-3 \div (-3) = 1 \qquad -6 \div (-3) = 2 \qquad -9 \div (-3) = 3$

Dividing Signed Numbers

The quotient of two numbers with like signs is positive.

$4 \div \frac{1}{2} = 8 \qquad -8 \div (-4) = 2$

The quotient of two numbers with unlike signs is negative.

$-12 \div 2 = -6 \qquad \frac{2}{15} \div \left(-\frac{1}{5}\right) = -\frac{2}{3}$

Think About It

Division is the same as multiplying by the reciprocal.

$-8 \div 4 = -8 \cdot \left(\frac{1}{4}\right) = -2$

$-30 \div (-6) = -30 \cdot \left(-\frac{1}{6}\right) = 5$

Example

Find the quotient. Use the rules for dividing signed numbers.

PROBLEM 1 $-27 \div (-3)$

SOLUTION The dividend and divisor are negative. The signs are alike, so the quotient is positive.

$-27 \div (-3) = +(27 \div 3) = 9$

ANSWER $-27 \div (-3) = 9$

PROBLEM 2 $-5.5 \div 2$

SOLUTION The dividend is negative and the divisor is positive. The signs are unlike, so the quotient is negative.

$-5.5 \div 2 = -(5.5 \div 2) = -(2.75)$

ANSWER $-5.5 \div 2 = -2.75$

→ Simplifying Expressions with Signed Numbers

Multiplying and Dividing Multiple Signed Numbers

If there are an odd number of negative terms, then the answer is negative.
If there are an even number of negative terms, then the answer is positive.

Think About It

Because division can be written as multiplication, the rules for multiplying multiple signed numbers also apply to expressions that include both multiplication and division.

Follow the order of operations and multiply or divide the terms in pairs from left to right.

Example

Simplify the expression.

PROBLEM 3 $-3 \cdot 5.6 \div (-2)$

SOLUTION There are an even number of negative terms, so the answer will be positive.

$-3 \cdot 5.6 \div (-2)$
$-16.8 \div (-2)$
8.4

ANSWER
$-3 \cdot 5.6 \div (-2) = 8.4$

PROBLEM 4 $24 \div 2 \cdot \left(-\frac{1}{3}\right)$

SOLUTION There is only one negative term, so the answer will be negative.

$24 \div 2 \cdot \left(-\frac{1}{3}\right)$
$12 \cdot \left(-\frac{1}{3}\right)$
-4

ANSWER
$24 \div 2 \cdot \left(-\frac{1}{3}\right) = -4$

Finding the Mean with Negative Numbers

Example

PROBLEM 5 A spelunker starts at a depth of -135 m. As he climbs up and down, he marks the change in his depth every hour. The changes are $+12$ m, $+7$ m, -14 m, -14 m, and -6 m. The net change in the spelunker's depth is -15 m. What is the mean depth change per hour?

SOLUTION Divide the net depth change by the number of hours.
$-15 \div 5 = -(15 \div 5) = -3$

ANSWER The mean depth change per hour is -3 m.

Remember

The *mean* of a set of values is the sum of the values divided by the number of values in the set.

T O P I C

Problem Set

Find the quotient.

1. **Stepping Stones** $20 \div (-5)$

   The signs are [____], so the quotient is [____].

   $20 \div (-5) =$ [ ]

2. $-12 \div (-4)$

3. $-35 \div 5$

4. $-12 \div (-6)$

5. $48 \div 8$

6. $81 \div (-9)$

7. $-110 \div (-11)$

8. $56 \div 8$

9. $7.6 \div (-2)$

10. $3 \div (-0.25)$

11. $-8 \div \left(-\frac{1}{4}\right)$

12. $-7 \div (-3.5)$

13. $20 \div \left(-\frac{1}{5}\right)$

14. $-\frac{2}{3} \div (-15)$

15. $19.75 \div (-1.25)$

16. $-17.25 \div 0.75$

17. $\frac{2}{5} \div \left(-\frac{3}{10}\right)$

18. **Challenge** $-109.5 \div \frac{3}{2}$

Simplify the expression.

19. **Stepping Stones** $8 \cdot (-1.2) \div 3$

    $8 \cdot (-1.2) \div 3$

    [ ] $\div 3$ Multiply.

    [ ]   Divide.

20. $18 \cdot \left(-\frac{1}{3}\right) \div (-2)$

21. $-35 \div 7 \cdot 4.6$

22. $-\frac{2}{3} \div (-4) \cdot (-3)$

23. $\frac{1}{2} \cdot 72 \div 4$

24. $0.8 \cdot (-0.4) \div 5$

25. $-84 \div 12 \cdot \left(-\frac{2}{7}\right)$

26. $-2.5 \cdot (-8) \div 4 \cdot (-8.6)$

27. $-96 \div (-8) \cdot \left(-\frac{2}{3}\right) \div \left(-\frac{1}{4}\right)$

28. $24 \div \frac{2}{3} \cdot (-5) \cdot (-3)$

29. $20.5 \cdot (-4) \div 10 \cdot (-2) \div \frac{1}{3}$

30. $-4.2 \div (-3) \cdot 7 \div (-2) \cdot (-5.5)$

31. $40.6 \div (-2) \cdot (-3) \div (-1) \cdot 1.2$

32. $70.5 \div (-0.5) \cdot 12 \div (-10) \cdot 120.1$

33. $-\frac{1}{5} \cdot (-450) \div \left(-\frac{4}{5}\right) \cdot (-80) \div (-20)$

34. **Challenge** $-\frac{4}{5} \div (-0.2) \cdot \frac{3}{8} \div (-2.5)$

Solve.

35. Stepping Stones The low temperatures for the past 5 days were $-3°C$, $-1°C$, $-13°C$, $-15°C$, and $-8°C$. The sum of these low temperatures is $-40°C$. What was the average low temperature over the past 5 days?

To find the average low temperature, divide the sum of the temperatures by the number of days: $-40 \div 5$.

The signs are different, so the quotient will be [   ] .

$-40 \div 5 = \square$

The average low temperature for the past 5 days was $\square$°C.

36. Rasheem keeps track of the monthly profit and loss for his lawn mowing business. For the past 4 months, the profit or loss was $-\$150$, $-\$70$, $-\$10$, and $+\$85$. The sum of the profits or losses over the past 4 months is $-\$145$. What was his average profit or loss?

37. A scientist measures the position of a glacier with positive measurements representing the glacier's advance. Her findings for 5 months were -0.6 m, -0.7 m, $+0.2$ m, $+0.1$ m, and -0.4 m. The net change in the glacier's position was -1.4 m. What was the mean monthly change in position?

38. Challenge The low temperatures for the past 7 days were $-13°C$, $-11°C$, $-4°C$, $0°C$, $+4°C$, $+5°C$, and $+5°C$. What was the average low temperature over the past 7 days?

Choose the answer.

39. What is the quotient?

$$-72 \div (-8)$$

A. 80   C. -9

B. 9   D. -80

40. What is the value of the expression?

$$6 \cdot (-3.6) \div (-3)$$

A. -64.8 C. 7.2

B. -7.2 D. 64.8

41. A business reports a net income of $-\$5760$ over a 6-month period. What is the average income per month for that period?

A. $-\$5766$ C. $\$960$

B. $-\$960$ D. $\$5754$

Properties of Signed Numbers

Properties you used with whole numbers can help you calculate with signed numbers.

➔ **Extending the Number Properties**

You have learned that these properties are true for whole numbers. They are also true for signed numbers including all integers, decimals, and fractions.

Number Properties

Commutative property of addition: $a + b = b + a$

Associative property of addition: $(a + b) + c = a + (b + c)$

Commutative property of multiplication: $a \cdot b = b \cdot a$

Associative property of multiplication: $(a \cdot b) \cdot c = a \cdot (b \cdot c)$

Distributive properties: $a \cdot (b + c) = ab + ac$ and $a \cdot (b - c) = ab - ac$

Tip

Use these everyday words to remember the names of the properties:

To *commute* means "to change locations."

To *associate* means "to group together."

Example

Complete the statement.

PROBLEM 1 $-3.8 + 4.5 + 3.8 = -3.8 + \boxed{} + 4.5$

SOLUTION The order of the addends is changed.

ANSWER $-3.8 + 4.5 + 3.8 = -3.8 + \mathbf{3.8} + 4.5$

PROBLEM 2 $-2 \cdot (-4 \cdot 11) = [-2 \cdot (-4)] \cdot \boxed{}$

SOLUTION The grouping of the factors is changed.

ANSWER $-2 \cdot (-4 \cdot 11) = [-2 \cdot (-4)] \cdot \mathbf{11}$

Think About It

Subtraction is not commutative:

$3 - 6 \neq 6 - 3$.

But you can rewrite subtraction as addition. Then it is commutative:

$3 + (-6) = -6 + 3$.

These are more properties that apply to all signed numbers.

More Number Properties

The following properties are true for any number a:

Inverse property of addition: $a + (-a) = 0$

Inverse property of multiplication: $a \cdot \frac{1}{a} = 1$ (as long as a is not zero)

Identity property of addition: $a + 0 = a$

Identity property of multiplication: $1 \cdot a = a$

Zero property of multiplication: $0 \cdot a = 0$

Example

PROBLEM 3 Marta had $147 in her checking account last month. This month her balance was $0. Identify her account activity during the month.

SOLUTION Write an equation to represent the situation. $147 + a = 0$, where a represents the money deposited or withdrawn. The inverse property of addition shows that $a = -147$.

ANSWER Marta withdrew $147 from her account.

➔ Using the Order of Operations

Use the same order of operations for signed numbers as you used for whole numbers. Do operations inside parentheses, evaluate exponents, multiply and divide from left to right, and then add and subtract from left to right.

Example

Simplify the expression.

PROBLEM 4 $-45 \cdot (-16 + 16) \cdot 38$

SOLUTION

$$-45 \cdot (-16 + 16) \cdot 38 = -45 \cdot 0 \cdot 38 \qquad \text{Add inside parentheses.}$$
$$= 0 \qquad \text{Multiply.}$$

ANSWER $-45 \cdot (-16 + 16) \cdot 38 = 0$

Tip

Use PEMDAS to help you remember the order of operations.

Parentheses

Exponents

Multiply

Divide

Add

Subtract

T O P I C

Problem Set

Complete the statement.

1. **Stepping Stones** $2.5 \cdot (-6) = \boxed{} \cdot 2.5$

   Two numbers can be multiplied in either order. That property of numbers is the _____ property of multiplication. The missing number is $\boxed{}$.

2. $-4.2 \cdot (-3) = \boxed{} \cdot (-4.2)$

3. $[3 + (-1)] + 9 = 3 + [(-1) + \boxed{}]$

4. $[7 + (-8)] + (-2) = 7 + [\boxed{} + (-2)]$

5. $[6 \cdot (-3)] \cdot (-7) = 6 \cdot [\boxed{} \cdot (-7)]$

6. $[0.5 \cdot (-1)] \cdot 12 = \boxed{} \cdot (-1 \cdot 12)$

7. $-1.6 + 2.7 = \boxed{} + (-1.6)$

8. $-5.4 + (-0.3) = -0.3 + \boxed{}$

9. $\frac{5}{6} \cdot \boxed{} = 0$

10. $\boxed{} \cdot \frac{1}{3} = 1$

11. $-8 + 0 = \boxed{}$

12. $-5 + \boxed{} = -5$

13. $7.6 \cdot \boxed{} = 7.6$

14. $1 \cdot \boxed{} = -1.8$

15. $-2(3 + 6) = \boxed{} - 12$

16. $-8(5 + 2) = -40 - \boxed{}$

17. $\boxed{} + 7 = 0$

18. $3 + \boxed{} = 0$

19. $\frac{1}{8} \cdot \boxed{} = 1$

20. **Challenge** $0 \cdot \boxed{} = 0$

21. **Challenge** $\frac{4}{5} \cdot \frac{5}{4} \div \boxed{} = 1$

Use the distributive property to complete the statement.

22. **Stepping Stones** $55 + 88 = 11 \cdot (5 + \boxed{})$

    The number 11 is a common factor. Since $88 \div 11 = \boxed{}$, the missing number is $\boxed{}$.

23. $90 + 70 = 10 \cdot (9 + \boxed{})$

24. $27 + 63 = 9 \cdot (\boxed{} + 7)$

25. $24 + 40 = 8 \cdot (3 + \boxed{})$

26. $18 + 42 = 6 \cdot (\boxed{} + 7)$

27. $24 + 60 = 12 \cdot (\boxed{} + \boxed{})$

28. $96 + 56 = 8 \cdot (\boxed{} + \boxed{})$

29. $84 + 76 = 4 \cdot (\boxed{} + \boxed{})$

30. **Challenge** $-30 + 18 = -6(\boxed{} + \boxed{})$

Use the distributive property to simplify.

31. Stepping Stones $-6 \cdot 47$

Use the distributive property to break the second factor into a sum.

$$-6 \cdot 47 = -6(40 + \square)$$
$$= (-6 \cdot 40) + (-6 \cdot \square)$$
$$= \square + \square$$
$$= \square$$

32. $63 \cdot (-5)$

33. $7 \cdot (-88)$

34. $-3 \cdot (-104)$

35. $-20 \cdot (-49)$

Simplify the expression.

36. Stepping Stones $-2 \cdot (6 - 15)$

$$-2 \cdot (6 - 15) = -2 \cdot \square = \square$$

37. $-4 \cdot (-3 + 8)$

38. $3 + 2 \cdot (-8)$

39. $-4 + 6 \cdot (-1)$

40. $-12 \cdot \frac{1}{3} \cdot 3 + 8$

41. $-25 \cdot 6 \cdot \frac{1}{6} + 5$

42. $6.2 + 8 \cdot (-0.4)$

43. $6 + 2.5 \cdot (-12)$

44. $\frac{1}{3} - \frac{4}{5} \cdot \frac{5}{9}$

45. $-\frac{5}{6} + \frac{1}{2} \cdot \left(-\frac{4}{3}\right)$

Choose the answer.

46. Which equation shows the commutative property of multiplication?

A. $-5 + 5 = 0$

B. $-5 \cdot (-1) = 5 \cdot 1$

C. $-5 \cdot (-1) = -1 \cdot (-5)$

D. $-5 + (-1) = -1 + (-5)$

47. Which number makes the statement true?

$$45 + 57 = 3 \cdot (\square + 19)$$

A. 15

B. 19

C. 45

D. 57

48. What is the value of the expression?

$$-2 + 6 \cdot (-10)$$

A. -62

B. -40

C. 40

D. 120

49. Which equation shows the zero property of multiplication?

A. $-8 + 8 = 0$

B. $-8 \cdot 0 = 0$

C. $-8 \cdot 0 = -8$

D. $-8 + 0 = -8$

Inequalities

Equations are good models when quantities are equal. But sometimes two amounts aren't equal!

➤ Modeling with Inequalities

When two numbers, quantities, or expressions are not equal, you can use an inequality to show how they are related.

> **Definition**
>
> An **inequality** shows that two quantities are not equal. Symbols for inequality include > (is greater than) and < (is less than).

Remember

A variable is a letter or other symbol that stands for an unknown number.

To model a situation with an inequality, start by choosing a variable.

Example

Write an inequality to model the situation.

PROBLEM 1 A liquid in a science experiment must be kept at a temperature greater than $-5.6°F$. Write an inequality that describes the possible temperatures for the liquid.

SOLUTION Let t = the temperature in degrees Fahrenheit.
Write a word expression. t must be greater than -5.6.
Write the inequality. $t > -5.6$

ANSWER $t > -5.6°F$

PROBLEM 2 Greg has $24.75 in his pocket for a trip to a museum. Write an inequality that describes the possible amounts he can spend if he wants to still have some money when he leaves the museum.

SOLUTION Let x = the amount Greg spends.
Write a word expression. x must be less than $24.75.
Write the inequality. $x < 24.75

ANSWER $x < 24.75

➔ Graphing Inequalities on Number Lines

The solution to an equation such as $x + 3 = 9$ is just one number. An inequality usually has many solutions. One way to show all the solutions is to use a number line.

Example

Write and graph an inequality to model the situation.

PROBLEM 3 Stan needs more than $4\frac{2}{3}$ yards of fabric for his craft project. Show the possible amounts of fabric he can buy.

SOLUTION Let $n =$ the number of yards he needs.

Write a word expression. n must be more than $4\frac{2}{3}$.
Write the inequality. $n > 4\frac{2}{3}$

Draw the graph. Use an open circle to show that $4\frac{2}{3}$ is not included.

ANSWER $n > 4\frac{2}{3}$

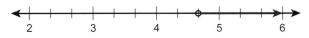

PROBLEM 4 Every dog in Laura's survey must be less than 84.5 cm in height. Show the possible heights for the dogs in her survey.

SOLUTION Let $h =$ height in centimeters.

Write a word expression. h must be less than 84.5.
Write the inequality. $h < 84.5$

Draw the graph. It shows all the possible heights for the dogs.

ANSWER $h < 84.5$

Problem Set

Write an inequality to model the situation. Describe any values that make the inequality true but that don't make sense for the actual situation.

1. **Stepping Stones** A scientific study includes butterflies with wingspans more than $3\frac{1}{8}$ inches long. Show the possible wingspans.

   Let w stand for the wingspan in inches. Then w must be greater than ☐. The inequality is w ☐ $3\frac{1}{8}$.

2. The pieces of wood used in a building project must be less than $15\frac{3}{4}$ feet long. Show the possible lengths.

3. Matt wants to run more than 12.25 kilometers each weekend. Show the possible distances he may run.

4. The county budget should be less than $2.3 million. Show the possible amounts for this budget.

5. A severe weather warning is issued when temperatures fall below $-18.5°C$. Show the possible temperatures when the alert is issued.

6. Pamela owes less than $42.25 on the payments for her new bike. Show the possible amounts she owes. Use a negative number for her debt.

7. **Challenge** Children 20.5 inches tall or shorter cannot go on a ride at a park. Show the heights of the children who can go on this ride.

Draw a number line. Use it to graph an inequality for the situation. Describe any values that make the inequality true but that don't make sense for the actual situation.

8. **Stepping Stones** Temperatures less than $-8.5°C$ may cause problems with a company's outdoor machinery. Show the temperatures where problems may occur.

   Draw an open circle to show -8.5 degrees.

   Make an arrow to the ☐ to show all the numbers less than ☐.

9. A company doesn't want to lose $6.5 million or more. Show the possible profits and losses for the company.

10. Valerie plans to study more than $1\frac{1}{4}$ hours each night. Show the possible number of hours she might study.

11. Miguel's goal is to practice the piano more than $3\frac{1}{2}$ hours per week. Show the possible number of hours he might practice.

12. An apartment complex allows small dogs that weigh less than 20 pounds. Show the possible weights of dogs that would be allowed.

13. For fishermen to keep a caught lobster, some states require that the lobster have a body shell length of at least 8.5 cm. Show the possible shell lengths of lobsters that cannot be kept.

14. Water boils at a temperature of 100°C. Show the possible temperatures of some water that isn't boiling.

15. A basketball coach makes his team run extra laps if their free-throw percentage in a game is less than 80%. The team didn't have to run extra laps after its last game. Show the possible free-throw percentages for the team.

Choose the answer.

16. Which inequality models this situation? The distance between two buildings must be greater than 2.75 meters.

   A. $d - 2.75 = 0$

   B. $d + 2.75 = 0$

   C. $d > 2.75$

   D. $d < 2.75$

17. Which situation is shown on this number line?

   A. a temperature that is less than -33.5°C

   B. a temperature that is less than -32.5°C

   C. a temperature that is greater than -33.5°C

   D. a temperature that is greater than -32.5°C

Chapter 12 Review

Choose the answer.

1. What is the sum?
$$2.4 + (-6.8)$$
   A. -4.4 C. 4.4
   B. -9.2 D. 9.2

2. What is the difference?
$$-5.9 - 3.7$$
   A. -2.2 C. 2.2
   B. -9.6 D. 9.6

3. Blair opens his investment account with $500. He loses $15.45 the first month, and then gains $35.68 the second month. If his net gain after 3 months is $40, how much money did he gain in the third month?
   A. $11.13   C. $34.17
   B. $60.23   D. $19.77

4. What is the product?
$$-4 \cdot (-12)$$
   A. -48 C. 48
   B. 3 D. -3

5. What is the product?
$$-5 \cdot (-2) \cdot 2 \cdot (-3)$$
   A. 60 C. -20
   B. -60 D. 30

6. What is the quotient?
$$-4.8 \div 12$$
   A. -7.2 C. -0.4
   B. 7.2 D. 0.4

7. What is the quotient?
$$-25 \div (-0.5)$$
   A. 50 C. 12.5
   B. -50 D. -12.5

8. Which equation shows the associative property of multiplication?
   A. $13.9 + (4.4 + 7) = (13.9 + 4.4) + 7$
   B. $13.9 + 4.4 + 7 = 13.9 + 7 + 4.4$
   C. $13.9 \cdot (4.4 \cdot 7) = (13.9 \cdot 4.4) \cdot 7$
   D. $13.9 \cdot 4.4 \cdot 7 = 13.9 \cdot 7 \cdot 4.4$

9. What is the value of the expression?
$$14 + (-6) \cdot (-8)$$
   A. 62 C. -34
   B. 34 D. -64

10. The number line shows which inequality?

   A. $p < -4$ C. $p < 4$
   B. $p > 4$ D. $p > -4$

Add or subtract.

11. $5 + (-6)$

12. $-8 + 8$

13. $14 - (-3)$

14. $-11 - 16$

15. $3.4 + (-8.7)$

16. $-7.9 - (-12)$

Solve.

17. A football team gains 118 rushing yards in the first half of the game, and then loses 21 rushing yards in the second half. What is the team's net number of rushing yards for the game?

18. Martin gains 45 points in the first round, loses 13 points in the second round, and gains 26 points in the third round. What is Martin's score after three rounds?

Simplify the expression.

19. $4 \cdot (-8)$

20. $-7 \cdot (-6)$

21. $-1.2 \cdot (-6.3) + 4$

22. $-2.7 \cdot 5.5 \cdot (-4.1)$

23. $-36 \div 6$

24. $-72 \div (-8)$

25. $5 + (-10) \div 2.5$

26. $-7.6 \div (-0.4) - 1$

Use properties to find the value of the variable.

27. $-8.4 + (-0.9) = -0.9 + d$

28. $-4.67 + m = 0$

29. $\frac{5}{6} \cdot g = 1$

30. $30 + 90 = 10 \cdot (3 + c)$

Simplify the expression.

31. $-6 \cdot [5 + (-8)]$

32. $\frac{3}{4} \cdot 2 \cdot \left(-\frac{1}{2}\right) + \frac{1}{4}$

33. $8.4 + 6 \cdot (-3.3)$

34. $\frac{1}{2} - \frac{1}{2} \cdot \left(-\frac{1}{2}\right)$

Write an inequality to represent the situation.

35. A movie is recommended for children over the age of 13.

36. Hedo wants to spend less than $22.50 on a new shirt.

Graph the inequality on a number line.

37. $p > \frac{1}{2}$

38. $g < -2.5$

CHAPTER REVIEW

Problem	Topic Lookup	Problem	Topic Lookup
1–2, 11–16	Adding and Subtracting Signed Numbers	6–7, 23–26	Dividing Signed Numbers
3, 17–18	Net Gains and Losses	8–9, 27–34	Properties of Signed Numbers
4–5, 19–22	Multiplying Signed Numbers	10, 35–38	Inequalities

13 Making and Moving Figures

Two men from Southampton, England, say that they used only planks, rope, hats, and wire to make the first crop circles in the 1970s. Crop circle designs range from the simple to the complex, but anyone who makes crop circles needs to know about circles and transformations.

In This Chapter

You will construct and transform figures. For constructions, you will use paper folding as well as a compass and a straightedge. For transformations, you will use coordinates and other methods.

Chapter Topics

- ► Foundations for Chapter 13
- ► Folded-Paper Construction
- ► Compass and Straightedge Construction
- ► Translation
- ► Reflection
- ► Rotation
- ► Translating with Coordinates
- ► Reflecting with Coordinates
- ► Figures on a Coordinate Plane
- ► Chapter 13 Review

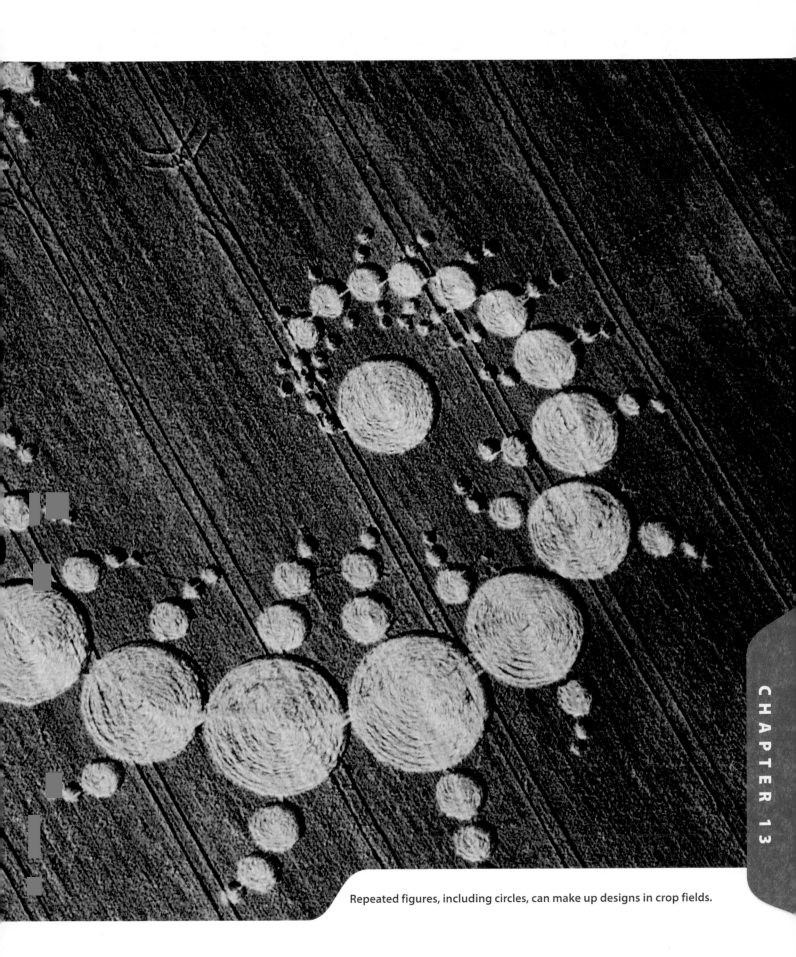

Repeated figures, including circles, can make up designs in crop fields.

Foundations for Chapter 13

➤ Identifying Regular Polygons

Definitions

A **polygon** is a closed figure formed by three or more straight sides in a plane. Each side intersects two other sides only at their endpoints.

In a **regular polygon**, all the sides are congruent and all the angles are congruent.

Determine whether a polygon is regular by using what you are told about the figure or by seeing the way its sides and angles are marked.

Example A

State whether the polygon is regular. Explain your answer.

PROBLEM A-1

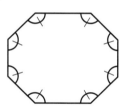

SOLUTION The angles are all congruent. The side lengths are not shown to be congruent.

ANSWER The polygon is not regular because the sides are not known to be congruent.

PROBLEM A-2

SOLUTION The sides are all shown to be congruent, and the angles are all shown to be congruent.

ANSWER The polygon is regular because it has congruent sides and congruent angles.

Problem Set A

State whether the polygon is regular. Explain your answer.

1.
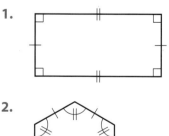

2.
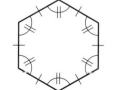

3.
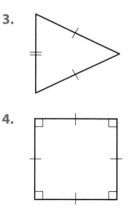

4.

➔ Identifying Quadrilaterals

Definition

A **quadrilateral** is a polygon with four sides.

Use this flowchart to classify a quadrilateral.

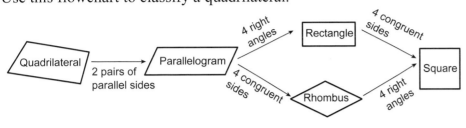

Example B

Write all the names that apply: *parallelogram*, *rhombus*, *rectangle*, and *square*.

PROBLEM B-1

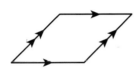

SOLUTION The figure has two pairs of parallel sides that are not all congruent. The figure has no right angles.

ANSWER The quadrilateral is a parallelogram.

PROBLEM B-2

SOLUTION The figure has two pairs of parallel sides, 4 congruent sides, and 4 right angles.

ANSWER The quadrilateral is a parallelogram, rectangle, rhombus, and square.

Problem Set B

Write all the names that apply: *parallelogram*, *rhombus*, *rectangle*, and *square*.

1.

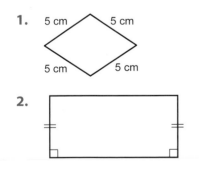

2.

3.

4.

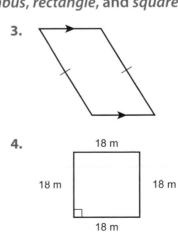

FOUNDATIONS

→ Finding Points on a Coordinate Plane

Definition

An **ordered pair** (x, y) shows the location of a point on a coordinate plane. The first number is the **x-coordinate**. The second number is the **y-coordinate**.

To describe the location of a point, look to the x-axis to find its x-coordinate. Then look to the y-axis to find the point's y-coordinate.

Example C

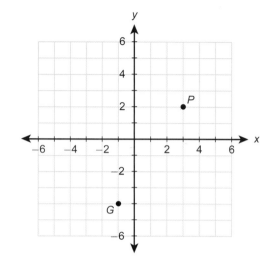

PROBLEM C-1 Find the coordinates of point P.

SOLUTION From P, look down to the x-axis. Point P is above 3. Look left to the y-axis. Point P is across from 2.

ANSWER The coordinates for point P are $(3, 2)$.

PROBLEM C-2 Plot point G at $(-1, -4)$ on a coordinate plane.

SOLUTION Start at the origin. The x-coordinate is -1, so move 1 unit left on the x-axis. The y-coordinate is -4, so move 4 units down. Write G next to the point.

ANSWER Point G is shown on the coordinate plane.

Problem Set C

Find the coordinates of the point on the coordinate plane.

1. point A

2. point B

3. point C

4. point D

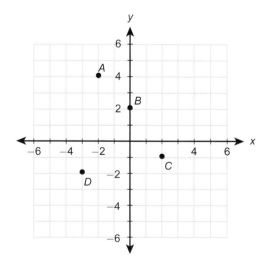

Plot the point on a coordinate plane.

5. point E at $(-2, 0)$

6. point F at $(1, -3)$

7. point H at $(4, 5)$

8. point J at $(-3, -1)$

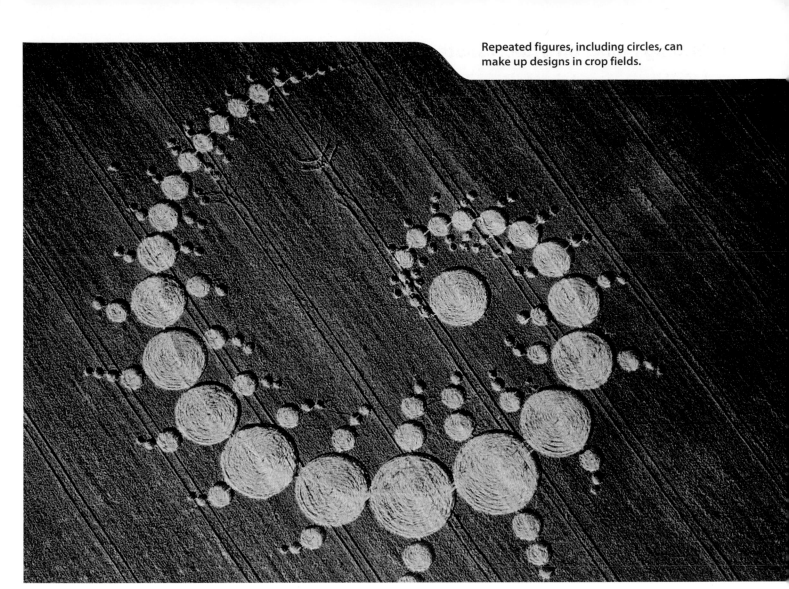

Planting the Seed

When you slide, flip, or turn a figure to create another figure, you are using transformations. Transformations can help you create interesting designs.

Folded-Paper Construction

You don't need a protractor or a ruler to make some figures. All you need is a piece of paper.

➜ Constructing Angles

> **Definition**
>
> A **construction** is something that has been made or put together.

To construct a right angle, draw a ray on a piece of paper. Fold the paper along the ray, and the crease represents the other side of a 180° angle. Fold the ray over on itself, and the crease represents the other side of a 90° angle.

> **Remember**
>
> The rays that make up the sides of a 180° angle form a straight line.

Example

PROBLEM 1 Construct a 90° angle with a piece of paper.

SOLUTION Draw a ray on a piece of paper. Fold the ray over on itself. Open the paper.

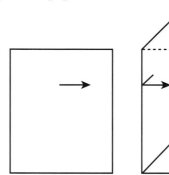 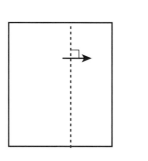

ANSWER The crease forms a 90° angle with the ray.

The ray is basically a straight angle. Folding the paper across the vertex bisects the straight angle, or cuts it into two equal angles. The straight angle measures 180°, so the result of folding is two 90° angles.

> **Tip**
>
> Lightweight paper that you can see through, such as tracing paper, works best for folded-paper constructions.

→ Constructing Bisectors of Segments and Angles

On a piece of paper, fold a line segment or an angle to make a bisector.

Example

PROBLEM 2 Construct a bisector of the angle.

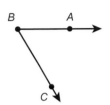

SOLUTION Copy the angle onto a sheet of paper. Fold the angle at its vertex so that one side of the angle overlaps the other. Open the paper. Place point D on the crease to label the new ray, which is $\overrightarrow{BD}$.

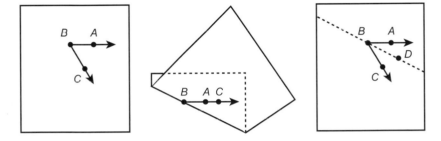

New angles ABD and CBD have been formed.
$m\angle ABD = m\angle CBD$

ANSWER $\overrightarrow{BD}$ represents a bisector of $\angle ABC$.

TOPIC

Problem Set

Construct the angle with a sheet of paper.

1. 90°

2. 180°

3. **Challenge** 45°

Copy the line segment onto a sheet of paper. Construct a bisector of the line segment.

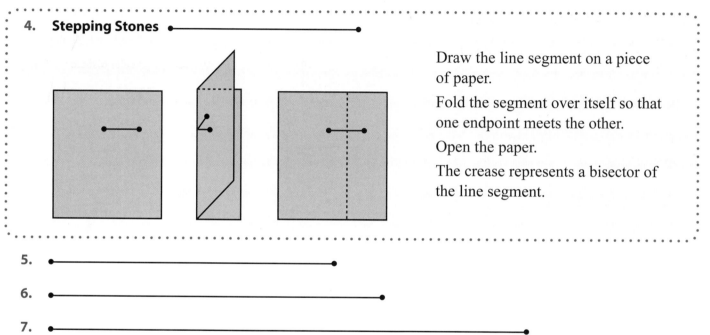

4. **Stepping Stones**

Draw the line segment on a piece of paper.

Fold the segment over itself so that one endpoint meets the other.

Open the paper.

The crease represents a bisector of the line segment.

5.

6.

7.

Copy the angle onto a sheet of paper. Construct a bisector of the angle.

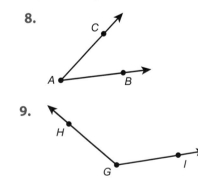

8.

9.

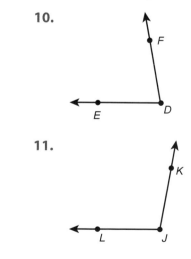

10.

11.

Use the diagram to solve.

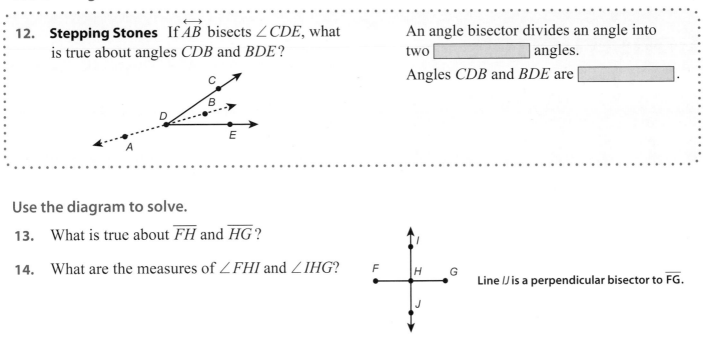

12. **Stepping Stones** If $\overleftrightarrow{AB}$ bisects $\angle CDE$, what is true about angles CDB and BDE?

An angle bisector divides an angle into two [_____] angles.

Angles CDB and BDE are [_____].

Use the diagram to solve.

13. What is true about $\overline{FH}$ and $\overline{HG}$?

14. What are the measures of $\angle FHI$ and $\angle IHG$?

Line IJ is a perpendicular bisector to $\overline{FG}$.

Choose the answer.

15. Which figure shows a construction of an angle bisector?

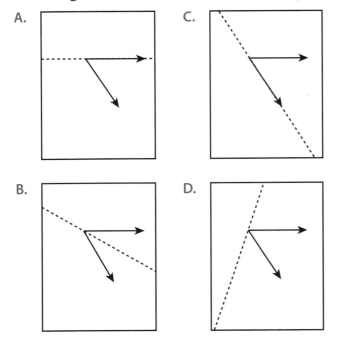

A.

C.

B.

D.

Compass and Straightedge Construction

You have worked with geometric figures. Now use a standard set of tools to construct some figures.

➔ Constructing Perpendicular Bisectors

Definition

In geometry, a **construction** is a method showing how a figure can be drawn accurately with a specified set of tools. A drawing compass and a straightedge are traditional tools for mathematical constructions.

Remember

A bisector is a line, segment, or ray that divides a line segment, angle, or other figure into two equal parts.

Use a compass and a straightedge to construct the perpendicular bisector of a line segment.

Example

PROBLEM 1 Construct a perpendicular bisector of a line segment.

SOLUTION Use a straightedge to draw a line segment. Place the compass on one endpoint of the segment, and set the width to about $\frac{2}{3}$ the width of the segment. The width doesn't need to be exact.

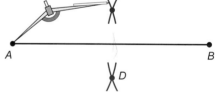

With the compass still at the end, draw one arc above and another arc below the segment. Without changing the width of the compass, move the compass to the other endpoint of the segment. Draw arcs, one each above and below the segment. The two arcs above and the two arcs below the segment should intersect.

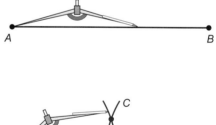

Use a straightedge to draw a line segment connecting the points where the arcs intersect.

ANSWER The constructed vertical line segment is a perpendicular bisector of the original line segment.

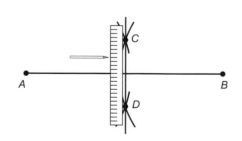

➔ Constructing Regular Polygons

You can construct regular polygons such as an equilateral triangle, a
square, and a hexagon by using a compass and a straightedge.

Example

PROBLEM 2 Construct an equilateral triangle.

SOLUTION Set the width of the compass to be the length of one side
of the triangle. Mark a point that will be one vertex of the triangle
(P in the figure). Place the compass on the vertex, and draw an arc in
the area where each of the other vertices will be.

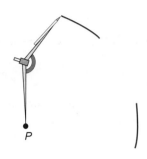

Mark a point on one of the arcs to represent a second vertex of the
triangle (Q in the figure). Place the compass on the second vertex, and
draw an arc that intersects the other arc you drew. The intersection of
the two arcs will be the third vertex of the triangle (R in the figure).

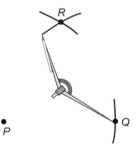

Connect the vertices using a straightedge.

ANSWER The figure formed is an equilateral triangle.

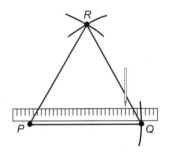

In Problem 2, because the opening of the compass never changes, you
know that all the arcs marked by the compass have the same radius, so
$PQ = QR = PR$.

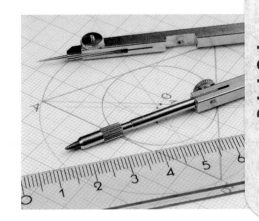

Problem Set

Construct a line segment with the given length, and then construct its perpendicular bisector.

1. 4 cm

2. 6 cm

3. 7 in.

4. $5\frac{1}{2}$ in.

5. 5 cm

6. 9.5 cm

Construct an equilateral triangle with the given side length.

7. 5 cm

8. 8 cm

9. 3 in.

10. $4\frac{3}{4}$ in.

11. 7.5 cm

12. 11 cm

Construct a square with the given side length.

13. Stepping Stones 5 cm

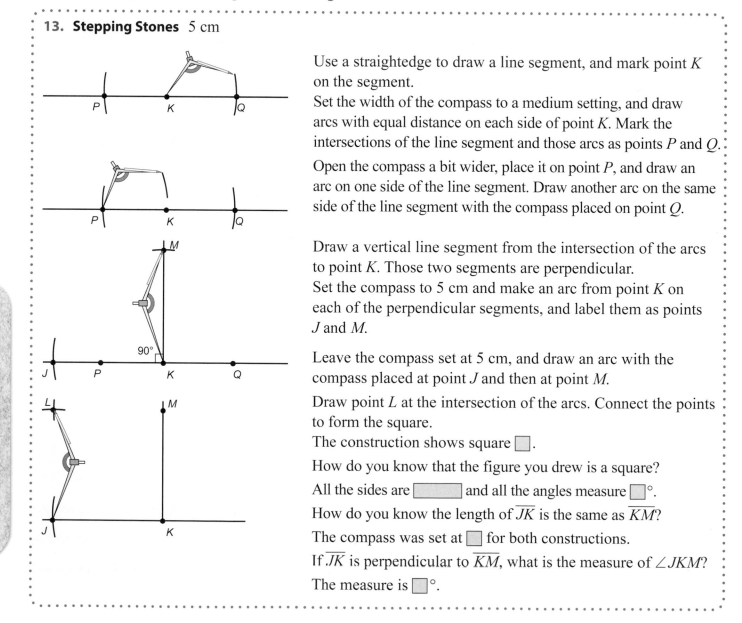

Use a straightedge to draw a line segment, and mark point K on the segment.
Set the width of the compass to a medium setting, and draw arcs with equal distance on each side of point K. Mark the intersections of the line segment and those arcs as points P and Q.

Open the compass a bit wider, place it on point P, and draw an arc on one side of the line segment. Draw another arc on the same side of the line segment with the compass placed on point Q.

Draw a vertical line segment from the intersection of the arcs to point K. Those two segments are perpendicular.
Set the compass to 5 cm and make an arc from point K on each of the perpendicular segments, and label them as points J and M.

Leave the compass set at 5 cm, and draw an arc with the compass placed at point J and then at point M.

Draw point L at the intersection of the arcs. Connect the points to form the square.
The construction shows square ☐.
How do you know that the figure you drew is a square?
All the sides are ☐☐☐☐ and all the angles measure ☐°.
How do you know the length of $\overline{JK}$ is the same as $\overline{KM}$?
The compass was set at ☐ for both constructions.
If $\overline{JK}$ is perpendicular to $\overline{KM}$, what is the measure of $\angle JKM$?
The measure is ☐°.

14. 3 cm

15. 7 cm

16. 6 in.

17. 5 in.

18. 8.8 cm

19. 12.5 cm

Construct a hexagon with the given side length.

20. **Stepping Stones** 5 cm

Draw a line segment that is 5 cm long.

Set the compass the width of the line segment, and draw arcs above the segment from each endpoint of the segment. The arcs should intersect.

Move the compass to the point of intersection, keeping its width the same, and draw a circle.

Beginning at one end of the segment, place the compass and mark an arc to cross the circle. The point of intersection is the next vertex of the hexagon.

Move around the circle, marking arcs until you have all 6 vertices. Connect the points of intersection of the arcs and the circle.

The construction shows a regular [_____] with side length [__] cm.

21. 4 cm

22. 8 cm

23. 3 in.

24. 4 in.

25. 4.5 cm

26. 6.7 cm

Translation

If you have ever used a stencil to make a pattern of repeated figures, you have made translations.

→ Describing Translations

A transformation is a way to create new figures from an original. Sometimes the new figure is exactly like the original, but it has been moved to a new location. Making an exact copy of a figure in a new location without rotating or flipping is called a translation.

Definitions

A **transformation** of a figure is a change in its position, shape, or size. A **translation** is a transformation that moves every point of a figure the same distance and the same direction.

> **Tip**
>
> In any transformation, the new figure is called the image. The original figure is the pre-image.
>
> The image of point A is written as A'. It is read "A prime."

Example

PROBLEM 1 State which figure is a translation of the gray shape.

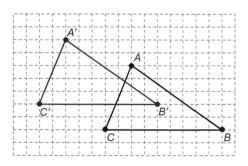

Figure 1   Figure 2   Figure 3   Figure 4

SOLUTION Find a figure with the same size but a different location. The correct answer cannot be rotated or reflected.

ANSWER Figure 4 is the translation.

PROBLEM 2 Describe the translation that changes $\triangle ABC$ into $\triangle A'B'C'$.

SOLUTION Choose one vertex and describe how it is moved. Point A moves 5 units to the left and then 2 units up to A'.

ANSWER The translation is left 5 and up 2.

TOPIC

➥ Sketching Translations

When you sketch a translation, remember that each point must move the same distance and the same direction.

Example

PROBLEM 3 Translate *ABCD* 3 units to the right, and then 4 units down.

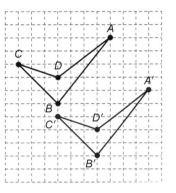

SOLUTION Translate each vertex, one at a time.
Move point *A* right 3, and then down 4. Label it point *A'*.

Move points *B*, *C*, and *D* in the same way.

Connect the vertices to make the new figure.

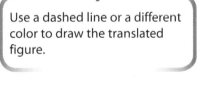

ANSWER The translated figure is *A'B'C'D'*.

Another way to describe a translation is with an arrow called a vector. The vector shows how far and in which direction each point moves.

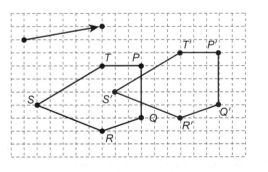

Definition

A **vector** is a line segment with a direction.

> **Tip**
> Use a dashed line or a different color to draw the translated figure.

Example

PROBLEM 4 Use the vector to translate the figure.

SOLUTION Decide what motion the vector shows. It shows right 6 and up 1.

Translate each vertex, one at a time.

Connect the translated vertices to make the translated figure.

ANSWER The translated figure is *P'Q'R'S'T'*.

T O P I C

Problem Set

State which figure is a translation of the gray shape.

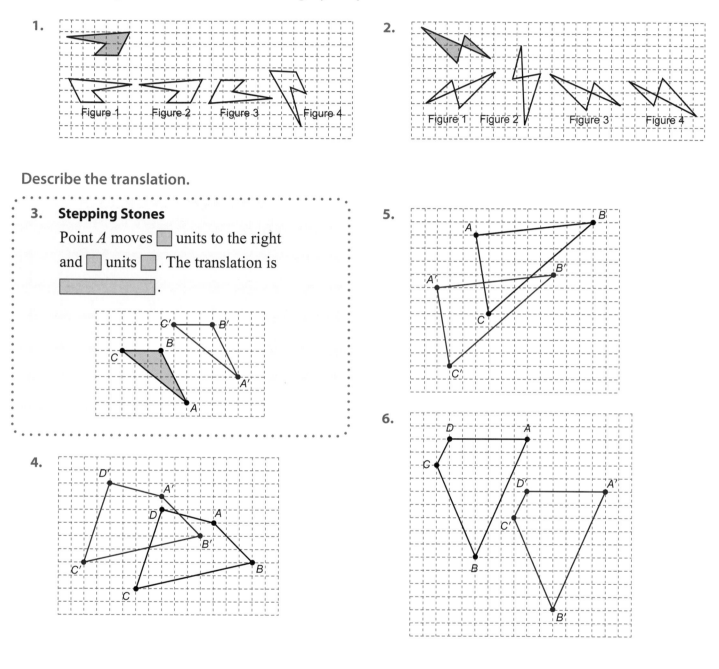

1.

Figure 1   Figure 2   Figure 3   Figure 4

2.

Figure 1   Figure 2   Figure 3   Figure 4

Describe the translation.

3. **Stepping Stones**

   Point *A* moves ☐ units to the right and ☐ units ☐. The translation is

   ☐.

5.

4.

6.

Copy the figure onto a sheet of paper, and draw the image of a translation of it by the given amount.

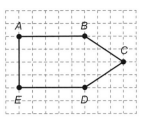

7. **Stepping Stones** 4 right, 2 up

Translate each point ☐ units right and ☐ units up. Connect the image points to form the figure.

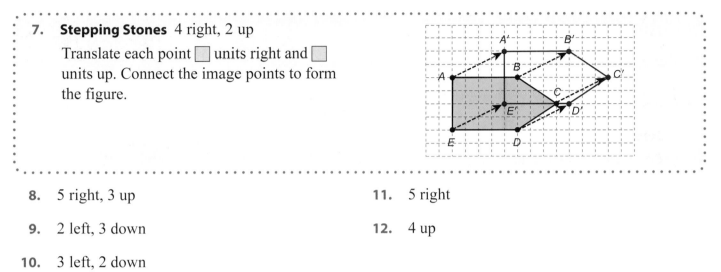

8. 5 right, 3 up

9. 2 left, 3 down

10. 3 left, 2 down

11. 5 right

12. 4 up

Use the vector to translate the figure.

13.

14.

15. **Challenge** Use grid paper. Draw a pentagon and three different vectors. Translate the pentagon by each vector. Use different colors, and label your translations.

Choose the answer.

16. Which figure is a translation of the gray shape?

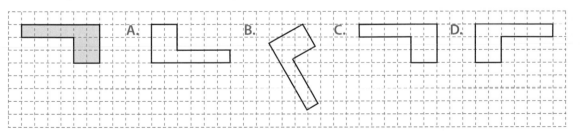

Reflection

When you look in a mirror, an object and its reflection seem to be the same distance from the mirror.

➡ Describing Reflections

A reflection changes both the location and the orientation of an object.

Definition

A **reflection** is a transformation that flips a figure across a **line of reflection**.

In this figure, equivalent polygons are reflected across a vertical line. What changes is the distance of each figure from the line of reflection.

To describe a reflection, locate the line of reflection.

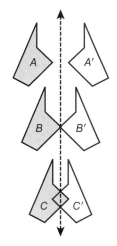

Example

PROBLEM 1 Describe the reflection that changes $\triangle ABC$ into $\triangle A'B'C'$.

SOLUTION Draw the line of reflection so that it is halfway between each vertex and its image point. The line of reflection is shown here as a dotted line.

Choose any vertex. Tell how far it is from the line of reflection.

ANSWER The line of reflection is horizontal.
It is 2 units below vertex B.

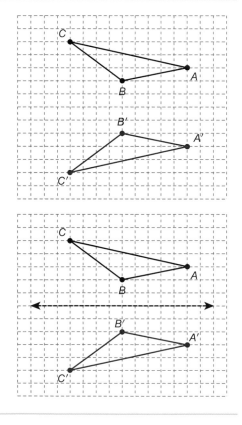

TOPIC

➡ Sketching Reflections

To sketch a reflection, use the fact that each point and its image point must be the same distance from the line of reflection.

Tip

Use a dashed line or a different color to draw the reflected figure.

Example

PROBLEM 2 Reflect *ABCD* across the horizontal line.

SOLUTION Mark the locations of each reflected vertex. Point *D'* should be on line *m*.

Point *A'* should be 3 units above line *m*.

Point *B'* should be 3 units above line *m*.

Point *C'* should be 6 units above line *m*.

Connect the vertices to make the reflected figure.

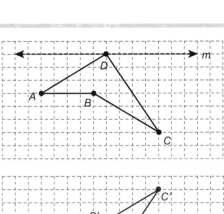

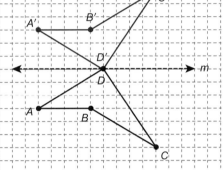

ANSWER The reflected figure is *A'B'C'D'*.

PROBLEM 3 Reflect rectangle *ABCD* across a vertical line that is 2 units away from point *A*.

SOLUTION Draw the line of reflection. It is shown here as a dotted line.

Reflect each vertex, one at a time, across the line of reflection.

Connect the reflected vertices to make the reflected rectangle.

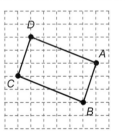

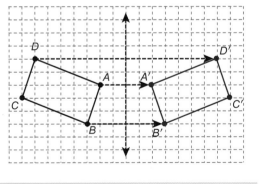

ANSWER The reflected rectangle is *A'B'C'D'*.

TOPIC

Problem Set

Describe the reflection by locating the line of reflection.

1. Stepping Stones

The line of reflection is [   ].

It passes through vertex [ ].

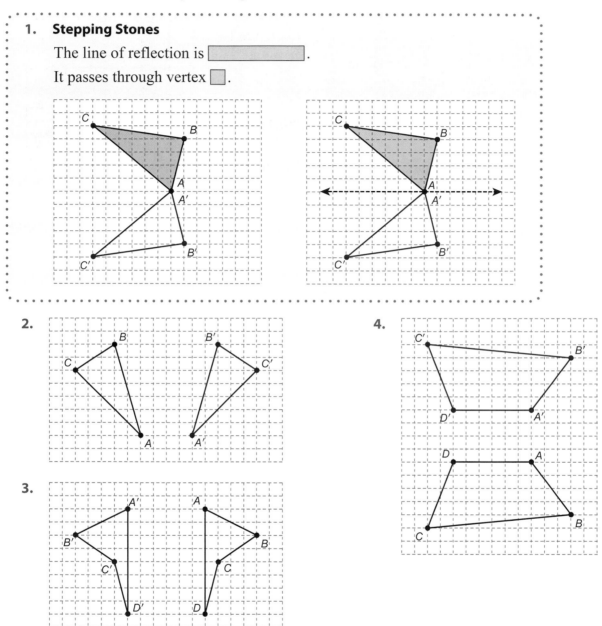

Copy the figure onto a sheet of paper. Then reflect the figure across the line.

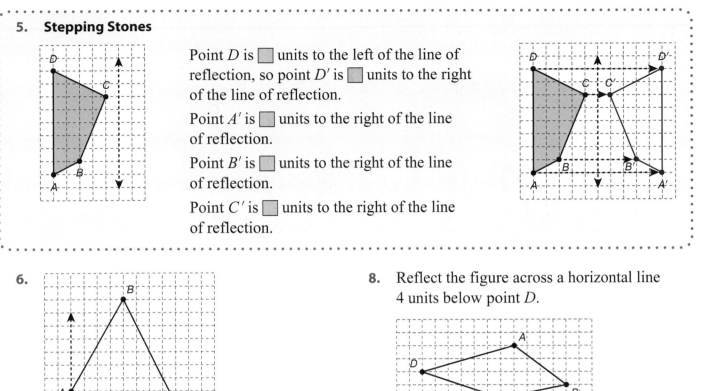

Point D is ▢ units to the left of the line of reflection, so point D' is ▢ units to the right of the line of reflection.

Point A' is ▢ units to the right of the line of reflection.

Point B' is ▢ units to the right of the line of reflection.

Point C' is ▢ units to the right of the line of reflection.

6.

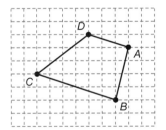

8. Reflect the figure across a horizontal line 4 units below point D.

9. Reflect the figure across a vertical line 3 units to the right of point B.

7.

Solve.

10. Challenge Use grid paper. Draw a horizontal line and mark point P on it. Draw $\triangle PQR$ and reflect it across the line.

Choose the answer.

11. The figure is reflected across the dotted line. Which point does not change location?

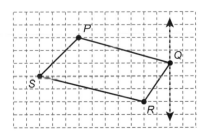

    A. point P **C.** point R

    B. point Q **D.** point S

Rotation

If you stick a pin through a piece of paper, you can turn the paper around the pin's point.

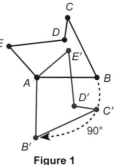

Figure 1

➡ Describing Rotations

Like a reflection, a rotation changes both the location and the orientation of an object. The figures show the same polygon rotated 90° $\left(\frac{1}{4} \text{ turn}\right)$ clockwise. In Figure 1, the center of rotation is vertex A. In Figure 2, it is point P.

> ### Think About It
>
> The point at the center of rotation can be anywhere: on a vertex, on a side, outside the polygon, or inside the polygon.

Definition

A **rotation** is a transformation that turns a figure about a given point. The point is called the **center of rotation**.

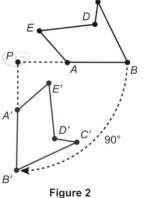

Figure 2

To describe a rotation, you need the location of the center, the fraction of a complete turn or degree measure of the rotation, and whether the direction of the rotation is clockwise or counterclockwise.

Example

PROBLEM 1 The figure shows a rotation of $\triangle ABC$. Describe the rotation by identifying the direction, the amount of turn, and the center.

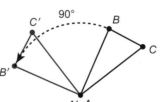

SOLUTION Choose one side of the triangle. Look to see how it moves. Side AB rotates counterclockwise through an angle of 90°. The fraction of the complete turn is a $\frac{1}{4}$ turn around center point A.

ANSWER $\frac{1}{4}$ turn counterclockwise about point A

> ### Tip
>
> Here are some rotations and their degree measures.
>
> | | |
> |---|---|
> | $\frac{1}{4}$ turn | 90° |
> | $\frac{1}{2}$ turn | 180° |
> | $\frac{3}{4}$ turn | 270° |
> | $\frac{1}{3}$ turn | 120° |
> | $\frac{1}{6}$ turn | 60° |
> | whole turn | 360° |

Example

PROBLEM 2 Describe the rotation that changes $\triangle ABC$ into $\triangle A'B'C'$.

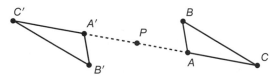

SOLUTION Draw a dotted line to connect a vertex and its image point.

The center of rotation is on the line that contains side AC. The amount of turn is from $\overline{AP}$ to $\overline{A'P}$.

So side AC rotates $\frac{1}{2}$ turn, or 180°.

ANSWER $\frac{1}{2}$ turn about point P

> **Tip**
>
> When a rotation is 180°, or $\frac{1}{2}$ turn, you do not need to describe it as clockwise or counterclockwise. The result is the same.

➔ Sketching Rotations

To sketch a $\frac{1}{4}$-turn rotation, use the corner of a piece of paper or an index card to make a right angle.

> **Tip**
>
> Tracing paper can be used to create, check, or describe rotations.

Example

PROBLEM 3 Rotate this figure by a $\frac{3}{4}$ turn clockwise. Put the center of rotation 3 units below point B.

SOLUTION Mark the center of rotation at point P. Draw a dotted line to connect it to point B. Draw a line and mark the location of the rotated line segment $A'B'$. Then draw in the circle.

ANSWER The rotated figure is line segment $A'B'$ and its adjoining circle.

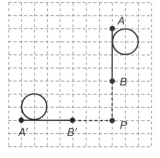

> **Think About It**
>
> A $\frac{3}{4}$ turn clockwise is equivalent to a $\frac{1}{4}$ turn counterclockwise.

Problem Set

Describe the rotation by identifying the center, the direction, and the amount of turn. Write both the fraction of a whole turn and the number of degrees.

1. **Stepping Stones**

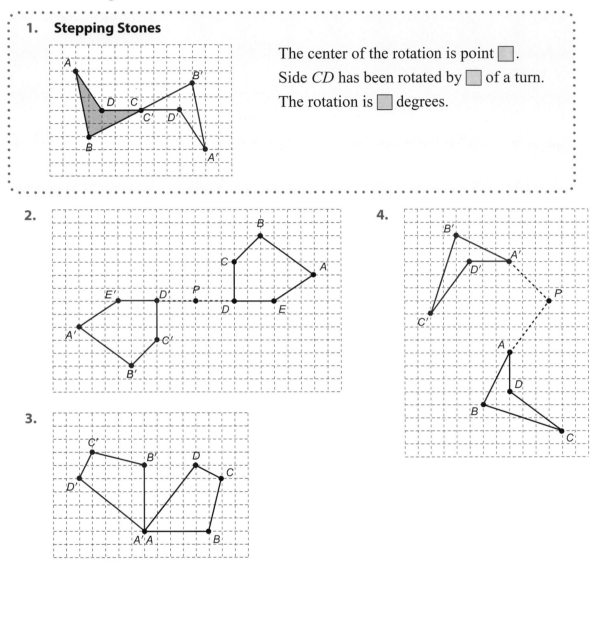

The center of the rotation is point ☐.

Side *CD* has been rotated by ☐ of a turn.

The rotation is ☐ degrees.

2.

3.

4.

Sketch the rotation.

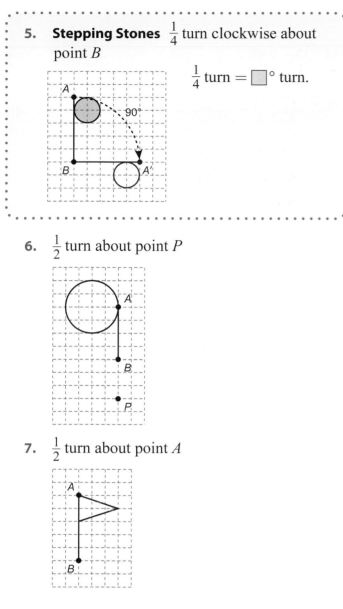

5. **Stepping Stones** $\frac{1}{4}$ turn clockwise about point B

$\frac{1}{4}$ turn = $\boxed{}$° turn.

6. $\frac{1}{2}$ turn about point P

7. $\frac{1}{2}$ turn about point A

8. $\frac{1}{4}$ turn counterclockwise about point P

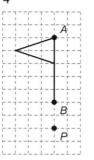

9. $\frac{3}{4}$ turn counterclockwise about point P

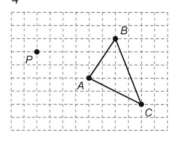

10. $\frac{1}{4}$ turn clockwise about point P

11. **Challenge** Use grid paper. Draw square $ABCD$. Mark a point P outside the square. Use point P to make a pentagon that has A, B, C, D, and P as vertices. Rotate your pentagon $\frac{1}{4}$ turn clockwise about point P.

Choose the answer.

12. The polygon $ABCD$ was rotated 60° about point P. Which best describes this rotation?

   A. $\frac{1}{3}$ turn clockwise

   B. $\frac{1}{6}$ turn clockwise

   C. $\frac{1}{3}$ turn counterclockwise

   D. $\frac{1}{6}$ turn counterclockwise

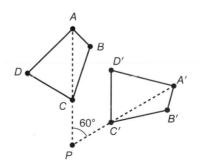

Translating with Coordinates

You can use coordinates to translate points and other figures.

➡ Translating Points

The figure shows point P at $(7, 7)$. A short way to write the point label is $P(7, 7)$. There are four translations in the figure. Translation a is right 3, up 4. The translated point shows that 3 is added to the x-coordinate of P, and 4 is added to the y-coordinate, so the translated point is $(10, 11)$.

Look at the figure to see how the other translations change the coordinates of point P. Studying the figure will help you learn these translation rules.

- To move **right** n units, **add** n to the x-coordinate.
- To move **left** n units, **subtract** n from the x-coordinate.
- To move **up** n units, **add** n to the y-coordinate.
- To move **down** n units, **subtract** n from the y-coordinate.

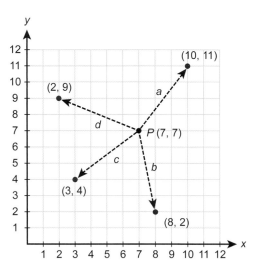

Example

PROBLEM 1 The point $A(-2, 4)$ is translated right 4, down 7. Write the coordinates of the translated point.

SOLUTION

The point moves 4 units to the right.
Add 4 to the x-coordinate.
$-2 + 4 = 2$

The point moves 7 units down.
Subtract 7 from the y-coordinate.
$4 - 7 = -3$

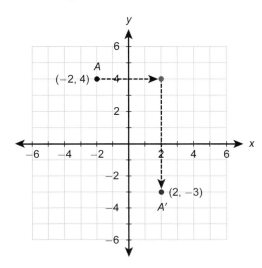

> **Tip**
>
> Add if a translation is to the right or up. Subtract if a translation is to the left or down.

ANSWER The translated point is $A'(2, -3)$.

CHECK Graph the point and its translation on a coordinate system. Use arrows to show the horizontal and vertical movements. ✓

TOPIC

➔ Translating Polygons

To translate a polygon using coordinates, translate each vertex. Then connect the vertices to make the translated polygon.

Example

PROBLEM 2 Polygon $ABCD$ is translated left 2, up 5. Write the coordinates of the translated vertices.

SOLUTION Use the figure to write the coordinates of the vertices.

$A(-2, 1), B(1, 4), C(5, -2), D(2, -5)$

Subtract 2 from each x-coordinate.

$(-2, 1)$	$(1, 4)$	$(5, -2)$	$(2, -5)$
↓	↓	↓	↓
$(-4, 1)$	$(-1, 4)$	$(3, -2)$	$(0, -5)$

Now, with each new x-coordinate determined, add 5 to each y-coordinate.

$(-4, 1)$	$(-1, 4)$	$(3, -2)$	$(0, -5)$
↓	↓	↓	↓
$(-4, 6)$	$(-1, 9)$	$(3, 3)$	$(0, 0)$

ANSWER $A'(-4, 6), B'(-1, 9), C'(3, 3), D'(0, 0)$

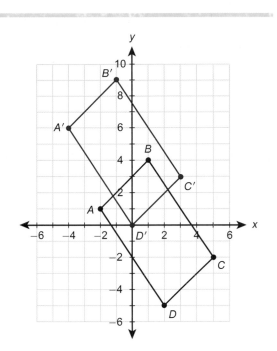

PROBLEM 3 A triangle has vertices at $A(4, 7), B(-3, 3),$ and $C(5, -1)$. The triangle is translated left 2, down 4. Write the coordinates of the translated vertices.

SOLUTION Subtract 2 from each x-coordinate. Subtract 4 from each y-coordinate.

$(4, 7)$	$(-3, 3)$	$(5, -1)$
↓	↓	↓
$(2, 3)$	$(-5, -1)$	$(3, -5)$

ANSWER $A'(2, 3), B'(-5, -1), C'(3, -5)$

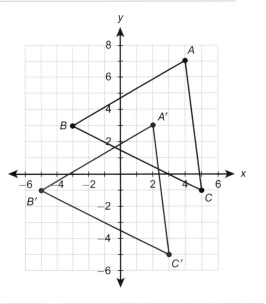

TOPIC

Problem Set

Write the coordinates of the translated point.

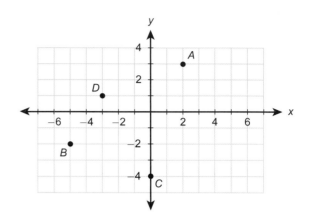

1. **Stepping Stones**

   $A(2, 3)$ translated right 5, up 2

   $A(2, 3) \rightarrow (2 + \boxed{}, 3 + \boxed{}) = (\boxed{}, \boxed{})$

2. $B(-5, -2)$ translated right 3, down 1

3. $C(0, -4)$ translated left 2, down 6

4. $D(-3, 1)$ translated left 4, up 0

Write the coordinates of the translated point.

5. Point E translated left 3, down 1

6. Point F translated right 2, down 4

7. Point G translated right 0, up 5

8. Point H translated left 6, up 1

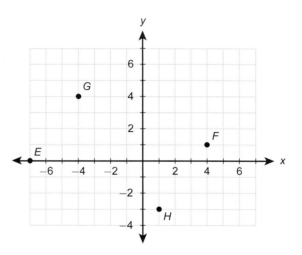

Solve.

9. A triangle with vertices at $(-5, 7)$, $(-4, -3)$, and $(3, -2)$ is translated right 4, down 9. What are the coordinates of the vertices of the translated triangle?

10. A square with vertices at $(-5, 4)$, $(-7, 0)$, $(-3, -2)$, and $(-1, 2)$ is translated left 5, down 1. What are the coordinates of the vertices of the translated square?

11. **Challenge** A triangle with vertices at $(-8, -3)$, $(-4, 5)$, and $(-11, 8)$ is translated so that one vertex ends up on the x-axis and another vertex ends up on the y-axis. Describe the translation.

Write the coordinates of the vertices of the translated figure.

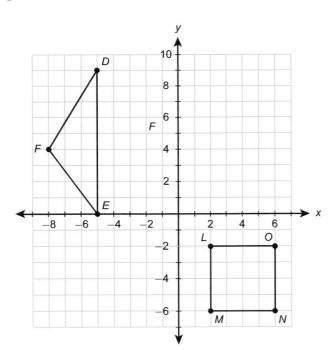

13. $\triangle DEF$ translated right 5, down 3

14. $LMNO$ translated left 3, down 6

15. $LMNO$ translated right 4, up 8

Write the coordinates of the vertices of the translated figure.

16. The square is translated right 5, down 2.

17. The square is translated left 4, down 10.

18. Rectangle $ECJK$ is translated left 5, up 3.

19. Rectangle $ECJK$ is translated right 3, down 5.

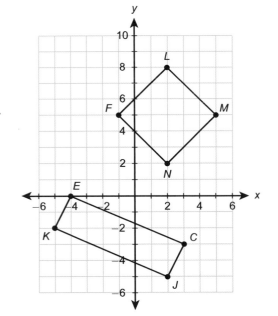

Choose the answer.

20. A point at $(3, -6)$ is translated left 8, up 5. What are the coordinates of the translated point?

    A. $(-5, -11)$ C. $(5, -11)$

    B. $(-5, -1)$ D. $(11, -1)$

21. A point is translated from $(2, 8)$ to $(5, -2)$. Which directions describe the translation?

    A. left 3, up 10   C. right 7, up 6

    B. left 7, down 6   D. right 3, down 10

Reflecting with Coordinates

When a point is reflected across the *x*-axis or the *y*-axis, the coordinates change in a special way.

➡ Reflecting Points Across Axes

In the figure, point P is reflected across each axis. When it is reflected across the *x*-axis, only the *y*-coordinate changes. The *y*-coordinates are opposites.

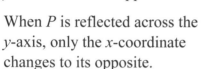

When P is reflected across the *y*-axis, only the *x*-coordinate changes to its opposite.

The figure can help you learn these reflection rules:

- To reflect a point across the *x*-axis, change the *y*-coordinate to its opposite.
- To reflect a point across the *y*-axis, change the *x*-coordinate to its opposite.

Example

PROBLEM 1 The point $A(-3, -4)$ is reflected across the *x*-axis. Write the coordinates of the reflected point.

SOLUTION Change the *y*-coordinate to its opposite.

$(-3, -4) \rightarrow (-3, 4)$

ANSWER The reflected point is $A'(-3, 4)$.

CHECK Graph the point and its reflection on a coordinate system. Use an arrow between the two ordered pairs to show how the point moves during the transformation. ✓

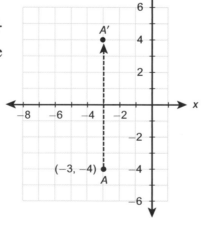

➧ Reflecting Polygons Across Axes

To reflect a polygon across the *x*- or the *y*-axis, reflect each vertex. Then connect the vertices to make the reflected polygon.

Example

PROBLEM 2 A triangle with vertices at $A(1, -6)$, $B(-3, 0)$, and $C(7, -3)$ is reflected across the *x*-axis. Write the coordinates of the reflected vertices.

SOLUTION Change each *y*-coordinate to its opposite.

$(1, -6)$ $(-3, 0)$ $(7, -3)$
   ↓   ↓   ↓
$(1, 6)$ $(-3, 0)$ $(7, 3)$

ANSWER

$A'(1, 6), B'(-3, 0), C'(7, 3)$

CHECK Graph the triangle and its reflection on a coordinate plane. ✓

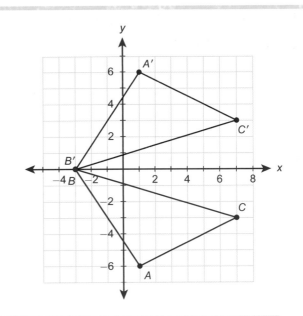

PROBLEM 3 A triangle with vertices at $A(-2, 6)$, $B(4, -2)$, and $C(6, 4)$ is reflected across the *y*-axis. Write the coordinates of the reflected vertices.

SOLUTION Change each *x*-coordinate to its opposite.

$(-2, 6)$ $(4, -2)$ $(6, 4)$
   ↓   ↓   ↓
$(2, 6)$ $(-4, -2)$ $(-6, 4)$

ANSWER $A'(2, 6), B'(-4, -2), C'(-6, 4)$

CHECK Graph the triangle and its reflection on a coordinate plane. ✓

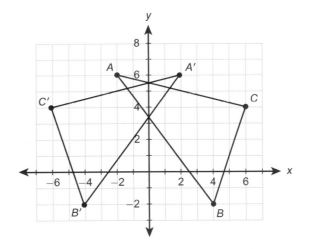

Problem Set

Write the coordinates of the reflected point.

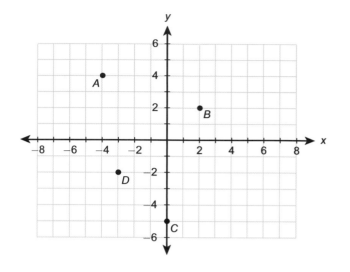

2. Reflect point B across the x-axis.

3. Reflect point C across the x-axis.

4. Reflect point B across the y-axis.

5. Reflect point C across the y-axis.

6. Reflect point D across the y-axis.

Write the coordinates of the vertices of the reflected figure.

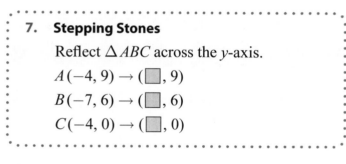

8. Reflect $IJLQ$ across the x-axis.

9. Reflect $\triangle ABC$ across the x-axis.

10. Reflect $IJLQ$ across the y-axis.

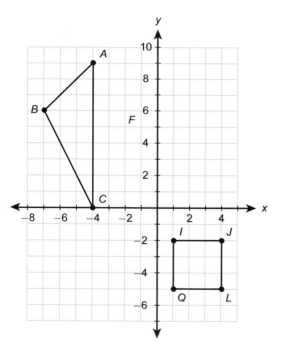

Write the coordinates of the vertices of the reflected figure.

11. The triangle is reflected across the *x*-axis.

12. The square is reflected across the *y*-axis.

13. The triangle is reflected across the *y*-axis.

14. The square is reflected across the *x*-axis.

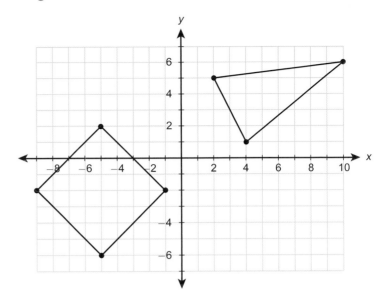

Solve.

15. A triangle with vertices at $(-5, 7)$, $(-4, -3)$, and $(3, -2)$ is reflected across the *x*-axis. What are the coordinates of the vertices of the reflected triangle?

16. A square with vertices at $(-5, 4)$, $(-7, 0)$, $(-3, -2)$, and $(-1, 2)$ is reflected across the *y*-axis. What are the coordinates of the vertices of the reflected square?

17. **Challenge** A triangle with vertices at $(-4, 9)$, $(2, 5)$, and $(-4, -4)$ is reflected across the *y*-axis and then reflected across the *x*-axis. What is the final location of the vertex at the right angle?

Choose the answer.

18. Which is the best description of the transformation shown in the figure?

    A. A pentagon is reflected across the *x*-axis.

    B. A pentagon is reflected across the *y*-axis.

    C. A quadrilateral is reflected across the *x*-axis.

    D. A quadrilateral is reflected across the *y*-axis.

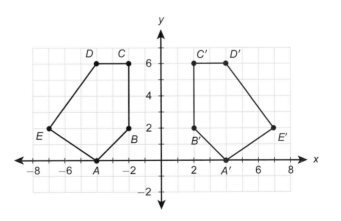

19. Which of these points does not change its location when it is reflected across the *y*-axis?

    A. $(-3, -4)$ C. $(0, 6)$

    B. $(4, -2)$ D. $(-6, 0)$

Figures on a Coordinate Plane

Some problems about figures on a coordinate plane will ask you to find missing vertices.

Think About It

A horizontal line contains all points with the same *y*-coordinates.

A vertical line contains all points with the same *x*-coordinates.

➡ Completing Rectangles and Squares

When the problems are about rectangles and squares, use the fact that opposite sides are parallel.

Example

PROBLEM 1 Three vertices of rectangle *ABCD* are $A(-4, 2)$, $B(3, 2)$, and $C(3, -3)$. Find the coordinates of the fourth vertex.

SOLUTION
Plot the three given points.

Point *D* will have the same *x*-coordinate as point *A*.

Point *D* will have the same *y*-coordinate as point *C*.

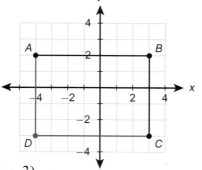

ANSWER The fourth vertex is $D(-4, -3)$.

PROBLEM 2 Three vertices of square *PQRS* are $P(-2, -1)$, $Q(2, 3)$, and $R(6, -1)$. Find the coordinates of the fourth vertex.

SOLUTION
Plot the three given points.

Look at how point *Q* could be translated to become point *P*, and apply the same translation to point *R*.

Translate point *Q* 4 units down and 4 units left to become point *P*.

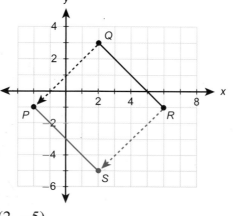

$R(6, -1) \rightarrow (6 - 4, -1 - 4) = (2, -5)$

ANSWER The fourth vertex is $S(2, -5)$.

➔ Completing Parallelograms and Triangles

To solve missing-vertex problems, use the properties of figures.

Example

PROBLEM 3 Three vertices of a parallelogram are $A(-4, -2)$, $B(-2, 3)$, and $C(6, 3)$. Find the coordinates of the fourth vertex.

SOLUTION Plot the three given points.
Look at how point B could be translated to become point A, and apply the same translation to point C. Translate point B 2 units left and 5 units down to point A.

$C(6, 3) \rightarrow (6 - 2, 3 - 5) = (4, -2)$

ANSWER The fourth vertex is $D(4, -2)$.

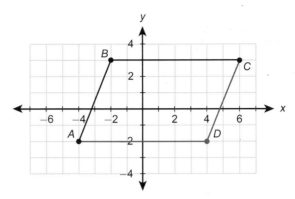

PROBLEM 4 The vertices of a right triangle are $D(-6, 3)$, $E(4, -2)$, and $F(4, y)$. Find the value of y.

SOLUTION Plot points D and E.
The x-coordinate of point F is 4, so F must be on the vertical line that passes through $(4, 0)$. Draw this vertical line.

For $\overline{DF}$ to meet $\overline{EF}$ at a right angle, $\overline{DF}$ must be horizontal. So the y-coordinates of points D and F are the same.

ANSWER The y-coordinates of D and F are 3. The third vertex is $F(4, 3)$.

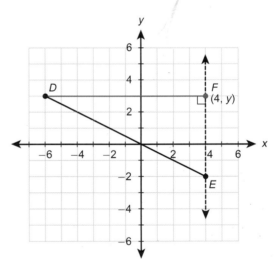

TOPIC

Problem Set

Three vertices of a rectangle are given. Find the coordinates of the fourth vertex.

1. **Stepping Stones** $A(-7, 6)$, $B(2, 6)$, $C(2, 3)$

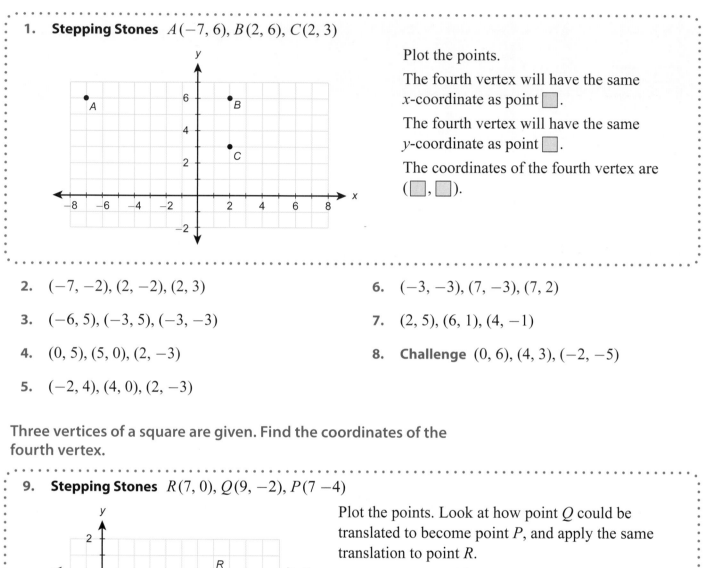

Plot the points.

The fourth vertex will have the same x-coordinate as point ▢.

The fourth vertex will have the same y-coordinate as point ▢.

The coordinates of the fourth vertex are (▢, ▢).

2. $(-7, -2)$, $(2, -2)$, $(2, 3)$

3. $(-6, 5)$, $(-3, 5)$, $(-3, -3)$

4. $(0, 5)$, $(5, 0)$, $(2, -3)$

5. $(-2, 4)$, $(4, 0)$, $(2, -3)$

6. $(-3, -3)$, $(7, -3)$, $(7, 2)$

7. $(2, 5)$, $(6, 1)$, $(4, -1)$

8. **Challenge** $(0, 6)$, $(4, 3)$, $(-2, -5)$

Three vertices of a square are given. Find the coordinates of the fourth vertex.

9. **Stepping Stones** $R(7, 0)$, $Q(9, -2)$, $P(7 -4)$

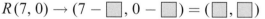

Plot the points. Look at how point Q could be translated to become point P, and apply the same translation to point R.

Translate point Q ▢ units down and ▢ units left to become point P.

$R(7, 0) \rightarrow (7 - \boxed{}, 0 - \boxed{}) = (\boxed{}, \boxed{})$

The coordinates of the fourth vertex are (▢, ▢).

10. $(-2, 1)$, $(1, -2)$, $(4, 1)$

11. $(4, 3)$, $(4, -2)$, $(-1, -2)$

12. $(-3, 3)$, $(-6, 0)$, $(-9, 3)$

13. $(5, 1)$, $(0, -2)$, $(-3, 3)$

14. $(2, 4)$, $(2, -2)$, $(-4, -2)$

15. $(8, -4)$, $(4, -8)$, $(0, -4)$

Find the coordinates of a fourth vertex.

16. Stepping Stones $P(-6, 1), C(1, 4), G(1, -1)$

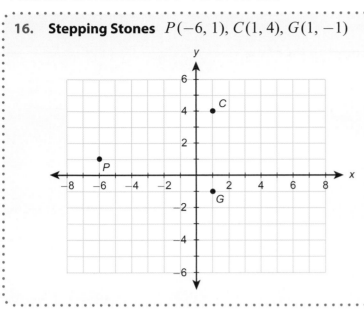

Plot the points. Look at how point C could be translated to become point G, and apply the same translation to point P.

Translate point C ▢ units down to become point G.

$P(-6, 1) \rightarrow (-6, 1 - ▢) = (-6, ▢)$

The coordinates of the fourth vertex are $(-6, ▢)$.

17. $(2, 2), (6, -3), (-4, -3)$

18. $(2, 6), (6, 3), (-1, -1)$

19. $(2, 5), (2, -2), (-3, 0)$

20. $(2, 6), (3, -3), (-2, 0)$

Solve.

21. The vertices of a right triangle are $(4, 8)$, $(8, 5)$, and $(x, 5)$. Find the value of x.

22. The vertices of a right triangle are $(7, 2)$, $(-2, -2)$, and $(-2, y)$. Find the value of y.

23. Challenge A hexagon has a line of symmetry on the line that has the equation $y = x - 4$. Four of the vertices are $(-4, -8), (-2, -2)$, $(4, 4)$, and $(7, 3)$. What are the coordinates of the other two vertices?

Choose the answer.

24. Three vertices of a rectangle are located at $(3, 2), (-2, 2)$, and $(-2, 5)$. What are the coordinates of the fourth vertex?

A. $(3, 5)$ C. $(3, -1)$

B. $(-2, -1)$ D. $(3, 7)$

25. Three vertices of a parallelogram are located at $(6, -3), (-3, -3)$, and $(0, 1)$. Which coordinates could describe the location of the fourth vertex?

A. $(1, 9)$ C. $(8, 2)$

B. $(8, 1)$ D. $(9, 1)$

Chapter 13 Review

Choose the answer.

1. Which figure is a translation of the gray figure?

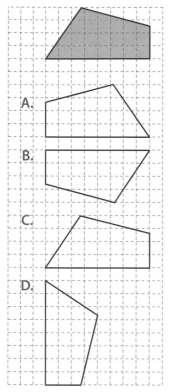

A.

B.

C.

D.

2. What are the coordinates of point P' if $\triangle PRG$ is reflected across the x-axis?

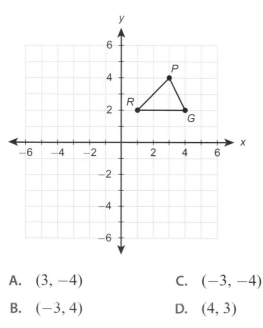

A. $(3, -4)$ C. $(-3, -4)$

B. $(-3, 4)$ D. $(4, 3)$

3. Figure $ABCD$ is rotated to create figure $A'B'C'D'$. Which directions describe the rotation?

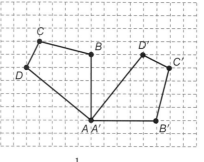

A. Rotate $\frac{1}{2}$ turn clockwise.

B. Rotate $\frac{1}{2}$ turn counterclockwise.

C. Rotate $\frac{1}{4}$ turn clockwise.

D. Rotate $\frac{1}{4}$ turn counterclockwise.

4. A point is translated from $(-4, 6)$ to $(5, -6)$. Which directions describe the translation?

A. left 9, up 12

B. right 1

C. right 9, down 12

D. left 1, down 12

5. Which point does **not** change its location when it is reflected across the y-axis?

A. $(3, 0)$ C. $(-3, 0)$

B. $(3, 3)$ D. $(0, 3)$

6. Three vertices of a square are located at $(1, 0)$, $(1, -3)$, and $(-2, 0)$. Where is the fourth vertex located?

A. $(-2, -3)$ C. $(-3, -2)$

B. $(2, -3)$ D. $(3, -2)$

Copy the figure onto a sheet of paper. Fold the paper to construct a bisector of the figure.

7. •——————————•

8.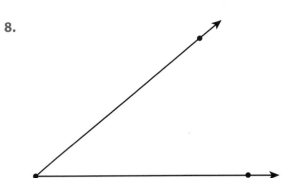

Use a compass and straightedge to construct a figure with the given measure.

9. line segment 7 cm long, with perpendicular bisector

10. equilateral triangle with side length 10 cm

11. square with side length $3\frac{1}{2}$ in.

12. regular hexagon with side length 6 cm

Transform $\triangle ABC$ as described.

13. Translate using the given vector.

14. Reflect across $\overleftrightarrow{DE}$.

15. Rotate $\frac{1}{2}$ turn about point A.

16. Translate 4 units right, 2 units down.

17. Reflect across the y-axis.

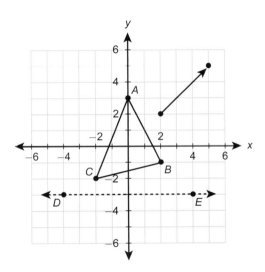

Give the coordinates of the point that would form the fourth vertex of a rectangle.

18. $(3, -7), (0, -7), (0, 0)$

19. $(2, 2), (-2, -2), (-2, 2)$

20. $(1, 5), (1, -3), (-3, 5)$

Problem	Topic Lookup	Problem	Topic Lookup
7–8	Folded-Paper Construction	3, 15	Rotation
9–12	Compass and Straightedge Construction	4, 16	Translating with Coordinates
1, 13	Translation	5, 17	Reflecting with Coordinates
2, 14	Reflection	6, 18–20	Figures on a Coordinate Plane

14 Patterns, Primes, and Puzzles

Prime numbers are used for many things. One of the most interesting uses is for encoding and decoding information. During the Second World War, the Allies were able to decode German messages with the help of Polish and British code breakers.

In This Chapter

You'll identify and extend various types of patterns, including patterns involving exponents. Next you will use primes to solve problems, and then you'll solve and create mathematical puzzles.

Chapter Topics

- ▶ Foundations for Chapter 14
- ▶ Addition Patterns
- ▶ Multiplication Patterns
- ▶ Exponents and Patterns
- ▶ Compound Interest
- ▶ Primes and Composites
- ▶ Using Prime Factorization
- ▶ Figuring Out Math Puzzles
- ▶ Creating Math Puzzles
- ▶ Chapter 14 Review

The Enigma machines helped the Allies break enemy codes.

CHAPTER 14   PATTERNS, PRIMES, AND PUZZLES   **487**

Foundations for Chapter 14

➔ **Identifying if Values Make Equations True**

Definitions

An **equation** is a number sentence indicating that two expressions have the same value.

A **variable** is a symbol that represents a value.

When you **substitute** for a variable in an equation, you replace the variable with a value.

To tell whether a value of a variable makes an equation true, substitute the value for the variable and simplify. If both sides of the equation are equal, the value makes the equation true.

Example A

Identify whether the given value of the variable makes the equation true.

PROBLEM A-1 $2x - 4 = 8; x = -2$

SOLUTION

$2x - 4 = 8$	Write the equation.
$2(-2) - 4 \stackrel{?}{=} 8$	Substitute -2 for x.
$-4 - 4 \stackrel{?}{=} 8$	Multiply.
$-8 \stackrel{?}{=} 8$	Subtract.
$-8 \neq 8$	Compare.

ANSWER The value $x = -2$ does not make the equation $2x - 4 = 8$ true.

PROBLEM A-2 $14 + 5x = 29; x = 3$

SOLUTION

$14 + 5x = 29$	Write the equation.
$14 + 5 \cdot 3 \stackrel{?}{=} 29$	Substitute 3 for x.
$14 + 15 \stackrel{?}{=} 29$	Multiply.
$29 \stackrel{?}{=} 29$	Add.
$29 = 29$	Compare.

ANSWER The value $x = 3$ makes the equation $14 + 5x = 29$ true.

Problem Set A

Identify whether the given value of the variable makes the equation true.

1. $13 - 3c = 1; c = 4$

2. $4m = 38; m = 9$

3. $27 = -g + 4; g = 23$

4. $\frac{p}{2} + 9 = 12; p = 6$

5. $2k - 4.5 = 6.5; k = 5.5$

6. $3a + \frac{1}{4} = 1; a = \frac{1}{4}$

7. $-5r - 6 = -26; r = 4$

8. $45 - 2.4d = 69; d = 10$

9. $14x = -36; x = -3$

10. $-y + \frac{3}{8} = -\frac{1}{8}; y = \frac{1}{2}$

➔ Checking for True Equations

You can find whether a set of *x*-values and their corresponding *y*-values make a given equation true by substituting the values for *x* and *y*, and then simplifying the equation.

Example B

PROBLEM B-1 Match the equation $y = 3x + 7$ with the table of values that makes the equation true.

x	10	13	16	22
y	1	2	3	5

x	1	2	3	5
y	10	13	16	22

SOLUTION Substitute values from each table into the equation to see if the values make the equation true.

Try (10, 1) from the first table.

$1 \overset{?}{=} 3 \cdot 10 + 7$ Substitute 10 for *x* and 1 for *y*.

$1 \overset{?}{=} 30 + 7$ Multiply.

$1 \overset{?}{=} 37$ Add.

$1 \neq 37$

Try (1, 10) from the second table.

$10 \overset{?}{=} 3 \cdot 1 + 7$ Substitute 1 for *x* and 10 for *y*.

$10 \overset{?}{=} 3 + 7$ Multiply.

$10 \overset{?}{=} 10$ Add.

$10 = 10$

To complete the solution, you need to check every pair of values in the second table. They all must make the equation true.

ANSWER The values in the second table make the equation true.

Problem Set B

Match the equation with the table of values that makes the equation true.

1. $y = 4x - 9$

x	1	3	5	7	9
y	40	24	8	−8	−24

2. $y = \frac{x}{2} + 5$

x	0	2	4	6	8
y	−9	−1	7	15	23

3. $y = -8(x - 6)$

x	−4	−2	0	2	6
y	3	4	5	6	8

➔ Describing Rules for Patterns

Definitions

A **pattern** is an ordered list of values or objects, which can include numbers, shapes, or letters, that are related to each other by a specific rule.

Each value or object in the pattern is called a **term**.

Example C

Describe a rule for the pattern and give the next two terms in the pattern.

PROBLEM C-1 A, BB, CCC, DDDD, . . .

SOLUTION The pattern is made of the letters of the alphabet, in order. Each term has the same number of letters as the term's place in the pattern.

The fifth and sixth terms will be using the letters E and F.

ANSWER A rule for the pattern is that each term is a successive letter of the alphabet, repeated a number of times equal to the term's place in the pattern. The next two terms are EEEEE and FFFFFF.

PROBLEM C-2

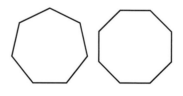

SOLUTION The pattern shows regular polygons with 3, 4, 5, and 6 sides. The number of sides increases by 1 with each term. The next two terms will be regular polygons with 7 and 8 sides.

ANSWER A rule for the pattern is that each term is a regular polygon with one more side than the previous term. Here are the next two terms:

Problem Set C

Describe a rule for the pattern and give the next two terms in the pattern.

1. A, BB, A, BB, A, . . .

4. x, X, y, Y, x, X, y, Y, . . .

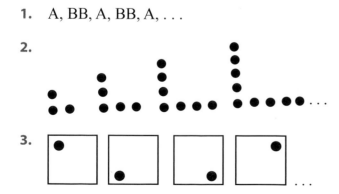

Enigma machines use patterns to encode and decode messages.

Planting the Seed

You can use mathematical reasoning to decode patterns and solve many kinds of problems.

Addition Patterns

Many lists of numbers have patterns. If you can find the pattern, you can predict more numbers in the list.

➡ Describing Addition Patterns

Definitions

Each number in a pattern is a **term**. The **term number** describes the position of a term in the pattern. An **addition pattern** is formed by adding the same number to each term.

Addition patterns can be shown with figures as well as with lists of numbers.

Tip

Three dots are used to show that a sequence never ends. For example, 2, 4, 6, 8, . . . shows the sequence of even numbers, which never ends.

Example

Solve.

PROBLEM 1 Describe this addition pattern.
3.25, 3.75, 4.25, 4.75, . . .

SOLUTION Write the first term. Identify two adjacent terms and subtract the first one from the second one.
$3.75 - 3.25 = 0.5$

ANSWER The first term is 3.25. Each term is obtained by adding 0.5 to the previous term.

PROBLEM 2 Write the addition pattern shown by these figures. Then find the next number in the pattern.

SOLUTION Write the number of dots in each figure: 1, 5, 9, 13

Look for the pattern. Four dots are added each time. Add 4 to get the next term: $13 + 4 = 17$

ANSWER 1, 5, 9, 13, 17

Think About It

If a positive number is added each time, the addition pattern is increasing. If a negative number is added each time, the pattern is decreasing.

TOPIC

➔ Writing Terms in Addition Patterns

An addition pattern can be described in different ways. Sometimes the term number n is used in a word or algebra expression. For example, the expression $3n$ results in the pattern 3, 6, 9, 12, ...

Term Number n	1	2	3	4
Term Value $3n$	3	6	9	12

Example

Write the first five terms of the addition pattern.

PROBLEM 3 An addition pattern is given by the formula $5n - 2$.

SOLUTION Substitute the term numbers 1, 2, 3, 4, and 5. Evaluate each expression.

1st term:	2nd term:	3rd term:	4th term:	5th term:
$n = 1$	$n = 2$	$n = 3$	$n = 4$	$n = 5$
$5 \cdot 1 - 2$	$5 \cdot 2 - 2$	$5 \cdot 3 - 2$	$5 \cdot 4 - 2$	$5 \cdot 5 - 2$
$5 - 2$	$10 - 2$	$15 - 2$	$20 - 2$	$25 - 2$
3	8	13	18	23

ANSWER The first five terms of the addition pattern are 3, 8, 13, 18, 23.

PROBLEM 4 Lee has studied 25 words from his spelling-bee list, and he plans to study 10 more words each night. Write an addition pattern that shows how many words he will have studied after five more nights.

SOLUTION Start with 25. Add 10 five times.

$25 + 10 = 35$
$35 + 10 = 45$
$45 + 10 = 55$
$55 + 10 = 65$
$65 + 10 = 75$

ANSWER After five more nights, Lee will have studied 75 words.

Problem Set

Describe the addition pattern and find the next two terms.

1. **Stepping Stones** 8, 13, 18, 23, 28, . . .

   The first term is ☐. The number added to each term is ☐.

   To find the next two terms, apply the pattern to the last term.

   $28 + 5 = ☐$

   $☐ + 5 = ☐$

2. 25, 28, 31, 34, 37, . . .

3. 7, 17, 27, 37, 47, . . .

4. 16, 27, 38, 49, 60, . . .

5. 12.4, 15.4, 18.4, 21.4, 24.4, . . .

6. 8.8, 28.8, 48.8, 68.8, 88.8, . . .

7. 3.2, 3.6, 4.0, 4.4, 4.8, . . .

8. 6.5, 7.1, 7.7, 8.3, 8.9, . . .

9. **Challenge** 5, 3, 1, −1, −3, . . .

10. **Challenge** 12, 7, 2, −3, −8, . . .

Write the addition pattern shown by the figure. Then find the next term.

11.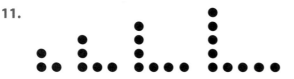

12.

Write the first five terms of the pattern.

13. **Stepping Stones** $4n$

   Substitute the term numbers 1, 2, 3, 4, and 5, and evaluate each expression.

1st term:	2nd term:	3rd term:	4th term:	5th term:
$n = 1$	$n = 2$	$n = 3$	$n = 4$	$n = 5$
$4 \cdot 1 = ☐$	$4 \cdot 2 = ☐$	$4 \cdot 3 = ☐$	$4 \cdot 4 = ☐$	$4 \cdot 5 = ☐$

   The first terms of the pattern are ☐, ☐, ☐, ☐, ☐.

14. $2.5n$

15. $17n$

16. $\frac{3n}{2}$

17. $9n - 1$

18. $12n + 6$

19. **Challenge** $-3n + 0.25$

PROBLEM SET

Find the given term in the addition pattern.

20. the sixth term in the pattern that begins 18, 31, 44, 57

21. the 10th term in the pattern with the formula $2n + 5$

22. the 10th term in the pattern with the formula $8n - 3$

23. the 25th term in the pattern with the formula $4n + 10$

24. **Challenge** The fourth and fifth terms in an addition pattern are 29 and 36. Find the first term.

25. **Challenge** The fourth and fifth terms in an addition pattern are 35 and 39. Find the first term.

Solve.

26. Rebecca buys a bean plant that is 7 cm tall. It grows 2 cm each week. Write the addition pattern that shows how tall the plant will be at the end of 4 weeks.

27. Joshua has $245 and plans to save $75 each month. Write the addition pattern that shows how much he will have at the end of the first 6 months.

28. Angelita has written 10 pages of a book. She plans to write 8 pages each day. Write the addition pattern that shows how much she will have finished at the end of the first 10 days.

29. The temperature at noon is 24°C. The temperature drops 0.5°C each hour for the next 5 hours. Write the addition pattern that shows the temperature at 5:00 p.m.

30. Max has $430 in his savings account, and he withdraws $14 each week. Write the addition pattern that shows how much money Max has in his account after 6 weeks.

31. **Challenge** The Fibonacci pattern starts with two 1s: 1, 1. Then each following term is the sum of the previous two terms. Write the first 10 numbers in the Fibonacci pattern.

Choose the answer.

32. Which formula describes the pattern?
    7, 8, 9, 10, 11, . . .
    A. $n + 6$ C. $n + 7$
    B. $7n$ D. $2n + 5$

33. What is the sixth term in the addition pattern that begins 0.3, 1.8, 3.3, 4.8?
    A. 1.5   C. 7.8
    B. 6.3   D. 9.3

Multiplication Patterns

You can predict numbers in a multiplication pattern, just like you do in an addition pattern.

⇒ Describing Multiplication Patterns

Like addition patterns, multiplication patterns can be shown with lists of numbers or figures.

> **Definition**
>
> A **multiplication pattern** is formed by multiplying each term by the same factor to get the next term.

> **Tip**
>
> When the terms have commas, use semicolons to more clearly separate the terms.

Example

PROBLEM 1 Describe this multiplication pattern:
4; 20; 100; 500; 2500; 12,500; . . .

SOLUTION Divide one term by the previous term to find the factor used.

$$20 \div 4 = 5 \qquad 100 \div 20 = 5 \qquad 500 \div 100 = 5$$

ANSWER The first term is 4. Then each term is multiplied by 5 to find the next term.

PROBLEM 2 Write the multiplication pattern shown by these figures. Then find the next number in the pattern.

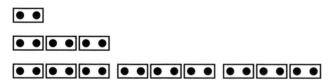

SOLUTION Write the number of dots in each row: 2, 6, 18

Look for the pattern. Each term is multiplied by 3 to get the next term.

$$2 \cdot 3 = 6 \qquad 6 \cdot 3 = 18$$

Multiply 18 by 3 to get the next term.
$$18 \cdot 3 = 54$$

ANSWER 2, 6, 18, 54

➔ Writing Terms in Multiplication Patterns

The factor used to create a multiplication pattern does not have to be a whole number. It can be a decimal, a fraction, or a negative number.

Example

Write the first four terms of the multiplication pattern.

PROBLEM 3 The first term is 32. Each term is multiplied by 20.

SOLUTION Start with 32. Multiply by 20 three times.

$32 \cdot 20 = 640$ $640 \cdot 20 = 12{,}800$ $12{,}800 \cdot 20 = 256{,}000$

ANSWER 32; 640; 12,800; 256,000

PROBLEM 4 A multiplication pattern starts with 45. Then each term is multiplied by 0.1.

SOLUTION Start with 450. Multiply by 0.1 three times.

$450 \cdot 0.1 = 45$ $45 \cdot 0.1 = 4.5$ $4.5 \cdot 0.1 = 0.45$

ANSWER 450, 45, 4.5, 0.45

➔ Application: Population Growth

Example

PROBLEM 5 The population of a certain type of insect will double every 3 months if no steps are taken to control the population growth. If the population is 35,000 at the beginning of the year, how many insects will there be at the end of the year?

SOLUTION Find the number of times the population will double.
12 months ÷ 3 months = 4

Write the multiplication pattern that begins with 35,000. Multiply 35,000 by 2 to double it. Each new population is doubled, so multiply each term by 2. Show four additional terms because the population doubles 4 times in 1 year.

$35{,}000 \cdot 2 = 70{,}000$
$\phantom{35{,}000 \cdot 2 = }70{,}000 \cdot 2 = 140{,}000$
$\phantom{35{,}000 \cdot 2 = 70{,}000 \cdot 2 = }140{,}000 \cdot 2 = 280{,}000$
$\phantom{35{,}000 \cdot 2 = 70{,}000 \cdot 2 = 140{,}000 \cdot 2 = }280{,}000 \cdot 2 = 560{,}000$

ANSWER There will be 560,000 insects at the end of the year.

> **Tip**
> Multiplication patterns can increase very rapidly. You may want to use a calculator to find some of the greater terms.

Problem Set

Describe the multiplication pattern and find the next two terms.

1. **Stepping Stones** 2, 6, 18, 54, 162, . . .

   The first term is ☐. Each term is multiplied by ☐.

   To find the next two terms, apply the pattern to the last term.

   $162 \cdot 3 =$ ☐

   ☐ $\cdot 3 =$ ☐

2. 1, 5, 25, 125, 625, . . .

3. 4; 40; 400; 4000; 40,000; . . .

4. 5; 100; 2000; 40,000; 800,000; . . .

5. 20; 60; 180; 540; 1620; . . .

6. 25; 100; 400; 1600; 6400; . . .

7. 40, 20, 10, 5, 2.5, . . .

8. 100, 50, 25, 12.5, 6.25, . . .

9. 0.5; 5; 50; 500; 5000; . . .

10. 0.2, 1, 5, 25, 125, . . .

11. **Challenge** 4, −8, 16, −32, 64, . . .

Write the multiplication pattern shown by the figures. Then find the next term.

12.

13.

Write the first four terms in the multiplication pattern.

14. **Stepping Stones** The first term is 2, and then each term is multiplied by 6.

    $2 \cdot 6 =$ ☐, $12 \cdot 6 =$ ☐, ☐ $\cdot 6 =$ ☐

15. The first term is 4, and then each term is multiplied by 3.

16. The first term is 3, and then each term is multiplied by 8.

17. The first term is 5, and then each term is multiplied by 4.

18. The first term is 8, and then each term is multiplied by 3.

19. The first term is 10, and then each term is multiplied by 6.

20. The first term is 30, and then each term is multiplied by 9.

21. The first term is 25, and then each term is multiplied by 8.

22. The first term is 3.2, and then each term is multiplied by 5.

23. The first term is 1.8, and then each term is multiplied by 3.

24. The first term is 20, and then each term is multiplied by 0.2.

25. The first term is 50, and then each term is multiplied by 0.8.

26. The first term is 8, and then each term is multiplied by -3.

27. The first term is 12, and then each term is multiplied by -5.

Solve.

28. Michelle does 6 sit-ups each day this week. Each week she will increase the daily number of sit-ups by a factor of 2. How many sit-ups will Michelle be doing in 5 weeks?

29. Andy has a piece of string that is 4 m long. He cuts it in half, and then cuts each piece in half. How long will each piece be if he cuts the strings in half 4 times?

30. This month, 200 people visited a new website. If that number increases by a factor of 2.5 every month, how many people will visit the website in the next 6 months?

31. The population of a herd of wild deer increases by a factor of 3 every 5 years. The current population is 18 deer. What will the population be in 20 years?

32. Every 10 years the population of a town is predicted to increase by a factor of 1.2. The population now is 3000. What will the population be in 50 years?

33. Every 50 years the population of a country is predicted to increase by a factor of 5. The population now is 2.3 million. What will the population be in 200 years?

34. **Challenge** Find the 10th term in the pattern that begins 0.0008, 0.004, 0.02.

Choose the answer.

35. Which formula describes the pattern?
     4, 12, 36, 108, . . .

A. Start with 4 and add 8 each time.

B. Start with 4 and multiply by 3 each time.

C. Start with 4 and subtract 8 each time.

D. Start with 4 and divide by 3 each time.

36. What is the next term in the multiplication pattern that begins 22, 66, 198?

A. 33   C. 1782

B. 594   D. 5346

Exponents and Patterns

Formulas for multiplication patterns can use exponents.

➡ Calculating Powers

An exponent is a way of showing repeated multiplication. In the expression 6^3, the exponent is 3. It shows that 6 is used as a factor 3 times. So $6^3 = 6 \cdot 6 \cdot 6$.

Definitions

An **exponent** tells how many times a number, the **base**, is used as a factor. A **power** has two parts, a base and an exponent.

Example

Expand and evaluate.

PROBLEM 1 $(1.2)^4$

SOLUTION Use 1.2 as a factor 4 times.
$1.2 \cdot 1.2 \cdot 1.2 \cdot 1.2 = 2.0736$

ANSWER 2.0736

PROBLEM 2 the third power of 20

SOLUTION
$20^3 = 20 \cdot 20 \cdot 20 = 8000$

ANSWER 8000

➡ Using the Order of Operations

When an expression has several operations, you use the order of operations to simplify or evaluate it.

Order of Operations

1. Perform operations that are inside parentheses.
2. Evaluate expressions with exponents.
3. Multiply or divide.
4. Add or subtract.

TOPIC

Example

PROBLEM 3 Simplify: $30 - 6 \cdot 4 + (5 - 2)^3$

SOLUTION

$30 - 6 \cdot 4 + (5 - 2)^3$	Subtract $5 - 2$ inside the parentheses.
$30 - 6 \cdot 4 + (3)^3$	Evaluate the power $(3)^3$.
$30 - 6 \cdot 4 + 27$	Multiply: $6 \cdot 4$
$30 - 24 + 27$	Add and subtract.
33	

ANSWER $30 - 6 \cdot 4 + (5 - 2)^3 = 33$

➜ Applications: Multiplication Patterns

An exponent indicates repeated multiplication, so an exponent can be used to describe a multiplication pattern. The letter n is often the variable chosen to represent the term number.

Remember

A multiplication pattern is formed by multiplying each term by the same factor.

Example

PROBLEM 4 Write the first four terms of the multiplication pattern given by the formula $5 \cdot 3^n$.

SOLUTION Substitute the term numbers 1, 2, 3, and 4. Evaluate each expression.

$n = 1$	$n = 2$	$n = 3$	$n = 4$
$5 \cdot 3^1$	$5 \cdot 3^2$	$5 \cdot 3^3$	$5 \cdot 3^4$
$5 \cdot 3$	$5 \cdot 9$	$5 \cdot 27$	$5 \cdot 81$
15	45	135	405

ANSWER 15, 45, 135, 405

CHECK Each term is 3 times the term before it, so the terms look like they are part of a multiplication pattern. ✓

Problem Set

Expand and evaluate the power.

1. **Stepping Stones** 15^2

   $15^2 = 15 \cdot 15$

   $\quad = \square$

2. 35^2

3. the fourth power of 5

4. 2^8

5. the third power of 2.5

6. $(1.6)^2$

7. $(0.4)^2$

8. the fourth power of 0.9

9. **Challenge** $\left(\dfrac{2}{3}\right)^4$

Simplify the expression.

10. **Stepping Stones** $6^3 - 8 \cdot 4$

    The first operation to begin simplifying the expression is $\boxed{}$.

    $6^3 - 8 \cdot 4 = (\square \cdot \square \cdot \square) - 8 \cdot 4$

    The next operation to perform is $\boxed{}$.

    $\quad = \square - \square$

    The last operation is $\boxed{}$.

    $\quad = \square$

11. $5^4 + 18 \div 3$

12. $(7 + 2)^2 - 6$

13. $11 + (8 - 3)^2 \cdot 10$

14. $20 - 4 \cdot 6^2$

15. $600 - (2 + 1)^4 \cdot 5$

16. $3 \cdot 7 \cdot 2^3$

17. $(15 - 6)^2 - 6^2$

18. $(8 - 2)^2 + (3 + 4)^3$

19. $(15 - 5)^3 - (5 \cdot 6)^2$

20. $9 \cdot 3 + (3 + 1)^3$

21. $45 \div 9 - (7 - 5)^4$

22. **Challenge** $\left(\dfrac{3}{4} - \dfrac{1}{2}\right)^2 + \left(\dfrac{1}{2}\right)^3$

Write the first four terms in the multiplication pattern given by the formula.

23. **Stepping Stones** $6 \cdot 2^n$

$n = 1$	$n = 2$	$n = 3$	$n = 4$
$6 \cdot 2^1 = \square$	$6 \cdot 2^2 = \square$	$6 \cdot 2^3 = \square$	$6 \cdot 2^4 = \square$

24. $2 \cdot 4^n$

25. $10 \cdot 5^n$

26. $20 \cdot 8^n$

27. $3 \cdot 10^{n+1}$

28. $6 \cdot 20^{n+1}$

29. **Challenge** $2.5 \cdot 4^{n-1}$

30. **Challenge** $0.5 \cdot 8^{n-1}$

Find the given term in the multiplication pattern.

31. the first term in the pattern with the formula $24 \cdot 3^{n-1}$

32. the first term in the pattern with the formula $40 \cdot 6^{n-1}$

33. the third term in the pattern with the formula $5 \cdot 7^{n-1}$

34. the third term in the pattern with the formula $2 \cdot 8^{n-1}$

35. the 10th term in the pattern with the formula $12 \cdot 2^{n-1}$

36. the 10th term in the pattern with the formula $2 \cdot 3^{n-1}$

37. **Challenge** A multiplication pattern begins with the terms 4, 12, and 36. Find the 10th term in this pattern.

Choose the answer.

38. What is the value of the expression?
$$200 - 4^2 + 9 \cdot 10$$
   A. 274   C. 1750

   B. 282   D. 1930

39. Which formula describes the pattern?
$$6, 12, 24, 48, \ldots$$
   A. $3n$ C. $3 \cdot 2^n$

   B. n^2 D. n^3

Compound Interest

Exponents are used in formulas for calculating interest that grows quickly.

➡ Calculating Compound Interest

You have used the simple interest formula $I = Prt$ to find interest and the total amount earned. Sometimes a bank pays interest on both the original principal and the interest already earned. That type of interest is called compound interest.

> **Definition**
>
> **Compound interest** is paid on both the principal (the original amount of money) and the interest an account has already earned.

To compute compound interest, add the interest for each period to the principal before calculating the interest for the next period.

Example

Juan deposited $5000 at Corner Bank, which pays 6% interest compounded annually.

PROBLEM 1 What is Juan's final account balance after leaving the money in Corner Bank for 3 years?

SOLUTION Use the formula $I = Prt$.

Year 1
starting principal: $5000
interest: $5000 · 0.06 · 1 = $300
ending principal: $5000 + $300 = $5300

Year 2
starting principal: $5300
interest: $5300 · 0.06 · 1 = $318
ending principal: $5300 + $318 = $5618

Year 3
starting principal: $5618
interest: $5618 · 0.06 · 1 = $337.08
ending balance: $5618 + $337.08 = $5955.08

ANSWER The final balance is $5955.08.

> **Remember**
>
> Interest is an amount paid for the use of money.
>
> I = interest = Prt
>
> P = principal
>
> r = interest rate
>
> t = time in years
>
> A = sum of principal and interest

TOPIC

➔ Using a Formula for Compound Interest

Look at how Juan's money increased in Problem 1.
$5000(1.06), $5000(1.06)(1.06), $5000(1.06)(1.06)(1.06), ...

There is a formula for compound interest that uses the time in years as an exponent. The formula lets you compute A, the total money you have after t years when the interest is compounded annually.

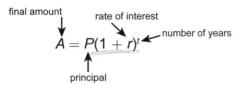

In the formula, P is the principal, the money you start with or your first deposit. The interest rate is r and the number of years is t.

Example

PROBLEM 2 Shalmar has a bank account with a principal of $1000. Her bank compounds the interest once a year at an interest rate of 4%. How much does she have in the account at the end of 3 years?

SOLUTION Substitute the given values into the compound interest formula.

$$P = \$1000 \qquad r = 4\% \qquad t = 3 \text{ years}$$

$A = P(1 + r)^t$	Use the formula.
$= \$1000 \cdot (1 + 0.04)^3$	Substitute.
$= \$1000 \cdot (1.04)^3$	Simplify inside parentheses.
$= \$1000 \cdot 1.124864$	Evaluate the power.
$\approx \$1124.86$	Round to the nearest cent.

ANSWER She has $1124.86 at the end of 3 years.

Problem Set

For each investment with interest compounded annually, find the final balance and the total interest earned.

1. **Stepping Stones** $300 for 2 years at 4%

   Year 1

   starting principal: $300

   interest: $300 · 0.04 = $☐

   ending principal: $300 + $☐ = $☐

   Year 2

   starting principal: $☐

   interest: $☐ · 0.04 = $☐

   ending balance: $☐ + $☐ = $☐

2. $500 for 2 years at 8%

3. $400 at 6% for 2 years

4. $8000 at 3% for 2 years

5. $1000 for 3 years at 2%

6. $4000 for 3 years at 5%

7. $1200 at 10% for 2 years

8. $3600 at 15% for 2 years

9. $10,000 at 3% for 3 years

10. $12,000 for 2 years at 12%

11. $12,500 at 6% for 3 years

12. $20,000 at 5.4% for 3 years

13. $70,600 for 3 years at 4.2%

14. $47,400 for 3 years at 2.6%

For each investment with interest compounded annually, find the final balance using the formula $A = P(1 + r)^t$.

15. **Stepping Stones** $400 for 5 years at 8%

$$A = P(1 + r)^t$$
$$= \$400 \cdot (1 + \boxed{})^5$$
$$= \boxed{}$$

16. $600 for 4 years at 5%

17. $700 at 3% for 20 years

18. $1200 at 4% for 20 years

19. $5000 for 5 years at 3.2%

20. $8000 for 8 years at 4.6%

21. $36,000 at 3% for 4.5 years

22. $92,000 at 6% for 8.5 years

23. $25,000 for 15 years at 1.4%

24. $35,000 for 20 years at 2.3%

Sunshine Bank offers 6% simple interest on deposits. Tangerine Bank offers 5% interest compounded annually. State the difference in final balances if the amount is deposited in each bank for the given time period.

25. $1,000 for 2 years

26. $2,000 for 2 years

27. $5500 for 2 years

28. $6300 for 3 years

29. $10,000 for 3 years

30. $16,800 for 3 years

31. $20,000 for 4 years

32. $23,400 for 4 years

Solve.

33. **Challenge** How much do you need to invest for 10 years at 3% interest to have a total balance of $75,000?

34. **Challenge** Choose the investment that would earn more interest. The interest is compounded annually.
3% for 4 years or 4% for 3 years

35. **Challenge** Choose the investment that would earn more interest. The interest is compounded annually.
7% for 10 years or 10% for 7 years

Choose the answer.

36. Tricia invested $8500 at 3% interest compounded annually. How much interest will she earn in 3 years?

    A. $255.00   C. $9288.18

    B. $788.18   D. $10,174.50

37. Bertram invested $12,000 at 6% interest compounded annually. What will be his total balance at the end of 2 years?

    A. $1483.20   C. $13,483.20

    B. $12,720.00   D. $18,720.00

Primes and Composites

All whole numbers greater than 1 are either prime or composite.

➡ Identifying Prime and Composite Numbers

Definitions

A **prime number** is a whole number greater than 1 that has only two whole-number factors, 1 and itself.

A **composite number** is a whole number greater than 1 that is not prime.

You can find the factors of a number to determine if it is prime or composite.

Example

State whether the number is prime or composite.

PROBLEM 1 24

SOLUTION Find the factors of 24.

Factors of 24: 1, 2, 3, 4, 6, 8, 12, 24

The number 24 has more than two whole-number factors.

ANSWER The number 24 is a composite number.

PROBLEM 2 17

SOLUTION Factors of 17: 1, 17

The number 17 has only two whole-number factors, 1 and itself.

ANSWER The number 17 is a prime number.

Tip

Once you find more than two whole-number factors of a number, you know the number is composite since a prime number has only two whole-number factors.

TOPIC

Using Examples to Test Conjectures

Test a conjecture by finding examples. But examples alone do not prove a conjecture. If there is a single counterexample, the conjecture is not true.

Example

PROBLEM 3 Use examples to test the conjecture.

Conjecture: All numbers greater than 1 that can be written as $2^n - 1$ are prime.

SOLUTION Test for $n = 2$, 3, and 4.

For $n = 2$, $2^2 - 1 = 4 - 1 = 3$; 3 is prime.
For $n = 3$, $2^3 - 1 = 8 - 1 = 7$; 7 is prime.
For $n = 4$, $2^4 - 1 = 16 - 1 = 15$; 15 is not prime.

ANSWER The conjecture is false by the example $n = 4$.

Finding Examples to Support Conjectures

After a conjecture is made, it can be helpful to find examples that support the conjecture.

Example

PROBLEM 4 Find an example that supports the conjecture.

Conjecture: Every odd number greater than 5 can be written as the sum of three prime numbers.

SOLUTION Think of an odd number greater than 5. Then find three prime numbers whose sum is that odd number.

$7 = 2 + 2 + 3$ 7 is an odd number greater than 5. 2 and 3 are prime numbers.

ANSWER An example that supports the conjecture is $7 = 2 + 2 + 3$.

T O P I C

Problem Set

State whether the number is prime or composite.

1. **Stepping Stones** 20

   Factors of 20: 1, ☐, ☐, ☐, ☐, 20

   The number 20 has ☐ than two whole-number ☐.

   The number 20 is a ☐ number.

2. 29

3. 14

4. 22

5. 19

6. 2

7. 33

8. 27

9. 15

10. 94

11. 71

12. 73

13. 57

14. 72

15. **Challenge** 39

State whether each example supports the conjecture or shows that the conjecture is not true.

16. **Stepping Stones** Conjecture: Every number greater than 2 can be written as the sum of two prime numbers.

    Values to consider: 6, 8, 12

    $6 = 3 +$ ☐, so the value 6 ☐ the conjecture.

    $8 = 3 +$ ☐, so the value 8 ☐ the conjecture.

    $12 = 5 +$ ☐, so the value 12 ☐ the conjecture.

17. Conjecture: The sum of two even numbers is even.
    Values to consider: 2 and 4; 12 and 20; 16 and 44

18. Conjecture: The sum of an odd number and any other number is even.
    Values to consider: 3 and 5; 9 and 11; 10 and 15

19. Conjecture: Every odd number can be written as the sum of three prime numbers.
    Values to consider: 5, 9, 15

20. Conjecture: Every even number can be written as the difference of two prime numbers.
    Values to consider: 4, 10, 30

21. Conjecture: Every odd number can be written as the difference of two prime numbers.
    Values to consider: 5, 7, 9

22. Conjecture: Between any two square numbers, there is always a prime number.
    Values to consider: 4 and 9; 9 and 16; 16 and 25

23. Conjecture: Between any two even numbers, there is always a prime number.
    Values to consider: 12 and 14; 14 and 16; 30 and 32

24. Conjecture: The product of any two prime numbers also is prime.
    Values to consider: 1 and 3; 5 and 13; 11 and 23

Find an example that supports the conjecture, and give a counterexample where possible.

25. **Stepping Stones** All prime numbers can be written as the sum of 1 and another number squared.

    $1 + 6^2 = \blacksquare$

26. The sum of all the factors of a number, except for the number itself, is less than the number.

27. The sum of any two consecutive integers is a composite number.

28. If the sum of the digits of a number is divisible by 3, then the number is also divisible by 3.

29. The sum of 2 and any integer is an even number.

30. Beginning with 1, the sum of consecutive odd numbers is a perfect square.

31. If the dimensions of a rectangle are doubled, then its area will be 4 times as great as its original area.

32. Any number that is divisible by 2 is divisible by 6.

33. Beginning with 1, the sum of the cubes of consecutive whole numbers is equal to the sum of those numbers squared.

34. **Challenge** Conjecture: 1 less than 2 raised to a prime-number power is a prime number.

Choose the answer.

35. Which number is prime?

    A. 2
    B. 12
    C. 49
    D. 51

36. Which equation supports the conjecture that every even number is the difference between two prime numbers?

    A. $8 = 14 - 6$
    B. $16 = 23 - 7$
    C. $26 = 47 - 21$
    D. $38 = 69 - 31$

Using Prime Factorization

The prime factorization of a number can be used to help solve many types of problems.

➤ Finding the LCM and GCF

Definition

The **prime factorization** of a number is the multiplication expression showing the number as a product of its prime factors.

$$24 = 2 \cdot 2 \cdot 2 \cdot 3 \qquad 15 = 3 \cdot 5 \qquad 23 = 1 \cdot 23$$

You can use prime factorizations to help find the least common multiple (LCM) and the greatest common factor (GCF) of two or more numbers.

Example

Find the LCM or GCF of the given numbers.

PROBLEM 1 LCM of 12 and 20

SOLUTION Find the prime factorizations. Multiply each of the prime factors the greatest number of times they appear in any one prime factorization.

$$12 = 2 \cdot 2 \cdot 3 \qquad 20 = 2 \cdot 2 \cdot 5$$

The most times that 2 appears in either factorization is twice. The most times that 3 and 5 appear in either factorization is once.

$$2 \cdot 2 \cdot 3 \cdot 5 = 60$$

ANSWER The LCM of 12 and 20 is 60.

PROBLEM 2 GCF of 36 and 24

SOLUTION Find the prime factorizations. Multiply each factor that has a match.

$36 = 2 \cdot 2 \cdot 3 \cdot 3$
$24 = 2 \cdot 2 \cdot 2 \cdot 3$

> 2 has two matches. 3 has one match.

$$2 \cdot 2 \cdot 3 = 12$$

ANSWER The GCF of 36 and 24 is 12.

> **Remember**
>
> The LCM is the least number, other than 0, that is a multiple of two or more whole numbers. The GCF is the greatest whole number that is a common factor of two or more whole numbers.

➡ Finding Possible Dimensions of Figures

If you know the volume of a figure, you can use prime factorization to help find its possible whole-number dimensions.

Example

PROBLEM 3 Find four possible whole-number dimensions for a rectangular prism with a volume of 54 in³.

SOLUTION Find the prime factorization of the volume, and include 1 as a factor.

$$54 = 1 \cdot 2 \cdot 3 \cdot 3 \cdot 3$$

Since the volume of a rectangular prism is given by $V = lwh$, rewrite the prime factorization in every way possible with only three factors. One factor is for the length, one for the width, and one for the height. Use the associative property to put the prime factors in different groups each time. Multiply within the groups and rewrite as the product of the grouped factors.

$54 = (1 \cdot 2 \cdot 3) \cdot 3 \cdot 3 = 6 \cdot 3 \cdot 3$	Rewrite $1 \cdot 2 \cdot 3$ as 6.
$54 = 1 \cdot (2 \cdot 3 \cdot 3) \cdot 3 = 1 \cdot 18 \cdot 3$	Rewrite $2 \cdot 3 \cdot 3$ as 18.
$54 = 1 \cdot 2 \cdot (3 \cdot 3 \cdot 3) = 1 \cdot 2 \cdot 27$	Rewrite $3 \cdot 3 \cdot 3$ as 27.
$54 = 2 \cdot 3 \cdot (1 \cdot 3 \cdot 3) = 2 \cdot 3 \cdot 9$	Rewrite $1 \cdot 3 \cdot 3$ as 9.

ANSWER Four possible sets of whole-number dimensions for a rectangular prism with volume 54 in³ are the following:

6 in. by 3 in. by 3 in.
1 in. by 18 in. by 3 in.
1 in. by 2 in. by 27 in.
2 in. by 3 in. by 9 in.

> **Remember**
>
> You find the volume V of a rectangular prism by using $V = lwh$, where l represents its length, w represents its width, and h represents its height.

Problem Set

Find the prime factorization of the number.

1. **Stepping Stones** 20

   $20 = 5 \cdot \boxed{} \cdot \boxed{}$

   The prime factorization of 20 is

   $\boxed{} \cdot \boxed{} \cdot \boxed{}$.

2. 19

3. 16

4. 28

5. 30

Find the LCM or GCF of the given numbers.

6. **Stepping Stones** LCM of 16 and 28

   $16 = 2 \cdot 2 \cdot 2 \cdot \boxed{}$ The most times that 2 appears in either factorization is $\boxed{}$.

   $28 = 2 \cdot 2 \cdot \boxed{}$ The most times that 7 appears in either factorization is $\boxed{}$.

   $2 \cdot 2 \cdot 2 \cdot 2 \cdot 7 = \boxed{}$

   The LCM of 16 and 28 is $\boxed{}$.

7. GCF of 7 and 14

8. GCF of 10 and 12

9. LCM of 15 and 10

10. LCM of 24 and 40

11. GCF of 18 and 30

12. GCF of 36 and 27

13. LCM of 16 and 26

14. LCM of 32 and 27

15. GCF of 56 and 40

16. GCF of 200 and 75

17. LCM of 8, 12, and 16

18. **Challenge** GCF of 72, 360, 12, and 52

Find at least three possible sets of whole-number dimensions for a rectangular prism with the given volume.

---

19. Stepping Stones 16 m^3

Write the prime factorization, and include 1 as a factor.

$16 = 1 \cdot 2 \cdot 2 \cdot \boxed{} \cdot 2$

Since the volume of a rectangular prism is given by $V = lwh$, rewrite the prime factorization so it has only three factors, one for the $\boxed{}$, one for the $\boxed{}$, and one for the $\boxed{}$.

$16 = (1 \cdot 2 \cdot 2) \cdot \boxed{} \cdot 2 = 4 \cdot \boxed{} \cdot 2$

$16 = 1 \cdot (2 \cdot 2 \cdot \boxed{}) \cdot 2 = 1 \cdot \boxed{} \cdot 2$

$16 = 1 \cdot (2 \cdot 2) \cdot (2 \cdot 2) = 1 \cdot 4 \cdot \boxed{}$

$16 = 1 \cdot 1 \cdot (2 \cdot 2 \cdot 2 \cdot 2) = 1 \cdot 1 \cdot \boxed{}$

Four possible sets of whole-number dimensions are $\boxed{}$ m by $\boxed{}$ m by $\boxed{}$ m, $\boxed{}$ m by $\boxed{}$ m by $\boxed{}$ m, $\boxed{}$ m by $\boxed{}$ m by $\boxed{}$ m, and $\boxed{}$ m by $\boxed{}$ m by $\boxed{}$ m.

---

20. 18 cm^3

21. 24 cm^3

22. 27 m^3

23. 40 in^3

24. 56 mm^3

25. 42 ft^3

26. 50 mm^3

27. 30 m^3

28. 54 cm^3

29. 44 km^3

30. 75 mm^3

31. 126 m^3

32. 135 cm^3

33. 60 in^3

34. 104 mm^3

35. 72 yd^3

36. 108 m^3

37. 112 cm^3

38. Challenge 168 cm^3

Choose the answer.

39. What is the LCM of 24 and 20?

A. 48

B. 80

C. 120

D. 240

40. Which set of dimensions is possible for a rectangle with a volume of 45 cm^3?

A. 3 cm by 3 cm by 3 cm

B. 3 cm by 5 cm by 3 cm

C. 6 cm by 5 cm by 2 cm

D. 9 cm by 5 cm by 2 cm

Figuring Out Math Puzzles

Math puzzles might seem like magic. But you solve them with math operations rather than magic.

➔ Solving the Four 4s Puzzle

The goal of the four 4s puzzle is to find the simplest expression that can be written using only four 4s to produce a given value. Numbers like 44 can be used, but each 4 counts as one of the four 4s. Different versions of the puzzle allow different math symbols to be used in the expression.

Example

Write an expression with the given value, using only four 4s and any of the operation symbols: $+$, $-$, $\cdot$, and $\div$. You may also use grouping symbols.

PROBLEM 1 7

SOLUTION Think about how to break down 7 into numbers that could be composed using the operation symbols and 4s.

$$7 = 8 - 1$$

$$8 = 4 + 4 \qquad 1 = 4 \div 4$$

$$7 = (4 + 4) - (4 \div 4)$$

ANSWER The expression $4 + 4 - 4 \div 4$ has a value of 7 and uses only four 4s.

PROBLEM 2 24

SOLUTION Think about how to break down 24 into numbers that could be composed using the operation symbols and 4s.

$$24 = 16 + 8$$

$$16 = 4 \cdot 4 \qquad 8 = 4 + 4$$

$$24 = (4 \cdot 4) + (4 + 4)$$

ANSWER The expression $4 \cdot 4 + 4 + 4$ has a value of 24 and uses only four 4s.

Think About It

More advanced mathematical operations can be included to solve the four 4s puzzle for every integer value up to 100.

TOPIC

➔ Solving Triomino Puzzles

Triomino puzzles are made of a series of triangles that show a number on each corner and a result in the center. A specific set of operations is performed on the numbers in the corners to give the number in the center. To solve the puzzle, find the operations that generate the center number from the corner numbers on each triomino, and then apply those same operations in the same order to find the missing number.

Example

PROBLEM 3 Find the missing number.

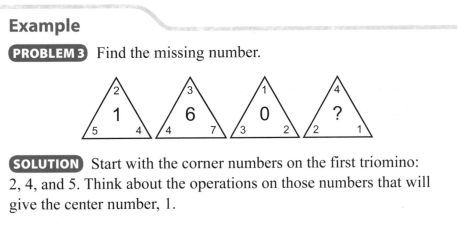

SOLUTION Start with the corner numbers on the first triomino: 2, 4, and 5. Think about the operations on those numbers that will give the center number, 1.

$2 + 4 - 5 = 1$

Check the operations on the second and third triominoes.

$3 + 7 - 4 \overset{?}{=} 6$ $1 + 2 - 3 \overset{?}{=} 0$

      $6 = 6 ✓$ $0 = 0 ✓$

Apply the operations to the corner numbers on the last triomino.

$4 + 1 - 2 = 3$

ANSWER The solution to the puzzle is 3.

Problem Set

Write an expression with the given value, using only four 4s and any of the following: $+$, $-$, $\cdot$, $\div$, exponents, and parentheses.

1. **Stepping Stones** 10

   Think about how to break down 10 into numbers that could be composed using four 4s.

   $10 = 40 \div \square$

   Write 40 with three 4s: $40 = \square - 4$

   So $10 = (\square - 4) \div \square$.

   The expression $(\square - 4) \div \square$ has a value of 10.

2. 0

3. 1

4. 16

5. 3

6. 4

7. 5

8. 8

9. 15

10. 2

11. 36

12. 6

Find the missing number.

13. **Stepping Stones**

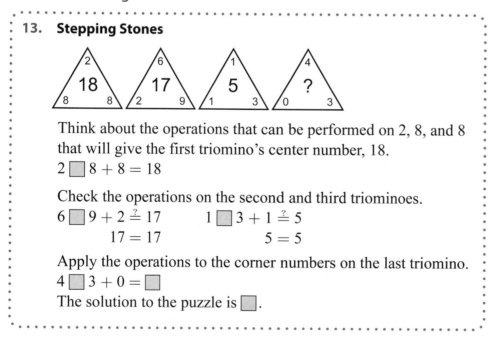

Think about the operations that can be performed on 2, 8, and 8 that will give the first triomino's center number, 18.

$2 \square 8 + 8 = 18$

Check the operations on the second and third triominoes.

$6 \square 9 + 2 \overset{?}{=} 17 \qquad 1 \square 3 + 1 \overset{?}{=} 5$

$\qquad 17 = 17 \qquad\qquad\quad 5 = 5$

Apply the operations to the corner numbers on the last triomino.

$4 \square 3 + 0 = \square$

The solution to the puzzle is $\square$.

14.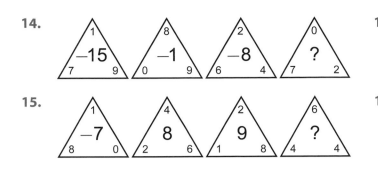

16.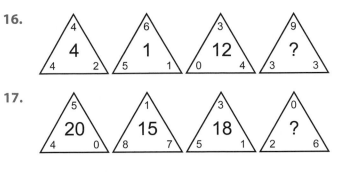

15.

17.

Triangles 14: 1 / 7 −15 9 ; 8 / 0 −1 9 ; 2 / 6 −8 4 ; 0 / 7 ? 2

Triangles 15: 1 / 8 −7 0 ; 4 / 2 8 6 ; 2 / 1 9 8 ; 6 / 4 ? 4

Triangles 16: 4 / 4 4 2 ; 6 / 5 1 1 ; 3 / 0 12 4 ; 9 / 3 ? 3

Triangles 17: 5 / 4 20 0 ; 1 / 8 15 7 ; 3 / 5 18 1 ; 0 / 2 ? 6

Choose the answer.

18. Which expression has a value of 17?

- A. $4 \div 4 \cdot 4 + 4$
- B. $4 \cdot 4 + 4 \div 4$
- C. $4 - 4 \cdot 4 + 4$
- D. $4 + 4 - 4 \div 4$

19. What is the missing number?

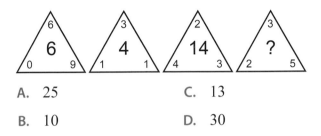

Triangles 19: 6 / 0 6 9 ; 3 / 1 4 1 ; 2 / 4 14 3 ; 3 / 2 ? 5

- A. 25
- B. 10
- C. 13
- D. 30

Creating Math Puzzles

Magic squares have been around for more than 3000 years. Here's how to make your own.

➥ Creating a Magic Square with Operations

The 3×3 grid of numbers at the right is considered a magic square because the sum of the 3 numbers in any column, row, or diagonal is the same. The magic sum in this square is always 3 times the middle number in the square.

You can create your own 3×3 magic square using the given square.

8	1	6
3	5	7
4	9	2

Example

PROBLEM 1 Create a 3×3 magic square with a center number of 8.

SOLUTION Find how the middle number on the square can be changed to become 8. Then apply that change as a constant to the other numbers in the square.

$5 + 3 = 8$, so add 3 to each of the other numbers.

11	4	9
6	8	10
7	12	5

ANSWER The magic square is shown above.

CHECK Find the sums in rows, columns, and diagonals. The magic sum should be 3 times the middle number 8: $8 \cdot 3 = 24$

$11 + 4 + 9 = 24 ✓$ $11 + 8 + 5 = 24 ✓$ $11 + 6 + 7 = 24 ✓$

Think About It

Because the magic square is defined by its sums, the properties of operations let you perform any operation with a constant on every number in the square to create a new square.

TOPIC

➡ Creating a Magic Square by Rearranging Numbers

You can create a new magic square by carefully rearranging the numbers in an existing magic square. Rearrange the numbers by transforming the entire grid using a rotation, a reflection, or a combination of a rotation and a reflection.

Example

The magic sum of the 4×4 magic square at the right is 34.

The gray section will help you see the transformation of the square in the problems.

7	12	1	14
2	13	8	11
16	3	10	5
9	6	15	4

PROBLEM 2 Create a new magic square using rotation of the existing square.

SOLUTION Rotate the numbers in the grid 90° clockwise.

ANSWER

9	16	2	7
6	3	13	12
15	10	8	1
4	5	11	14

CHECK Find the sums in rows, columns, and diagonals.

$9 + 6 + 15 + 4 = 34$ ✓
$9 + 16 + 2 + 7 = 34$ ✓
$9 + 3 + 8 + 14 = 34$ ✓

PROBLEM 3 Create a new magic square using reflection of the existing square.

SOLUTION Reflect the numbers on the grid horizontally.

ANSWER

14	1	12	7
11	8	13	2
5	10	3	16
4	15	6	9

CHECK Find the sums in rows, columns, and diagonals.

$14 + 11 + 5 + 4 = 34$ ✓
$14 + 1 + 12 + 7 = 34$ ✓
$14 + 8 + 3 + 9 = 34$ ✓

Think About It

The magic sum does not change when you rotate or reflect the grid. The commutative property of addition allows you to add the numbers in any direction and get the same sum.

Problem Set

Complete the magic square.

1.

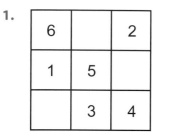

6		2
1	5	
	3	4

2.

	4	5
2		10
		3

Create a new magic square using the given operation.

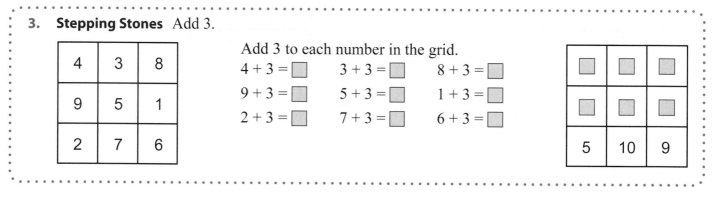

3. Stepping Stones Add 3.

4	3	8
9	5	1
2	7	6

Add 3 to each number in the grid.

$4 + 3 = \square$ $3 + 3 = \square$ $8 + 3 = \square$

$9 + 3 = \square$ $5 + 3 = \square$ $1 + 3 = \square$

$2 + 3 = \square$ $7 + 3 = \square$ $6 + 3 = \square$

$\square$	$\square$	$\square$
$\square$	$\square$	$\square$
5	10	9

4. Add 4.

8	3	10
9	7	5
4	11	6

6. Subtract 3.

6	21	18
27	15	3
12	9	24

5. Multiply by 3.

1	15	14	4
12	6	7	9
8	10	11	5
13	3	2	16

7. Challenge Multiply by 4.

8	2.5	4.5	2
1	5.5	3.5	7
1.5	5	3	7.5
6.5	4	6	0.5

Create a new magic square using a rotation, a reflection, or a combination of rotation and reflection. Give the transformation or transformations used.

8. Stepping Stones

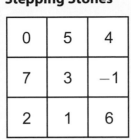

Reflect the grid vertically.
In the first column, switch 0 with ☐.
In the middle column, switch 5 with ☐.
In the last column, switch 4 with ☐.
The grid was reflected.

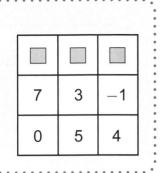

9.

8	18	4
6	10	14
16	2	12

11.

−4	−3	−8
−9	−5	−1
−2	−7	−6

10.

9	10	5
4	8	12
11	6	7

12. Challenge

30	8	16	6
2	20	12	26
4	18	10	28
24	14	22	0

Choose the answer.

13. What is the magic sum of the magic square?

A. 4   C. 12

B. 8   D. 16

5	0	7
6	4	2
1	8	3

Chapter 14 Review

Choose the answer.

1. Which rule describes the pattern?
   $$-3, -2, -1, 0, 1, \ldots$$
   A. $n + 1$ C. $-3n$
   B. $n - 4$ D. $n - 1$

2. What is the 7th term in the addition pattern that begins $\frac{1}{4}, \frac{3}{4}, 1\frac{1}{4}, 1\frac{3}{4}$?
   A. $2\frac{1}{2}$ C. $2\frac{3}{4}$
   B. $2\frac{1}{4}$ D. $3\frac{1}{4}$

3. Which rule describes the pattern?
   $$5, 9, 13, 17, 21, \ldots$$
   A. $4n + 1$ C. $5n$
   B. $n + 5$ D. $5n - 1$

4. What is the sixth term in the multiplication pattern that begins 6, 12, 24, 48?
   A. 96   C. 240
   B. 192   D. 288

5. What is the value of the expression?
   $$20 + 3^2 - 4 \cdot 10$$
   A. 250   C. 70
   B. -11 D. -14

6. Which rule describes the pattern?
   $$1, 4, 9, 16, \ldots$$
   A. $3n$ C. $2n$
   B. n^2 D. n^3

7. Marcus invests $7500 at 4% interest, compounded annually. How much interest will he earn in 3 years?
   A. $900   C. $612
   B. $936.48   D. $324.48

8. Kate invests $500 at 3% interest, compounded annually. What is her total balance after 2 years?
   A. $530   C. $515.45
   B. $515   D. $530.45

9. Which number is prime?
   A. 14   C. 18
   B. 17   D. 20

10. Which set of dimensions is possible for a right rectangular prism with volume 36 cm³?
    A. 4 cm by 4 cm by 4 cm
    B. 4 cm by 3 cm by 3 cm
    C. 4 cm by 3 cm by 2 cm
    D. 4 cm by 4 cm by 3 cm

Write the first five terms of each addition pattern.

11. First term is 1, and then 7 is added each time.

12. First term is 0.5, and then 6.2 is added each time.

13. First term is -21, and then 7 is added each time.

14. First term is $\frac{3}{8}$, and then $\frac{1}{8}$ is added each time.

Write the first four terms of each multiplication pattern.

15. The first term is 2, and then each term is multiplied by 3.

16. The first term is 6, and then each term is multiplied by 1.5.

Simplify the expression.

17. $15 + 6 \cdot (-3)^3$

18. $(4 - 3)^4 + 8 \cdot 9$

19. $4^2 - 5^2 + 7 \cdot 6$

20. $12 \div 3 + (8 + 2)^2$

Find the total amount, including principal and annually compounding interest.

21. $400 at 5% for 2 years

22. $1000 at 3% for 4 years

23. $4000 at 3.5% for 3 years

24. $6500 at 2.75% for 4 years

State whether the number is prime or composite.

25. 33   26. 41   27. 182   28. 133

Find the LCM or GCF of the given numbers.

29. LCM of 4 and 6

30. LCM of 12 and 50

31. GCF of 12 and 20

32. GCF of 16 and 18

Find the missing number that follows the rule.

33.
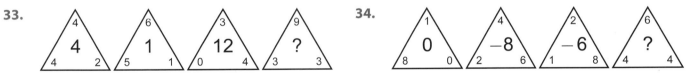

34.

Use an operation to create a new magic square. Then use a transformation on the original square to create another new magic square.

35.

6	7	2
1	5	9
8	3	4

Problem	Topic Lookup
1–2, 11–14	Addition Patterns
3–4, 15–16	Multiplication Patterns
5–6, 17–20	Exponents and Patterns
7–8, 21–24	Compound Interest

Problem	Topic Lookup
9, 25–28	Primes and Composites
10, 29–32	Using Prime Factorization
33–34	Figuring Out Math Puzzles
35	Creating Math Puzzles

Pronunciation Guide

The table below provides sample words to explain the sounds associated with specific letters and letter combinations used in the respellings in this book. For example, *a* represents the short "a" sound in *cat*, while *ay* represents the long "a" sound in *day*.

Letter combinations are used to approximate certain more complex sounds. For example, in the respelling of *trapezoid*—TRA-puh-zoyd—the letters *uh* represent the vowel sound you hear in *shut* and *other*.

Vowels

a	short a: **a**pple, c**a**t
ay	long a: c**a**ne, d**ay**
e, eh	short e: h**e**n, b**e**d
ee	long e: f**ee**d, t**ea**m
i, ih	short i: l**i**p, act**i**ve
iy	long i: tr**y**, m**i**ght
ah	short o: h**o**t, f**a**ther
oh	long o: h**o**me, thr**ow**
uh	short u: sh**u**t, **o**ther
yoo	long u: **u**nion, c**u**te

Letter Combinations

ch	**ch**in, an**ci**ent
sh	**sh**ow, mi**ss**ion
zh	vi**s**ion, a**z**ure
th	**th**in, heal**th**
<u>th</u>	**th**en, hea**th**er
ur	b**ir**d, f**ur**ther, w**or**d
us	b**us**, cr**us**t
or	c**our**t, f**or**mal
ehr	**er**ror, c**are**
oo	c**oo**l, tr**ue**, r**u**le
ow	n**ow**, **ou**t
ou	l**oo**k, p**u**ll, w**ou**ld
oy	c**oi**n, t**oy**
aw	s**aw**, m**au**l, f**a**ll
ng	so**ng**, fi**ng**er
air	**A**ristotle, b**a**rrister
ahr	c**ar**t, m**ar**tyr

Consonants

b	**b**utter, **b**aby
d	**d**og, cra**d**le
f	**f**un, **ph**one
g	**g**rade, an**g**le
h	**h**at, a**h**ead
j	**j**udge, gor**g**e
k	**k**ite, **c**ar, bla**ck**
l	**l**ily, mi**l**e
m	**m**om, ca**m**el
n	**n**ext, ca**nd**id
p	**p**rice, co**pp**er
r	**r**ubber, f**r**ee
s	**s**mall, **c**ircle, ha**ss**le
t	**t**on, po**tt**ery
v	**v**ase, **v**ivid
w	**w**all, a**w**ay
y	**y**ellow, ka**y**ak
z	**z**ebra, ha**z**e

PRONUNCIATION

Glossary

absolute value the distance from 0 to the graph of a number on a number line; the absolute value of a number a is denoted by $|a|$

acute angle an angle that measures greater than 0° and less than 90°

acute triangle a triangle with 3 acute angles

addend one of the two or more numbers that are added to find a sum

addition pattern a pattern formed by adding the same addend to each term to get the next term

adjacent angles two angles in the same plane that have a common side and a common vertex, but no common interior points

algebraic expression an expression that includes at least one variable, such as $x + 4$ or $6 \cdot y$

algorithm a step-by-step way to solve a problem

angle the figure formed by two rays, called sides, that share the same endpoint

approximate solution an estimate for the answer to a problem

area the number of square units in the interior of a figure

arrangement the order or placement of numbers or objects

average the sum of the data divided by the number of data values; the mean of the data

axis a number line that appears in a graph, such as the x-axis or y-axis in a coordinate plane; the plural of axis is axes

bar graph a graph that uses bars to display and compare data

base a number that is raised to some power; for example, in 5^3 the base is 5

base of a cylinder one of the parallel, congruent faces of the cylinder; a base of a cylinder is a circle

base of a figure the bottom side or face of a geometric figure

base of a parallelogram the side of a parallelogram that is chosen as the bottom side; any side of a parallelogram can be its base

base of a prism one of the parallel, congruent faces of the prism; a base of a prism is a polygon

bias the error that can arise when a sample is not representative of the population

biased sample a sample that is not representative of the population

bisector a line that divides a line segment, an angle, or another figure into two equal parts

boundary number the upper or lower limit used to round a number to a given place value

box-and-whisker plot a diagram that shows the distribution or spread of data with the minimum, the maximum, and the three quartiles of the data

capacity a measure indicating an amount a container can hold

center of rotation the point about which a figure is rotated

chord a line segment that connects any two points on a circle

circle the set of all points in a plane that are equidistant from a given point in the plane, called the center

circle graph a circular chart that shows divisions according to how data results are distributed

circumference distance around a circle

clockwise in the same direction that the hands on a clock rotate

clustering finding addends that are nearly alike in order to use a product to estimate their sum

coefficient a number that is multiplied by a variable in a variable expression; in an expression such as $3ab$, the numerical coefficient of ab is 3

combination a collection of items in which the order of the items is not important

common factor a factor that is the same for two or more integers

compass a tool used to draw circles and to measure in constructions

complementary angles two angles that have a combined measure of 90°

complementary events two or more nonoverlapping events that together cover all possible outcomes

composite number a whole number greater than 1 that is not prime

compound interest interest paid on both the principal (the original amount of money) and the interest an account has already earned

cone a three-dimensional figure with one base that is a circle, a curved lateral surface, and a point called a vertex

congruent angles angles that have the same measure

congruent figures figures that have the same size and shape

conjecture an idea that might be true on the basis of observations but is not yet proven to be true

consecutive whole numbers whole numbers that increase by 1, such as the numbers 3, 4, and 5

constant of variation the constant rate in the direct variation equation $y = kx$; the variable k represents the constant of variation and indicates the steepness of the graph

constant rate a rate that does not change over time

construction a method showing how a figure can be drawn accurately with a specified set of tools

continuous data values that all make sense within a range of data

convenience sampling sampling in which members of the population who are close at hand are selected

coordinate a location of a point on the number line or the coordinate plane that is designated by an x-value and a y-value

coordinate plane a plane that has an x-axis and a y-axis perpendicular to each other on which points can be located

counterclockwise in the opposite direction than the hands on a clock rotate

cross products the product of the numerator of one fraction and the denominator of a second fraction and the product of the denominator of the first fraction and the numerator of the second fraction

cube a solid figure made up of six square faces that meet at right angles

cube root a number that when multiplied by itself three times equals a given number

cubed the result of the operation where a number has been multiplied by itself two times, such as 5 cubed $= 5^3 = 5 \cdot 5 \cdot 5 = 125$; when the volume of a cube is found, the dimensions are cubed, and the volume is expressed in units cubed

cubic unit a cube whose edges are each one unit long; a cubic unit is used to measure volume

cylinder a three-dimensional figure with two congruent, parallel bases that are circles and a curved lateral surface that joins the bases

data numerical information that has been gathered; the term *data* is plural

data skewed left the graph of the distribution of data with a longer tail to the left side

data skewed right the graph of the distribution of data with a longer tail to the right side

decimal a number written with a decimal point

degree a unit used to measure angles

degree of accuracy the place value that is to be used to report an answer, such as in tens or hundredths

denominator the number in a fraction that is below the fraction bar

dependent event events for which one event's outcome affects the other event's probability

dependent variable the output variable

diameter a chord that passes through the center of a circle

difference the solution to a subtraction problem

dilation the change in size of a figure without a change in shape

direct variation a relationship between two quantities in which one quantity increases in proportion to the other; the relationship can be shown as a line on a graph

discount a decrease in the price of an item

discrete data values that are distinct or have distinct intervals; values between the intervals do not make sense as part of the data set

distributive property a rule that says that multiplying a number by a sum gives the same answer as multiplying the number by each addend of the sum and then adding the products

divide out a common factor to simplify an expression by dividing a numerator and denominator by a common factor

dividend the number to be divided; the dividend divided by the divisor equals the quotient

divisor the number that divides the dividend; the dividend divided by the divisor equals the quotient

domain in a relation, the set of allowable inputs (the set of first elements of the ordered pair in the relation)

equally likely having the same chance of happening

equation a number sentence that indicates that two expressions are equal

equiangular polygon a polygon with all angles congruent

equiangular triangle a triangle with three 60° angles

equilateral polygon a polygon with all sides congruent

equilateral triangle a triangle in which all 3 sides have equal length

equivalent having the same value, such as $\frac{1}{2}$, 0.5, and 50%

equivalent equations equations that have the same solution

equivalent fractions fractions that name the same number

equivalent ratios ratios that describe the same numerical relationship

estimate (n.) a very good guess or rough calculation of an answer, when the exact answer is not necessary

estimate (v.) to make a very good guess or rough calculation of an answer when the exact answer is not necessary

evaluate to find the value of an expression

event a set of one or more outcomes; an event is a subset of the sample space

exact solution a solution that is not an estimate or an approximation

experiment any process or action that has a result

experimental probability the probability given to events as the result of an experiment

exponent a number that shows how many times the base is used as a factor

expression one or more numbers and symbols that represent a numerical value, such as $2 + 3$, or 12, or $3y$, or $10 - w + 1$; an expression containing no variables is called a numerical expression and one containing one or more variables is called an algebraic expression

extrapolation the process of inferring, estimating, or predicting an unknown value that is outside of known values

extremes in a proportion, the first and last numbers or variables; in $a : b = c : d$ or $\frac{a}{b} = \frac{c}{d}$, a and d are the extremes

factor any of two or more numbers multiplied to form a product

favorable outcome the outcome you are investigating

flip the movement of a figure that shows the figure and its mirror image, sometimes called a reflection

formula a standard equation that is used to compute values, such as area, perimeter, or volume

fraction a number that shows part of a set, a point on a number line, a part of a whole, a quotient, or a ratio

frequency the number of times one item appears in a data set

frequency table a table that shows how often each item appears in a set of data

friendly numbers numbers such as 5 and 10, or multiples of 5 and 10, that are easier to add, subtract, multiply, and divide

graph a pictorial way to display data

greatest common factor (GCF) the greatest integer that is a factor of two or more given integers

height in a geometric figure, the length of an altitude that is perpendicular to a base

height of a triangle the length of the perpendicular segment that joins a base to the opposite vertex

histogram a graph with adjoining bars; used to show the frequency of data or data groups

hypotenuse the side opposite the right angle in a right triangle

image in a transformation, the new figure that results from the transformation

improper fraction a positive fraction whose numerator is greater than or equal to its denominator, or the opposite of such a fraction

independent event events for which one event's outcome has no effect on the other event's probability

independent variable the input variable

inequality a mathematical sentence formed by placing an inequality symbol between two expressions

input a number that will be used in a rule to determine the value of the output

integers the whole numbers and their opposites $\{\ldots -2, -1, 0, 1, 2, \ldots\}$

intercept the value at which a graph crosses one of the coordinate axes

interest the cost to borrow money or the amount earned by lending money

interest rate the percentage of the original amount of money on which the interest will be figured

interior angle any angle inside a polygon

interpolation the process of inferring, or estimating, an unknown value that is between known values

interquartile range (IQR) a measure of variation found by subtracting the first quartile Q_1 from the third quartile Q_3: $IQR = Q_3 - Q_1$; represents the range of the middle half of the data

intersecting lines lines that cross at one point

interval the distance between two points, as between two numbers on a number line

inverse operations opposite operations that undo each other; subtraction and addition are inverse operations; division and multiplication are inverse operations

irrational number any real number that is not rational; in decimal form, all irrational numbers are nonterminating and nonrepeating

irregular polygon a polygon that does not have all sides and angles equal in measure

isosceles triangle a triangle that has at least 2 sides equal in length; an equilateral triangle is a special type of isosceles triangle

label one of the informative indicators at various places on data displays such as tables and graphs

lateral face a face that is not a base

lateral surface the curved surface of a cylinder or cone; in a prism, any surface that connects the two bases; in a pyramid, any surface that rises from the base to the vertex

lateral surface area the sum of the areas of all surfaces of a three-dimensional figure except the base(s)

least common denominator (LCD) the least common multiple of two or more denominators

least common multiple (LCM) the least common nonzero number that is a multiple of two or more nonzero given numbers; used for the least common denominator

leg of a right triangle one of the two sides of a right triangle that form the right angle

like denominators denominators that are exactly the same in two or more fractions

like terms terms in which only the numerical coefficients are different

line a straight path of points that extends without end in both directions

line graph a display in which a set of information is shown as a series of points connected by straight line segments; a line graph is used to reveal trends

line of reflection the line across which a figure is reflected

line plot a number line that shows all the data values with a mark or marks above each data value to show how many times that data value occurred

line segment a part of a line that includes any two points on the line and all the points in between those two points

linear equation an equation whose graph is a line

lower bound estimate an estimate for a problem that is less than the actual solution could be

lowest terms a fraction whose numerator and denominator have no common factor other than 1 or −1

magic square a square made up of an equal number of rows and columns of numbers such that the sum of any column, row, or diagonal is the same

maximum the greatest value for a data set

mean the average of a set of data; the sum of the data divided by the number of data values

mean absolute deviation the average distance of all the data values from the mean of the data

means in a proportion, the second and third numbers or variables; in $a : b = c : d$ or $\frac{a}{b} = \frac{c}{d}$, b and c are the means

measure of center a measure that represents the center of the distribution of values for a data set, such as mean, median, and mode

measure of spread a measure that represents the extent to which the values of a data set are spread out, such as the range

measure of variation a measure, such as the interquartile range, that compares the range or spread of data to a measure of center

median the middle number in a numerically ordered set of data with an odd number of data values, or the average of the two middle numbers in a numerically ordered set of data with an even number of data values

minimum the least value for a data set

minuend a number from which another number is subtracted

mixed number a whole number and a proper fraction that show a single amount

mode the data values that occur most often in a set of data; data may have 0, 1, or many modes

multiple of a number the product of the given number and a counting number

multiplication pattern a pattern formed by multiplying each term by the same factor to get the next term

multiplicative inverses two numbers whose product is 1; also called reciprocals

mutually exclusive events events that cannot happen at the same time

negative correlation a trend that develops with two variables when the value of one variable increases while the other value decreases; in a scatter plot, the data points form a pattern that slants down

negative sign the sign (–) indicating that a number's value is less than zero, such as –6

net a two-dimensional pattern that can be folded into a three-dimensional figure

net gain or net loss the sum of the individual values when a situation includes several gains and losses

number line a line on which each point represents a number

numerator the number or expression in a fraction that is above the fraction bar

numerical expression an expression with no variables that represents a certain number

obtuse angle an angle that measures greater than 90° and less than 180°

obtuse triangle a triangle with an obtuse angle

opposites a pair of numbers whose distance on both sides of zero is the same, such as –5 and +5

order of operations the order in which operations must be computed when more than one operation is involved

ordered pair a pair of numbers in which the first number is the x-coordinate and the second number is the y-coordinate of the location of a point

origin the location of 0 on the number line and the location of (0, 0) on a coordinate plane

outcome the result of an experiment or one of the several possible results in a probability experiment

outlier a data value that has a value much less than or much greater than the rest of the data

output the result of applying a function rule to the value of an input

parallel lines lines in the same flat surface that never intersect

parallelogram a quadrilateral with two pairs of parallel sides

percent a ratio that compares a number to 100

percent of change ratio of the amount of change to the original amount, expressed in percent form

perfect square a rational number whose square root is also a rational number

perimeter distance around a figure; the perimeter of a polygon is the sum of the lengths of all the sides

perpendicular lines lines that intersect and form angles that measure 90°

place value the value of a digit depending on its position, or place, in a number

plane a flat surface with infinite length and width but no thickness

point a location in space with no length, width, or depth

point on a coordinate plane a dot that marks a coordinate; a location on a coordinate plane, designated by an x-value and a y-value

polygon a closed plane figure made up of line segments that meet only at their endpoints

population a group on which data results are collected

positive correlation a trend that describes when two variables increase or decrease together; in a scatter plot, the data points form a pattern that slants up

positive sign the sign $(+)$ indicating that a number's value is greater than zero, such as $+6$; the positive sign is not always shown

power a product in which all the factors are the same; for example, 16 is the fourth power of 2, because $2 \cdot 2 \cdot 2 \cdot 2 = 16$

power of ten any number that can be written in the form 10^n, where n is an integer

precision an indication of how exact a calculation or measurement is

predict to state how future events will happen

pre-image the original figure in a transformation

prime factorization an expression showing a positive integer as a product of its prime factors

prime number a whole number greater than 1 that has only two whole-number factors, 1 and itself

principal money that earns interest at a given rate over time; the principal is the original amount of money on which the interest is based

principal square root the nonnegative square root, indicated by the square root sign

prism a three-dimensional figure whose surfaces, called faces, are polygons; at least two faces are parallel and congruent and are called bases, and all other faces are parallelograms or rectangles

probability a number from 0 to 1 that describes how likely an event is to occur

product the answer to a multiplication problem

proportion an equation stating that two ratios are equal

protractor a tool to measure the degrees in an angle

pyramid a three-dimensional figure with one base that is a polygon and all other faces (called lateral faces) are triangles that meet at a single vertex

quadrant one of the four regions into which the coordinate axes separate the coordinate plane

quadrilateral a polygon with 4 sides

quartile one of the three values that separate an ordered data set into four equal parts; the second quartile Q_2 is the median of the data set; the first quartile Q_1 is the median of the lower half of the data set; the third quartile Q_3 is the median of the upper half of the data set. **Note:** A quartile also refers to the entire set of data in any quarter of the data.

quotient the answer to a division problem

radius a line segment that connects the center of a circle to a point on the circle; the plural of radius is radii (RAY-dee-iy)

range the set of possible outputs (the set of second elements of the ordered pairs in the relation)

range of a data set the difference of the maximum and minimum values in the data set

rate a ratio that compares quantities of different kinds of units

ratio a comparison of two quantities using division

rational number any number that can be expressed as a ratio $\left(\frac{a}{b}\right)$ where a and b are integers and b is nonzero

ray part of a line that begins from an endpoint and extends infinitely in one direction

reasonableness the sense that an answer is correct, given the facts

reasoning the series of thoughts and steps used to understand a problem, to create a plan to solve the problem, to reach a solution, and to accurately explain results

reciprocals two numbers whose product is 1

rectangle a parallelogram with 4 right angles; a square is a special type of rectangle

reflection a transformation of a figure by flipping it across a line or line segment, creating a mirror image of the figure

regular polygon a polygon with all its sides congruent and all its angles congruent

relation a set of ordered pairs

relatively prime numbers two or more numbers that have no common factors other than 1

remainder the amount left over after dividing

replacement set the given set of numbers that a variable may represent

representation a way of displaying information, such as a model, a number, a graph, or an equation

rhombus a parallelogram with 4 congruent sides; a square is a special type of rhombus

right angle an angle that measures 90°

right triangle a triangle with a right angle

rise the change in the y-coordinates (the vertical change) when moving from one point on a line to another point on the line

rotation a transformation of a figure by turning it about a given point

round (v.) to change a number to the nearest place value asked in a problem; for example, the result of rounding 532 to the nearest ten would be 530

ruler a tool to measure length, typically marked in centimeters or inches

run the change in the x-coordinates (the horizontal change) when moving from one point on a line to another point on the line

sale price the price of an item after a discount

sales tax a percent of the price of an item paid to a government when the item is sold

sample (n.) a portion of a group or population

sample (v.) to collect data on a part of a population to determine information about the entire population

sample space the set of all possible outcomes of an experiment

scale factor a ratio of one measure to another, where both measures are the same unit of measure

scalene triangle a triangle that has no sides equal in length

scatter plot a graph that displays two sets of data as points; scatter plot points represent ordered pairs

semicircle half of a circle

side of a polygon one of the line segments that are the boundaries of a polygon

similar figures figures that have the same shape but not necessarily the same size

simple interest interest earned or paid only on the principal, or initial deposit

simple random sampling sampling in which all members of the population have an equal probability of selection

simplest form of a fraction a fraction in which the numerator and the denominator have no common factor other than 1 or –1; also called a fraction in lowest terms

simplify a numerical expression to evaluate, or find, the value of the expression

slide the movement of a figure along a line without turns or flips, also known as translation

slope a number that describes the steepness of a line, computed as the ratio of the change in the y-coordinates to the change in the x-coordinates (the ratio of rise to run) when moving from one point on the line to another point on the line

solution the answer to a problem or the process used to find the answer

solution set the set of all solutions to a given open sentence

solve to determine the answer to a problem

speed the ratio of distance traveled to time

square a parallelogram with 4 congruent sides and 4 right angles

square root a factor of a number that when multiplied by itself results in the number; the nonnegative square root is called the principal square root and is indicated by the square root sign

square unit a square with sides of a particular side length, such as a square meter, used to measure area

squared the result of the operation where a number has been multiplied by itself, such as 5 squared $= 5^2 = 5 \cdot 5 = 25$; when the area of a square is found, the dimensions are squared, and the area is expressed in units squared

stem-and-leaf plot data display that lists the last digits (leaves) of the data values to the right of the earlier digits (stems)

straight angle an angle that measures exactly 180°; a straight angle is a line

strategy a technique used to solve a problem, such as working backward or drawing a diagram

stratified random sampling sampling in which the population is first organized into separate categories, and then each is sampled as an independent subpopulation

substitution the replacement of an equivalent value for another

subtrahend a number that is subtracted from another number

sum the result of an addition; the numbers added are addends

supplementary angles two angles that have a combined measure of 180°

surface area the sum of the areas of all surfaces of a three-dimensional figure

surface of a solid figure all of the polygons that are faces of the solid figure

survey a strategy for collecting data by asking questions of a group of people

systematic sampling sampling in which the population is ordered, and then members are selected at regular intervals through that ordered list

tax a sum of money collected by a government

term a part of an expression that can be a number, a variable, or a product of numbers and variables

term in a pattern each number or object in a pattern

term number the position of a term in a pattern

tessellation a pattern of shapes that fit together with no overlaps or gaps and can extend to fill a figure

theoretical probability the ratio of the number of favorable outcomes to the total number of possible outcomes

three-dimensional object a figure with length, width, and height; often called 3-D

tip an amount of money given to someone who provides a service

transformation (geometric) a movement or change of a figure, such as a translation, reflection, rotation, or dilation

transformation (of an equation) any change to an equation that results in an equivalent equation

translation the movement of a figure along a line without turns or flips, sometimes called a slide

trapezoid a quadrilateral with exactly one pair of parallel sides

tree diagram a branching diagram used in probability to show outcomes of several events that occur one after the other

trend a consistent pattern in data

triangle a polygon with 3 sides

turn the movement of a figure a certain number of degrees around a given point, sometimes called a rotation

two-dimensional shape a figure with length and width, but no height; often called 2-D

unbiased sample a sample that is representative of the population

unit an object or an amount used to measure, such as kilograms as a standard unit for mass

unit rate a rate that has a denominator of 1 unit

unlike denominators denominators that are different in two or more fractions

upper bound estimate an estimate for a problem that is greater than the actual solution could be

variable a symbol used to represent one or more numbers

variable expression an expression that involves a variable

vector a line segment with a direction indicated with an arrow

vertex the common endpoint of the two rays or segments that form an angle less than 180°; the vertex of a 180° angle is any point along the line; the plural of vertex is vertices

vertical angles two nonadjacent angles formed by intersecting lines

volume the amount of space taken up by a three-dimensional object; measured in cubic units

whole numbers zero and the counting numbers (0, 1, 2, 3, 4, 5, 6, and so on)

x-axis the horizontal axis on a coordinate plane, perpendicular to the y-axis

x-coordinate the first number in an ordered pair of numbers that designates the location of a point on the coordinate plane

x-intercept the x-coordinate of a point where a graph intersects the x-axis

y-axis the vertical axis on a coordinate plane, perpendicular to the x-axis

y-coordinate the second number in an ordered pair of numbers that designates the location of a point on the coordinate plane

y-intercept the y-coordinate of a point where a graph intersects the y-axis

Venn diagram a drawing that shows relationships among sets of numbers or objects

Symbols

$\sqrt{a}$	principal square root of a	$|x|$	absolute value of x
$\sqrt[3]{a}$	cube root of a	$-a$	opposite of a
A'	A prime; the result of transforming point A	a^n	a to the nth power
$\ldots$	continuation of a pattern	%	percent
Q_1	first quartile	$\pm$	plus or minus
x_1	first value of x	$a:b$	ratio of a to b
π	pi	$\circ$	degree or degrees
( )	parentheses	$\overline{AB}$	line segment AB
[ ]	brackets	AB	length of line segment AB
$\approx$	is approximately equal to	$\overrightarrow{AB}$	ray AB
$=$	is equal to	$\overleftrightarrow{AB}$	line AB
$\neq$	is not equal to	$\triangle ABC$	triangle ABC
$\cong$	is congruent to	$\angle ABC$	angle ABC
$\sim$	is similar to	$m\angle ABC$	measure of angle ABC
$<$	is less than	⌐	right angle
$>$	is greater than	$\perp$	perpendicular

Properties

Real Number Properties

Let a, b, and c be any real numbers.

Addition Property: **Addends with Like Signs**	For all $a > 0$ and $b > 0$, $a + b = \|a\| + \|b\|$. For all $a < 0$ and $b < 0$, $a + b = -(\|a\| + \|b\|)$.
Addition Property: **Addends with Unlike Signs**	For all $a > 0$ and $b < 0$, If $\|a\| > \|b\|$, then $a + b = \|a\| - \|b\|$. If $\|a\| < \|b\|$, then $a + b = -(\|b\| - \|a\|)$.
Addition Property of Equality	If $a = b$, then $a + c = b + c$ and $c + a = c + b$.
Subtraction Property of Equality	If $a = b$, then $a - c = b - c$.
Multiplication Property of Equality	If $a = b$, then $c \cdot a = c \cdot b$ and $a \cdot c = b \cdot c$.
Division Property of Equality	If $a = b$ and $c \neq 0$, then $\frac{a}{c} = \frac{b}{c}$.
Transitive Property	If $a = b$ and $b = c$, then $a = c$.
Substitution Property of Equality	If $a = b$, then a may be replaced with b in any expression or equation.

	Addition	**Multiplication**
Commutative Properties	$a + b = b + a$	$a \cdot b = b \cdot a$
Associative Properties	$(a + b) + c = a + (b + c)$	$(a \cdot b) \cdot c = a \cdot (b \cdot c)$
Inverse Properties	$a + (-a) = 0$ and $(-a) + a = 0$	$a \cdot \frac{1}{a} = 1$ and $\frac{1}{a} \cdot a = 1, a \neq 0$
Identity Properties	$a + 0 = a$ and $0 + a = a$	$a \cdot 1 = a$ and $1 \cdot a = a$
Distributive Property	$a(b + c) = ab + ac$	

Absolute Value Equations

If $\|x\| - a$ for some positive number a, then $x - a$ or $x = -a$.

Properties of Exponents

Let a be a nonzero number, and let n be an integer.

If n is a positive integer, $a^n = a \cdot a \cdot a \cdot \ldots \cdot a$ (n factors).

Square Root Properties

For nonnegative values of m, n, and p, if $m < n < p$, then $\sqrt{m} < \sqrt{n} < \sqrt{p}$.

For real numbers a and b, $\sqrt{ab} = \sqrt{a} \cdot \sqrt{b}$ and $\sqrt{a} \cdot \sqrt{b} = \sqrt{ab}$.

Reciprocal Properties

For any nonzero real number a, $a \cdot \frac{1}{a} = 1$.

For all nonzero real numbers a and b, the reciprocal of $\frac{a}{b}$ is $\frac{b}{a}$.

For any nonzero real number a, $\frac{1}{-a} = \frac{-1}{a} = -\frac{1}{a}$.

For all nonzero real numbers a and b, $\frac{1}{ab} = \frac{1}{a} \cdot \frac{1}{b}$.

Division Properties

For any real number a and nonzero real number b, $a \div b = a \cdot \frac{1}{b}$.

For all real numbers a and b and nonzero real number c, $\frac{a+b}{c} = \frac{a}{c} + \frac{b}{c}$.

For all $a > 0$ and $b > 0$, $a \div b > 0$.

For all $a < 0$ and $b < 0$, $a \div b > 0$.

For all $a < 0$ and $b > 0$, $a \div b < 0$.

Comparison Property of Rational Numbers

For nonzero integers a and c and positive integers b and d,

$\frac{a}{b} > \frac{c}{d}$ if and only if $ad > bc$.

$\frac{a}{b} < \frac{c}{d}$ if and only if $ad < bc$.

Means-Extremes Product Property

Let a, b, c, and d be real numbers.

$\frac{a}{b} = \frac{c}{d}$ if and only if $ad = bc$, given that b and d are not 0.

Formulary

Geometric Formulas

Circle

Circumference $C = \pi d = 2\pi r$

Area $A = \pi r^2$

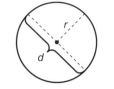

Cone

Volume $V = \frac{1}{3}Bh = \frac{1}{3}\pi r^2 h$

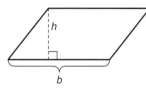

Cylinder

Volume $V = Bh = \pi r^2 h$

Surface Area $SA = 2\pi r^2 + 2\pi rh$

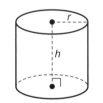

Parallelogram

Area $A = bh$

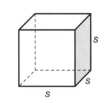

Prism: Cube

$V = s^3$

Surface Area $SA = 6s^2$

Prism: Rectangular

Volume $V = lwh$

Surface Area $SA = 2lw + 2lh + 2wh$

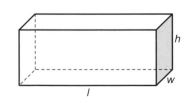

FORMULARY

Pyramid

Volume $\quad V = \frac{1}{3}Bh$

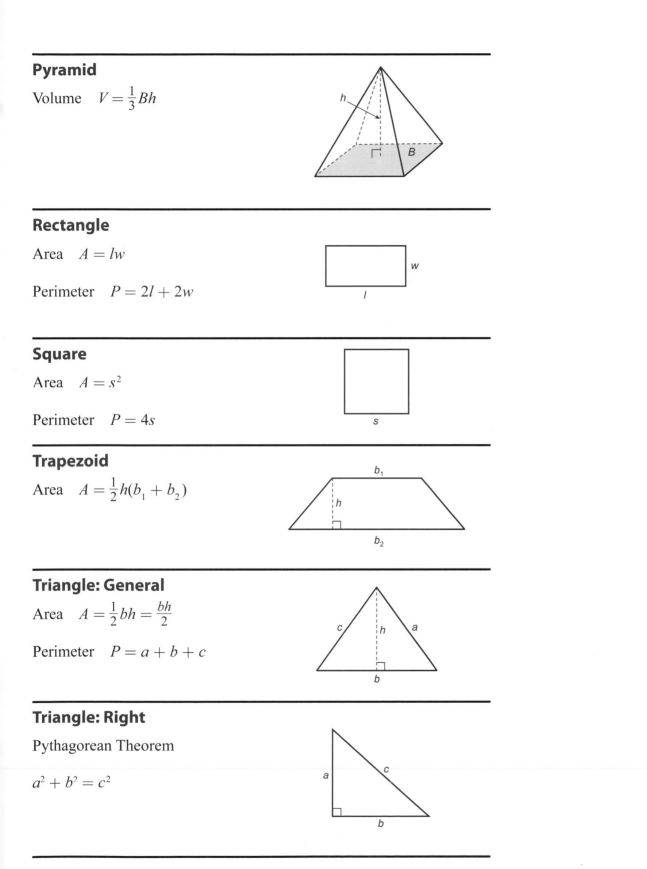

Rectangle

Area $\quad A = lw$

Perimeter $\quad P = 2l + 2w$

Square

Area $\quad A = s^2$

Perimeter $\quad P = 4s$

Trapezoid

Area $\quad A = \frac{1}{2}h(b_1 + b_2)$

Triangle: General

Area $\quad A = \frac{1}{2}bh = \frac{bh}{2}$

Perimeter $\quad P = a + b + c$

Triangle: Right

Pythagorean Theorem

$a^2 + b^2 = c^2$

Points on a Coordinate Plane

Vertical Distance

Same x-value: $d = |y_2 - y_1|$

Horizontal Distance

Same y-value: $d = |x_2 - x_1|$

Statistics

Mean

$$\bar{x} = \frac{x_1 + x_2 + \ldots + x_n}{n}$$

Median

Arrange the values in order from least to greatest.
Odd number of values: the middle value
Even number of values: the average of the middle two values

Mode

The value or values that occur most often in a set of data.
If no one value occurs most often, then there is no mode for the set.

Range

range = maximum − minimum

Probability

Simple Theoretical Probability

$$P(E) = \frac{\text{number of outcomes in event } E}{\text{total number of outcomes in sample space } S} = \frac{n(E)}{n(S)}$$

Combined Probabilities

For mutually exclusive events A and B,
$P(A \text{ or } B) = P(A) + P(B)$.

For independent events C and D,
$P(C \text{ and } D) = P(C) \cdot P(D)$.

Conversions

Conversion for Length

English Units

1 ft = 12 in.
1 yd = 36 in.
1 yd = 3 ft
1 mi = 5280 ft

Metric Units

1 cm = 10 mm
1 m = 100 cm
1 km = 1000 m

Conversion of Cubic Units

English Units

$1 \text{ ft}^3 = 1728 \text{ in}^3$
$1 \text{ yd}^3 = 27 \text{ ft}^3$

Metric Units

$1 \text{ cm}^3 = 1000 \text{ mm}^3$
$1 \text{ m}^3 = 1{,}000{,}000 \text{ cm}^3$

Scale Factor Formulas

If SA_F is the surface area of a figure that is enlarged or reduced with a scale factor, then the surface area of the scaled image, SA_I, is $SA_I = (\text{scale factor})^2 \cdot SA_F$.

Other Formulas

Percent of Change

$$\text{percent of change} = \frac{\text{amount of change}}{\text{original amount}} \cdot 100\%$$

Simple Interest

$I = Prt$, where I is the amount of interest, P is the principal, r is the annual interest rate, and t is the time in years.

Compound Interest

$A = P(1 + r)^t$, where P is the principal (the money you start with or your first deposit), r is the interest rate, and t is the number of years.

Selected Answers

Chapter 1   Problem Solving

Page 4
1. 7   **3.** 12   **5.** 19   **7.** 56   **9.** 4   **11.** 20   **13.** 12   **15.** 36

Page 5
1. true   **3.** not true   **5.** not true   **7.** not true   **9.** true
11. true   **13.** not true   **15.** true

Page 6
1. 13   **3.** 25   **5.** 30   **7.** 96   **9.** 600   **11.** 15   **13.** 13   **15.** 800

Pages 8–11
1. 2   **3.** 10   **5.** 10.7   **7.** 9   **9.** 42   **11.** 12.6
13.

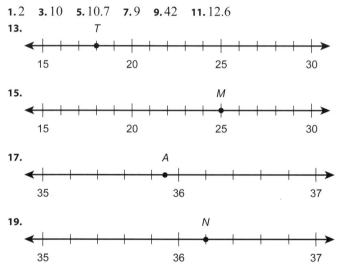

21. $52 > 49$ **23.** $57 > 48$ **25.** $48 < 52 < 54$
27. $36.2 < 37$ **29.** $35.8 < 36.4$ **31.** $36.4 < 36.9 < 37.4$
33. D   **35.** D

Pages 12–15
1. addends   **3.** product   **5.** subtrahend   **7.** difference
9. 7 and $4z$ are addends; 4 and z are factors   **11.** $5h$ is a subtrahend; 5 and h are factors   **13.** 81 is the dividend; 2 is the quotient   **15.** $5c$ is the minuend; $6d$ is the subtrahend; 5 and c are factors; 6 and d are factors   **17.** 27   **19.** 0   **21.** 38
23. 44   **25.** 4   **27.** 7   **29.** 1   **31.** The first step should have been to divide the numbers 14 and 2. Then the second step should have been to subtract the numbers 20 and 7. The correct result is 13.   **33.** You should multiply before adding. The numbers 2 and 4 were added to get 6. Then 3 was multiplied by 6 to get 18. Instead, multiply 3 by 2 to get 6. Then add 6 and 4 to get a result of 10.   **35.** You should subtract inside the parentheses before dividing. The numbers 6 and 3 were divided to get 2. Then 2 was subtracted from 18 to get 16. Instead, subtract 6 from 18 to get 12. Then divide 12

by 3 to get a result of 4.   **37.** You should subtract inside the parentheses before multiplying. The numbers 4 and 6 were multiplied to get 24. Then 5 was subtracted from 24 to get 19. Instead, subtract 5 from 6 to get 1. Then multiply 4 by 1 to get a result of 4.   **39.** A   **41.** A

Pages 16–19
1. commutative property of addition   **3.** distributive property   **5.** symmetric property   **7.** commutative property of multiplication   **9.** symmetric property   **11.** associative property of multiplication   **13.** commutative property of multiplication   **15.** associative property of addition   **17.** distributive property   **19.** commutative property of addition   **21.** commutative property of multiplication   **23.** distributive property   **25. A.** commutative property of multiplication;   **B.** Multiply;   **C.** Multiply.   **27. A.** distributive property;   **B.** Multiply;   **C.** Add.   **29. A.** distributive property;   **B.** Subtract within parentheses;   **C.** Multiply.   **31. A.** commutative property of addition;   **B.** associative property of addition;   **C.** Add;   **D.** Add.   **33.** 39   **35.** 58   **37.** 23   **39.** 77   **41.** 180   **43.** 161   **45.** 423   **47.** 420   **49.** 384   **51.** 380   **53.** D   **55.** D

Pages 20–23
1. $5 + 7$ **3.** $6 \cdot 8$ **5.** $30 - 17$ **7.** $8 \cdot 10$ **9.** $11 \cdot n$
11. $n - 1$ **13.** $12 + t$ **15.** $40 - a$ **17.** $12 \cdot h$ **19.** $2 \cdot s$
21. $14 + w$ **23.** $s \div 2$ **25.** $3 \cdot v$ **27.** Sample answer: 3 times the number n; the product of 3 and the number n
29. Sample answer: 18 divided by the number h; 18 divided into h equal groups   **31.** Sample answer: the number m more than 25; 25 increased by the number m **33.** Sample answer: the number d times 5; the product of 5 and the number d
35. Sample answer: the number w less than 11; the difference between 11 and w **37.** Sample answer: the number p more than 17; the sum of 17 and the number p **39.** Sample answer: You take some money m shopping and buy a $20 gift certificate for your friend. The expression $m - 20$ represents how much money you have left.   **41.** Sample answer: You exercise 45 minutes each day for d days. The expression $45d$ represents the total amount of time spent exercising.
43. B   **45.** A

Pages 24–27
1. $8 + 5 \cdot 6$ **3.** $20 \div (1 + 4)$ **5.** $2n - 12$ **7.** $n - 5 + 30$
9. $(10 - n) \div 3$ **11.** $(6 + x) \div 5$ **13.** $75 \div (x - 10)$
15. $50 + (65 \cdot 3)$ **17.** $350 - (85 \cdot w)$ **19.** Sample answer: There are 3 piles of coins with the same coins in each pile. Each pile has some quarters and 7 dimes.
21. Sample answer: Arthur's grandmother is 2 years younger than 6 times as old as he is.   **23.** Sample answer: Jocelyn

bought 5 packs of apple juice boxes and 11 single boxes of grape juice.   **25.** Sample answer: Cho had 36 pounds of sand and removed 2 scoops of it.   **27.** Sample answer: Sarah bought 7 bags that hold 3 oz of granola each. She divided each bag equally among her friends.   **29.** Sample answer: Some people in Lilly's building own dogs. Three times as many people own cats.   **31.** C   **33.** A

Pages 28–31

1. 11   **3.** 38   **5.** Paige   **7.** 13   **9.** 80   **11.** 32 foam balls and 48 straws   **13.** 44,640 min   **15.** 14 chickens and 3 cows   **17.** 36   **19.** 37.5 min   **21.** C

Pages 32–35

1. 13; information needed: number of cherry and number of plum trees; information not needed: number of apple trees   **3.** 9 miles; information needed: miles on Friday and Saturday; information not needed: amount of time on Friday   **5.** 4 to 1; information needed: lemonade and orange juice amounts; information not needed: amount of strawberries   **7.** 10; information needed: number of fish and number of birds; information not needed: number of hamsters   **9.** $94; information needed: amount saved and cost of player; information not needed: amount saved per week from allowance   **11.** the cost of the sandwich   **13.** the number of people on the bus to begin with   **15.** the total number of students in Patrick's neighborhood   **17.** D

Pages 36–39

1. 90   **3.** 700   **5.** 7   **7.** 8.1   **9.** 24.62   **11.** 560   **13.** 55,000   **15.** 500.2   **17.** about 100   **19.** about 10,000   **21.** about 40   **23.** about 1000   **25.** about 1600   **27.** about 120   **29.** about $280   **31.** about 8   **33.** about 80   **35.** about 4   **37.** about 30   **39.** about 1100   **41.** about 800   **43.** about 30   **45.** about 60   **47.** lower bound estimate: 2700; upper bound estimate: 3000   **49.** lower bound estimate: 0; upper bound estimate: 200   **51.** lower bound estimate: 15; upper bound estimate: 40   **53.** A   **55.** D

Pages 40–43

1. 19.1 m   **3.** 6.6 kg   **5.** $5.99 per lb   **7.** $43.94   **9.** 8 h   **11.** estimate; No   **13.** estimate; Yes   **15.** estimate; No   **17.** estimate; Yes   **19.** estimate; Yes   **21.** C

Pages 44–45

1. B   **3.** B   **5.** A   **7.** B   **9.** B   **11.** B
13.

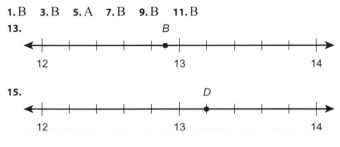

17. 78   **19.** 4   **21.** 158   **23.** 48   **25.** $24 \div (n - 6)$
27. $13w - 25$ **29.** 11.55 h   **31.** about 100   **33.** about 9100

Chapter 2   Distance: Addition Equations

Page 48

1. 60   **3.** 86   **5.** 948   **7.** 11.33   **9.** 1229   **11.** 3.53   **13.** 12.02   **15.** 34.36

Page 49

1. 45   **3.** 4.2   **5.** 1.5   **7.** 292   **9.** 3.597   **11.** 298   **13.** 44   **15.** 208

Page 50

1. Either convert the meters to kilometers or convert the kilometers to meters. Once one value is converted, the measures can be added.   **3.** Yes   **5.** Either convert the liters to milliliters or convert the milliliters to liters. Once one value is converted, the measures can be subtracted.   **7.** Yes   **9.** No

Pages 52–55

1. inches; centimeters   **3.** inches; centimeters   **5.** inches, feet; centimeters, meters   **7.** feet, yards; meters   **9.** inches; millimeters, centimeters   **11.** feet; meters   **13.** inches; centimeters   **15.** miles; kilometers   **17.** miles; kilometers   **19.** 4 mi   **21.** 4 yd   **23.** 96 in.   **25.** 1500 cm   **27.** 36 ft   **29.** 3.5 m   **31.** 5.92 m   **33.** 700,000 cm   **35.** 24 in.; 2 ft   **37–43.** Answers will vary.   **45.** C

Pages 56–59

1. $P = 2(10.2) + 2(6.5)$; $P = 2(10.2 + 6.5)$; 33.4 m
3. $P = 2(3.2) + 2(0.5)$; $P = 2(3.2 + 0.5)$; 7.4 m
5. $P = 2(13) + 2\left(4\frac{1}{2}\right)$; $P = 2\left(13 + 4\frac{1}{2}\right)$; 35 ft   **7.** 62 cm
9. 72 in.   **11.** 128 m   **13.** 22 ft   **15.** 35 yd   **17.** 0.016 m
19. 22 m   **21.** 12.6 m   **23.** 101.86 cm   **25.** 68 m   **27.** C

Pages 60–63

1. 3 m   **3.** 8 in.   **5.** 3 km   **7.** 5.8 cm   **9.** 0.51 m
11. $y = 5$ **13.** $a = 16$ **15.** $26 = c$ **17.** $q = 28$ **19.** $n = 1.5$
21. $15.3 = m$ **23.** $y = 26.$ 24   **25.** $x = 2\frac{4}{21}$ **27.** $n - 17 = 49$; $n = 66$ **29.** $p + 66 = 72$; $p = 6$ **31.** $e + 0.75 = 2.5$; $e = 1.75$ h   **33.** C

Pages 64–67

1. $n + 142.7 = 436.2$; $n = 293.5$; 293.5 mi
3. Sample equation: $f + 12 = 38$; $f = 26$; 26 m
5. Sample equation: $t - 51 = 127$; $t = 178$; $178
7. Sample equation: $e + 1029 = 10,724$; $e = 9695$; 9695 ft
9. Sample equation: $f + 18.7 = 29$; $f = 10.3$; 10.3 m
11. Sample equation: $x + 5 + 20 + 10 = 96$; $x = 61$; 61 min
13. Sample equation: $s + 26 = 34.95$; $s = 8.95$; $8.95
15. Sample equation: $n + 9.4 = 152.3$; $5.7 + 6.4 + 8.9 + 11.1 + 13.5 + 16 + n = 152.3 - 9.4$; $n = 81.3$; 81.3 lb
17. A

Pages 68–71

1. -8 **3.** -1 **5.** -25 **7.** -5 **9.** -110 **11.** -24
13. -3 **15.** -1007 **17.** $-8 < -3$ **19.** $-2 > -3$
21. $2 > -2$ **23.** $-15 < 4$ **25.** $-31 < -26$ **27.** $-12 < 3290$
29. $-13 < -5 < -4$ **31.** $-9 < -7 < -5$
33. $-2 > -17 > -18$ **35.** $-47 > -65 > -96$

37. $-6444 < -4 < 367$ **39.** -11 **43.** -16 **47.** $-11{,}000$
49. C

Pages 72–75

1. $|-12| = 12$; the opposite of -12 is 12.   **3.** $|5| = 5$; the opposite of 5 is -5.   **5.** $|-19| = 19$; the opposite of -19 is 19.   **7.** $|-17| = 17$; the opposite of -17 is 17.   **9.** $|1| = 1$; the opposite of 1 is -1.   **11.** $|57| = 57$; the opposite of 57 is -57.   **13.** $|-179| = 179$; the opposite of -179 is 179.
15. $|1534| = 1534$; the opposite of 1534 is -1534.
17. $|-989{,}006| = 989{,}006$; the opposite of $-989{,}006$ is 989,006.   **19.** 5   **21.** 18   **23.** 24   **25.** 21   **27.** 4   **29.** 5
31. 251   **33.** 164   **35.** 9 and 21   **37.** 9 and 33   **39.** -7 and 17
41. -9 and 65   **43.** -23 **45.** 43 and -43 **47.** The water will reach the rosebush but not the palm tree.   **49.** C

Pages 76–79

1. 1   **3.** 2   **5.** 0   **7.** -21 **9.** 4   **11.** -99 **13.** 74   **15.** 303
17. -3.2 **19.** -48.6 **21.** 10   **23.** -14 **25.** -3 **27.** -1530
29. -25 **31.** -429.25 **33.** $-8°C$ **35.** 130 m   **37.** $-\$100$
39. $\$1900$ **41.** $-\$900$ **43.** A   **45.** B

Pages 80–83

1. $x + 2 - 2 = -4 - 2$; $x + 0 = -6$; $x = -6$ **3.** $2 = b$
5. $d = -5$ **7.** $t = -4$ **9.** $b = -5$ **11.** $-13 = x$ **13.** $y = -18$
15. $-14 = d$ **17.** $a = 11$ **19.** $r = 15$ **21.** $g = 20$ **23.** $y = -4.7$
25. $b = -1\frac{3}{4}$ **27.** $-22 + t = 85$; $t = 107$; \$107
29. $a + (-14) = -2$; $a = -2 + 14$; $12°C$ **31.** $-50 + 400 = e$; $350 = e$; 350 m   **33.** B   **35.** D

Pages 84–85

1. D   **3.** B   **5.** A   **7.** C   **9.** B   **11.** feet; meters
13. millimeters   **15.** 32 in.   **17.** 5.2 m   **19.** $y = 5$
21. $a = 19$ **23.** $w = 245 + 317$; $w = 562$; 562 m
25. $-6 < -5$ **27.** $-7 < -2 < 7$ **29.** 30   **31.** -8
33. -110 **35.** -12 **37.** 4   **39.** $k = -6$ **41.** $t = -956$

Chapter 3   Area: Multiplication Equations

Page 88

1. 4 cm^2 **3.** 49 square units   **5.** 9 ft^2 **7.** 225 in^2

Page 89

1. 900   **3.** 1369   **5.** 440.2   **7.** 639,240   **9.** 1,863,274
11. 6.90727

Page 90

1. 27   **3.** 0.7   **5.** 63 r 6   **7.** 18 r 13   **9.** 78 r 7   **11.** 178

Pages 92–95

1. 12 cm^2 **3.** 12 m^2 **5.** 15 cm^2 **7.** 9 in^2 **9.** 81 yd^2; 729 ft^2
11. 576 in^2; 4 ft^2 **13.** 27 yd^2; 243 ft^2 **15.** 0.2 m^2; 200,000 mm^2
17. D

Pages 96–99

1. 36 cm^2 **3.** 18 m^2 **5.** 18 m^2 **7.** 442 in^2 **9.** 0.9416 mi^2
11. 28,980 cm^2 **13.** $A = 27 \cdot 10$; $A = 10 \cdot 27$; 270 cm^2
15. 224 yd^2 **17.** 297 yd^2 **19.** 960.4375 yd^2 **21.** 6480 ft^2
23. 4896 ft^2 **25.** B

Pages 100–103

1. parallelogram, rectangle   **3.** parallelogram, rectangle, rhombus, square.   **5.** none   **7.** 144 mm^2 **9.** 299 ft^2
11. 143.38 cm^2 **13.** 112 m^2 **15.** 0.72 m^2 **17.** 15.87 m^2 **19.** B

Pages 104–107

1. For $b = 12$ in., $h = 5$ in.; for $b = 5$ in., $h = 12$ in.; for $b = 13$ in., $h = 4.6$ in.   **3.** For $b = 12$, $h = 3$; for $b = 7.2$, $h = 5$; for $b = 6$, $h = 6$ **5.** 330 ft^2 **7.** 245 m^2 **9.** 2.16 cm^2
11. 24.57 in^2 or 24.3 in^2 (depends on how the area is calculated)
13. 9 cm^2 **15.** 24.5 km^2 **17.** 28.03125 mi^2
19. 268,125 cm^2 **21.** 245,000,000,000 cm^2
23. Triangle B has a base of 3 cm and a height of 9 cm. Triangle A has a base of 3 cm, but its height is the leg of a right triangle. The hypotenuse of the right triangle is 9 cm, so both legs must be shorter than 9 cm. When you use equal base lengths, Triangle B has a longer height, so Triangle B has a greater area.   **25.** A

Pages 108–111

1. 539 cm^2 **3.** 275 cm^2 **5.** 147 cm^2 **7.** 420 mm^2 **9.** 5.265 m^2
11. 28 cm^2 **13.** 83 km^2 **15.** A

Pages 112–115

1. 12 cm   **3.** 9 in.   **5.** 3 ft   **7.** 9 cm   **9.** 2.6 cm   **11.** $p = 4$
13. $d = 7$ **15.** $m = 17$ **17.** $r = 19.5$ **19.** $c = 16.6$
21. $437 = 23 \cdot w$; $w = 19$; 19 in.   **23.** $3y = 75$; $y = 25$; 25 yd
25. $570 = 30 \cdot h$; $h = 19$; 19 cm   **27.** $35.28 = 2w^2$; $l = 8.4$; 8.4 ft by 4.2 ft   **29.** A

Pages 116–119

1. 11 in.   **3.** 4 mi   **5.** 8 m   **7.** 12 cm   **9.** 16 mm   **11.** 6   **13.** 9
15. 10   **17.** 4   **19.** 50   **21.** 40 yd   **23.** 80 yd   **25.** 3 ft   **27.** A
29. B

Pages 120–121

1. A   **3.** D   **5.** B   **7.** B   **9.** 0.0016 m^2; 16 cm^2 **11.** 184 in^2
13. 11.75 m^2 **15.** 227.5 mm^2 **17.** 36 ft^2 **19.** $w = 9$ **21.** 12 m

Chapter 4   Working with Rational Numbers

Page 124

1. $\frac{1}{2}$ **3.** $\frac{3}{7}$ **5.** $\frac{3}{4}$

Page 125

1. $\frac{2}{3}$ **3.** $\frac{7}{8}$ **5.** $\frac{1}{2}$ **7.** $\frac{4}{5}$ **9.** $1\frac{2}{5}$ **11.** 1

Page 126

1. three tenths; $0 + 0.3$ **3.** two and sixteen hundredths; $2 + 0.1 + 0.06$ **5.** 0.14; $0.1 + 0.04$ **7.** 1.2; $1 + 0.2$
9. 47.39; forty-seven and thirty-nine hundredths   **11.** 103.08; one hundred three and eight hundredths

Pages 128–131

1. 20   **3.** 9   **5.** 6   **7.** 30   **9.** 70   **11.** Sample answer: $\frac{3}{4} = \frac{6}{8} = \frac{9}{12}$
13. Sample answer: $\frac{4}{5} = \frac{8}{10} = \frac{12}{15}$ **15.** Sample answer: $\frac{6}{5} = \frac{12}{10} = \frac{18}{15}$ **17.** Sample answer: $\frac{3}{7} = \frac{6}{14} = \frac{9}{21}$
19. Sample answer: $\frac{5}{1} = \frac{10}{2} = \frac{15}{3}$ **21.** 15   **23.** 18

25. 24 **27.** 25 **29.** 10 **31.** $\frac{4}{15} < \frac{2}{6}$ **33.** $\frac{5}{7} < \frac{11}{14}$ **35.** $\frac{9}{24} = \frac{3}{8}$
37. $\frac{6}{8} < \frac{7}{9}$ **39.** $\frac{5}{8} > \frac{12}{20}$ **41.** C **43.** B

Pages 132–135

1. $4\frac{2}{3}$; $\frac{14}{3}$ **3.** $1\frac{3}{4}$; $\frac{7}{4}$ **5.** $\frac{38}{9}$ **7.** $\frac{21}{4}$ **9.** $\frac{33}{16}$ **11.** $\frac{31}{8}$ **13.** $\frac{9}{5}$
15. $\frac{103}{20}$ **17.** $\frac{27}{10}$ **19.** $3\frac{3}{5}$ **21.** $5\frac{2}{6}$, or $5\frac{1}{3}$ **23.** $2\frac{1}{10}$ **25.** $3\frac{1}{4}$
27. $3\frac{2}{5}$ **29.** $1\frac{3}{6}$, or $1\frac{1}{2}$ **31.** $5\frac{3}{4}$ **33.** C **35.** B

Pages 136–139

1. 0.375 **3.** 0.16 **5.** 0.35 **7.** 1.06 **9.** $0.8\overline{3}$ **11.** $0.\overline{88}$
13. $0.5\overline{3}$ **15.** 11.1875 **17.** $7\frac{4}{10}$ **19.** $2\frac{7}{10}$ **21.** $\frac{1}{100}$
23. $\frac{35}{100}$, or $\frac{7}{20}$ **25.** $\frac{4}{100}$, or $\frac{1}{25}$ **27.** $5\frac{905}{1000}$, or $5\frac{181}{200}$
29. $\frac{3}{10} > 0.25$ **31.** $\frac{4}{12} > 0.32$ **33.** $3\frac{3}{8} < 3.45$ **35.** $0.36 > \frac{3}{16}$
37. $\frac{27}{24} < 1.3 < 1\frac{2}{5}$ **39.** $2\frac{1}{2} < 3.5 < 3.7$ **41.** B **43.** B

Pages 140–143

1. $1\frac{1}{8}$ **3.** $4\frac{7}{8}$ **5.** $16\frac{1}{3}$ **7.** $22\frac{7}{15}$ **9.** 79 **11.** $P = 37\frac{1}{2}$
13. $P = 82\frac{1}{4}$ yd **15.** $P = 261\frac{1}{2}$ ft **17.** $y = 30$ mi
19. $x = 13\frac{5}{8}$ **21.** D

Pages 144–147

1. $4\frac{3}{12}$, or $4\frac{1}{4}$ **3.** $2\frac{3}{16}$ **5.** $6\frac{25}{32}$ **7.** $\frac{3}{12}$, or $\frac{1}{4}$ **9.** $1\frac{1}{10}$ **11.** $\frac{73}{48}$, or $1\frac{25}{48}$ **13.** $\frac{16}{17}$ **15.** $\frac{16}{9}$, or $1\frac{7}{9}$ **17.** $\frac{23}{14}$, or $1\frac{9}{14}$ **19.** The area is $10\frac{1}{8}$ square feet. *A* represents the area of the rectangle, $10\frac{1}{8}$ square feet; *l* represents its length, $4\frac{1}{2}$ ft; and *w* represents its width, $2\frac{1}{4}$ ft **21.** The area is $30\frac{5}{9}$ square yards. *A* represents the area of the rectangle, $30\frac{5}{9}$ square yards; *l* represents its length, $8\frac{1}{3}$ yd; and *w* represents its width, $3\frac{2}{3}$ yd **23.** The area is $\frac{3}{128}$ square mile. *A* represents the area of the triangle, $\frac{3}{128}$ square mile; *b* represents its base, $\frac{1}{8}$ mi; and *h* represents its height, $\frac{3}{8}$ mi **25.** The area is $39\frac{3}{8}$ square feet. *A* represents the area of the parallelogram, $39\frac{3}{8}$ square feet; *b* represents its base, $10\frac{1}{2}$ ft; and *h* represents its height, $3\frac{3}{4}$ ft **27.** C

Pages 148–151

1. $\frac{3}{2}$ **3.** $\frac{3}{8}$ **5.** $\frac{11}{12}$ **7.** $\frac{4}{3}$ **9.** $\frac{2}{1}$ **11.** $\frac{1}{6}$ **13.** $\frac{4}{11}$ **15.** $2\frac{1}{4}$ **17.** 2
19. 16 **21.** $\frac{1}{6}$ **23.** $8\frac{8}{9}$ **25.** $3\frac{1}{4}$ **27.** $\frac{3}{5}$ **29.** $\frac{15}{53}$
31. The diagram shows a rectangle with an area of 9 in² and a width of $2\frac{1}{4}$ in. The division sentence shows that the length of the rectangle is 4 in. **33.** The diagram shows a rectangle with an area of $71\frac{7}{8}$ in² and a length of $12\frac{1}{2}$ in. The division

sentence shows that the width of the rectangle is $5\frac{3}{4}$ in.
35. The ribbon that is $18\frac{1}{3}$ ft long is being cut into smaller pieces that are 3 ft long. The division sentence shows that a ribbon $18\frac{1}{3}$ ft long can be cut into 6 equal, 3 ft pieces, and there will be $\frac{1}{3}$ ft left over. **37.** B

Pages 152–155

1. $x = 12$ **3.** $z = 9$ **5.** $b = 18$ **7.** $p = 64$ **9.** $r = 34$
11. $y = 36$ **13.** $b = 22\frac{1}{2}$ **15.** $p = 13\frac{1}{2}$ **17.** $r = 22\frac{4}{5}$
19. $g = 47\frac{1}{4}$ **21.** $x = 2\frac{22}{35}$ **23.** 54 baseball cards **25.** 22 pizzas
27. 29 min **29.** $225\frac{7}{8}$ lbs **31.** $248\frac{9}{10}$ min **33.** C

Pages 156–157

1. B **3.** A **5.** A **7.** B **9.** C **11.** C **13.** 12 **15.** $\frac{29}{7}$ **17.** $2\frac{1}{8}$
19. $\frac{5}{6} > 0.83$ **21.** 8 **23.** The missing side length is $10\frac{1}{2}$ yd.
25. $\frac{19}{18}$, or $1\frac{1}{18}$ **27.** $9\frac{1}{2}$ **29.** The painter can complete 32 whole doors and 1 half of another door.

Chapter 5   Solids

Page 160

1. 64 **3.** 729 **5.** 1728 **7.** 0.125 **9.** 1,000,000,000

Page 161

1. 8 cubic units **3.** 125 cubic units **5.** 512 cubic units
7. 1000 cubic units **9.** 1,000,000 cubic units

Page 162

1. 250 unit cubes **3.** 1944 cubic units **5.** 108 cubic units

Pages 164–167

1. 0.2 **3.** 4 **5.** 7 **7.** 8 **9.** 0.3 **11.** estimate, 0.71
13. estimate, 2.92 **15.** 8 cm **17.** 4 in. **19.** 10 m **21.** 0.5 cm
23. about 0.41 km **25.** 2,000,000 cm³ **27.** 8640 in³
29. 162 yd³ **31.** 2.5 cm³ **33.** 168.75 yd³ **35.** 1019.25 ft³
37. about 1.69 yd³ **39.** D

Pages 168–171

1. 36 cm³ **3.** 120 in³ **5.** 144 m³ **7.** 648 m³ **9.** 1029.6 m³
11. 648 in³ **13.** 63 cm³ **15.** 0.0072 m³ **17.** Ricardo can use the box. **19.** D

Pages 172–175

1. The net matches Figure 1. **3.** The net can be folded into Figure 3. **5.** The net can be folded into Figure 5. **7.** 100 mm²
9. 4 m² **11.** A cube with faces that each have an area of 5 in² has a greater surface area. **13.** The problem is about the amount needed to cover a surface. The situation involves surface area. **15.** The problem is about the amount of wrapping paper needed to cover all the sides of the box holding the present. The situation involves surface area.

17. The problem is about how much planting soil is needed to fill a garden. The situation involves volume.   **19.** A

Pages 176–179
1. 3920 cm²   **3.** 1350 in²   **5.** 336 ft²   **7.** 87,600 m²
9. 1,623,102 ft²   **11.** 105 cm²   **13.** 1600 yd²
15. 112.32 cm²   **17.** C

Pages 180–183
1. The surface area does not change. The number representing the surface area would decrease.   **3.** The surface area does not change. The number representing the surface area would increase.   **5.** 972 in²   **7.** 7500 yd²   **9.** 12 ft³
11. 17,664 m²   **13.** Prism 1: 3 m by 2 m by 4 m; Prism 2: 2 m by 1 m by 12 m   **15.** Possible answer: Rectangular prisms with dimensions of 2 mm by 4 mm by 4 mm and 8 mm by 4 mm by 1 mm have the same volume of 32 mm³, but different surface areas.   **17.** Possible answer: Rectangular prisms with dimensions of 2 ft by 4 ft by 10 ft and 4 ft by 5 ft by 4 ft have the same volume of 80 ft³, but different surface areas.   **19.** Possible answer: Rectangular prisms with dimensions of 2 m by 2 m by 10 m and 2 m by 4 m by 5 m have the same volume of 40 m³, but different surface areas.   **21.** Possible answer: Rectangular prisms with dimensions of 2 cm by 3 cm by 9 cm and 3 cm by 3 cm by 6 cm have the same volume of 54 cm³, but different surface areas.   **23.** Possible answer: Rectangular prisms with dimensions of 2 m by 9 m by 9 m and 3 m by 6 m by 9 m have the same volume of 162 m³, but different surface areas.   **25.** Possible answer: Rectangular prisms with dimensions of 3 cm by 5 cm by 15 cm and 5 cm by 5 cm by 9 cm have the same volume of 225 cm³, but different surface areas.   **27.** Possible answer: Rectangular prisms with dimensions of 2 cm by 4 cm by 67 cm and 67 cm by 8 cm by 1 cm have the same volume of 536 cm³, but different surface areas.   **29.** D

Pages 184–185
1. B   **3.** A   **5.** B   **7.** D   **9.** 4 m   **11.** 0.001 m³   **13.** 64 cm³
15. 6144 cm³
17. 520 m²

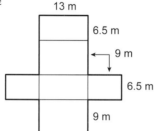

19. 768 cm³   **21.** Possible answer: Rectangular prisms with dimensions of 2 m by 3 m by 8 m and 3 m by 4 m by 4 m have the same volume of 48 m³, but different surface areas.
23. Possible answer: Rectangular prisms with dimensions of 2 cm by 6 cm by 10 cm and 4 cm by 5 cm by 6 cm have the same volume of 120 cm³, but different surface areas.

Chapter 6   Comparisons: Ratios

Page 188
1. $\frac{3}{2}$ **3.** $\frac{19}{8}$ **5.** $\frac{20}{3}$ **7.** $\frac{39}{8}$ **9.** $\frac{13}{4}$

Page 189
1. $5\frac{3}{10}$ **3.** $7\frac{2}{5}$ **5.** $2\frac{1}{50}$ **7.** $9\frac{1}{10}$ **9.** $18\frac{13}{20}$ **11.** $165\frac{29}{50}$

Page 190
1. $\frac{4}{2}$ or 2   **3.** $\frac{4}{10}$ or 0.4   **5.** $\frac{3}{2}$ or 1.5   **7.** $\frac{3}{7}$ or about 0.43
9. $\frac{6}{4}$ or 1.5   **11.** $\frac{4}{10}$ or 0.4

Pages 192–195
1. 4 to 3 or 4 : 3 or $\frac{4}{3}$ **3.** $\frac{4}{7}$, 4 to 7, or 4 : 7   **5.** $\frac{3}{5}$, 3 to 5, or 3 : 5
7. $\frac{2}{1}$, 2 to 1, or 2 : 1   **9.** $\frac{1}{2}$, 1 to 2, or 1 : 2   **11.** $\frac{2}{1}$, 2 to 1, or 2 : 1
13. 28 days   **15.** $\frac{5}{4}$ or 5 to 4   **17.** $\frac{9}{5}$ or 9 to 5   **19.** $\frac{6}{1}$ or 6 to 1
21. $\frac{1}{4}$ or 1 to 4   **23.** 48 min   **25.** 315 mi   **27.** 6 c   **29.** 10 c
31. C   **33.** A

Pages 196–199
1. 3%   **3.** 5%   **5.** 78%   **7.** 8.5%   **9.** 345%   **11.** 300%
13. 0.8   **15.** 0.23   **17.** 0.125   **19.** 1.73   **21.** 14.93
23. 80%   **25.** 75%   **27.** 62%   **29.** 175%   **31.** about 258%
33. $\frac{7}{10}$ **35.** $\frac{1}{10}$ **37.** $\frac{1}{20}$ **39.** $\frac{9}{20}$ **41.** $2\frac{9}{20}$ **43.** $\frac{9}{20}$ or 45%
45. $\frac{6}{13}$ or about 46%   **47.** A

Pages 200–203
1. 270   **3.** 216   **5.** 15   **7.** 940   **9.** 443.7   **11.** 1.84   **13.** 0.345
15. 65   **17.** 1500   **19.** 120   **21.** 4000   **23.** 88   **25.** 126 people
27. 4750 people   **29.** 700 movies   **31.** 45   **33.** 35% of 180
35. C   **37.** C

Pages 204–207
1. $61   **3.** $144   **5.** $6   **7.** $34.90   **9.** $86.36   **11.** $168
13. $544   **15.** $18   **17.** $342   **19.** $1829.64   **21.** 16%
23. about 25.9%   **25.** about 10.5%   **27.** about 50.4%
29. about 22.7%   **31.** The jacket costs $9.50 less at Store A.
33. A   **35.** C

Pages 208–211
1. $3.20   **3.** $3.30   **5.** $2.56   **7.** about $13.38   **9.** $63
11. $202.40   **13.** $2693.45   **15.** $454.52   **17.** $12; $16
19. $2.70; $3.60   **21.** $20.10; $26.80   **23.** $3.93; $5.23
25. $13.80   **27.** $8.05   **29.** $16.20   **31.** B   **33.** A

Pages 212–215
1. $200   **3.** $1248   **5.** $472.50   **7.** $14,300
9. about $10,305.44   **11.** about $3931.88   **13.** $968
15. $725   **17.** $5880   **19.** $40,131.60   **21.** $1293.60
23. 22.5%   **25.** 19%   **27.** 9%   **29.** 50%   **31.** A   **33.** C

Pages 216–219

1. The ratios form a proportion.
3. The ratios form a proportion.
5. The ratios do not form a proportion.
7. The ratios form a proportion.
9. The ratios form a proportion.
11. The ratios do not form a proportion.
13. The ratios do not form a proportion.
15. The ratios do not form a proportion.
17. The ratios do not form a proportion.
19. The ratios form a proportion.
21. The ratios do not form a proportion.
23. The ratios do not form a proportion.
25. The ratios do not form a proportion.
27. The ratios form a proportion.
29. The ratios do not form a proportion.
31. The ratios form a proportion.
33. The ratios form a proportion.
35. The ratios form a proportion.
37. The ratios do not form a proportion.
39. The ratios do not form a proportion.
41. C

Pages 220–223

1. Yes   **3.** The ratios do not form a proportion.   **5.** The ratios form a proportion.   **7.** The ratios do not form a proportion.
9. The ratios form a proportion.
11. The ratios do not form a proportion.
13. The ratios do not form a proportion.
15. The ratios form a proportion.
17. The ratios form a proportion.
19. The ratios do not form a proportion.
21. The ratios form a proportion.
23. $y = 10$ **25.** $z = 1$ **27.** $b = 21$ **29.** $p = 8$ **31.** $r = 48$
33. $y = 24$ **35.** 36 people   **37.** 12 boxes   **39.** 192 gal of orange juice   **41.** D   **43.** C

Pages 224–227

1. 2   **3.** $\frac{1}{4}$ **5.** They are similar figures.   **7.** 42 cm   **9.** 15 mm
11. 4   **13.** 35 in.   **15.** 13.25 cm   **17.** D

Pages 228–229

1. B   **3.** D   **5.** C   **7.** D   **9.** A   **11.** $\frac{2}{3}$, 2 to 3, or 2 : 3
13. 70%   **15.** 7.2   **17.** $65.60   **19.** $62.40   **21.** $575
23. The ratios do not form a proportion.   **25.** $p = 36$

Chapter 7   Angles and Circles

Page 232

1. Sample answer: $\angle BAD$ **3.** Sample answer: ray EA
5. Sample answer: $\angle 2$ **7.** Sample answer: ray BE
9. Sample answer: $\angle CAB$

Page 233

1. $m\angle HGJ = 45°$ **3.** $m\angle QKP = 160°$

Page 234

1. acute   **3.** right   **5.** obtuse

Pages 236–239

1. An adjacent angle is $\angle HLI$.   **3.** Sample answer: $\angle HLI$
5. complementary   **7.** supplementary   **9.** a vertical pair
11. adjacent   **13.** a vertical pair   **15.** neither   **17.** neither
19. complementary   **21.** 30°   **23.** 123°   **25.** B

Pages 240–243

1. 156°   **3.** 90°   **5. A.** 40°   **B.** 35°   **7. A.** 52°   **B.** 38°
9. 120°   **11.** 120°   **13. A.** 88°   **B.** 74°   **15.** 10°, 100°, 125°, and 125°   **17.** A

Pages 244–247

1. regular   **3.** The polygon is not regular because the sides and angles are not congruent.   **5.** The polygon is not regular because the sides and angles are not congruent.   **7.** 24 cm
9. 16.8 km   **11.** 12 cm   **13.** 72 cm   **15.** 2904 mm   **17.** $7\frac{1}{3}$ yd
19. 6 cm   **21.** 6 ft   **23.** 3.5 km   **25.** D

Pages 248–251

1. The chords are $\overline{PQ}$ and $\overline{RT}$; the radii are $\overline{OR}$, $\overline{OS}$, and $\overline{OT}$; and the diameter is $\overline{RT}$.   **3.** The chords are $\overline{GJ}$, $\overline{HI}$, $\overline{IL}$, and $\overline{JK}$; the radii are $\overline{OG}$, $\overline{OI}$, $\overline{OJ}$, and $\overline{OL}$; and the diameters are $\overline{GJ}$ and $\overline{IL}$.   **5.** 4 in.   **7.** 20 in.   **9.** 24 yd   **11.** 14 ft
13. 9.9 km   **15.** 20.85 m   **17.** 10 m   **19.** 6 ft   **21.** 5.4 m   **23.** A

Pages 252–255

1. 14π cm   **3.** exactly 4π km   **5.** exactly 18π m   **7.** exactly 7π ft   **9.** exactly 63.28π m   **11.** about 25.1 in.   **13.** about 25.1 mm   **15.** about 18.8 km   **17.** about 39.2 cm   **19.** about 42.7 cm   **21.** 8 m; 4 m   **23.** 36 cm; 18 cm   **25.** about 11.1 yd; about 5.55 yd   **27.** about 6 km; about 3 km   **29.** 9π m
31. 32π in.   **33.** about 30π m   **35.** B

Pages 256–259

1. exactly 64π m²   **3.** exactly 9π km²   **5.** exactly 25π m²
7. exactly 20.25π ft²   **9.** exactly 135.4896π m²   **11.** approximately 50.2 in²   **13.** about 113 mm²   **15.** about 452 km²
17. about 359 cm²   **19.** about 191 cm²   **21.** exactly 18π m²
23. exactly 1π cm²   **25.** exactly 18π yd²   **27.** exactly 0.16π km²
29. exactly 256π ft²   **31.** exactly 30.25π m²   **33.** exactly 128π m²
35. D

Pages 260–263

1. exactly 99π cm³; approximately 311 cm³   **3.** exactly 63π cm³; approximately 198 cm³   **5.** exactly 1339.56π mm³; approximately 4210 mm³   **7.** exactly 43.03125π in³; approximately 135 in³   **9.** exactly 117π cm³; approximately 368 cm³
11. exactly $54,432\pi$ ft³; approximately 171,000 ft³   **13.** exactly 5220π cm³; approximately 16,400 cm³   **15.** exactly 49π in³; approximately 154 in³   **17.** Because the volumes and the bases are the same, the heights of the figures must also be the same.   **19.** approximately 10.6 m   **21.** approximately 7.18 cm
23. exactly 72.25π cm³   **25.** exactly 121.5π in³
27. exactly 156.4289965π m³   **29.** C

1. A   3. B   5. A   7. C   9. A   11. a vertical pair and supplementary   13. supplementary   15. 90°   17. 30 ft
19. 3.5 m long   21. Sample answer: $\overline{AD}$ 23. about 22.0 mm
25. about 28.3 m²   27. exactly 405π cm³; approximately 1270 cm³

Chapter 8   Probability

Page 268

1. certain   3. likely   5. certain   7. impossible

Page 269

1. one out of two, $\frac{1}{2}$, 0.5 or 50%   3. 3 out of 6 $= \frac{3}{6}$, or $\frac{1}{2} =$
0.5 $= 50\%$ 5. one out of three, $\frac{1}{3}$, about 0.33, or 33%
7. 1 out of 6 $= \frac{1}{6} \approx 0.17 = 17\%$

Page 270

1. Two of the 6 sections of the spinner are white.
3. There are no purple marbles in the bag.   5. There are no black marbles in the bag.   7. Five of the marbles in the bag are green, blue, or white.

Pages 272–275

1. 8 students   3. 3 students   5. 5 more students
7. 7 campers   9. 11 campers   11. 7 recipes
13. 1 more recipe   15. 23 recipes   17. 3   19. 4   21. 3
23. 13 families   25. 6 different combinations   27. C

Pages 276–279

1. $\frac{3}{6}$ or $\frac{1}{2}$ 3. $\frac{1}{2}$ 5. $\frac{1}{3}$ 7. 0   9. $\frac{1}{4}$ 11. $\frac{3}{4}$ 13. $\frac{1}{2}$ 15. $\frac{3}{4}$
17. $\frac{6}{25}$ 19. $\frac{1}{25}$ 21. 1   23. 10 times   25. 18 times
27. Answers will vary. Tables must show 20 pieces of data representing pennies and nickels.   29. Answers will vary. Tables must show 24 pieces of data representing 1, 2, 3, 4, 5, or 6.   31. Answers will vary. Tables must show 30 pieces of data representing pennies, dimes, and quarters.   33. A   35. B

Pages 280–283

1. $\frac{3}{5}$ 3. $\frac{3}{7}$ 5. 250 books   7. 38 machine parts   9. $\frac{1}{10}$
11. $\frac{51}{100}$, or about $\frac{1}{2}$ 13. $\frac{14}{25}$ 15. about 4 M tiles, 3 A tiles, and 3 H tiles   17. about 9 nickels   19. about 3 quarters   21. B

Pages 284–287

1. 7 times   3. 12 times   5. 16 times   7. 18 times   9. 60 times
11. 328 times   13. 16 times   15. B

Pages 288–291

1. 88%; the probability is experimental   3. The theoretical probability is 0.1%.   5. The theoretical probability is 80%.   7. The experimental probability is 65%.   9. The theoretical probability is 20%.   11. The experimental probability will get closer to 25%.   13. The experimental probability

will remain at or close to 25%.   15. about 250 times that an orange marble will be drawn   17. A

Pages 292–295

1. dependent   3. dependent   5. independent   7. independent
9. independent   11. $\frac{1}{48}$ 13. $\frac{1}{24}$ 15. $\frac{7}{75}$ 17. $\frac{1}{3}$ 19. C

Pages 296–299

1. tails   3. an even number   5. $\frac{4}{6}$ 7. $\frac{1}{3}$ 9. $\frac{1}{3}$ 11. $\frac{2}{3}$ 13. $\frac{5}{6}$
15. There is no complementary event, because the event "a multiple of 5" represents a probability of 1 since all the numbers on the spinner are multiples of 5.   17. $\frac{1}{3}$ 19. $\frac{1}{6}$
21. $\frac{5}{12}$ 23. $\frac{3}{4}$; No   25. 80%; not complementary   27. 100%; complementary   29. 1; complementary   31. 75%; not complementary   33. A   35. A

Pages 300–301

1. C   3. D   5. B   7. D   9. 17 children   11. 26 children
13. 1   15. 24 times   17. independent   19. $\frac{3}{16}$ 21. The probability of a 5 is $\frac{1}{6}$, the complement of the event is rolling a 1, 2, 3, 4, or 6; the probability of the complement is $\frac{5}{6}$, and the sum of the probabilities is 1.   23. The probability of a number less than 7 is 1, and there is no complementary event.

Chapter 9   Statistics

Page 304

1. The minimum is 1, the maximum is 9, the range is 8, the mean is about 4.9, and the median is 5.   3. The minimum is 37, the maximum is 208, the range is 171, the mean is 100.5, and the median is 92.5.

Page 305

1. 8   3. 17   5. 119

Page 306

1. mode   3. median   5. mode

Pages 308–311

1. $\frac{7}{24}$ 3. $\frac{9}{20}$ 5. 15 people   7. $\frac{1}{4}$ 9. 12.5%   11. $\frac{1}{3}$
13. 5 people
15.

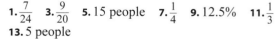

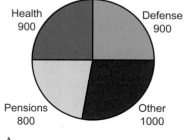

**U.S. Federal Spending
(billions of dollars)**

Health 900   Defense 900   Pensions 800   Other 1000

17. A

Pages 312–315

1. 0.2 m **3.** Weeks 3 and 4 **5.** Ohio, Illinois, Michigan, Indiana **7.** $\frac{18}{29}$ **9.** 3 people **11.** line plot **13.** line graph **15.** bar or circle graph **17.** line graph **19.** bar graph or line plot **21.** line plot **23.** C

Pages 316–319

1.

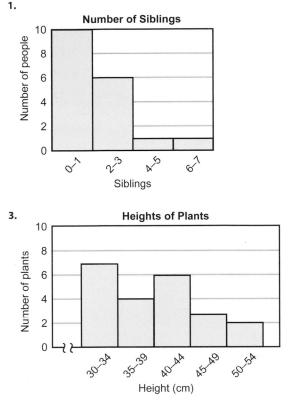

5. 21 watermelons **7.** 24 cantaloupes **9.** 16 cantaloupes **11.** 20 games **13.** 15 games **15.** 32 adults **17.** C

Pages 320–323

1. mean = 58; median = 59; mode = 59 **3.** mean = 82.375; median = 85; mode: none **5.** mean ≈ 558; median = 542; mode = 535 **7.** The mean decreased by about 5, and the median did not change. **9.** mean **11.** median **13.** median **15.** B

Pages 324–327

1. maximum = 30; minimum = 12; median = 22 **3.** first quarter: 2; second quarter: 8; third quarter: 5; fourth quarter: 3 **5.** fourth quarter **7.** maximum = 63; minimum = 49; median = 54 **9.** first quarter: 2; second quarter: 3; third quarter: 1; fourth quarter: 8 **11.** lower quartile = 28; upper quartile = 38 **13.** maximum = 22; minimum = 3; median = 12 **15.** second, third, and fourth quarters

17.

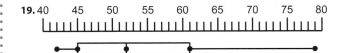

19.

21. B

Pages 328–331

1. 14 **3.** 20 **5.** 8 **7.** 4 **9.** about 7.2 **11.** 11.25 **13.** The IQR shows that the spread of the middle 50% of the data is 15. If this problem were about miles driven, the MAD shows that the average number of miles away from the overall average is about 6.85. **15.** C

Pages 332–335

1. upper extreme **3.** lower extreme **5.** both extremes **7.** outlier 31: mean increased by 4, median unchanged; outlier 0: mean decreased by about 1.2, median decreased by 0.5 **9.** outlier 0: mean decreased by 2.95, median decreased by 0.35; outlier 26.5: mean increased by 1.5, median increased by 0.15 **11.** skewed left **13.** skewed right **15.** The mean decreases by $33,850. **17.** D

Pages 336–339

1. is not representative **3.** not representative **5.** representative **7.** not representative **9.** not representative **11.** The survey is likely to find that people exercise more than they actually do. **13.** The survey is likely to find that households have more members than is actually true for the general population. **15.** The survey is likely to find a current basketball player. **17.** The survey is likely to find that people enjoy more movies only for adults than they actually do. **19.** Not representative; samples are more likely to prefer the swings or the slide. **21.** representative **23.** Not representative; the sample is likely to show that people are more happy with the amount of plowing than they really are, because the roads in the center of town will likely be better plowed than those in other parts of the city. **25.** C

Pages 340–343

1. simple random sample **3.** systematic sample **5.** convenience sample **7.** stratified random sample **9.** convenience sample **11.** systematic sample **13.** systematic sample **15.** stratified random sample **17.** convenience sample **19.** stratified random sample **21.** convenience sample **23.** systematic sample **25.** C

Pages 344–347

1. The data for years 1993, 1996, and 1998 are missing. **3.** The scale of the graph does not start at 0, so the difference among scores is smaller than the bars' heights indicate. **5.** The survey might have included more girls than boys, so the results show more interest for sports that are typically enjoyed by more girls than boys. **7.** The question is biased against classical music by calling it "boring," and suggesting that most teenagers dislike listening to it. **9.** Residents in a wealthy part of town might want to discourage low-income housing in their town because of fears that it might negatively affect their property values, so the results are likely to show less support for the housing.

11. The median distance does not show the outlier of 1 mile.

13. The median weight is higher than the mean because it is not as affected by the low weights of 11, 12, 13, and 16.

Pages 348–349

1. C   **3.** D   **5.** C   **7.** C   **9.** B   **11.** 25%   **13.** line graph
15. 17 rock samples   **17.** about 25.2   **19.** 59 is an outlier.

Chapter 10   The Second Dimension

Page 352

1. 41   **3.** 54   **5.** 21.9

Page 353

1, 3.

5, 7.

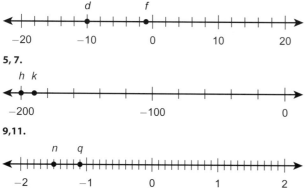

9, 11.

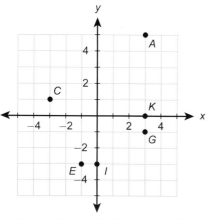

Page 354

1. $3\frac{2}{5}$ **3.** 4   **5.** 3.25   **7.** 4

Pages 356–359

Odd problems 1–11:

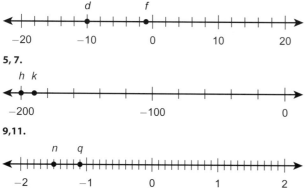

13. $(-4, -1)$ **15.** $(3, 5)$ **17.** $(0, 4)$ **19.** $(2, -5)$
21. Quadrant II   **23.** y-axis   **25.** Quadrant III   **27.** Quadrant I
29. x-axis   **31.** Quadrant IV   **33.** points $K(-2, 2)$ and $M(-2, -2)$; possible answer: $(-2, 0)$

35. Answers will vary. Sample answer: $\overleftrightarrow{AB}$ is a vertical line that can be described by the equation $x = 3$.

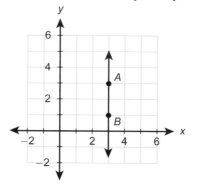

37. Answers will vary. Sample answer: The points form a diagonal line.

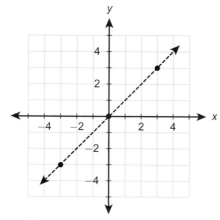

39. D

Pages 360–363

1. 3   **3.** 5   **5.** 4   **7.** 5   **9.** 6   **11.** 5   **13.** $d = |0 - (-3)| = 3$
15. 3   **17.** $(3, 1)$
19. $(1, 1)$

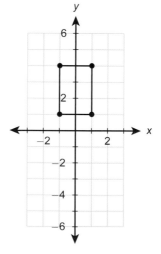

21. $(-2, -2)$

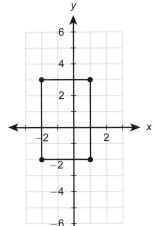

23. $(-3, 1)$

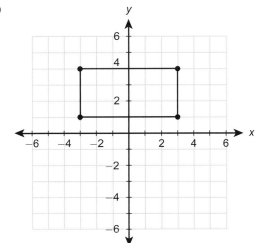

25. $(1, 5)$

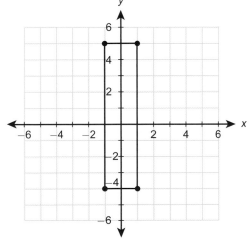

27. $(1, 1)$

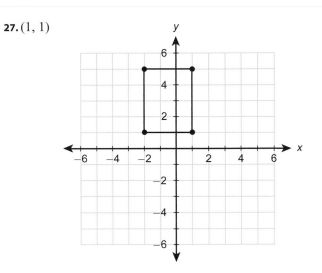

29. C

Pages 364–367

1. The points on the graph show the solutions to the equation $2x + y = -3$ because the x-value and y-value of each make the equation true. **3.** The points are not all solutions to the equation. **5.** The points all are solutions to the equation because each pair of values makes the equation true.

7. $(0, 0)$, $(2, -4)$, and $(5, -10)$ **9.** $(0, -1)$, $(1, 2)$, and $(2, 5)$

11.

x	x + 4	y	(x, y)
0	0 + 4	4	(0, 4)
1	1 + 4	5	(1, 5)
2	2 + 4	6	(2, 6)

13.

x	−3x	y	(x, y)
−2	−3 · (−2)	6	(−2, 6)
0	−3 · 0	0	(0, 0)
2	−3 · 2	−6	(2, −6)

15. Points will vary. Sample points are shown.

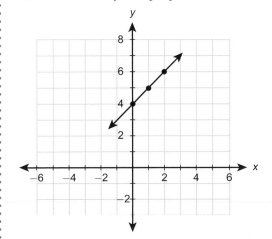

17. Points will vary. Sample points are shown.

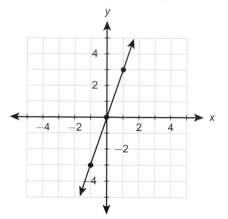

19. Points will vary. Sample points are shown.

x	$\frac{5x}{4}$	y	(x, y)
4	$\frac{5 \cdot 4}{4}$	5	(4, 5)
0	$\frac{5 \cdot 0}{4}$	0	(0, 0)
−4	$\frac{5 \cdot (−4)}{4}$	−5	(−4, −5)

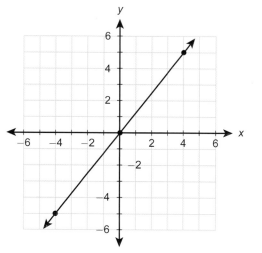

21. C

Pages 368–371

1. The independent variable is time. The dependent variable is distance.

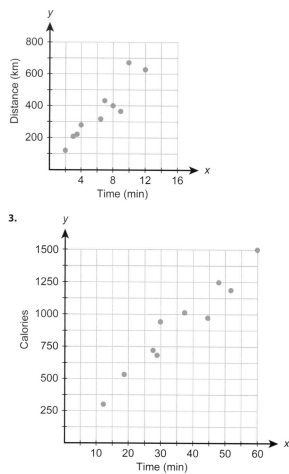

3.

5. The independent variable is number of football games played and the dependent variable is amount earned.
7. The independent variable is time, and the dependent variable is distance.   **9.** The independent variable is the amount of water flowing into the pool, and the dependent variable is water depth.   **11.** The independent variable is the person's age, and the dependent variable is the amount of time on the Internet.   **13.** The independent variable is the number of sunny days, and the dependent variable is the yearly profit.   **15.** B

1. The scatter plot shows no correlation. **3.** The scatter plot shows no correlation. **5.** The more months that pass, the greater the amount of money that will be in the savings account. **7.** Answers will vary. Sample answer: The more time that is spent playing sports, the greater the number of calories that are needed.

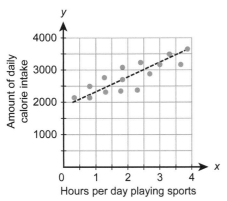

9. Answers will vary. Sample answer: People buy more ice cream as the temperature increases.

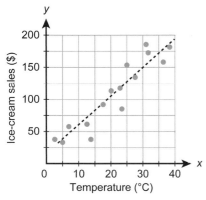

11. Answers will vary. Sample answer: The greater the elevation, the lower the expected temperature.

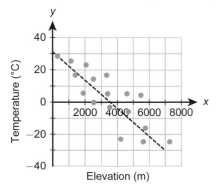

13. B

Pages 376–377

1. B **3.** A **5.** B **7.** (2, 1) **9.** (−1, −1) **11.** (0, 2) **13.** 4 **15.** No. The graph does not represent points with y-coordinates that are 2 times the x-coordinates. **17.** (8, −1), (12, 3), and (14, 5)

19.

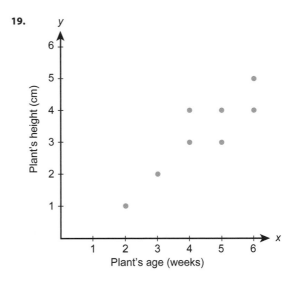

Chapter 11   Rates

Page 380

1. Sample answer: Something travels a distance of 55 miles for each hour of travel time. **3.** Sample answer: Someone can peel or process 9 apples during a 10-minute period. **5.** Sample answer: Each load requires 4 scoops of something. **7.** Sample answer: Each group of 22 players has 3 balls.

Page 381

1. 150 km **3.** 27,900 km

Page 382

1. 64 boxes **3.** 84 doors

Pages 384–387

1. $\frac{30}{5}$ **3.** 190 seconds ÷ 38 sit-ups **5.** 27 minutes ÷ 81 laps **7.** 160 pages ÷ 8 days **9.** $p = \frac{180}{12}$ **11.** $p = \frac{\$24}{12\ lb}$ **13.** $c = \frac{280.5\ cal}{4.25\ h}$ **15.** $2 **17.** 310 mi **19.** 66 players **21.** $4121.60 **23.** D

Pages 388–391

1. $16\frac{2}{3}$ pages/day **3.** 3 pencils/pack **5.** 50 m/h **7.** $8\frac{1}{2}$ mi/min **9.** 2.4 girls/boy **11.** $809.75/couch **13.** $76\frac{2}{3}$ words/min **15.** 54 m/s **17.** $72\frac{2}{3}$ heartbeats/min **19.** $662\frac{8}{11}$ people/km² **21.** $4 **23.** 132 softballs **25.** 147 box jumps **27.** 18 laps **29.** $13\frac{1}{3}$ walls **31.** 135 flowers **33.** $1064 **35.** 15 mi **37.** $75,295 **39.** A

Pages 392–395

1. $11.99/football; 0.084 footballs/dollar **3.** $0.98/kg; about 1.02 kg/dollar **5.** 9.6 calories/min; about 0.104 min/calorie **7.** 2.5 white cars/red car; 0.4 red cars/white car **9.** 18.7 students/teacher; about 0.053 teachers/student **11.** 57.4 points/game; about 0.017 games/point **13.** $7.90/kg; about 0.127 kg/dollar **15.** 86.7 km/h; about 0.012 h/km **17.** Greg **19.** the 10-pack **21.** Brand B

23. Rebecca   **25.** Melinda   **27.** Ingrid   **29.** dollars/night
31. kg/dollar   **33.** A

Pages 396–399

1. 112.5 km   **3.** 32 m   **5.** 40 mi/h   **7.** $t = 19$ h   **9.** $r = 5$ m/s
11. $t = 10$ h   **13.** $r = 6.25$ mi/h   **15.** $t = 15$ s   **17.** $t = 15$ h
19. $d = 0.575$ km   **21.** 8.5 h   **23.** about 5.08 km/h   **25.** about
17 km/h; about 3.5 min/km   **27.** B

Pages 400–403

1. 24 cakes

3	6	15	24	30
1	2	5	8	10

3. 20 h

10	20	50	100	200
1	2	5	10	20

5. 5 buttons/minute; 300 buttons   **7.** $\frac{1}{5}$ h/tree; 30 h
9. 1440 boxes   **11.** 30 trees trimmed/day   **13.** 50 hours
15. 500 s, or 8 min 20 s   **17.** 60 baskets/day   **19.** 1920 tons
21. $13\frac{1}{3}$ days, or 13 days 8 hours   **23.** D

Pages 404–407

1. Table 1   **3.** Table 1   **5.** Table 1

7.

Weeks	Chairs
0	0
1	200
10	2000
52	10,400

9.

Days	Miles
0	0
1	3.5
7	24.5
30	105

11.

x	y
0	0
1	5.2
10	52
20	104

13.

Days	Minutes
0	0
1	25
3	75
4	100

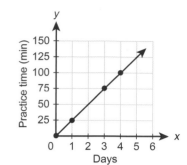

15.

Hours	Miles
0	0
1	75
2	150
5	375

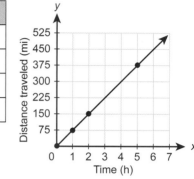

17. A

Pages 408–411

1. Josh's rate, $8/h, is less than Clay's rate, $15/h.   **3.** Fiona's rate, 15 pages/h, is greater than Albert's rate, 5 pages/h.

5.

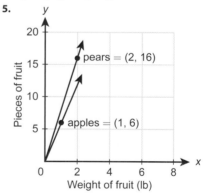

7.

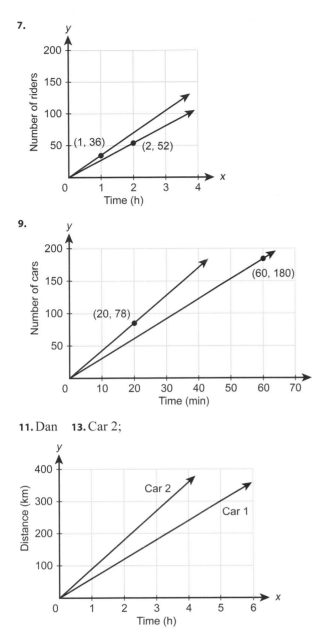

9.

11. Dan **13.** Car 2;

15. D

Pages 412– 413

1. C **3.** C **5.** D **7.** D **9.** $p = 312$ pages $\div$ 13 days
11. \$9/book **13.** 56 min **15.** $r = 16$ km/h **17.** 16 min
19. $y = 14x$ **21.** The line will be steeper than line a but less steep than line b.

23.

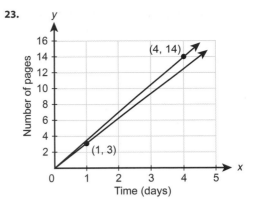

Chapter 12   Working with Positives and Negatives

Page 416

1, 3.

5, 7.

9, 11.

Page 417

1. 7 **3.** $-1\frac{2}{3}$ **5.** -4.01 **7.** $-\frac{1}{12}$ **9.** $4\frac{1}{4}$ **11.** $\frac{2}{5}$ **13.** $-\frac{3}{5}$
15. $-\frac{1}{3}$ **17.** $-\frac{8}{25}$

Page 418

1. 6 **3.** -11 **5.** -20 **7.** -52 **9.** -16 **11.** 0 **13.** -27
15. -152

Pages 420– 423

1. -7.1 **3.** 3.8 **5.** 6.9 **7.** -23.11 **9.** -3.5 **11.** -3.32
13. 1.67 **15.** -10.95 **17.** $-\frac{7}{16}$ **19.** -4.9 **21.** -30.2
23. 32.12 **25.** -28.93 **27.** -3.06 **29.** -26.35 **31.** 12.6
33. 2.75 **35.** 38 **37.** -0.1 **39.** -1.096 **41.** 5 **43.** $-5.7°C$
45. B **47.** D

Pages 424– 427

1. profit of \$8300 **3.** 850 ft loss **5.** about \$1.34 gain
7. $-9 + (-4) + 5 + n = 10$; 18 yd
9. $3.2 + 1.8 + 6.4 - 4.5 - 2.7 + n = 7.5$;
\$3.3 million profit **11.** $873 - 456 - 329 = p$; \$88 profit
13. $-126 + 345 - 280 - 164 = p$; \$225 loss
15. $925.62 - 75.6 - 450 + 750 + 875 - 35.25 = b$;
\$1989.77 **17.** C

Pages 428–431

1. -24 **3.** -45 **5.** 64 **7.** 44 **9.** -84 **11.** 4 **13.** -4
15. $-\frac{1}{3}$ **17.** $\frac{5}{28}$ **19.** -355.074 **21.** 192 **23.** -100 **25.** 84
27. $1\frac{1}{2}$ **29.** 252 **31.** 12 **33.** 42 **35.** -320 **37.** $-75{,}600$
39. negative **41.** 3 **43.** 305 m **45.** A

Pages 432–435

1. -4 **3.** -7 **5.** 6 **7.** 10 **9.** -3.8 **11.** 32 **13.** -100
15. -15.8 **17.** $-\frac{4}{3}$ **19.** -3.2 **21.** -23 **23.** 9 **25.** 2
27. 32 **29.** 49.2 **31.** -73.08 **33.** -450 **35.** $-8°C$
37. -0.28 m **39.** B **41.** B

Pages 436–439

1. -6 **3.** 9 **5.** -3 **7.** 2.7 **9.** 0 **11.** -8 **13.** 1 **15.** -6
17. -7 **19.** 8 **21.** 1 **23.** 7 **25.** 5 **27.** $2; 5$ **29.** $21; 19$
31. -282 **33.** -616 **35.** 980 **37.** -20 **39.** -10 **41.** -20
43. -24 **45.** $-1\frac{1}{2}$ **47.** A **49.** B

Pages 440–443

1. $w > 3\frac{1}{8}$ **3.** $d > 12.25$ km; very high values, such as
$100{,}000$ km **5.** $t < -18.5°C$; values below $-273.15°C$
7. $h > 20.5$ in.; very high values, such as 1000 in.
9.

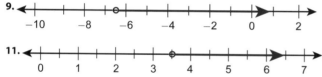

11.

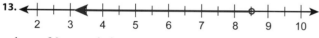

values above 168 h

13.

values of 0 cm or below

15.

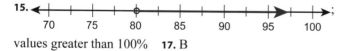

values greater than 100% **17.** B

Pages 444–445

1. A **3.** D **5.** B **7.** A **9.** A **11.** -1 **13.** 17 **15.** -5.3
17. 97 yd **19.** -32 **21.** 11.56 **23.** -6 **25.** 1 **27.** -8.4
29. $\frac{6}{5}$ **31.** 18 **33.** -11.4 **35.** $a > 13$
37.

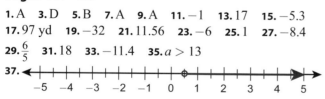

Chapter 13   Making and Moving Figures

Page 448

1. Not regular; sides are not congruent. **3.** Not regular; sides are not congruent.

Page 449

1. parallelogram, rhombus **3.** parallelogram

Page 450

1. $(-2, 4)$ **3.** $(2, -1)$
5, 7.

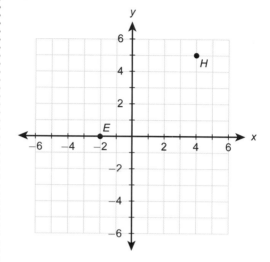

Pages 452–455

1.

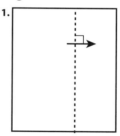

3.

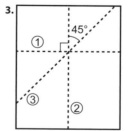

5.

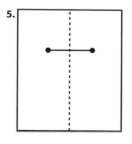

7.

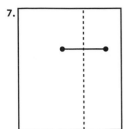

9.

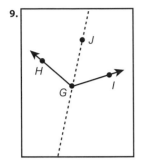

11.

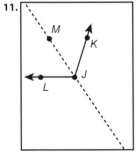

13. They are congruent.   **15.** B

Pages 456–459

1, 3, 5. Note: Circled numbers indicate steps for constructing a bisector.

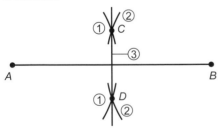

7, 9, 11. Note: Circled numbers indicate steps for constructing an equilateral triangle.

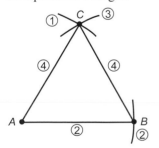

13, 15, 17, 19. Note: Circled numbers indicate steps for constructing a square.

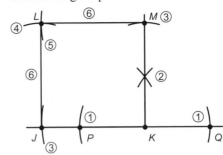

21, 23, 25. Note: Circled numbers indicate steps for constructing a hexagon.

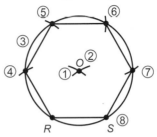

Pages 460–463

1. Figure 2   **3.** right 4, up 2   **5.** left 3, down 4
7. 4 units right and 2 units up

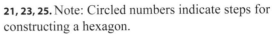

9.

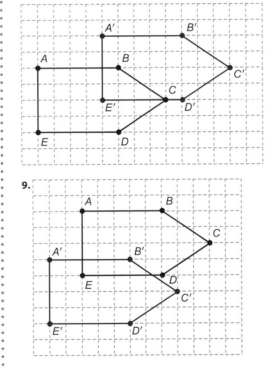

11.

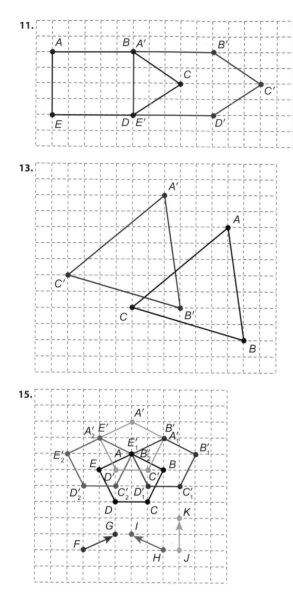

13.

15.

7.

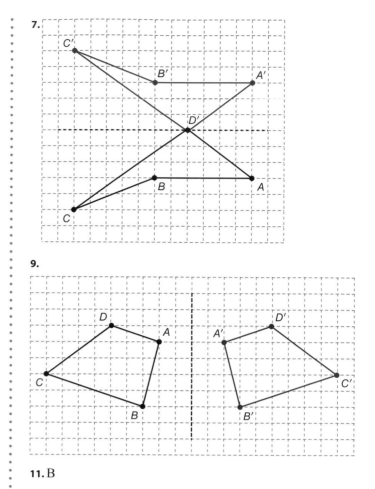

9.

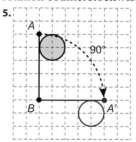

11. B

Pages 468– 471

1. $\frac{1}{2}$ turn, or 180° rotation, about point *C* **3.** $\frac{1}{4}$ turn, or 90° rotation counterclockwise, about point *A*

5.

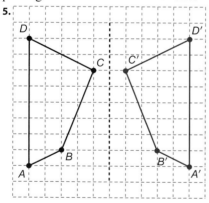

Pages 464– 467

1. horizontal line passing through vertex *A* **3.** vertical line passing 3 units to the left of vertex *A*

5.

7.

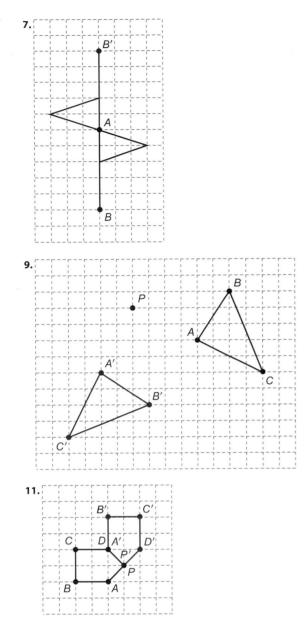

9.

11.

Pages 472–475

1. $(7, 5)$ 3. $(-2, -10)$ 5. $(-10, -1)$ 7. $(-4, 9)$
9. $(-1, -2), (0, -12),$ and $(7, -11)$ 11. Possible answer:
right 4, up 3 13. $D'(1, 6), E'(1, -3), F'(-2, 1)$
15. $L'(6, 6), M'(6, 2), N'(10, 2), O'(10, 6)$ 17. $F'(-5, -5),$
$L'(-2, -2), M'(1, -5), N'(-2, -8)$ 19. $E'(-1, -5),$
$C'(6, -8), J'(5, -10), K'(-2, -7)$ 21. D

Pages 476–479

1. $(4, 5)$ 3. $(0, 5)$ 5. $(0, -5)$ 7. $A'(4, 9), B'(7, 6),$
$C'(4, 0)$ 9. $A'(-4, -9), B'(-7, -6), C'(-4, 0)$
11. $(2, -5), (10, -6), (4, -1)$ 13. $(-2, 5), (-10, 6), (-4, 1)$
15. $(-5, -7), (-4, 3), (3, 2)$ 17. $(4, -9), (-2, -5), (4, 4)$

Pages 480–483

1. $(-7, 3)$ 3. $(-6, -3)$ 5. $(-4, 1)$ 7. $(0, 3)$ 9. $(5, -2)$
11. $(-1, 3)$ 13. $(2, 6)$ 15. $(4, 0)$ 17. $(-8, 2), (0, -8),$ or
$(12, 2)$ 19. $(-3, -7), (-3, 7),$ or $(7, 3)$ 21. $x = -2$
23. $(8, 0)$ and $(2, -6)$ 25. D

Pages 484–485

1. C 3. C 5. D

7.

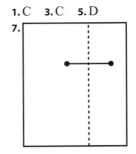

9. Note: Circled numbers indicate steps for constructing
a bisector.

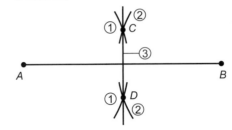

11. Note: Circled numbers indicate steps for constructing
a square.

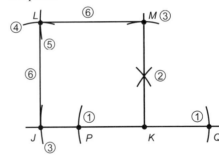

13.

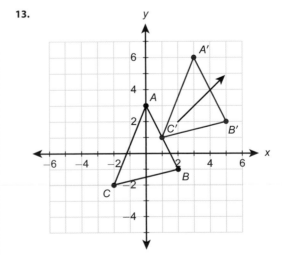

15.

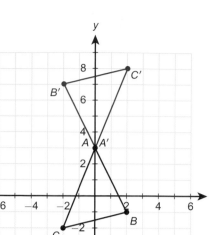

17.

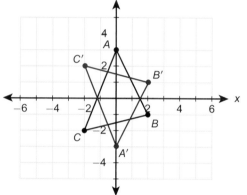

19. $(2, -2)$

Chapter 14   Patterns, Primes, and Puzzles

Page 488

1. Yes   **3.** No   **5.** Yes   **7.** Yes   **9.** No

Page 489

1. second table   **3.** first table

Page 490

1. The terms A and BB are repeated; BB, A   **3.** The dot moves counterclockwise to the next corner;

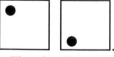

5. The triangle and circle alternate;

Pages 492–495

1. Add 5; 33, 38   **3.** Add 10; 57, 67   **5.** Add 3; 27.4, 30.4   **7.** Add 0.4; 5.2, 5.6   **9.** Add -2; -5, -7

11. Add 2;   **13.** 4, 8, 12, 16, 20

15. 17, 34, 51, 68, 85   **17.** 8, 17, 26, 35, 44
19. $-2.75, -5.75, -8.75, -11.75, -14.75$ **21.** 25
23. 110   **25.** 23   **27.** $245, $320, $395, $470, $545, $620, $695   **29.** 24°C, 23.5°C, 23°C, 22.5°C, 22°C, 21.5°
31. 1, 1, 2, 3, 5, 8, 13, 21, 34, 55   **33.** C

Pages 496–499

1. Multiply by 3; 486; 1458   **3.** Multiply by 10; 400,000; 4,000,000   **5.** Multiply by 3; 4860; 14,580   **7.** Multiply by 0.5; 1.25, 0.625   **9.** Multiply by 10; 50,000; 500,000
11. Multiply by -2; -128, 256   **13.** Multiply by 3;

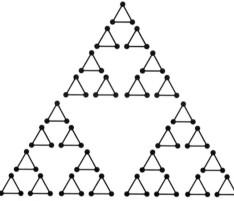

15. 4, 12, 36, 108   **17.** 5, 20, 80, 320   **19.** 10, 60, 360, 2160
21. 25; 200; 1600; 12,800   **23.** 1.8, 5.4, 16.2, 48.6
25. 50, 40, 32, 25.6   **27.** 12, -60, 300, -1500, 7500
29. 25 cm   **31.** 1458 deer   **33.** 1.4375 billion people   **35.** B

Pages 500–503

1. 225   **3.** 625   **5.** 15.625   **7.** 0.16   **9.** $\frac{16}{81}$ **11.** 631   **13.** 261
15. -2525 **17.** 45   **19.** 100   **21.** -11 **23.** 12, 24, 48, 96
25. 50, 250, 1250, 6250   **27.** 300; 3000; 30,000; 300,000
29. 2.5, 10, 40, 160   **31.** 24   **33.** 245   **35.** 6144   **37.** 78,732
39. C

Pages 504–507

1. $324.48; $24.48   **3.** $449.44; $49.44   **5.** $1061.21; $61.21
7. $1452; $252   **9.** $10,927.27; $927.27   **11.** $14,887.70; $2387.70   **13.** $79,874.45; $9,274.45   **15.** $587.73
17. $1264.28   **19.** $5852.86   **21.** $41,121.60
23. $30,797.07   **25.** $97.50   **27.** $96.25   **29.** $223.75
31. $489.88   **33.** $55,807.04   **35.** 7% for 10 years   **37.** C

Pages 508–511

1. composite   **3.** composite   **5.** prime   **7.** composite
9. composite   **11.** prime   **13.** composite   **15.** composite
17. All given values support the conjecture.   **19.** The values 9 and 15 support the conjecture; the value 5 shows the conjecture is not true.   **21.** The value 5 supports the conjecture, but the values 7 and 9 show the conjecture is not true.

23. The value pairs 12 & 14 and 30 & 32 support the conjecture, but the value pair 14 & 16 shows the conjecture is not true.   **25.** 37   **27.** Sample supporting example: $4 + 5 = 9$; Sample counterexample: $2 + 3 = 5$ **29.** Sample supporting example: $2 + 4 = 6$; Sample counterexample: $2 + 3 = 5$
31. 3-meter square: $A = 3 \text{ m} \cdot 3 \text{ m} = 9 \text{ m}^2$; 6-meter square: $A = 6 \text{ m} \cdot 6 \text{ m} = 36 \text{ m}^2$ **33.** $1^3 + 2^3 = 9$, $(1 + 2)^2 = 9$; $5^3 + 6^3 = 341$, $(5 + 6)^2 = 121$ **35.** A

Pages 512–515

1. $5 \cdot 2 \cdot 2$ **3.** $2 \cdot 2 \cdot 2 \cdot 2$ **5.** $2 \cdot 3 \cdot 5$ **7.** 7   **9.** 30   **11.** 6
13. 208   **15.** 8   **17.** 48
19. 4 m by 2 m by 2 m, 1 m by 8 m by 2 m, 1 m by 4 m by 4 m, and 1 m by 1 m by 16 m
21. 4 cm by 2 cm by 3 cm, 2 cm by 2 cm by 6 cm, and 2 cm by 12 cm by 1 cm
23. 10 in. by 2 in. by 2 in., 5 in. by 4 in. by 2 in., and 5 in. by 8 in. by 1 in.
25. 2 ft by 3 ft by 7 ft, 6 ft by 7 ft by 1 ft, and 1 ft by 2 ft by 21 ft
27. 3 m by 5 m by 2 m, 15 m by 2 m by 1 m, and 3 m by 1 m by 10 m
29. 2 km by 2 km by 11 km, 1 km by 4 km by 11 km, and 1 km by 1 km by 44 km
31. 7 m by 9 m by 2 m, 21 m by 3 m by 2 m, and 7 m by 3 m by 6 m
33. 5 in. by 2 in. by 6 in., 5 in. by 4 in. by 3 in., and 10 in. by 2 in. by 3 in.
35. 9 yd by 4 yd by 2 yd, 3 yd by 6 yd by 4 yd, and 18 yd by 2 yd by 2 yd
37. 14 cm by 4 cm by 2 cm, 28 cm by 2 cm by 2 cm, and 28 cm by 4 cm by 1 cm   **39.** C

Pages 516–519

1. $(44 - 4) \div 4$ **3.** Sample answer: $44 \div 44$ **5.** Sample answer: $(4 + 4 + 4) \div 4$ **7.** Sample answer: $(4 \cdot 4 + 4) \div 4$
9. Sample answer: $44 \div 4 + 4$ **11.** Sample answer: $44 - 4 - 4$
13. 7   **15.** 6   **17.** 0   **19.** C

Pages 520–523

1.

6	7	2
1	5	9
8	3	4

3.

7	6	11
12	8	4
5	10	9

5.

3	45	42	12
36	18	21	27
24	30	33	15
39	9	6	48

7.

32	10	18	8
4	22	14	28
6	20	12	30
26	16	24	2

9. Sample answer using rotation;

16	6	8
2	10	18
12	14	4

11. Sample answer using reflection

−2	−7	−6
−9	−5	−1
−4	−3	−8

13. C

Pages 524–525

1. B   **3.** A   **5.** B   **7.** B   **9.** B   **11.** 1, 8, 15, 22, 29
13. −21, −14, −7, 0, 7   **15.** 2, 6, 18, 54, 162   **17.** −147
19. 33   **21.** $441   **23.** $4434.87   **25.** composite
27. composite   **29.** 12   **31.** 4   **33.** 24
35. Sample answer:

8	9	4
3	7	11
10	5	6

2	7	6
9	5	1
4	3	8

Illustrations Credits

All illustrations © K12 Inc. unless otherwise noted.
Cover: © Glen Allison, The Image Bank/Getty Images.

Chapter 1: 2–3 © Javier Pierini/Digital Vision/Getty Images. 7 © Javier Pierini/Digital Vision/Getty Images. 21 © OJO Images Ltd./Alamy. 25 Hemera Technologies/Thinkstock. 29 © Angus Plummer/iStockphoto.com. 33 © GlobalP/iStockphoto.com. 40 Photodisc/Thinkstock.

Chapter 2: 46–47 © David Stubbs/Aurora/Getty Images. 51 © David Stubbs/Aurora/Getty Images. 52 © Scott Leigh/iStockphoto.com. 55 © Philip Atherton/iStockphoto.com. 57 © Casara/iStockphoto.com. 61 Jupiterimages/Thinkstock. 69 © Tammy616/iStockphoto.com. 73 © brittak/iStockphoto.com.

Chapter 3: 86–87 © James Lauritz/moodboard/Corbis. 91 © James Lauritz/moodboard/Corbis. 97 © Ron Chapple Studios/Dreamstime.com. 105 © GlowImages/Alamy. 113 Getty Images/Thinkstock.

Chapter 4: 122–123 © B.A.E. Inc./Alamy. 127 © B.A.E. Inc./Alamy. 149 2010/Steve Cukrov/BigStockPhoto. 153 © Tanya Constantine/Blend Images/Corbis.

Chapter 5: 158–159 © Ellen Isaacs/Alamy. 163 © Ellen Isaacs/Alamy. 169 © Sally A. Morgan/Ecoscene/Corbis. 173 © Karima Lakhdar/123RF. 183 © Francesco Dazzi/Dreamstime.com.

Chapter 6: 186–187 © Ian Cuming/Photo Researchers, Inc. 191 © Ian Cuming/Photo Researchers, Inc. 192 © Алексей Сергеев/iStockphoto.com. 193 © Artville. 197 © Corey Hochachka/Design Pics/Corbis. 201 © Leonard F. Wilcox/Alamy. 205 © Andrius Kavaliunas/iStockphoto.com. 209 © Hill Street Studios/Getty Images. 213 Comstock/Thinkstock. 221 © Zoe Fieldhouse/Dreamstime.com. 225 2010/Rob Marmion/BigStockPhoto.

Chapter 7: 230–231 © Ziggy Folkmanis/Alamy. 235 © Ziggy Folkmanis/Alamy. 245 © GeoEye/Space Imaging. 249 2010/Anthony Berenyi/BigStockPhoto. 253 © Carlos Alvarez/iStockphoto.com. 257 © Sebastian Kaulitzki/123RF. 260 2010/Jean-louis Bouzou/123RF.

Chapter 8: 266–267 © Matthew Brown/iStockphoto.com. 271 © Matthew Brown/iStockphoto.com. 280 Stockbyte/Thinkstock. 281 © Flashback Studio/iStockphoto.com. 284 2010/James Steidl/BigStockPhoto. 285 © Bradcalkins/Dreamstime.com. 288 2010/James Steidl/BigStockPhoto. 289 © Jim Barry/iStockphoto.com. 293 © K12 Inc.

Chapter 9: 302–303 Jupiterimages/Thinkstock. 307 Jupiterimages/Thinkstock. 313 © Czalewski/Dreamstime.com. 325 © Ocean/Corbis. 341 © Eye Wire.

Chapter 10: 350–351 © Pankaj and Insy Shah/Getty Images. 355 © Pankaj and Insy Shah/Getty Images. 369 Digital Vision/Thinkstock. 373 © Ted Foxx/Alamy.

Chapter 11: 378–379 © Sofia Gentiletti/Getty Images. 383 © Sofia Gentiletti/Getty Images. 385 BananaStock/Thinkstock. 389 © Bart Coenders/iStockphoto.com. 393 Noel Hendrickson/Thinkstock. 397 John Foxx/Thinkstock. 401 © Carmen Martínez Banús/iStockphoto.com.

Chapter 12: 414–415 © msenbg/Fotolia. 419 © msenbg/Fotolia. 425 © Steve Cole/iStockphoto.com. 433 © Salajean/Dreamstime.com. 440 © Jupiterimages.

Chapter 13: 446–447 © Masterfile. 451 © Masterfile. 453 © eskaylim/iStockphoto.com. 457 © Dreamstime.com.

Chapter 14: 486–487 James King–Holmes/Bletchley Park Trust/Photo Researchers, Inc. 491 James King–Holmes/Bletchley Park Trust/Photo Researchers, Inc. 497 John Foxx/Thinkstock. 513 © Diane Labombarbe/iStockphoto.com.

Index

INDEX

Precision, **40**
  in problem solving, 40–43
Predictions
  experimental probability and,
    280–281, 284–285
Prime factorization, **512**–515
Prime numbers, **508**–511
  and composite numbers, 508–511
  prime factorization, **512**–515
Principal for interest calculation, **212**
Prisms, **168**
  finding surface area, 176
  relating volume of, 261
  volumes of, 168–171, 181, 261, 513
Probability, 266, 268–271, **269**, **276**,
    300–301
  comparing theoretical and
    experimental, 288–289
  complementary events, **296**–299
  counting, 272–275
  dependent events, **292**–295
  determining likelihood, 268
  experimental, **280**–283, 284,
    288–289
  experiments and, 276–279
  finding probabilities, 276–277, 293
  finding the sum of probabilities,
    297
  independent events, **292**–295
  interpreting, 270
  law of large numbers and,
    288–291
  making predictions from
    experiments, 280–281
  theoretical, **284**–287, 288–289
  using tree diagrams, **272**–273
  using Venn diagrams, **272**, 273
Problem solving, 2, 4–7, 44–45, *see*
    also Addition and subtraction
    equations; Division equations;
    Multiplication equations
  absolute value and, 46, 72–75
  equations and, 5
  estimation and reasonableness,
    36–39
  evaluating expressions with
    variables, 6
  expressions and, 4
  finding and correcting errors, 13
  identifying information in word
    problems, 32–35
  order of operations and, 12–15, 24,
    25, 437

positive and negative number
    operations, 46, *see also*
    Working with positives and
    negatives
  precision and, 40–43
  strategies for, 28–31, 60–61
  translating between words and
    math, 20–23
  using nets, 173
  using number lines, 8–11
  using number properties, 16–18
  word problems, 20–27, 32–35
Products, **12**, **89**, *see also*
    Multiplication
  algebraic notation of, **12**
Properties, number, **16**
  solving problems using, 16–18,
    60–61
Proportion, **216**–219, *see also* Ratios
    and proportions
  application to maps, 225
  cross multiplying and cross
    products, 220, 221
  reducing and enlarging figures,
    224–227
  solving, 220–223
  using common denominators to
    find, 216
Protractor, using, 233
Purchases
  calculating sales tax, 208
Puzzles
  creating math puzzles, 520–523
  finding possible dimensions of
    figures, 513
  four 4s puzzle, 516
  magic square puzzles, 520–521
  solving math puzzles, 516–519
  Triomino puzzle, 517
Pyramid, **177**
  finding surface area, 177

Q

Quadrants, **357**
Quadrilaterals, **449**
  angle sum property, 241
  area, 100–103
  classifying, **100**, 449
Quotient, **12**, **90**, *see also* Division

R

Radius, **248**, 249, 256
  circumference and, 252–255

Range, **304**
Rates, 378, **380**–383, 412–413
  average-speed problems, 396–399
  as comparisons, 384–387
  considerations in using, 385
  constant-rate problems, 400–403
  direct variation equations and
    graphs, 404–411
  expressing situations correctly, 384
  relating distance, rate, and time, 381
  relating work, rate, and time, 382
  solving unit-rate problems, 392–395
  unit rates, 388–391, 404–411
  using the work formula, **401**
Rational numbers, 122, 124–127,
    156–157, **188**
  adding and subtracting fractions,
    125, 140
  areas with fractions, 144–147
  changing division to multiplication
    with reciprocals, 148–149
  comparing, 136–139
  converting fractions and decimals,
    136–137, 189, 354
  converting mixed numbers and
    improper fractions, 133, 140,
    188
  dividing fractions, 148–151
  equivalent fractions, 128–131, **129**,
    216
  expressing fractions in simplest
    form, 124, 125, 133
  fractions with unlike denominators,
    140
  improper fractions, **132**, 133
  mixed numbers, **132**, 133, 140, 188
  multiplying fractions, 144–145
  perimeters with fractions, 140–143
  ratios and, *see* Ratios and
    proportions
  reciprocals, **148**–149
  relating fraction division problem
    situations, 149
  representing, 132–135
  solving problems with fraction
    division, 152–155
  translating among different forms of
    decimals, 126
  using a number line for comparing
    and ordering, 137
  using LCD to compare fractions, 129
  writing mixed numbers as improper
    fractions, 188

INDEX